Regional Geography

of Anglo-America

C. LANGDON WHITE

Professor of Geography
School of Humanities
Stanford University

EDWIN J. FOSCUE

Professor of Geography
Southern Methodist University

REGIONAL

GEOGRAPHY

of

ANGLO-AMERICA

SECOND EDITION

PRENTICE-HALL, INC.
Englewood Cliffs, N. J.

77084

Preface

Rᴇɢɪᴏɴs are formed by man as he adjusts himself to his natural environment rather than by arbitrary survey lines resulting from historical settlement and the various acts of Congress. Canada and the United States are not compact, single economic units, but each consists of numerous parts, each having its own economy based upon a distinctive natural environment. Few generalizations are applicable to the whole of the United States or Canada. Since regions vary in location, climate, landforms, soils, water, minerals, fauna and flora man tends to think and react differently in each region in dealing with such factors.

Geographic contiguity and similarity of economic and defense problems have created a sense of interdependence between Canada and the United States. Moreover, American movies, radios, magazines, mechanical devices, and the friendship resulting from movement back and forth across the border, have created a strong community of interest between the two peoples.

The reader of this volume will see how a people took possession of the land and how the land took possession of a people. He will become aware of the fact that the population is by no means evenly distributed through this living space, and that geographic factors are largely responsible for the uneven distribution.

The flowering of civilization in Anglo-America is partly a reflection of the degree to which man has levied tribute against the natural resources. From the Atlantic to the Pacific and from the Arctic to the Gulf, the white man has been a destroyer. Pioneers could not think about the distant future; but the day of the pioneer is past. Today no more good virgin land, well-located or potentially productive, stands ready for the plow. There are no new frontiers. The future standard of living of Anglo-Americans depends upon how well they use the land they already have. It is for this reason that conservation of natural resources is discussed repeatedly throughout the book.

Since December 7, 1941, Canada and the United States with their common heritage have been moving toward similar goals. Geographic factors and the rapidly changing technology of modern warfare have developed a common war and defense strategy. It was clear that mutual endeavor and good faith based on an understanding of the problems of the two countries would augur for success in the struggle for enduring peace and prosperity.

This book is not a simple compendium of facts. Wherever possible, facts are shown by maps or photographs, since most human knowledge is gained through the eye, and the language of pictures and maps is universal.

The textual material has been used in the classroom many times by both authors. Frequently a significant question or comment by a keen student has been incorporated. So have many ideas of professors who have used the book. Both authors have traveled widely over the continent and have carried on field investigations in many of the regions.

Agreement has been lacking among geographers on suitable names for the various regions of Anglo-America. Accordingly, a number of Anglo-America's leading geographers were consulted, and the titles used here are those suggested by the largest number of persons.

So many changes have taken place in Anglo-America since the original text was published, and particularly since the close of World War II, that the authors have considered it desirable to rewrite almost all of the material, thus making this a new edition rather than merely a revision of the old text. Most of the maps have been redrawn and, with a few exceptions, all photographs are new. Before the revision of *Regional Geography of Anglo-America* was begun, however, questionnaires were sent to all colleges and universities where the first edition had been used, and replies were received from more than 80 per cent. Among other things, the questionnaire asked for suggestions on reorganization, and many of these suggestions were incorporated into the new edition.

An improvement has been made by dividing the long chapter on the American Manufacturing Belt into two chapters and placing them at the beginning of the book immediately following the introduction. This change seemed desirable since a consideration of the great industrial centers should precede and not follow the other geographic regions in which they are also located.

The two introductory chapters in the original text have been transferred to the end of the book and now appear as appendices. In this new location they are available as reference material for anyone who desires further information on the physical appearance of Anglo-America or on its settlement and development, but they no longer interrupt the continuity of the regional descriptions. Also, some of the original regions have been combined where it seemed that combination would simplify and clarify the text.

To conserve space, the sections on cities have been reduced to statistical tables and appear at the end of each of the regional chapters. An additional feature of this new edition also appears at the end of each regional chapter in the form of a selected bibliography designed to enable the reader to consult easily-accessible outside references.

Finally, the text has been printed in a new double-column format designed to make the type more readable, and also to make possible the use of larger maps and photographic illustrations.

Acknowledgments

In writing this book, the authors have leaned heavily upon many geographers and colleagues in the closely related natural and social sciences. They have benefited also from the labors of numerous government employees who have collected statistical material, carried on surveys, and made maps. They have drawn especially upon articles in the professional geographical journals. Accordingly, the number to whom they are grateful is so large that only a general acknowledgment is possible. When quotations are used, the sources are cited in appropriate footnotes. The authors wish especially to express thanks to the men and women who have given specific chapters a critical reading. They were consulted because they live within a given region or have made that region their special field of research and are, therefore, especially familiar with it. The authors wish to make clear, however, that these critics are not responsible for any mistakes in fact or philosophy.

J. W. Alexander, University of Wisconsin
Stanley A. Arbingast, University of Texas
Ruth Baugh, University of California at Los Angeles
Nels A. Bengtson, University of Nebraska
Kenneth Bertrand, Catholic University of America
Donald J. Bogue, Miami University
William T. Chambers, Stephen F. Austin State College
W. G. Cunningham, American Can Company
Samuel N. Dicken, University of Oregon
Sigismond Diettrich, University of Florida
Loyal Durand, Jr., University of Tennessee
John Garland, University of Illinois
Frederick K. Hare, McGill University
H. Bowman Hawkes, University of Utah
Leslie Hewes, University of Nebraska
Harold A. Hoffmeister, University of Colorado
Preston E. James, Syracuse University
George H. T. Kimble, American Geographical Society
Trevor Lloyd, Dartmouth College
Howard H. Martin, University of Washington
Donald E. Meinig, University of Utah
Elbert E. Miller, University of Utah
E. Willard Miller, Pennsylvania State College
Merle Prunty, University of Georgia
Donald F. Putnam, University of Toronto
J. Lewis Robinson, University of British Columbia
Francis J. Schadegg, Eastern Washington College of Education
Earl B. Shaw, Worcester State Teachers College
James W. Watson, Department of Mines and Technical Surveys, Ottawa

The authors also wish to thank Eileen B. Sheldon, who devoted many months of her time to problems connected with this volume, and Juliet B. Hay, who gave generously of her time in preparing the maps for the second edition of *Regional Geography of Anglo-America.*

C. Langdon White
Edwin J. Foscue

STANFORD, CALIFORNIA
DALLAS, TEXAS
JANUARY 4, 1954

Contents

Contents

Maps, Illustrations, and Tables

Maps and Illustrations

Tables

Regional Geography

of Anglo-America

1.

Anglo-America and Its Regions

Nᴏᴛ so very many years ago North America was regarded as those lands lying between the Arctic Ocean on the north and Colombia on the south. Today the Western Hemisphere is divided into two parts — Anglo-America and Latin America (Figure 1–1). This latter division is geographically sound, for the cultural chasm between the two Americas is wide and deep.

Anglo-America comprises the United States, Alaska, Canada, and Greenland.[1] Externally Canada and the United States look like compact economic units and our practice is to assume that they are sufficiently uniform throughout to make generalizations that are applicable to the whole nations. Close study and inspection reveal, however, that such a practice is not justifiable. If generalizations about the whole of the two nations are made, however, it should be realized that a vast number of unlike units are being arranged together. Actually these countries are mosaics composed of a very large number of dissimilar pieces, which geographers call "regions."

It is well known that people in the various regions differ from one another. There is no agreement as to why this is so, however. One school attributes these differences to the natural environment, asserting that the differences remain despite the mobility and fluidity of the people. Thus streams and counter streams of migrants have flowed and ebbed, mingled and fused from one end of Anglo-America to the other, and yet, they say, despite this migration and such levelers as identical motion pictures, television and radio programs, newspapers and magazines, Americans and Canadians are not "run-of-mine" peoples. The Southerner, Middle Westerner, New Englander, Great Plainsman, Westerner, and Newfoundlander are all individualistic. This school asserts that so long as the various parts of Anglo-America differ markedly in climate and soils, water supply and minerals, flora and fauna, geographical location and landforms, just so long will man behave differently in adjusting himself to these factors.

The other school does not deny the importance of the natural environment, but insists that the significance to man of the physical quality of the land is not something that remains the same for all men at all times; rather it is determined by the attitudes, objectives, and technical abilities of the settlers, and with each change in these elements of the culture, the physical land, or

[1] Quebec and Greenland are insular concentrations of French and Danish nationalities in the otherwise (except for the aborigines) predominantly Anglo continent.

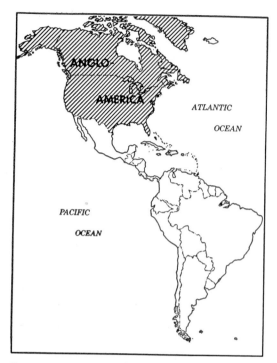

Figure 1–1. The Americas — Anglo and Latin. Authors in increasing numbers think less in terms of North America and South America and more in terms of Anglo-America and Latin America.

kind of natural environment. They had to unlearn much of what they formerly knew about farming; they even had to develop and use different tools. Today the region is politically unstable; it has a gambler's psychology owing to man's constant conflict with the vagaries of climate (wind, rain or lack of it, hail, blizzards, dust storms), and with insect pests. When his crops and livestock do well, the farmer reinvests his profits; but when things go badly with his farming operations, he calls upon his government for help or migrates in large numbers as he did during the days of the "Dust Bowl" (Figure 1–2). This region has accordingly witnessed a long pageant of political movements and events. Actually there is nothing wrong with the Great Plains folks; their tribulations stem from the fact that the people have geared their human geography in this region to the good years and not to the bad, or even to the average ones. The one thing with which these people have been equipped has been a super-abundance of hope — hope particularly for the following year's rainfall. In order to fulfill these hopes and bring stability to this region, the governments of both countries supply crop planting and many other kinds of advice.

Thus the United States and Canada are unions composed of many units, each with its own peculiar and distinctive economy, an economy based upon its own sources of wealth, each dominated by self-interest and competing with every other unit.

resource base, must be re-evaluated. According to this school the resulting differences in occupance are more closely related to culture than to nature. In short, this school believes that so long as the land remains relatively changeless, man, the active agent, decides how the land affects his use of it. The natural environment is passive.[2]

Regions are thus utilized for geographic study by both groups and eminent geographers belong to both.

These differences will be noted later in the chapters on specific regions. Compare, for example, the Great Plains Region with any other in Anglo-America. Small unrelated groups of settlers entered the Great Plains and, without an understanding of the climate, began adjusting themselves to this new

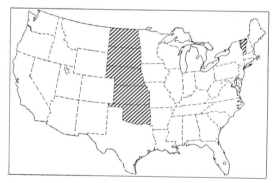

Figure 1–2. The states losing population during the years 1930–1940 — the decade of the "black blizzards." (Based on the U. S. Census.)

[2] Preston E. James, "Toward a Further Understanding of the Regional Concept," *Annals of the Association of American Geographers,* Vol. 42, September 1952, pp. 220-221.

It is the purpose of this book to treat Anglo-America by regions — to do so with broad sweeps of the brush, believing that by so doing readers will get the concept of regionalism. Many users of this book will not be professional geographers; some may be business men. Business men, however, do think in terms of regions and firms operating nationally usually employ region systems. Montgomery Ward and Company has mail-order houses in nine cities, each serving an assigned region. There are regions such as Federal Reserve Districts, Army Corps Areas, wholesale trade areas, and many others. In hundreds of ways business men have set up regions — regions that are operating reasonably well. By working with large units, regional geography can make a real contribution to national life.[3] This method of approach provides the best opening to an understanding of Anglo-America's fundamental achievement, for people live and work together as units of a geographical region far more than they do as citizens of a state or province. The Federal Reserve Act of 1913, which divided the United States into 12 Federal Reserve Districts, the boundaries of which sometimes divide states, led Harold U. Faulkner to remark that this gave "tacit recognition that the nation was fundamentally a group of economic sections rather than agglomeration of states."[4] For some time scholars have perceived a lack of uniformity in American life and attitudes and geographers, historians, political scientists, economists, and sociologists all recognize the significance of regions and of regionalism.

Geography, which links the data of the social sciences with those of the natural sciences, is a logical discipline for dealing with regions. It sees in the region not only the physical and biological, the social, political, and economic factors but it synthesizes them. In short it considers the region in its totality — not merely as things that are there but the processes and relationships now operating

and those presumably that will occur in the future. The geographer is

> . . . like the builder of a house who takes brick, stone, sand, cement, nails, wire, lath, boards, shingles, and glass — the products of many industries — and builds them into a symmetrical structure which is not any one of the many things that have entered into it, but is instead a house for the occupancy of man.[5]

Distinction Between Regionalism and Sectionalism

The words "region" and "section" are used synonymously by some professional social scientists. "Section" is a term with a connotation of regionality used particularly by some historians. Frederick J. Turner often used the two terms interchangeably.[6] The sociologists Odum and Moore speak of the divisive power of self-seeking *sections* and the integrating power of co-ordinated *regions* fabricated into a united whole.[7]

Among geographers, sectionalism is inseparably associated with politics, emotionalism, and sentiment: therefore, as currently used, it adds only confusion to the geographer's study of a real differentiation. Regionalism, on the other hand, provides the motif for economic planning.

The Geographical Region

The geographical region includes the totality of place and people in association. Whittlesey, James, and others use the term "compage" to include the region based on the totality of the human occupance. It is defined without reference to the physical regions or biotic regions with which it might be profitably compared. Preston James says:

> I would draw surface regions, climatic regions, vegetation regions, and *compages,* and then compare their area spread, never expecting

---

[3] "U. S. – Canadian Northwest Forgets About Frontiers," *Business Week,* October 11, 1952, pp. 84 ff.

[4] Harold U. Faulkner, *American Economic History,* p. 558, Harper & Bros., New York: 1943.

[5] J. Russell Smith, *School Geography and Regional Idea,* p. 2. Philadelphia: John C. Winston Co., 1934.

[6] Frederick Jackson Turner, *The Significance of Sections in American History,* p. 45. New York: Henry Holt & Co., 1943.

[7] H. W. Odum and H. E. Moore, *American Regionalism: A Cultural-Historical Approach to National Integration.* New York: Henry Holt & Co., 1938.

them to coincide. In fact, if they did, I would suspect something to be wrong because of the nature of regions.[8]

In every region there is a core area that gives it personality and individuality: it is here that the regional characteristics are best exemplified. The core possesses two qualities which may be blurred in the periphery:

a. It differs noticeably from neighboring core areas.

b. It exists as a recognizable and coherent segment of space defined by the criteria whereby it is selected.

Beyond the core lies a marginal area. Regional boundaries usually are not lines but rather transitional zones that partake of the character of adjoining regions or cores. The width may vary from a few feet to many miles. Thus the field geographer in making his reconnaissance survey seldom knows when he leaves one region and enters another. At some point, of course, he passes from one to the other, but the human eye probably cannot perceive it at the moment of change. The distinguishing features of one region grade or melt gradually into those of the neighboring region, save along a mountain range, along the shore of a large body of water, or at the border of a desert.

Regionalism is something the people who occupy the unit feel: it is a kind of collective consciousness. No region in Anglo-America corresponds exactly to state or provincial boundaries or with physical boundaries.

While almost all geographers agree that regional geography is the core of their subject — that it is even the final goal of the discipline, it has nonetheless been admitted that there is one glaring weakness — that the statistics (quantitative data concerning the functions and functioning of communities) of the Bureau of the Census are applicable only to statistical regions and very seldom indeed do the boundaries of geographical and statistical regions coincide. This is unfortunate, for the data should have a more specific meaning for the classes of problems with which they are concerned. The fact that

the boundaries of states, counties, townships, and other civil divisions are non-functional has fostered an attitude that the data collected for these units are seriously deficient for research use. Wishing to ameliorate this situation, the Bureau of the Census recently has designated new units such as metropolitan areas, industrial areas, and census tracts. In 1949 the Bureau of the Census, the Bureau of Agricultural Economics, and the Scripps Foundation for Research in Population Problems co-operated in studies leading first to the subdivision of all the 48 states into homogeneous areas called "state economic areas," which were designed for use in tabulating and summarizing statistics for states in terms of their principal parts. Since then the studies have been extended so that the "state economic areas" themselves have been combined into fairly homogeneous groups — "economic regions" and "subregions." These new divisions are intended to represent the fundamental physical structure of the United States economy.

In many respects they might be considered synonymous with geographic regions; certainly in most instances their cores are identical. If the geographers will try to see eye-to-eye with the three groups working on these "economic regions," the difficult problem of fitting statistics to regions might be well on the way to solution.[9]

Geographical regions obviously occur at different levels of subdivision. In this text the region sometimes consists of several minor areas called subregions.

Determination of Regions

The geographic region has already been

---

[8] Preston James, personal communication.

[9] Students interested in the new "economic regions" should consult:

Donald J. Bogue, "Economic Areas As a Tool for Research and Planning," *American Sociological Review*, Vol. 15, June 1950.

————, *State Economic Areas*, Bureau of the Census, Washington, D. C.: Government Printing Office, 1951.

————, *A Description of the Economic Regions and Economic Subregions of the United States.* Oxford, Ohio: Scripps Foundation for Research in Population Problems, August 22, 1951.

defined. Dividing a continent into regions is a matter of "scientific generalizing" and is not, as someone once remarked, "merely a pedagogical device to facilitate the presentation of geographical material to classes of students," although it may admittedly serve this latter purpose.

One recognizes a region by noting the intimate association existing between peoples of like interest and the area they occupy. Similarity of interest may and often does indicate a similarity of natural environmental conditions. In the American Manufacturing Belt, especially the part west of the Appalachians, a large segment of the population thinks and talks in terms of iron and steel and the many products derived from them; in fact, iron and steel are called the "barometer of industry," because nearly all manufacturing enterprises depend upon them in some way. East of the mountains, though iron and steel making still is important, manufacturing more nearly includes the whole gamut of fabricated products. In the Agricultural Interior to the west, however, the people are vitally interested in corn, oats, tobacco, fruit, hay, hogs, and beef and dairy cattle as the economic barometers of life. In either region, the natural environment is a factor in the popular interests.

The Cultural Landscape in Regional Analysis

Geographers deal with both natural and cultural landscapes. Everyone who has traveled, even if only slightly, has noted that the natural landscape changes from one part of the country to another. When two greatly unlike areas are neighbors, the geographer may separate them on his map by a line, thereby recognizing them as separate natural regions. Similarly, he may study the cultural or man-made landscape, and resolve it into separate cultural regions.

Whenever man comes into any area, he promptly modifies its natural landscape, "not in a haphazard way but according to the culture system which he brings with him . . . Culture is the agent, the natural area is the medium, the cultural landscape the result." [10]

Figure 1–3. Indian corn — showing the close adjustment on the part of man to the rainfall regime. Note the large hills widely spaced in each direction. The soil is sandy and the surface layers are dry in spring so that deep planting is necessary to place the seed in contact with moist soil. (Courtesy of Soil Conservation Service.)

He cuts down the forest, plows under the native grass, raises domesticated animals, erects houses and buildings, builds fences, constructs roads, railroads, telephone and telegraph lines, digs canals, builds bridges, and tunnels under mountains. All this constitutes the "cultural landscape."

Geography, however, consists of more than the mere distribution of men and things in the landscape. The distribution of races or climates or landforms by themselves is never geography. Rather it is ethnology, climatology, and geology or geomorphology respectively. Such distributions become geographically significant only as they function in the mutual relationship of mankind to natural environment, as these relations are themselves recorded in the landscape (Figure 1–3).

Are Regions Fixed?

In several of the fields or disciplines which are closely related to geography, the systems of regions that are studied are fixed by nature; climatic, pedologic, physiographic, and vegetation regions all are based on static or almost static natural boundaries. Geographic regions, however, are not fixed: instead of

[10] Isaiah Bowman, *Geography in Relation to the Social Sciences,* pp. 149-150. New York: Charles Scribner's Sons, 1934.

having hard-and-fast boundary lines, they have ever-changing ones. When man pushes wheat culture farther north in Canada or farther west in Kansas, or when he grows cotton farther north and west in Texas or Oklahoma, he is definitely responsible for changes in geographic regions, since bound-

ary lines of such areas must then be redrawn.

Sequent Occupance

"Sequent occupance" is a concept supporting the principle that the significance of the physical environment changes as attitudes, objectives, and technical abilities of the

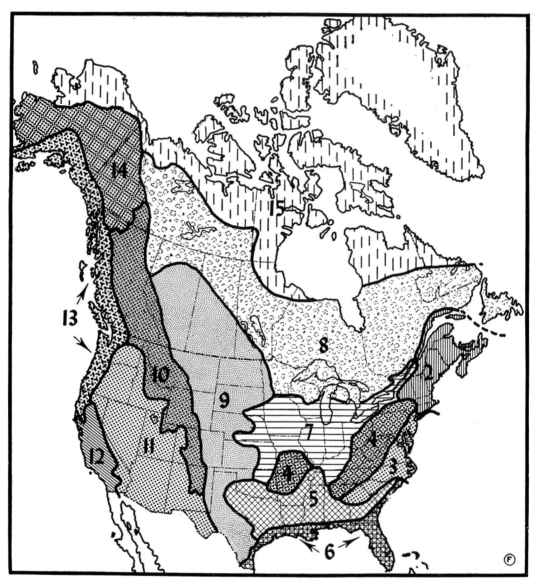

Figure 1–4. Geographic regions of Anglo-America. The numbers on the map correspond to the numbers of the regions listed on page 7. Note that region 1, *The American Manufacturing Belt,* is omitted from the map. For details concerning this region see Figures 3–2 and 3–3, pages 33 and 34.

people living in it change. It is a sequence of different modes of occupance.

One studies sequent occupance by studying the man-land relations within a period during which the culture of the people remained essentially unchanged. With any change such as the application of steam to transportation, a new period of sequent occupance comes in.

The Goal of Regional Geography

We have seen that Anglo-America is a fabric of regions. As we go from chapter to chapter we will see that it is the functioning of these interrelated areas that gives us our national life "with its phenomena of regional-national balance and integration."

The principal purpose of regional geography is to put the resources within it to the best possible use. Before this can be done, however, an inventory must be made of the resources. Regional study is useful in social science research and in governmental regional planning.

Every region has offered to its people a certain range of possibilities. The actual use made of these possibilities, however, depends to a very great extent upon the economic, social, and cultural heritage of the people. In other words, such additional factors as ideals, psychology, and inherited intellectual habits — all of which are derived from the stock from which they come — function along with the natural environment.

As each chapter which follows is considered in its turn, the reader will see that there is a mutual relationship (cultural, psychological, and economic) between the people of the region and the conditions of the natural environment. He will also get a broad picture of the current conditions of life in the different parts of the continent. Finally he will be convinced that the division of Anglo-America into geographical regions provides the best understanding for its fundamental achievement.

Regions of Anglo-America

On the basis of man's adjustment to the natural environment within specific areas, the continent may be divided into the following regions (Figure 1–4):

1. The American Manufacturing Belt
2. Northeastern Anglo-America
3. The Atlantic Coastal Plain and the Piedmont
4. The Appalachians and the Ozarks
5. The Cotton Belt
6. The Humid Subtropical Coast
7. The Agricultural Interior
8. The Northern Continental Forest
9. The Great Plains
10. The Rocky Mountains
11. Intermontane Basins and Plateaus
12. The Subtropical Pacific Coast
13. The North Pacific Coast
14. The Yukon-Kuskokwim Basins
15. The Tundra

Selected Bibliography

Donald Davidson, "Where Regionalism and Sectionalism Meet," *Social Forces,* Vol. 13, October 1934, pp. 23-31.

William B. Hesseltine, "Regions, Classes and Sections in American History," *Journal of Land and Public Utility Economics,* Vol. 20, 1944, pp. 35-44.

Preston James, "Toward a Further Understanding of the Regional Concept," *Annals of the Association of American Geographers,* Vol. 42, September 1952, pp. 195-222.

Merrill Jensen, *Regionalism in America.* Madison: University of Wisconsin Press, 1952.

B. G. Lewis, "Regionalism: A Plan of Uniting the

States More Effectively," *Forum,* Vol. 89, March 1933, 136-141.

L. Mumford, "Regionalism and Irregionalism," *Sociological Review,* October 1927, April 1928.

Frank W. Notestein, "Population," *Scientific American,* Vol. 185, September 1951, pp. 28-35.

H. W. Odum, "Regionalism vs. Sectionalism in the South's Place in the National Economy," *Social Forces,* Vol. 12, March 1934, pp. 338-354.

Robert S. Platt, "Field Approach to Regions," *Annals of the Association of American Geographers,* Vol. 25, 1935, pp. 153-174.

G. T. Renner, "Incentives and Objectives in Regional Planning," *American Planning and Civic Annual,*

Part II, pp. 105-111. Washington, D.C.: American Planning and Civic Association, 1936.

G. T. Renner and Mayme P. Renner, "Regionalism in American Life," *Teachers College Record*, Vol. 43, February 1942, pp. 337-357.

H. G. Roach, "Sectionalism in Congress, 1870-1890," *American Political Science Review*, Vol. 19, August 1925, pp. 500-526.

E. C. Whitley, "The Sequent Land Use at Bridgeport Bar Washington," *Pacific Northwest Quarterly*, Vol. 42, January 1951, pp. 32-39.

Raymond Schuessler, "Air Pollution in Our Chemical Age," *Think*, Vol. 17, December 1951.

J. C. Spurr, "More Than Half of U. S. Industrial Workers and Plants are in 53 Areas," *Printers Ink*, Vol. 231, No. 4, April 28, 1950, pp. 30-31, 48.

Eugene Van Cleef, "The City of Tomorrow," *Ohio Journal of Science*, Vol. 42, July 1942, pp. 151-158.

Derwent Whittlesey, "A Geographer's Approach to Urban Study," *Scientific Monthly*, Vol. 73, 1951, pp. 42-44.

2.

The City and Industrial
Geography[1]

THE great city is not new. Ancient Carthage, Alexandria, and Rome all had populations of half a million or more. But they were
political creations of great empires; the
majority of modern cities are the product of
economic-geographic conditions. Prior to the
era of steam, few cities had populations of
more than 100,000 inhabitants and it is
doubtful whether any city, even such renowned ones as Rome, Nanking, and Peking,
ever attained populations of as many as one
million. It was not until significant social and
economic changes were wrought by the Industrial Revolution that the modern city
became possible. On the other hand, the
wholesale growth of cities is quite recent,

[1] Viewed *geographically* a city is an area of the
earth that is in sharp contrast in appearance, characteristics, and functions to its rural surroundings.
The core is its distinguishing feature — the quality
that gives it personality; its actual boundaries often
are difficult to determine. Cities differ one from another much as do people. They are classified functionally as (1) industrial, (2) commercial, (3)
mining, (4) resort, (5) political, (6) residential,
(7) transportational, (8) university, and (9) health.
It should be realized, of course, that almost every
large city is more or less multi-functional, and its
classification as a commercial or a manufacturing
city does not imply the absence of other functions.

because the strategic quality of a place is
measurable solely in terms of transportation
and communication, and these have come
into being only in modern times. So long as
transport facilities were backward, large
numbers of people could not be confined to a
small area and at the same time be fed and
clothed. Thus at the time of the first census,
in 1790, the United States was 75 per cent
rural.

The principal difference between urban
growth in the Old World and in the United
States and Canada is the slow evolution of
cities in the former and their rapid growth
in the latter. In the Old World they grew
over a period of centuries from town economies to their present urban caste. In the
New World they started as wilderness communities on the outskirts of civilization,
bridging the gap from primitive agriculturalism to mature urbanism in little more than
a century. Thus Anglo-American cities have
almost no past; nearly all have grown up in
response to the same influences and they are
among themselves far more homogeneous
than European cities. There are, of course,
variations among them but these variations
are slight indeed. The major influence in

the growth of modern American and Canadian cities has been manufacturing.

Historical Development of Anglo-American Cities

Colonial Period to 1865. In early colonial days small cities sprang up along the Atlantic Seaboard, mostly in what are now New England and the Middle Atlantic States in the United States, and in the Maritime Provinces and Lower St. Lawrence Valley in Canada. This was natural because these areas were nearest England and France, particularly the former, whence came capital goods and many consumer goods. Merchandising establishments were, accordingly, more advantageously located in port cities from which goods could be more readily distributed to interior settlements. Here, too, were the favored locations for assembling raw materials for export and for performing what little processing was necessary prior to shipment abroad. Boston, Philadelphia, New York and several other Atlantic cities throve and, as the United States and Canada grew, the cities increased in importance.

This was less true in the Colonial South, where life centered in the plantation, rather than in the town, as in New England. The local isolation and the economic self-sufficiency of the plantation were antagonistic to the development of towns. Thus, nearly all settlements there were located on navigable streams and each planter owned a wharf accessible to the small shipping of that day; in fact one of the strongest reasons for the planter selecting his land as he did was to have it front on a water highway (Figure 5–2).

With independence the new nation (the United States) started its career without a single city as large as 50,000 inhabitants; and it was not until 1820 that it had a city of more than 100,000 persons, and not until 1880 that it recorded one in the million class.

From the close of the Revolutionary War until 1823, American industry suffered from economic chills and fevers. While the war of 1812 temporarily stimulated manufacturing, it was not until after 1823 that it really

boomed. It was the mechanization of spinning and weaving that set the pace. Influences were at work drawing farm youths to the cities; particularly was such migration rapid following the Civil War.

The large port cities especially, grew in size with the building of canals, roads, and railroads. Each began to develop its own railroad and push it westward toward Chicago. Boston alone of the major American ports was forced to content itself with connecting lines; its Boston and Albany never got beyond the Hudson River. There was very little railway development at this time in Maritime Canada. The Grand Trunk Railway, built after 1850 from Chicago through Toronto and Montreal, reached the Atlantic in the United States at Portland, Maine. Hence, Canada had few large Atlantic port cities.

The Period from 1865 to 1914: Era of Great Urban Growth in Anglo-America. As the United States and Canada grew, the coastal cities particularly in the former, became more and more important. At first manufacturing catered only to local markets; ultimately, however, it served national markets. The Civil War marked a definite turning point in manufacturing in America. The geographical division of labor, a basis for present-day regionalism, was beginning to become apparent by the end of the Civil War period. There next followed a quarter century of accelerated westward movement, rapid population increase, heavy immigration, and accelerated growth of urban centers. Cities found their functions multiplying as the growth of manufacturing became pronounced. Yet as late as 1890 the economy in Anglo-America was still dominantly agricultural, still highly dependent on trade with Europe.

1914-1930. During this period revolutionary things were happening. The continuous mechanization of farms resulted in a great population movement from farms, hamlets, and villages to cities. Manufacturing was concentrating more and more in cities during the early part of this period, but was moving away from the congested central parts of cities toward the latter part of the period.

The automobile industry was not only winning its position as an important new enterprise that soon was to become the nation's largest single industry in the value of its product, but was to become responsible for the explosion of cities and the birth of suburbs.

The method of mass production came into its own at this time, embracing particularly such industries as steel, paper, cement, glass, chemical, and others. And accompanying mass production came movements toward standardization, industrial research, and industrial management. Manufacturers turned their attention likewise to marketing techniques, particularly the popularization of installment selling. A stream of new products made their appearance — plastics, radio, and sound movies. Industry became more highly mechanized due to the comparative scarcity of labor. This resulted especially from the restriction of immigration in 1924. A wave of industrial consolidations also characterized this period. It was a different type, however, from those of the turn of the century. When one company absorbed a competitor during the 1920's, for example, it was to gain an advantage held by that competitor — a strategic location, highly specialized equipment, or a well-established market.

1930-1950. By 1930, however, there were more urban than rural people in the United States, and by 1950, 64 per cent of the 150,697,361 people in the nation resided in urban territory and only 36 per cent in rural territory.[2]

The proportion of farmers in the total population has been decreasing rapidly. In 1950 there were 23,577,000 rural farm dwellers, who comprised only 15.6 per cent of the total population. Even the number of farms had declined sharply. In 1950 there were 5,382,162 farms — 477,007 fewer than in 1945.[3] The area in farms, however, increased, there

having been 1,158,565,852 acres in 1950 and 1,141,615,364 in 1945 — an increase of 16,950,488 acres.

This shift in population from rural to urban areas has resulted in significant occupational changes in the nation; in short, in a little more than a century the United States has been transformed from a rural frontier settlement into a full-fledged industrial society. This change has greatly affected our civilization — our way of living and our ways of making a living. It is obvious that urbanization has become the outstanding feature of life today in much of Anglo-America.

Factors Stimulating the Founding, Growth, and Maintenance of Cities. Cities come into existence to serve the demands of regions, but their actual sites are determined by geographical conditions. In short, cities do not spontaneously come into existence without the operation of causal factors. They are thus the production of locations possessing a strategic quality. If we think in terms of the American Manufacturing Belt (see Chapter 3), 50 of its 400 odd cities are situated on the shores of the Atlantic Ocean and on the southern Great Lakes; not less than 210 are situated on rivers of considerable size and 30 on canals either used or abandoned. Altogether some 300 were originally located and grew up near waterways. Only 70 of the 400 have no such situation, and nearly all of these owe their development to important sites along railroads. Even the railroads did not differentiate the business of the river and lake cities, for at first they were conceived as supplements to water trade routes and were built to connect river towns with each other.

Important cities grew up especially at bulk-breaking points at the heads of navigation where goods and passengers had to shift from water to rail transport at a waterfall or

---

[2] Bureau of the Census, *Some Census Facts about the Urbanization of America*, Washington, D. C.: Government Printing Office, November 27, 1951.

[3] Possibly 200,000 of this decrease is attributable to the change in the definition of a "farm." In 1950 places of three or more acres were classed as farms only if agricultural products, exclusive of a home

garden, with a value of $150 or more were produced; and places with less than three acres were classed as farms only if the value of agricultural products sold was $150 or more. Bureau of the Census, *Farm Census Shows Less than 5,400,000 Farms in the United States*, Washington, D. C.: Government Printing Office, April 9, 1951.

a rapid, or a gradual shallowing in the stream beyond which boats could not go. The exact town site was often determined by the local terrain — a terrace, a convenient ferriage, a navigable tributary stream, or even by some historical accident — such as the wording of a charter or an agreement made with the aborigines. With the growth of manufacturing, many large water consuming industries located in cities having good supplies of industrial water.

The Nature of Cities

The Great City — The Metropolis. To use an expression of the late Professor J. Paul Goode, all of the *great* cities were born great. To be sure man helps make them what they are but without a favorable endowment to begin with, man alone could not make them great; their importance "rests on factors far behind man's puny story."[4] All are located at a unique place for enabling the urban functions to serve the articulated area. It may be said that such cities are of three kinds: (1) those performing comprehensive services for the tributary area; (2) those performing bulk-breaking services along transport routes; and (3) those engaged in special functions, such as mining, manufacturing, and commerce. Most cities, of course, represent a combination of the three. Modern mechanization, transportation, and interdependence enable much of the economic activity of mankind to be centered in cities.

All cities greatly influence the areas in which they are located but all, too, are helpless without the rural lands that sustain them. For every city workman and every member of his family, some four acres of reasonably productive land must be farmed to enable him and his family to maintain the American standard of living.[5] Assuming an average of three dependents per man, a factory employing 1,000 men is thus drawing on an agricultural area of 16,000 acres. Back of Cleveland,

Ohio, there must be some 3½ million acres in production. City folks are dependent every day for many necessities besides food and all are supplied at a price — a price that seems to go up with the size of the city.

But just as the city cannot exist without the country, neither can the country prosper without the city, for some settlements, for example, Des Moines, Dallas, and Salt Lake City, exist to supply the needs of the surrounding and distant country. In fact, this is true of nearly all Anglo-American cities outside the American Manufacturing Belt.

Cities also relieve the population pressure of the rural areas which no longer can afford to keep their surplus sons and daughters. The American machine-tending farmer now produces 400 times more food than he eats.

The Typical American City. Viewed from an airplane, a typical American city appears as a sprawling mass of structures of varying size, shape, and construction, crisscrossed by a checkerboard street pattern which here and there assumes irregularities. The blocks into which the city is divided seem to lack any organic grouping into units. The general impression is one of stereotyped monotony. Internal structure is repeated so often that broad generalizations seem valid especially if confined to cities of similar size, function, and regional setting. Within it the several portions are utilized for different functions. Heavy manufacturing gravitates to the flat lands somewhat removed from the city center, for it requires much space; if the area be a plain, this is no serious problem, but if it be hill country or mountain terrain, a valley must be utilized. Commerce, too, keeps to the flat land. Heavy industry will also be located with respect to railways and highways and to the water front if the city be a port. On level land is also the business section; residences usually are forced to the higher ground not far from the factories. Just outside the commercial core are the blighted areas and slums. Adjacent to this belt are the tenements and working men's homes, and beyond them the apartment houses, and finally the single homes with small yards. Cemeteries are located on the best drained land. Here and there are parks;

[4] J. Paul Goode, *The Geographic Background of Chicago.* Chicago: University of Chicago Press, 1926.

[5] Paul B. Sears, "Science and Natural Resources," *American Scholar*, Vol. 14, 1944–45, p. 485.

Figure 2-1. Lower Manhattan skyline looking west from the East River. Here is the greatest concentration of skyscrapers in the world. The skyscraper is an adjustment to a paucity of room. (Courtesy Port of New York Authority.)

some of these may be in the most highly congested areas and on the most expensive land; others may be well out from the core. Also there may be spacious metropolitan parks some distance from the city. On the periphery is the change from suburb to farm land. At especially favorable sites, partly obscured by woods, nestle imposing mansions and country clubs. In detail, of course, each city is unique.

Cities tend to swarm or cluster in groups as illustrated in the Boston Lowland, the Mohawk Valley and elsewhere. Many tend to be arranged in linear patterns along transportation lines.

Ills of the Large City. The big city everywhere is the object of criticism by thoughtful people. These critics insist that all cities are ailing and that they are not good places in which to live. They point to the smog, crowding, strain on family life, snarled traffic, segregation of minorities, juvenile delin-

quency, impersonality, and the failure to produce enough children to maintain themselves in the next generation. Nearly half of all metropolitan families are without children and only three American cities of 100,000 and more inhabitants have enough children to maintain their present populations.

Moreover as cities become larger, the cost of living rises and workers' real wages decline. The cities accordingly are hotbeds of labor strife.

The lack of control of city growth has thus led to extreme congestion, the debasement of housing standards because of space shortage, increasing distance between home and place of employment, and incurable deadlocks in traffic. In every large city are acres of slum areas, which foster crime and disease and threaten to topple the tax structure. There is no doubt but that many of the cities of Anglo-America have surpassed their optimum size.

The Skyscraper — Adjustment to Congestion. The skyscraper is a visible symbol of congestion and high land values. If building cannot be spread outward, it must spread upward or the city ceases to grow. No city has had to adapt itself to the skyscraper as has New York, for on Manhattan Island, space is restricted (Figure 2–1). In most cities almost indefinite lateral expansion is possible. Fortunately, Manhattan consists almost entirely of solid rock and hence provides the foundations for the skyscrapers which make New York's jagged skyline the most awe-inspiring man-made sight in the world.

While the skyscraper permits a great increase in the number of people who can live and work in a restricted area, it only adds to the confusion of the traffic, for most American cities grew so fast that little conscious thought was given to form or function or to the satisfactions they should provide. Their streets were designed for smaller cities, lower buildings, and fewer people and hence cannot carry the traffic load without friction and delays. Traffic assumes less than a snail's pace in the very places where speed and promptness are at a premium. Nowhere has the traffic dilemma been better presented than in an article in *Fortune*, where the reader suffers with one truck driver who maneuvers, frets, and battles to cover four miles and make 35 deliveries in eight hours (Figure 2–2).[6]

The Future of Cities

The Big City — Is It Doomed? Large cities are not reproducing themselves. Moreover, they have grown so big that the poor people live under tragic conditions. Most of the big ones are ailing to a greater or lesser degree, yet the average one seems to concern itself more with growing larger than with curing its sickness.

There are many persons who believe that the great city is doomed: some even believe that it is a "dinosaur." According to Oswald Spengler as civilization concentrates in a city, it dries up; as ancient Mediterranean civilization desiccated in Carthage and in Rome, its modern counterpart is drying up in New York, Chicago, and Pittsburgh.[7] Lewis Mumford, eminent scholar and planner warned those attending the convention of the American Institute of Architects in 1950 that the age of the big city was over.

The authors do not believe that large urban centers must necessarily die or disappear. With the passage of time all undergo change. Large cities are like middle-aged people — they suffer from fatty degeneration. Certain parts of cities decay but the entity does not die. Cities seem to be going through a relatively new stage in their evolution, a stage made possible by the automobile — that of spilling out from the center and over the corporate boundaries. Hence it would appear that with all its evils, the city

Figure 2–2. Traffic congestion in the garment-making area of New York City. Probably no other part of the city is so congested: the streets are actually clogged; trucks move at a snail's pace; the curb lanes are packed solidly with trucks; the sidewalks are cluttered. (Courtesy of *The New York Times.*)

[6] "A Day in New York's Traffic Jungle," *Fortune,* October 1946.

[7] Benton MacKaye, "End or Peak of Civilization?" *Survey Graphic,* Vol. 68, No. 13, October 1, 1932, p. 441.

is with us as a practical problem and is here to stay.[8]

The Garden City: Its Possibilities. Some 60 years ago, Ebenezer Howard, a London commuter, pondered the question — what it is that a human being needs to make him happy. He then appraised both the city and the country as to what each offers and denies to man. Boiled down his balance sheet was essentially as follows:

Man in order to be happy and socially valuable must be employed, have social contacts, access to nature, and an opportunity to own a piece of land. The present-day city offers a wide choice of jobs, makes social contacts easy but denies most of the other necessaries of the good life. The country, too, comes up wanting; it can offer few jobs and few social contacts.

Howard's solution for the inadequacies of

[8] "Big Cities' Big Future: They Still Grow, Despite Boom in Suburbs," *U. S. News and World Report*, August 8, 1952.

both city and country life was the garden city, where all land is held in public trust by developing companies, which are permitted to earn only five or six per cent on the investment. The garden city has surrounding it a permanent belt of agricultural land — a "green belt" closed forever to any kind of building. The average density of the residential area is about eight houses to the acre. All the workers, except those commuting to outside places, live within easy walking distance of their places of employment. Each garden city has its own group of diversified industries. The population must not exceed 60,000 persons.

Howard's idea was that of a town which should provide for the technical needs of industry along with the environmental needs of the family and the social and cultural needs of man in communities.

The social advantages of the garden city need no proof. England has been meeting a

Figure 2–3. Fairless Hills, an experiment in greenbelt living. This graceful, spacious city is considered to be one of the most perfectly planned communities in Anglo-America. It lies close to the big iron and steel works at Morrisville, where the men and some women are employed. (Courtesy of *United States Steel News*.)

considerable proportion of her acute need for housing during the post World War II period in this way.

A modification of the garden city has taken hold in America in the form of the "super block" — the planning of dwellings in neighborhood units. In it several typical city blocks are consolidated into one large community area with major thoroughfares forming the boundaries. Shopping centers, schools, playgrounds, churches, and community centers all are located *inside* the boundaries. The dangers and annoyances of heavy traffic are thus avoided (Figure 2–3).

City Planning. Throughout Anglo-America today there is great interest in city planning. Toledo, Syracuse, Portland, and many other cities have been active in this field.[9] Planning is regarded as the expression of the collective purpose of the people.[10]

Possibly every large city in Anglo-America today has its planning commission and is taking stock of itself. World War II and the subsequent "Cold War" did more than anything else to focus attention on the shortcomings and inadequacies of the modern metropolis. Great cities, abroad, once considered enduring, were, during the war flattened and all but wiped off the map in a single night of saturation bombing. Accordingly planning seems to be the only *practical* way out since international agreement, at least for a long time, appears to be but a hopeless dream. Modern planning is concerned with more than mere patching jobs; it is making an all-out attack on the under-

lying causes of the modern city's troubles.[11] Particularly is it tackling the problems of overcrowding and congestion in the interior and of unguided sprawling in the outskirts. It plans for the continuance of great cities.

Standard Metropolitan Areas. The "standard metropolitan area" in the 1950 Census replaces the former "metropolitan district," which included, in addition to the central city or cities, all adjacent and contiguous minor civil divisions or incorporated places with a population density of 150 or more per square mile. It might have included territory not included in the standard metropolitan area.

Standard metropolitan areas have been established and defined in connection with each city of 50,000 or more persons and may contain more than one city of 50,000 or larger. These may lie in more than one state. Each standard metropolitan area has as a nucleus the county or counties containing the central city or cities and are composed of whole counties.[12]

For more than a century the drift of people in metropolitan areas has been one of the outstanding traits of population distribution. More than half the population of continental United States, or a total of 83,929,863 persons lived in 168 such areas in 1950. It is these populous areas, these counties, that play so dominant a role in the nation's manufacturing (Figure 2–4).

It is seen that a standard metropolitan area includes far more land than is confined within its political or city limits. Geographically considered, however, this arrangement seems proper; flying over the area would convince one that the whole really constitutes one city. Thus New York City has expanded far beyond the city limits, crowding the arms and tributaries of New York Bay and Long Island Sound in both New Jersey and Connecticut. Chicago, too, is not just the city incased within definite political limits,

[9] "Syracuse Tackles Its Future," *Fortune,* May 1943, pp. 120 ff. "Future Toledo," *Life,* September 17, 1945, pp. 87 ff.

[10] An outline of master planning procedure was compiled in 1942 by the National Resources Planning Board, and, with the aid of consultants supplied by the Board, was demonstrated in 1942 and 1943 in Corpus Christi, Salt Lake City, and Tacoma. This outline in pamphlet form is *Action for Cities — A Guide for Community Planning,* Public Administration Service, 1313 East 60th Street, Chicago. See, also, "So You're Going to Plan a City," *Fortune,* January 1943, pp. 123 ff.

[11] Efficient city planning involves synthesizing the contributions of the architect, engineer, economist, biologist, geographer, geologist, physician, psychologist, political scientist, sociologist, and statistician.

[12] Bureau of the Census, *Population of Standard Metropolitan Areas, April 1, 1950,* p. 3. Washington, D. C.: Government Printing Office, November 5, 1950; and Robert C. Klove, "The Definition of Standard Metropolitan Areas," *Economic Geography,* Vol. 28, April 1952, pp. 95-104.

but extends along the shore of Lake Michigan for more than 100 miles and includes Waukegan, South Chicago, Whiting, and even Gary — all as much a part of it as the "loop."

Pittsburgh, capital of the world's iron and steel industry, means not the city *per se* but the Pittsburgh District, which includes besides Allegheny County, Beaver, Washington, and Westmoreland counties and all the

In many ways suburbs are as much a part of the city as though they shared in its municipal government. The big city everywhere appears to be losing out; it is growing outside its boundaries rather than inside. In the largest metropolitan areas the rate of growth in the outer rings is four times greater than the rate of growth in the central cities. In the Boston, Los Angeles, Pittsburgh, and San Francisco areas, the suburban residents

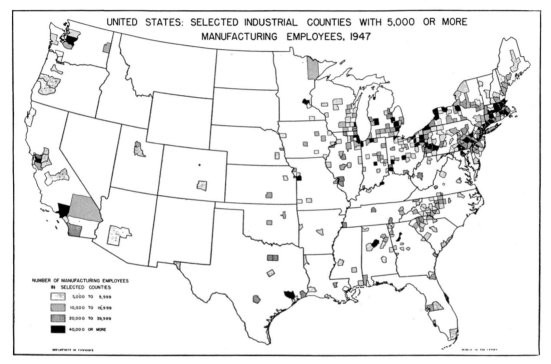

Figure 2–4. The counties shown on this map play the dominant role in the nation's manufacturing. (U. S. Bureau of the Census.)

cities, townships, and boroughs in their three river valleys. Here is an area with 2,213,000 people, all with much the same economic interests. Pittsburgh, defined politically, has only 677,000, or roughly about one third of this number. Pittsburgh is a splendid example — though an extreme one — of an actual city spreading beyond the municipal corporation.

Suburbs: The Overflow of Cities. No one thing connected with urban centers has been more important in recent years than the spilling out of people into the suburbs.

outnumber the city dwellers. The movement from cities to suburbs has been stimulated by the desire to get more fresh air and sunshine, lower taxes, cheaper land, and better parking accommodations.

This overflow of the cities began in the early 1920's with increased automobile ownership and better roads, but reached its greatest acceleration in the 1940's. During the period 1940-1950 the population of the United States increased about 19 millions and nearly half of this gain was in the suburbs of 168 metropolitan areas. The gain was 35 per cent for the suburbs and 13 per cent for the central cities.

Suburbanization has been made possible by improvements in transportation, especially by the automobile. The motor car was a mere curiosity in 1900, but in five decades it transformed cities, created metropolitan areas, attracted people from remote districts into the urban trade territory, and enticed city populations into suburbs. Car ownership increased from 29,500,000 in 1941 to 40,-160,000 in 1950. The suburb, however, must rely upon the central city for its economic and social well being:

> The model suburb, whether it is industrial or residential, however superior, aloof, and detached it may believe itself to be, has its basis of existence and draws much of its sustenance from the noisy, grimy city of which economically and culturally it is an integral part, but from which it has managed to remain independent politically.[13]

[13] National Resources Committee, *Our Cities: Their Role in the National Economy,* p. 35. Washington, D. C.: Government Printing Office, 1937.

Prospects for Future City Growth. People who can be objective in their thinking admit that the great cities have grown too big; places of abode are too crowded, and too close to the noise and fumes of the street, are constantly exposed to smoke and grime, get too little sunshine, and are bad for health. If this be true and, if 64 per cent of the total population of the United States is now urban, then the entire nation should be concerned regarding the future size and internal arrangement of our cities.

The ideal goal to work toward is a city with a population somewhere between 20,000 and 50,000. Separate small cities of this size, retaining their character and identity, possess real advantages and amenities and, by co-operative action, could provide the facilities and cultural attractions now available only to large and wealthy cities.

Cities and Manufacturing

We have seen that cities are functional and that from the standpoint of geography there

Figure 2–5. Cities Service Refinery on the Calcasieu River in Louisiana. About a decade ago this 2,300 acre site was a wilderness of brush and scrub pine. The river provides water for the cooling processes of the refinery and gives access for ocean-going tankers to the Gulf of Mexico. (Courtesy of Cities Service Company.)

are nine types. By and large, however, a close relation exists between manufacturing and cities, and most of Anglo-America's manufacturing is carried on in cities.

At first manufacturing was a home enterprise and, therefore, an unimportant factor in urbanization. But very soon—by the close of the eighteenth century—the factory system was introduced into New England through the fabrication of cotton and woolen textiles and of shoes. Thus began the concentration of factory workers and the birth of the industrial city.

Certain types of industries that are dangerous or unpleasant to have near large urban agglomerations either have been or are being located on the outskirts of large cities or in the country (Figure 2–5). These include plants making chemicals, explosives, synthetic rubber, paper and leather, and those engaged in oil refining and smelting.

The economic history of both Canada and the United States shows conclusively that manufacturing and urbanism are inclined to go hand in hand and that the dominant influence in the growth of the majority of their cities has been manufacturing, because growing factories and mills employ vast numbers of people. Industries also locate in cities because they require a great variety of materials and services, and these are most available in the large urban area.

Once the experimental period is past and commercial production has begun, manufacturing goes through two stages: (1) pronounced and increasing concentration in a given area during industrial youth, and (2) a redistribution or decentralization away from that area during maturity.

Concentration. When many units of the same industry locate in a given city, the industry is said to be *concentrated* there. The success of the initial plant generally indicates that the original location was a satisfactory one.

Concentration occurs when industry is young and fast-growing, for certain advantages accrue from having several plants located close together when they fabricate the same kind of products. Among these advantages are the following: the principal market

may be there or at least nearby; a pool of labor and all kinds of labor are assured; power, raw materials, and capital are all available (local bankers understand the industry well); service industries are present (machine repair and machine construction); and municipal and other ordinances are apt to favor the industry. This has been the case in the development of New England's shoe, textile, and brass industries, of Richmond's cigarette industry, and of Akron's rubber industry. The biggest single advantage was the low cost of manufacturing, whereas the biggest disadvantage, once the entire country became the market, was the high cost of distribution.

Inertia. Despite the trend towards decentralization, a strong force tends to perpetuate manufacturing in a given place once it has become thoroughly established. This is frequently described as the "inertia of invested capital." The situation is thus well stated:

It is very easy, on paper, to overrate or underrate the advantages or disadvantages of any producing district. Freight rates may be made to appear of paramount importance, for the thing is done on every working day of the Interstate Commerce Commission. The steel industry is largely a fixed thing. Plants cannot be moved, and the relative production of different districts can change only gradually, chiefly by growth at one point and decadence at another, a slow process at most.[14]

Decentralization. When industries reach technical maturity, they appear to find less advantage in the region or city than when they were young. Factors that contribute to decentralization are:

1. Shifts in population (some students of the geography of manufactures do not consider this to be an important factor).
2. Wide distribution of electrical power.
3. Sharply rising freight costs.
4. Widespread development of hard surface roads and the ease of moving raw materials by truck; 75 per cent of the

[14] Editorial, *The Iron Age*, Vol. 121, No. 24, June 14, 1925, p. 1704.

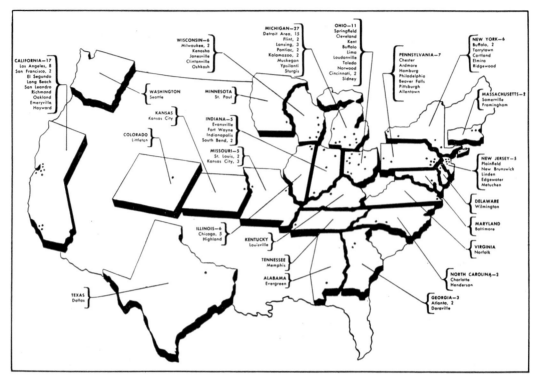

Figure 2–6. Automobile assembly plants. Materials for these plants come from all 48 states and some 60 foreign countries. The assembly plant charges a delivered price based on the completed car rather than on the cost of parts. (Courtesy *Automobile Facts.*)

nation's total freight tonnage now moves by truck.

5. High cost of living in congested areas.
6. Inequalities of the tax burden.
7. Standardization of industrial processes.
8. Labor troubles in large centers of concentration.
9. Cramped and inefficient plants and sites.
10. Changed financial status.
11. Elimination of the basing-point system in some industries.
12. Closer and more satisfactory relations between management and labor in smaller places.
13. Greater danger from bombing (in the event of war).
14. The popularity of the assembly plant.

The Assembly Plant. As the population shifts in the United States, many industries set up assembly plants in new market areas. Such an arrangement permits primary man-

ufacturing to be kept near the raw materials while the advantages of improved labor, markets, and reduced transport accrue through the assembly of the final product near the new market centers. Foremost among these industries has been the automotive. No product as heavy and competitive as the motor car can long be centered in one producing area for national sales. It has been able to do so for many years only because the automobile was a new thing that everyone wanted and hence was willing to pay freight charges from Detroit. While the Southern Michigan Automobile Subregion still is the automotive center of Anglo-America, assembly plants in other places play an ever increasing and important role in the industry (Figure 2–6).

Is Industry Really Abandoning the City? With so many factors encouraging decentralization, is industry actually abandoning the cities — the former centers of concentration? The answer appears to be in the negative: much of what is called decentral-izaton is not that but is recentralization or diffusion, where industries move to the out-skirts and the hinterlands of the large cities. By so doing, they acquire more appropriate locations as part of an even larger central-ized pattern, the metropolitan area. In most instances the close ties between the moved plants and the central cities continue.

Cities and Diversified Industry. Some cities are almost one-industry cities: Lynn—shoes; Akron—rubber; Youngstown—steel; Detroit—automobiles. Dependence upon a single industry, during depressions has meant suffering for the entire city as well as for the people of nearby farms and of the com-munities that supply parts. Actually, com-paratively few, if any, modern large Anglo-American cities are wholly dependent upon a single industry; yet the condition of the dominant one affects the life of the entire community. Thus Detroit with its growing automotive industry prior to 1929 flourished with a most reckless abandon, but after this date it encountered the toughest kind of de-pression problems and there was a decided out-movement of people during the 1930's.

Some cities are more diversified in their industrial enterprises. Thus Cleveland, Buf-falo, and Chicago have different "atmos-pheres" from Detroit, Akron, or Youngstown. Cleveland is primarily an iron and steel and metalworking center, with emphasis on pre-cision parts which go into automobiles, air-planes, household appliances, and industrial equipment. It makes about 25 per cent of the automotive parts used by the big auto-motive companies. It does not go into the "deepest valleys"—it does not suffer quite so much—during severe depressions as does the single-industry city.

Diversification then is the opposite of spe-cialization and involves the presence of con-trasting types of manufacture in the same general area.

The Big City, Manufacturing, and the Atomic Bomb

We know that most of the manufacturing of Anglo-America occurs in big cities and

their suburbs. We also know that a nation's political strength today is directly propor-tional to its industrial capacity. We know, too, that a very considerable percentage of our industries is to be found in concentrated areas (iron and steel in Pittsburgh, Youngs-town, Cleveland, and the Chicago area; au-tomobiles in Detroit; rubber in Akron, *ad infinitum*) and is, accordingly, vulnerable to attack by air.

Since not a single area in Anglo-America is immune from possible attack and since many industries are largely concentrated, most of our manufacturing capacity is highly vulner-able (Figure 2–7). The danger of a sneak attack becomes great because of the possible decisive advantage which could accrue to a powerful enemy by choosing his own time, place, and mode of attack.

The protection of industrial production is imperative for survival in case of war. For this reason the federal government has pressed for dispersal of those industries par-ticularly inseparable from the defense effort. Twenty-five per cent of our total population is concentrated in 12 urban areas of a mil-lion inhabitants or more and with a com-bined population of 37,595,460.[15]

Cities of 40,000 to 50,000 are considered too small to present attractive targets for atomic bomb attack. Such cities invariably are separated from each other by belts of open land that keep them from forming col-lective targets. It is these cities that now should be acquiring the new plants accord-ing to the National Security Resources Board.[16]

Great as the threat appears to be, little has been done to give either Canada or the United States a pattern of dispersed small cities located (1) singly, (2) in small clus-ters, and (3) in large metropolitan agglom-erations. The reason appears to be that most Americans and Canadians do not seriously entertain the theory that their cities will be bombed. Americans enjoyed the psychologi-

[15] Bureau of the Census, *Population of Urban-ized Areas, April 1, 1950.* Washington, D. C.: Gov-ernment Printing Office, February 1, 1951.

[16] National Security Resources Board, *Is Your Plant a Target?* Washington, D. C.: Government Printing Office, 1951.

Figure 2–7. An example of industrial vulnerability. In few areas in the world is manufacturing so concentrated as in parts of this region. An atomic bomb dropped on this area would inflict incalculable damage. (Courtesy of *The Military Engineer.*)

cal protection from their two great oceans so long and had the idea that they were safe so indelibly impressed upon their minds that they continue to live in a fool's paradise. Still another reason is that they escaped from the two worst wars in the world's history without invasion and have accordingly developed the idea that it can't happen here. As nations, neither yet thinks in terms of a round earth and short air routes (great circles) across the polar regions. Yet unless war can be prevented, or at least as long as atomic bombs can be used in war, it seems criminal from a military standpoint to permit urban areas to grow larger and larger.

The Geography of Manufactures

We have seen that cities and manufacturing are almost inseparable — that the greater part of our manufacturing takes place in urban centers. This does not result from mere chance; there are good reasons for it. The location of manufacturing is a matter of science and the wise selection of a place for a plant requires application of geographic principles. The best location for a factory involves relationships with areas of markets, materials, power, and labor which form an unshakable base upon which executives may make plans with confidence. Competition is the force that makes manufacturers pay careful attention to costs and to the location of the plant. The factors of cost are all-important because an industry dies if its costs of production become too high. In fact, the basic reason for spatial differentiation in the location of manufacturing is spatial differentiation in costs of manufacture operations.

Time changes all, and can make what is good factory location today bad factory location tomorrow. The science of industrial location is dynamic, not static.

In the location of any great industry, such as iron and steel, furniture, meat packing, agricultural implements, machine tools, chemical, rubber, textile, and others, there are the major factors (*concerned with location*), and the minor factors (*concerned with site*).

Major Factors in the Location of Manufacturing. Most great manufacturing industries in the United States were, with few exceptions, not purposely and deliberately located in their present situations. They sprang up for the most part in the home town of some individual who had sufficient capital to start a factory. The market was local. Transportation was poorly developed, and raw materials had to be procured near the plant. The better situated of these enter-

prises prospered, but many of those badly located lost money, withered, and finally disappeared. "A deserted or dismantled factory is a pathetic tribute to human incompetence or changing economic conditions. Mistakes are often irrevocable and moves always costly."[17]

Thus manufacturing as much as agriculture has been and is influenced by favorable or unfavorable natural environmental conditions. It is unthinkable that the great iron and steel industry of Anglo-America, in which billions of dollars are invested, emerged as a result of chance or human whim; yet so rapid have been the industrial changes in Anglo-America that some steel-plant locations represent definitely maladjusted loci under present conditions. Where this is the case, however, it is usually because subsequent changes, unforseen when the plants were started, have occurred. Industrial locational factors are both complex and numerous.

Proximity to market. According to many authorities, the most vital location factor in manufacturing is the market. Types of industries that located near their markets are:

1. The expansional ones, which make products more bulky than their raw materials, for example; agricultural implements, pianos, boxes, and barrels.

2. Those which make fragile or perishable products — ice cream, bakery goods, glass, and china ware. (Improved techniques of packing and shipping tend to make location less important with this type.)

3. Those which cater to rapidly changing technological devices — textile machinery, for example.

4. Those which supply a whimsical market such as women's millinery.

Some students of industrial location believe that the relation of markets to plant location has received too much emphasis. Generally speaking, however, the importance of this factor is in direct ratio to the transportation rate on the products.

---

[17] C. Langdon White and George T. Renner, *Geography: An Introduction to Human Ecology,* p. 639. New York: D. Appleton-Century Co., 1936.

Figure 2–8. Making charcoal — the fuel for reducing iron ore — in the early days. The charcoal burners stacked the sticks on end in a pile, plastered turf and loose earth over it, leaving a small chimney in the center, and then lighted the pile. The charring took three to ten days. (Courtesy of American Iron and Steel Institute.)

Proximity to raw materials. A major location factor for certain types of manufacturing has been and still is nearness to the source of raw materials. Since the cost of transporting raw materials is so very important, certain kinds of industries find it imperative to be near their raw materials. Especially does this hold for two types of industries — those handling perishable commodities and those where there is considerable loss of weight in the process. Canning, cheese making, and

Figure 2–9. Early American Furnace. The preferred location of early furnaces was on a stream next to a hillside. Note covered bridge to charging platform, water wheel, blast pipe to tuyere, and cast house at right. (Courtesy of *United States Steel News.*)

sugar milling are simple but good examples of the first, since their raw materials could not be shipped far without spoilage. Cement-making and smelting of ores are good examples of the second type.

Proximity to power. After machine manufacturing began and until 30 or 40 years ago, the dominant factor in locating a plant was the proximity to power, because, before the era of electricity and its transmission, industries had to be near a source of stationary power. The first iron furnaces were erected in the heart of a forest—the source of charcoal (Figure 2–8); when the timber was mined out, the furnace, which was a simple and relatively inexpensive structure (Figure 2–9), was abandoned and a new one constructed elsewhere in a tract of virgin timber. Another example is New England's widely scattered pioneer textile mills, which squatted beside almost every waterfall except in valleys too narrow and too steep to provide a site. Water power was at first indisputably the basic physical factor in establishing cotton manufacturing in New England. Still another example is the aluminum-smelting industry, which is a voracious consumer of electric power — using 20 times as much per ton as does the iron and steel industry. Demanding cheap power, the aluminum industry has frequently gone into areas rich in hydroelectric power but remote from large urban markets. More recently it has invaded the rich storehouse of natural gas in the Southwest.

The wider distribution of electric power has no doubt been a major factor in making

lar industry. Certainly Akron and New York City had advantages over any rival locations in the form of skilled and experienced labor for fabricating rubber goods and garments. The effect of this advantage tends to perpetuate the concentration of plants engaged in the same industry. With the passage of time, however, the enterprise and its main

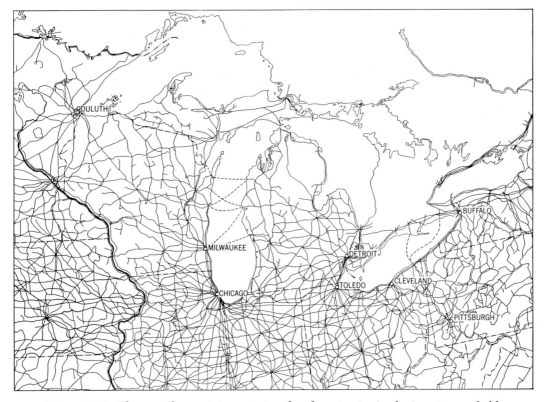

Figure 2–10. Chicago, the most important railroad center in Anglo-America, probably in the world, presents a bafflingly intricate maze of railway lines and facilities. The city serves as a terminal point for 21 trunk lines, which extend from Canada to the Mexican border and from the Atlantic to the Pacific. (Map drawn by David Dahle.)

many industries more foot-loose, for wherever a power line runs, there manufacturing and labor can make their home if other location factors are favorable.

Proximity to reservoirs of man power and skills. When an industry is young and its problems unfamiliar, it tends to be concentrated in those few places which provide the basic skills. Local concentration thus encourages the availability there of a particularly productive labor force for that particu-

center mature and the process becomes such that ordinary labor can be used. Dispersion of the industry then takes place.

Labor normally constitutes a factory's largest item of expense and savings in wages are quickly reflected in the profit account. Hence cities where labor is militant and highly organized tend to lose ground. Labor organizations have been a dominant factor in the decentralization of industry. However, labor, like manufacturing, is fast becoming nationally organized. Moreover, minimum wage laws passed by the federal government are leveling out local and sectional differences.

Labor has become highly mobile. Today more than 25 million men, women, and children live in states other than those in which they were born. Nearly 15 million civilians were migrants during the three years 1942–1944 and probably four million cross state lines every year in search of work. Almost half of California's population, for example, was born in other states.

Significance of transportation. Every outstanding transportation center is also a great manufacturing center (Figure 2–10). Every modern industry is located with proper regard to the "zone of minimum transportation cost." Some years ago Charles M. Schwab stated that the basic reason for manufactural decentralization away from one-industry cities was the desirability of median points between markets and raw materials.[18]

The significance of climate upon labor. The greatest amount of factory work is per-

formed when the temperature is between 40° and 70° F. Output is then constant. Above 75° output falls progressively. Twice as much work is done at 70° as at 93°.[19]

Before steel mills became greatly mechanized, workers became inefficient during the several weeks of "close" weather in July and August. Factory discipline suffered; workers became nervous, irritable, and tired; production suffered accordingly. Steel-mill workers now benefit from various appliances installed to make their tasks more comfortable, and modern machinery has made the work much easier, especially in summer. In many other industries, for example, textile and flour-milling, air conditioning has completely solved this problem (Figure 2–11).

Industrial water supply. Water is so critical in many industries that it merits consideration as a major location factor. Particularly is this true in the case of those industries making iron and steel, rubber, chemicals, and pulp and paper.

Probably more than five billion gallons of

---

[18] John A. Piquet, "The Effects of Industrial Plant Relocation," *Industrial Management,* Vol. 71, June 1926, p. 376.

[19] Massachusetts Development and Industrial Commission, *In Black and White: The Facts Concerning Industrial Advantages in Massachusetts,* p. 56. Boston: 1937.

Figure 2-11. A modern factory — a flour mill in Los Angeles. This four-story mill is one of the newest and most modern in Anglo-America. It is entirely pressurized in order to prevent the infiltration of dirt and impurities. (Courtesy of General Mills.)

water are utilized daily by the American iron and steel industry alone. Thirty tons are required to produce a single ton of pig iron. From 250,000 to 400,000 gallons are utilized in producing one ton of rayon. The total consumed by American industry is estimated at 25 billion gallons per day — about a fourth of the total water consumption of the nation. Quality is as important as quantity in many industries. Textile mills should have clean, soft water, and mills engaged in bleaching and dyeing need water of exceptional purity.

Most manufacturing districts have adequate water, but some are better off than others. Thus the iron and steel industries of Buffalo and Gary which utilize water from Lakes Erie and Michigan are better off than those of Sparrows Point and Fontana, which depend upon wells.

The Southwest, for example Texas, has recently discovered how important water is. With increasing industrialization — the area has suffered from the limited supply and the bad quality of much of it.

Capital. Capital is so mobile that it becomes available in almost any location where satisfactory financial returns from manufacturing are assured. In some industries, however, the amount needed is so great that only powerful corporations can afford to build plants. In the late 1940's, New England tried desperately to acquire an iron and steel industry of her own but all the major companies refused to locate there. Apparently New Englanders themselves have either been unable or unwilling to raise the necessary capital. To construct an integrated, well-balanced plant, including blast furnaces, coke ovens, open hearths, and rolling mills, costs well over 200 million dollars. Industries such as canning, meat packing, flour milling, and shoe and furniture manufacturing, on the other hand, require small capital; hence this factor is not always a major one in the location of a plant.

Minor Locational Factors. *Room and the cost of land.* Not infrequently an old well-established company, which started with what it considered to be an abundance of room, suddenly finds itself cramped. Un-

able or unwilling to purchase additional land at high prices, it often migrates. In Pittsburgh, some of the steel companies, hedged-in by rivers, steep hills, railroads, or neighboring plants, moved as far as 40 miles down the Ohio River so as to have plenty of room on low cost land.

Sometimes a firm profits by moving. One company, for example, bought its Chicago site in 1879 for $147,000, which it sold for $2,500,000 (enough to build the new factory) in 1908 when it moved to a suburb. It is interesting to note that in the great amount of advertising being carried on now in newspapers, magazines, and trade journals by railroads, cities, public utilities, and others much emphasis is being placed on this point.

The human factor. Difficult indeed is it to dissociate certain men from their industries and their cities. Man cannot succeed if the natural environmental factors do not favor a given industry, but often a given environment would not be used for a manufactural enterprise were it not for the vision, imagination, and determination of some man. Henry Ford could not have built up his great automobile empire had he gone to Bismarck, North Dakota, rather than Detroit. The following list is typically representative but by no means complete:

Andrew Carnegie..................steel — Pittsburgh
H. C. Frick.........coking coal, steel — Pittsburgh
Henry Ford...................automobiles — Detroit
B. F. Goodrich.................... ....rubber — Akron
Cyrus McCormick.......agricultural implements — Chicago
Ambrose Swasey......machine tools, telescopes — Cleveland
E. D. Libbey................................glass — Toledo
David Buick.....................automobiles — Flint
R. E. Olds.....................automobiles — Lansing
J. A. Dagyr...................................shoes — Lynn
John Deere...................steel plow — Moline
Samuel Slater...........cotton textiles — Pawtucket
Gustavus F. Swift..................meat — Chicago
P. D. Armour..................meat — Chicago

Taxation. Tax policies vary widely from state to state and from city to city. In order to secure lower taxes as well as more favorable conditions, Henry Ford, whose original factory was in Detroit, moved to the then small village of Highland Park.

Two Ohio cities, Cleveland and Lorain, vied during the depression of the 1930's for a steel plant: one to retain it, and the other to acquire it. Though several factors were involved, taxation was paramount. Cleveland's tax rate at the time was $2.76 per $100 valuation, Lorain's $2.20 — a differential of $0.56. Cleveland lost.

Cost of living. High cost of living makes high wages imperative. Accordingly, many industries have been moving from large cities to suburbs, small cities, towns, and villages, for labor is invariably cheaper in the smaller places. The cost of living presses hard upon city workers; the general cost of living — food, fuel, rent, and amusements — being at least 50 per cent higher than in smaller communities.[20]

Disposal of waste. About 28 per cent of American industries empty their solid wastes into streams. In fact this is a major reason why many industrial plants were located on rivers. When streams are inadequate, they fail to attract manufacturing plants. With increasing industrializaton, stream pollution has become in many places a major problem. When only one or two plants turn their wastes into a river, there may be no deleterious effects but when 50 or 100 large industries do so, then the stream may become a dead, vile thing — a scourge to all those living within its basin. Most industrial wastes are acid and many are highly toxic and poisonous. In some instances all fish are killed for scores of miles along a stream course. In some areas pollution has become so serious that it has alienated the inhabitants from the companies. The most progressive concerns are alert to public opinion and, seeing the handwriting on the wall, are of their own accord fighting stream pollution. Ford, for example, has recently spent more than $1.5 million on pollution control at its River

Rouge plant. In fact some cities and states, through regulatory agencies, now have laws and sanitary regulations against stream pollution.

General Location and Specific Site

In giving thought to industrial location, the company considers the *general location* and the *specific site*. The major factors usually determine the area within which conditions will be most satisfactory—that is where costs will be lowest with respect to assembly of raw materials and sale of the fabricated product in the market. Thus for many years the Lower Great Lakes Area has been considered the most scientific in Anglo-America for the manufacture of iron and steel. This does not, however, mean that *any* and *every* place in this large area would be satisfactory. Within it are great local differences; this introduces the problem of specific site which is concerned mostly with the minor locational factors. Some of these are physical, others social and political.

Let us now examine briefly a case history that is one of Anglo-America's finest examples of the application of the scientific method to an industrial location with reference to *both general location and specific site*:

GARY, INDIANA —
GREAT IRON AND STEEL CENTER

Position factors (general location)

1. Location in midst of a tremendous steel market.
2. Easy access to all raw materials.
3. A crossroads position, whereby the cheapest *direct route* between the coal and iron ore is crossed by the important Atlantic Seaboard-Chicago rail routes.
4. Proximity to Chicago enables management to transact business there conveniently.
5. Stimulating climate because of moderating influence of lake.
6. Densely populated surrounding general area; hence availability of a large and efficient *labor supply*.

Site Factors (specific site)

1. Fairly level and uniform topography

---

[20] The big-city dweller is by force of environment dependent daily on a thousand others for everything — food, heat, transit. He is supplied by middlemen at a price — a price that seems to increase with the size of the city.

(much freedom in planning the city — much room for expansion)

2. Location at extreme end of water route on Lake Michigan gives it an advantage over Milwaukee or even Chicago.
3. Adjacent lake provides an almost unlimited water supply.
4. Soil unproductive — much sand. This a real advantage; avoids necessity of paying high prices for first class agricultural land.
5. Distance from Chicago avoids high taxes and high land prices characteristic of a metropolis.
6. Laws less stringent in Indiana than in Illinois.

Proper and Improper Location: The Scientific Survey. Meat-packing plants are located in Omaha, flour mills in Buffalo, blast furnaces and steel mills in Gary and Pittsburgh, automobile plants in Detroit, and clothing establishments in New York City. These are, in each case, excellent locations.

Every industrialist is vitally interested in having his plant well situated. He must scrutinize each possible locus and compare production costs in all parts of the country. If the plant is badly located, the company pays for its error in high freight costs, labor troubles, inefficiency, and poor access and service to market. The industrialist may, accordingly, consider relocation, which always involves risks and uncertainties. Never should a move be undertaken without careful analysis of all advantages and disadvantages.

The science of industrial location is a relatively new one. Even though there are few industries in which one factor far outweighs any other, and even though there is wide scope for the exercise of judgment and discretion, it nevertheless is possible today to have a scientific survey made by trained personnel who go into the field and compare

[21] Among the business organizations equipped to locate an industry scientifically are Battelle Memorial Institute, Columbus, Ohio; Armour Research Foundation, Chicago; Franklin Institute, Philadelphia; Southern Research Institute, Birmingham; Midwest Research Institute, Kansas City; Southwest Research Institute of San Antonio, Texas; Arthur G. McKee Company, Cleveland; Austin Company, Cleveland; Stanford Research Institute, Menlo Park, California; Coverdale and Colpitts, New York City.

the advantages of a number of potential locations.[21]

A foreign rubber-tire manufacturing company, contemplating spending a million dollars on a new plant in the United States, knew it should locate somewhere in the American Manufacturing Belt. A careful scientific survey was made of some 20 cities — all possible locations. Each was graded for the specific requisites of the tire industry. Buffalo, with more points of advantage than any other city, got the plant. Some of the considerations which led to these conclusions were as follows: (1) There are fourteen lines of railroad operating into Buffalo. (2) The city is within easy access of power, fuel, and markets. (3) New York City, the nation's greatest port of entry and largest rubber-importing port, is within easy access. (4) Buffalo enjoys stable business conditions and its growth has been steady and normal over a period of years, free from the booms and mushroom growth of many other cities. (5) More than two hundred acres of land were available on the river making it possible to take advantage of any development in water transportation. (6) Cold water in unlimited quantity could be pumped directly from the Niagara River. (A huge supply of cold water is important because a rubber plant is a tremendous user of water.)

Thus industry has learned that in countries of huge size, varied resources, markets, and people, it no longer pays to locate factories just anywhere. There is a proper location for every industrial plant.

Treatment of Urban Centers

In the first edition of *Regional Geography of Anglo-America*, the cities of each region were included as an integral part of the regional study in each chapter. A considerable number of users of the book have suggested that the cities be listed in tabular form at the end of each chapter where they could be referred to easily and yet not interrupt the flow of the narrative. This procedure has been followed for all regions beginning with Chapter 4.

Selected Bibliography

"America's Changing Industrial Map," *Business Week,* August 7, 1948. pp. 65-72.

Anonymous, "The Obsolescence of Our Changing Cities," *Think,* Vol. 12, February 1946.

Tracy B. Augur, "Decentralization Can't Wait," *Tennessee Planner,* Vol. 9, October-December 1948, pp. 35-44.

"City Populations 'Exploded' During the Three Automobile Decades," *Automobile Facts,* Vol. 10, No. 1, December 1950–January 1951, pp. 4-5.

J. C. Cresswell, "Regional Study of Business Potentials in the Light of Migration of Industry, Population and Income Shifts," *Magazine of Wall Street,* Vol. 85, October 22, 1949.

"Dispersion of Facilities Sought for National Security," *World Oil,* Vol. 128, No. 9, January 1949, p. 44.

Chauncy D. Harris, "Suburbs," *American Journal of Sociology,* Vol. 49, July 1943, pp. 1-13.

Chauncy D. Harris, "A Functional Classification of Cities in the United States," *The Geographical Review,* Vol. 33, 1943, pp. 86-99.

Joyce Jackson, "Need for Basic Data in Selecting Plant Location," *Domestic Commerce,* Vol. 35, No. 6, June 1947, pp. 28-32.

Harold M. Mayer, "Geography and Urbanism," *Scientific Monthly,* Vol. 72, July 1951, pp. 40-42.

Dugald Macfadyen, "Sociological Effects of Garden Cities," *Social Forces,* Vol. 14, December 1935, pp. 250-256.

F. W. Mohlman, "Waste Disposal as a Factor in Plant Location," *Chemical Engineering Progress,* Vol. 46, July 1950.

National Security Resources Board, *National Security Factors in Industrial Location,* Document 66, Revised July 22, 1948, Washington, Mimeographed.

Office of Domestic Commerce, U. S. Department of Commerce, *Basic Industrial Location Factors,* Industrial Series No. 74. Washington, D. C.: June 1947.

3.

The American Manufacturing Belt

THE American Manufacturing Belt is the great industrial workshop of the nation (Figure 3–1). It is located mostly in northeastern United States but includes also parts of the provinces of Ontario and Quebec. A map showing the distribution of standard metropolitan areas, which indirectly portrays reservoirs of labor and the degree of industrialization, emphasizes the fact that manufacturing in Anglo-America has, for the most part, tended to concentrate in and near big cities. Urban agglomerations here, therefore, are predominantly industrial.

The Region

The American Manufacturing Belt is characterized by many areas of high manufacturing activity. Its dominant traits are urban interest and mode of life — themselves results of transport advantages and proximity to raw materials, power, labor, and markets. Actually the region consists of an insular concentration of industrial intensity in a sea of agriculture and dairying (Figure 3–2). There is no *total land* occupation by industrial plants, cities, and towns comparable with what is to be seen in the Agricultural Interior

with its even pattern of *farms, fields, pastures, and villages.* Farm land or pastures or wooded hills or mountains separate the various urban industrial centers one from another.

Thus manufacturing causes an intensive but spotty utilization of the land within any region dominated by it, in contrast to agriculture, which uses broad acres and covers them with a continuous pattern of farms. Within a given industrial area then, much less land is actually occupied by factories and mills than is generally supposed. In even so highly an industralized area as that engaged in making steel between Cleveland, Youngstown, and Pittsburgh, the so-called "Ruhr of America," only a relatively small part of the land is used industrially. In its space requirements, manufacturing is extremely modest, where as in its space utilization it is dynamic.

To a certain extent long rows of industrial cities are to be found along major transportation routes. One major route runs from New York Harbor up the Hudson to Albany and west to Buffalo. Here it breaks into two branches, one going north of Lake Erie through Canada to Detroit and Chicago, the

Figure 3–1. The American Manufacturing Belt leads Anglo-America in the manufacture of steel, and this industry is a "seed industry" whence all kinds of products come. From the steelmaker's furnaces pours metal for the thousands of things Americans consider *essentials*, from bridges to bicycles, from ships to scissors, from railroads to razors, from tunnels to tin cans. (Courtesy of Bankers Trust Company, New York.)

other south of Lake Erie through Cleveland and Toledo to Chicago. At Chicago routes fan out, though major stems extend northward to Milwaukee and southwestward to St. Louis (Figure 2–10). Coastwise routes extending from Baltimore to southern Maine early stimulated the growth of industry, making their tributary areas the original home of the American factory.

Manufacturing Districts

Though manufacturing has put its stamp on the American Manufacturing Belt, actual industrial production is spotty; in short there are large areas of meager manufactural equipment between numerous hives of industry. The belt is, therefore, divided into districts (Figure 3–3). But even within these, much of the land is not used for manufacturing. Possibly the best way to show manufactural use of the land is by districts.

Basis for Mapping Relative Manufacturing. No one factor suffices as an absolute measuring stick for manufacturing. Several factors have been used by different individuals. Sten De Geer based his boundaries on the number of wage earners in towns of more than 10,000 population.[1] Two weak-

[1] Sten De Geer, "The American Manufacturing Belt," *Geografiska Annaler*, Vol. 9, 1927, pp. 235-359.

nesses characterized this study: (1) manufacturing is not limited to cities of 10,000 or more persons, and (2) the study reflected the general distribution of population, since his wage earners were not all factory workers. Richard Hartshorne sensing the weakness above, decided that possibly ten per cent of the total population of any city might be engaged in manufacturing. He then took a

based on power per unit area.[3] Alfred J. Wright proposed that value added by manufacture be accepted as the criterion for the distribution and relative importance of manufacturing areas. Like De Geer he used cities with populations of 10,000 and more and like Strong insisted that *all* industries be included.[4] Clarence F. Jones believed that the county rather than the city of 10,000 or

Figure 3–2. The American Manufacturing Belt: an urban region of diversified industries.

figure of 500 workers in non-local industries as his minimum figure for an industrial city worthy of a place on his map.[2] Helen Strong, convinced that Hartshorne overemphasized concentration, included *all* manufacturing in her study. Her density of manufacturing was

more persons should be employed as the basic areal unit.[5] Chauncy Harris classified industrial cities functionally on the basis of employment in manufacturing.[6] The authors

[2] Richard Hartshorne, "A New Map of the Manufacturing Belt of North America," *Economic Geography*, Vol. 12, 1936, pp. 45-53.

[3] Helen Strong, "Regions of Manufacturing Intensity in the United States," *Annals of the Association of American Geographers*, Vol. 27, 1937, pp. 23-47.

[4] Alfred J. Wright, "Manufacturing Districts of the United States," *Economic Geography*, Vol. 14, 1938, pp. 195-200.

[5] Clarence F. Jones, "Areal Distribution of Manufacturing in the United States," *Economic Geography*, Vol. 14, 1938, pp. 217-222.

[6] Chauncy D. Harris, "A Functional Classification of Cities in the United States," *Geographical Review*, Vol. 33, 1943, pp. 86-99.

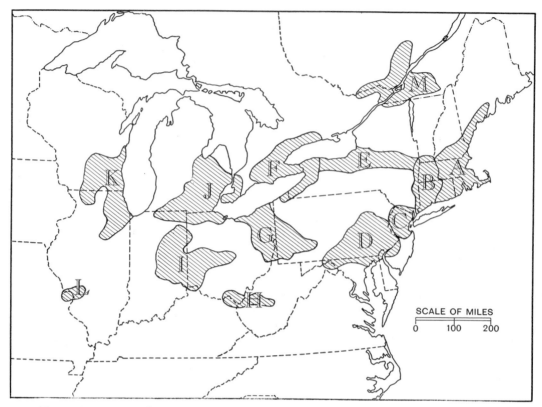

Figure 3–3. Principal manufacturing districts: (A) Eastern New England; (B) South-western New England; (C) Metropolitan New York; (D) Southeastern Pennsylvania; (E) the Mohawk Valley and the Ontario Plain; (F) the Niagara Frontier; (G) the Pittsburgh-Cleveland District; (H) the Great Kanawha Valley; (I) Inland Ohio-Indiana; (J) the Southern Michigan Automobile District; (K) the Chicago-Milwaukee District; (L) the St. Louis; (M) the Montreal – Ottawa – Trois Rivières District. (After Harts-horne and others.)

of this book use as the basis of their classification the regionalist's "feel" of the area; they draw a line around all large urban agglomerations (Figure 3–3).

Principal Districts of the American Manufacturing Belt

Eastern New England

The American industrial era had its beginning in this area's early cotton mills but the factory system did not attain prominence until the termination of the Civil War.[7] New England had the largest supply of potential factory workers (native-born and European

[7] Harvey Wish, *Society and Thought in Modern America: A Social and Intellectual History of the American People from 1865,* Vol. 2. New York: Longmans, Green and Co., 1952.

immigrants) and the greatest amounts of investment capital.

Included within this subregion are the industrial parts of Maine, New Hampshire, Rhode Island, Massachusetts, and Connecticut; in the last two states only those parts east of the Connecticut River are considered. Boston obviously is the dominating center. Of considerable importance also are Providence, Fall River and New Bedford.

This is an area of diversified light industry.

Formerly some type of manufacturing was followed in almost every village. Today most of the small mills are abandoned, but this district will not become one of ghost cities, for in spite of certain competitive weaknesses, it offers attractive conditions for the types of manufacturing that specialize in high-grade products that utilize skilled labor and are made from non-bulky or imported raw materials.

The Textile Industry: Cotton. New England was long the center of the nation's cotton textile industry and cotton-making still is important in every one of its states save Vermont. However, 75 per cent of all cotton textile workers and 90 per cent of the mills are in the two states, Rhode Island and Massachusetts. In fact Bristol County, Massachusetts, and Providence County, Rhode Island, have one half of New England's total active spindles. Here are the famous cotton-mill cities of Fall River, New Bedford, Pawtucket, and Woonsocket.

Among the early advantages of New England for the manufacture of cotton textiles were: (1) damp air, which is essential to prevent twisting and snarling during spinning and reduces breakage in weaving (in dry air frictional electricity causes the yarn to snarl and twist)[8]; (2) excellent water power facilities; (3) clean, soft water; (4) skilled labor, and (5) location in a major market area.

However, New England has yielded supremacy to the South in the manufacture of coarse and medium goods. It has lost scores of plants and millions of spindles. The decline which has been precipitous since 1920, results essentially from two conditions: (1) the failure to keep the plants as modern and efficient as those in the Southern Piedmont and (2) costlier labor and shorter working hours than in the South. This second factor involves also less freedom in terms of night work, for unions are strong in New England and extremely weak in the South.

Despite New England's loss of spindles, it is estimated that about one out of every five New England industrial workers is in

---

[8] The desired humidity is now supplied artificially.

textiles and that the area still makes the finest quality goods in America.

The Textile Industry: Wool. New England is the heart of the nation's woolen industry. In the early days it had local wool in addition to water power, clear, soft water, skilled labor, and an appreciable nearby market. Boston is the great wool-importing port of the nation, handling about 60 per cent of all the fiber used in the country. Almost half of the New England woolen mills are located in eastern Massachusetts with the other half shared by Maine and Rhode Island. The woolen industry falls naturally into two distinct branches — woolens and worsteds.

Woolen manufacturing is more concentrated than cotton manufacturing. Outstanding centers are Lawrence, Providence, Woonsocket, Holyoke, and Lowell, the first three being especially active in worsteds.

Unlike cotton-textile manufacturing, the woolen branch until recently had not migrated from New England, a circumstance attributable to the fact that the district is the style center for woolens and that the principal markets for such goods are obviously in the North. Recently, however, this trend has been reversed. Thirty-two mills closed in 1951, and the American Woolen Company, the nation's largest, operating 21 of its 24 mills in New England, announced in 1952 that it would move most of its plants into the South unless the differential in wages between New England and the South was closed and unless the amount of work given by employees for the wage paid was increased.

The Shoe Industry. New England leads the nation in shoe manufacturing, with eastern Massachusetts possessing the greatest concentration of plants. Adjoining parts of New Hampshire and Maine are important too. The chief locative factor is skilled labor, though access to leather and other materials and proximity to markets are important. Brockton, Haverhill, and Lynn are dominantly shoe towns — the first two concentrating on men's shoes, and the last on women's shoes.

New England cannot, however, indefinitely retain supremacy over other areas having large local markets and better access to raw materials. By 1950 New England's share of the national production had dropped to 32 per cent. So long as shoemaking depended upon skilled labor, New England dominated by virtue of its early start. However, mechanization, the system of leasing machinery, high labor costs, high rents, high taxes, difficulties with unions, all have fostered decentralization. Movement out of this district has been largely into the Middle West, though not to the exclusion of the Middle Atlantic States, the South, and the Pacific Coast. New York, Ohio, Illinois and Wisconsin all have become important in shoe manufacturing — a response to the westward migration of the center of population and hence of the market.

Metal Goods Industry. The manufacture of small metal wares finds almost ideal conditions here, for this industry utilizes skilled labor, caters to a national and international market, consumes little fuel, and assembles raw materials at comparatively little cost. This particular industry, making machine tools, electrical equipment, textile and other machinery, hardware, foundry products, and aircraft engines, all of which fit so well into the regional objective, gives employment to approximately 40 per cent of all New England factory labor.

Unfortunately, from the point of view of New Englanders, who want their own iron and steel production for supplying their metal-goods-industry materials — blooms, billets, bars, plates, sheets, slabs, and some wire — must be purchased from outside New England. Yet the nation's first iron and steel industry was born on the banks of the winding Saugus River near Lynn in 1646. This plant, comparable to contemporary ones in England, was productive until 1675 when it closed down because of the paucity and the high cost of materials and because of legal difficulties. Just recently this early industrial landmark has been restored. It was this plant at Saugus that spread a wave of iron-makers throughout New England and down the Atlantic Coast. During 1950 and 1951 there was much agitation for an integrated iron and steel plant in New England and, despite the

fact that many economists, engineers, and geographers believed such a mill could be economically and financially feasible as a branch operation of a major steel company and despite the fact that the Bethlehem Steel Corporation held an option to build a 250 million dollar plant in the New London-Waterford area, nothing happened. Bethlehem is reported to have reached its decision in response to a scientific survey made by a New York engineering firm. Another reason that has been advanced is the present custom followed by secondary steel industries of purchasing not more than half their requirements from a single primary iron and steel manufacturer.[9] Should New England consumers get only half their needs from the proposed New London plant, the mill would be unable to market its entire output in New England.

Some New England industrialists believe that two recent developments have changed the picture: (1) the termination of the basing-point system of pricing in the iron and steel industry; and (2) the discovery and the development of iron ore in Labrador and Quebec. They assert that iron ore, coking coal, and limestone can be assembled in New England on tide-water at less cost than at any center in the Middle West and that New England could use the entire output of the proposed plant. Apparently, however, New England capital is either unavailable or unwilling to undertake so great an investment — one in excess of 250 million dollars for an integrated plant.[10]

Southwestern New England

This district includes the parts of Massachusetts and Connecticut that lie west of the Connecticut Valley. Cities are strung along the Connecticut River like beads on a chain and additional important industrial centers lie in the smaller valleys of the Berk-

[9] John H. Thompson and Edward C. Higbee, *New England Excursion: Guidebook*, International Geographical Union, XVIIth International Geographical Congress, United States, 1952, p. 153. Washington, D. C.: 1952.

[10] "No Yankee Mill," *Business Week*, September 1, 1951, p. 25.

shire Hills. In this district factories specialize in diversified light products requiring high mechanical skill — machinery, tools, hardware, firearms, plastics, electrical goods, precision instruments, watches, and clocks. These are all products of high value and small bulk, which require little raw material and power and can easily stand transport charges to distant markets.

The Bridgeport area is an outstanding example of an area that manufactures diversified products. Its acres of factories pour out brassware, brake linings, electrical equipment, hardware, machinery, munitions, pharmaceuticals, rubber goods, tools, sewing machines, and typewriters.

From early days towns making the same products were in the same river valley, because expansion logically takes place along "topographic lines of least resistance." Thus the brass industry is strung along the Naugatuck Valley in Connecticut from Torrington to Bridgeport. The manufacture of metal products, especially electrical machinery and hardware, predominates in southwestern New England.

Metropolitan New York

The New York Metropolitan District, which comprises the small, concentrated area of New York City and its industrial suburbs, is one of superlatives. It is Anglo-America's most populous and cosmopolitan district and its most intense mixing-bowl. It has the best harbor and is the largest port, and it leads the entire continent in commerce, manufacturing, and finance. It also dictates the nation's styles and attracts the greatest number of tourists.

This district is located at the mouth of the navigable Hudson River on a well-protected deep-sea harbor and at the focus of major land and sea routes. By value it handles approximately one half of the nation's commerce. In 1951 foreign cargo passing through the port was worth 8 billion dollars. Its harbor consists of 7 bays, 4 rivers, 4 estuaries, and 42 different channels. The Hudson River scours out the mouth of the bay, keeping the channel deep. The direct water frontage is 771 miles, almost half of which has been developed. The harbor includes the Hudson River, the Upper Bay, the Narrows, the Lower Bay, Newark Bay, Kill Van Kull, Arthur Kill, East River, Flushing Bay, Harlem River, Buttermilk Channel, Bay Ridge Channel, Gravesend Bay, Sheepshead Bay, Sandy Hook Bay, and Raritan Bay. Most of these channels are deep enough to accommodate the largest ships afloat. Moreover, the harbor is kept deep with comparatively little dredging. The channel leading to the Atlantic is direct. The tidal range is so small that ships may come and go at almost any time. The rush of the tides from the sound to the ocean and back, however, is cursed by seamen because of the tricky whirlpool of Hell Gate, where two tides and a river meet and currents move back and forth with a velocity as great as six miles per hour. Staten Island and the bar of Sandy Hook afford fine protection from storms. Ice never blocks the harbor, though fog occasionally holds up traffic. At times the fog is so thick that ships and ferries cannot stir for several days.

New York is the only Atlantic port with an easy route through the Appalachians — the Hudson-Mohawk Depression (Figure 3-4). The Erie Canal (now the New York State Barge Canal) more than any other single factor contributed to New York's greatness as a port, for it made all the country between the Great Lakes and the Ohio River and between the Mississippi and the Atlantic tributary to the Atlantic Seaboard and largely to New York City. The New York Central Railroad, following the route of the Erie Canal, by 1851 had brought the steel rails from the Middle West almost to the tip of Manhattan. Other railroads have established marine and rail termini on the west side of the Hudson as near to the New York Central as possible. All 12 railroads serving the port maintain large fleets of lighters, barges, and tugboats. Cargoes are transferred to rail heads by lighters.

Congestion. The great amount of water, while advantageous to commerce, is a barrier to traffic between Manhattan and the rest of the New York area. For decades attempts have been made to mitigate the traffic congestion in and about the city. New York's subways, elevated lines, surface cars, busses and taxis handle more than 3 billion passengers annually. In 1950, 60 million cars crossed the Hudson River from New York to New Jersey and back via bridges and tunnels alone.

Because of the small area and the hordes

could move 200 to 600 miles by rail for what it costs to send it by lighter across New York Harbor.

Population. The white population of New York in 1626, the year Manhattan passed from the Indians, was less than 200. In 1950 the population of New York City had reached a total of 7,891,957. If we add

Figure 3–4. Scene in the Mohawk Valley — outstanding route into the interior. Note the concentration of parallel transportation facilities. In addition to the New York State Barge Canal, the Mohawk River, and two sets of railroad tracks there is, in the lower right-hand corner, a hard-surface road partly obscured by shrubbery. In its advertising the New York Central emphasizes the fact that it uses the only water-level route through the mountains. (Courtesy of the New York Central System.)

of human beings that come and go into the city daily, the most elaborate subway system ever conceived has been built, while above ground is operated an extensive bus system. Vehicular tunnels have been constructed — the longest in the world; great suspension and steel-arch bridges have been built across the rivers. Railroads enter Manhattan via tubes under the Hudson and East rivers. Local movement of goods over the area's water barriers is expensive; a ton of freight

to this population that included in the urbanized area, the total is 12,296,117. The greater part of this population is concentrated in Manhattan and Long Island and in the peninsulas of the Bronx and Bayonne.

New York's foreign-born population, representing every part of the globe, is extraordinarily high. More than one half of the foreign-born whites have come from eastern and southeastern Europe and less than a third from northwestern Europe.

New York City also draws heavily on the native white populations of all 48 states.

Commerce. New York, the greatest port in the world, has a ship entering and a ship leaving every ten minutes of the daylight hours. Possibly 400 ships line its docks daily.

The Hudson River, including the New Jersey side, handles more than half the port's business based on value, and yet it occupies only about ten miles out of a total of 771 for the entire port. The imports include chiefly fuel oil and gas, crude oil, raw sugar, fruits, coffee, flaxseed, raw natural rubber, raw silk, gypsum, and paper, whereas the principal exports are iron and steel scrap, refined petroleum products, automobiles and parts, wheat and flour, and livestock feeds. The chief commodities in the coastwise trade are crude oil, gasoline, and bituminous coal.

Statisticians estimate that one out of every ten persons gainfully employed in the New York district earns his living directly or indirectly from shipping or kindred enterprises.

Finance. New York City has become the financial center of the world, having replaced London following the First World War. Because New York is the financial center of the United States, many national concerns have selected it for their headquarters. This is true, for example, of the big oil, steel, and automobile companies whose actual manufacturing operations are carried on elsewhere. Very recently, however, a considerable post-war decentralization of industries, management, investment firms, and stores from over-crowded New York to the suburbs has occurred and is continuing.[11]

Manufacturing. New York's greatness depends more upon commerce than upon industry, more upon its great rail-end piers in Jersey City and its huge berths for enormous liners on lower Manhattan than upon its factories. Nonetheless, it is the nation's leading industrial center.

Unlike Chicago, Pittsburgh, and Cleveland, the New York area, because of competition for available land, does not manufacture heavy products such as pig iron and steel. Its industries are secondary rather than

basic, consisting of those fabricating such items as clothing, printed materials, refined petroleum products, chemicals, tobacco, metal goods, fertilizer, asphalt, metals, soap, sugar, and meat.

The Garment Industry. The garment industry, America's fourth largest based on value of products, operates in all but 7 of the 48 states. This industry, New York's largest, is highly concentrated in the center of the city between Forty-second Street on the north, Twenty-fifth Street on the south, Eighth Avenue on the west, and Fifth Avenue on the east. Three quarters of the 200,-000 Manhattan garment laborers work in an area 200 acres in size. This indicates that, unlike the steel and automobile industries, garment factories, which thrive in the crowded conditions of a city, do not need huge plants. The shops are generally small and there are 7,000 of them, the average employing only about 30 workers. More persons are employed in Manhattan's garment industry than in Detroit's automotive or Pittsburgh's steel industries. Probably no part of the city is so congested as the garment center; the streets are clogged (Figure 2–2) and overcrowding increases factory overhead. Hence a large part of the industry has moved into skyscrapers. The higher cost of housing here is reflected in higher wages — the differential between the Midwest and New York City ranging from 15 to 25 per cent. New York promises to remain the capital of the garment industry, however, so long as it can maintain itself as the style and buying center of the United States. The importance of the city in both the garment and textile industries is indicated by the fact that New York is also the foremost cotton-textile market in the world; each year it handles 10 billion yards of cotton goods and its mercantile houses and selling organizations distribute 90 per cent of the nation's cotton textiles.

About three fourths of the nation's women's clothing and about one third of the men's wear is made in New York City.

New York's advantages for making garments. If New York overwhelmingly dominates the garment industry, it must enjoy

[11] *Business Week,* November 22, 1952, p. 189.

advantages over competing cities. Foremost among these advantages are:

(1) The clothing industry is a *city industry,* for cities supply it with both *market* and *labor.* In a big city materials can be transferred quickly to different contractors and suppliers in various stages of production so that quick style changes can be met.

(2) Acceptance by the trade of New York City as the national clothing market. Buyers accordingly congregate from all parts of the nation to compare prices and goods of competing sellers.

(3) Ample room. Big tracts of land are not essential. Machine units may be housed in several hundred square feet.

(4) Auxiliary services. *Any item* needed by the industry is quickly available.

(5) Momentum of an early start.

The Chemical Industry. The New York area is probably the continent's largest single chemical center, with between 15 and 20 per cent of the industry, though at present there is much decentralization into the South, the Southwest, the Pacific Coast, the south shore of Lake Erie, the Great Kanawha Valley, and elsewhere. Most plants are very large and are growing larger.

The most important branch of the business in this district produces heavy chemicals including acids, ammonia, soda, and potash. The harbor location enables raw materials to be assembled from far distant areas. Furthermore, the finished products find a huge market close by.

The roomier New Jersey part of the area leads in the fabrication of heavy chemicals. The finer chemicals, particularly pharmaceuticals, are made mostly in Brooklyn.

Oil Refining. Metropolitan New York is an outstanding petroleum refining center, though less important than formerly. Most of the newer and larger refineries are being located either very close to heavily concentrated marketing areas, or on water routes with cheap access to concentrated markets and within relatively short pumping distances from the producing fields. Metropolitan New York exemplifies the first, the Texas-Louisiana Gulf Coast the second. Since it is cheaper to ship crude oil than refined prod-

ucts, many of the major oil companies carrying on business in the metropolitan district, have plants in the port. Vast quantities of crude oil are brought to this area by pipeline from the interior and by tanker from California, the Gulf Coast, and Caribbean Latin America. Dependence upon tankers was forcibly brought to the attention of nearly all Americans during World War II (summer of 1942) when German submarine packs sank many and drove others elsewhere. It was at this time that the government built the "Big Inch" and the "Little Big Inch" pipelines for overland transport of crude oil and gasoline from Texas to the East Coast.

New York's refineries are located on the New Jersey side of the Hudson River because of storage-space demands, obnoxious fumes, and fire and explosion hazards. Five New Jersey plants have plots averaging a square mile or more in extent. Bayonne is the principal refining center of the area. Several years ago, however, the Standard Oil Company (New Jersey) announced curtailment of refining operations at Bayonne in favor of expanding interests in the Gulf of Mexico area. It also partially dismantled its Eagle Works in New Jersey.

All refineries in the area are situated on the waterfront to facilitate imports of crude oil and exports of finished products. For the enterprise to be competitive, neither the incoming crudes nor the outgoing finished products can be handicapped by excessive freight charges.

Slaughtering of Livestock. This industry is presented because of its uniqueness. The unmistakable national trend in this business is for packing plants to locate near the growing and fattening grounds. New York ranks high only because it has a tremendous orthodox Jewish population which requires Kosher meats in sizable quantities.

In this area the animals are slaughtered and the meats prepared under the close supervision of the rabbi or a representative of the Jewish faith. The preparation of these meats is thus a religious rite. "Sticking" the animals is not permitted; the throat must be cut. After slaughter each animal is given a careful physical examination, particular at-

---

tention being given to lungs and stomachs and only healthy animals are accepted. The Hebrew word "Kosher" means "clean."

Cuts for the Kosher trade are usually sold within 72 hours after slaughter. Most of the cattle eaten in Metropolitan New York are raised in southwest Virginia and West Virginia and are fattened in Lancaster County, Pennsylvania.

Southeastern Pennsylvania

Southeastern Pennsylvania comprises the area from Philadelphia to Wilmington, together with Baltimore and smaller areas in New Jersey, Delaware, and Maryland. No other subregion shows such a combination of heavy and light manufacturing — everything from iron and steel to silk. Its factories turn out about ten per cent of the nation's fabricated goods. Though Philadelphia is the hub, much business and trade, especially in the Lehigh Valley, flows to New York City. Baltimore, southeasternmost point of this district as well as of the entire American Manufacturing Belt, is noted both for commerce and manufacturing. Industrial development in this district is no recent development; it is almost as old as that of New England.

Iron and Steel. This area, a major producer of iron and steel, has long been important and is benefiting from much new construction. Bethlehem Steel Corporation's plants at Sparrows Point and elsewhere are of long standing, but the United States Steel Corporation's mill at Morrisville, Pennsylvania, and National Steel Corporation's mill at nearby Paulsboro on the New Jersey side of the Delaware River south of Philadelphia are new. Plans are being made by two other big corporations to locate iron and steel mills between the Philadelphia-Camden area and Trenton. These new plants on navigable water, which is a locational trend away from the traditional location on or near the Lower Great Lakes, results primarily from three circumstances and a fourth possibility:

(1) The abolition of the basing-point system in selling iron and steel, which made it econom-

Figure 3–5. U. S. Steel Corporation's Fairless Works on the Delaware River near Morrisville, Pennsylvania. This 450 million dollar integrated mill was converted from farm land to steel production in less than two years. Never in American history had so huge a steel plant been constructed at one time. The industry here utilizes imported iron ore and supplies part of the big urban-industrial market extending from Philadelphia to New York and Boston. (Courtesy of United States Steel Corporation.)

ically unprofitable for Pittsburgh, Youngstown, Buffalo, Cleveland, and the Midwestern centers to compete with Sparrows Point, for example, for the big Atlantic Seaboard market — Boston to Baltimore [12].

(2) The decline in reserves of high grade ore in the Lake Superior District, and growing dependence upon Chile, Venezuela, Brazil, Liberia, and elsewhere.

(3) The big market along the seaboard — one of the largest in the world.

(4) Strategic location for reaching foreign markets if these should ever become important.

Morrisville, Pennsylvania. At Morrisville, the Delaware River makes a big bend, the stream changing direction (Figure 3–5). Here on a 3,800 acre tract of land, the United States Steel Corporation has constructed at

---

[12] In the steel industry it is the customer who pays the freight charges on the product from the mill. If the customer's plant be close to the steel mill, his charges are small; if far away, they will be high — a decisive handicap in competition.

a cost of more than 450 million dollars the Fairless Works, an integrated plant spreading over 2,000 acres, employing 6,000 workers and adding 1,800,000 ingot tons to the nation's annual steel capacity. The additional 1,800 acres are insurance for expansion should that become necessary. Never before has so complete a plant been constructed all at once. The project, which was on the drawing boards for 4,000 hours of engineering time, is one of the best examples in Anglo-America of the scientific location of industry.

The raw materials come from widely separated and distant sources: iron ore from Cerro Bolivar in Venezuela, coal from Pennsylvania and West Virginia and limestone from Pennsylvania.

Since the steel industry is a "seed industry," it is begetting tremendous growth in other types of manufactures — particularly those using and those selling to iron and

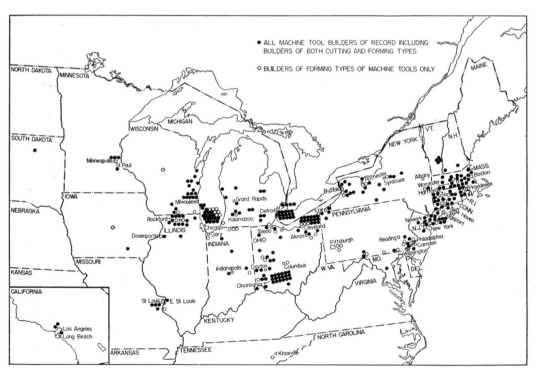

Figure 3–6. Distribution of the machine tool industry in the United States. The builders are scattered across the country from New England to the Mississippi River. Note particularly New England, the Middle Atlantic States, and the Middle West. (Map based on data from National Machine Tool Builders' Association.)

steel: factories benefiting each other tend to migrate to common centers.

Sparrows Point, Maryland. Until recently this was the world's largest and America's only important tidewater iron and steel industry. The plant was located here after a careful engineering study had indicated that Sparrows Point was the most desirable site on the Atlantic Seaboard. Though all of the raw materials come from some distance

major importance, the area under consideration — Delaware River and Bay, Chesapeake Bay and the New York area — build about three fifths of our tonnage.

The Delaware River, with yards at Philadelphia, Camden, Chester, and Wilmington, is the most important shipbuilding river in Anglo-America and hence merits the appelation — "the American Clyde." Nature endowed the Delaware more generously, how-

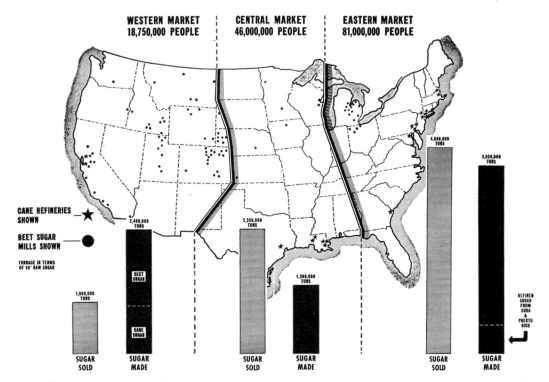

Figure 3–7. Sugar refining in the United States. Cane refineries are located at ports, where they handle imported raw sugar, except in the lower South, where home-grown cane is also used. Beet refineries almost invariably are located close to the source of beets. (Courtesy of California and Hawaiian Sugar Refining Corporation, Limited.)

(limestone from Pennsylvania, coal from the Virginias, and iron ore from Chile, Cuba, and Venezuela), Sparrows Point has probably the lowest pig iron manufacturing costs outside of Birmingham, though there is much disagreement among the various districts regarding the cost of assembling the basic raw materials at the stacks.

Shipbuilding. Except in wartime when the Pacific Coast and the Gulf Coast assume

ever, for this industry than she did the Clyde. If America does not approach Scotland in importance in shipbuilding, it is for economic rather than geographic reasons (it costs about twice as much to build ships here as there). Great shipyards also have grown up at Sparrows Point.

Industrial Machinery, Machine Tools, Locomotives, and other Machinery. In the manufacture of locomotives, Philadelphia leads the world and has for decades. The famous Baldwin Locomotive Works, formerly situated on a crowded site in Philadelphia, is now located in Eddystone, a suburb on the Delaware River.

This area also ranks high in the manufacture of all kinds of machinery including machine tools (Figure 3–6). This results from proximity to raw materials, early start, skilled labor, unexcelled transportation, and proximity to markets.

Aircraft. This area, particularly that near Baltimore, is important in aircraft manufacture. During World War II, the huge Martin Aircraft Corporation was among the nation's leaders. But the manufacture of aircraft also is important near Paterson, West Trenton, Lock Haven, and Philadelphia.

This industry located here for many reasons, among which were a superior labor pool, proximity to a large market for planes, availability of more adaptable buildings, seaplane base facilities in several instances, and needed capital.

Oil Refining. Southeastern Pennsylvania ranks very high in petroleum refining: in fact Pennsylvania ranks third – following Texas and California. Its plants are, however, smaller than several of those in Louisiana and Texas. Its great advantages are ability to receive crude oil cheaply and easily by pipeline or tanker and to serve easily and quickly the tremendous nearby market.

Other Manufactures. The excellent port facilities along the Delaware River have encouraged the localizing of manufacture in chemicals, chocolate, copper, cork products, leather, linoleum, soap, and cane sugar (Figure 3–7).

The Mohawk Valley and the Ontario Plain

The Mohawk Valley and the Ontario Plain occupy the great water-level route from Troy to Buffalo and are traversed by the main line of the New York Central Railroad, the New York State Barge Canal, and U. S. Highway 20 (Figure 3–4). The route through the Mohawk Valley is almost as level as the Ontario Plain. This results from

the fact that during glacial times (when the mouth of the St. Lawrence was choked by a glacier) the outlet for much of the Great Lakes watershed was by this route.

The area is almost completely urbanized – stimulated as a result first of the Erie Canal, built in 1825, and later by a series of short railroads that parallel the river and canal. Later these lines were consolidated and the area became one of the major traffic arteries of Anglo-America. Factories sprang up all along the route. Each city tends to specialize in several products and nearly every conceivable product is manufactured somewhere in the area. Thus Rochester makes cameras, optical goods, and men's clothing; Rome, copper and brass; Syracuse, shoes, soda and typewriters. Schenectady makes electrical equipment and locomotives; Cohoes, knit goods. Like the output of southwestern New England, nearly all of these products require skill. Few districts are so well located as this one with respect to (1) efficient and economical transportation facilities; (2) raw materials (brought easily and economically by railway, truck, or barge); (3) power – both hydroelectric and coal; (4) dense population, which assures an abundance of skilled labor; and (5) large markets. This district, however, lacks a capital of its own, and therefore lies within the orbit of New York City.

The Niagara Frontier

This subregion lies between Lakes Ontario and Erie in western New York and adjacent Ontario. It is complicated by the international boundary which, as a result of the tariff, plays a vital role in causing manufacturing to be more important on the Canadian side than otherwise would be the case. In the entire British Empire and Commonwealth, the Province of Ontario ranks second only to the United Kingdom in manufacturing, and threatens ere long to outdistance even it. The power from Niagara Falls is widely used on both sides of the border and has played an important part in the development of chemical, metallurgical, and other industries. Because of the international border there are two industrial capitals –

Buffalo on the American side and Toronto on the Canadian.

Iron and Steel. At Lackawanna, a part of metropolitan Buffalo, is one of America's greatest iron and steel industries. The Lackawanna Iron and Steel Company moved here from a location it had occupied at Scranton for 60 years. Like other Lower Lake cities, Buffalo is an economical meeting place for coal, iron ore, and fluxing limestone. Its blast furnaces and coke ovens are so placed on a ship canal that lake carriers deliver the raw materials economically directly to the stacks. It is claimed that this plant is second only to Detroit's among those in the Lower Lake iron and steel districts in the cost of assembling the three raw materials. The cost of laying down coal is considerably less than in competing areas while that for limestone and iron ore is identical. Lying in the heart of a great iron- and steel-consuming area, Buffalo plants deliver their finished products by barge, lake freighter, railway, and truck. This district can and does deliver steel to New York City at lower cost than any competitor west of the Appalachians. Besides

the huge Lackawanna plant, Buffalo has several smaller ones.

The Canadian portion of this district, the nation's outstanding in iron and steel fabrication, shows little promise of ever becoming a second Pittsburgh, Chicago, or even Youngstown, for its raw materials are too widely separated for economical assembly. Her coal lies far from the iron ore and the blast furnaces, except at Sydney, Nova Scotia, which is outside this region. Canada, accordingly, imports about as much coal from the United States as she mines. A growing market and considerable tariff protection, however, assure the nation a place of importance and Canada now ranks eighth in world output of steel.

Canada continues to import considerable steel from the United States and Europe (France, Belgium, Germany and Sweden) but she is increasing her productive capacity at a rate of about 300,000 tons of steel ingots per year. With this enlarged capacity, along with new sources of iron ore in Ontario, Quebec, and Labrador, she hopes soon to be able to reduce imports considerably.

Figure 3–8. Flour mills and elevators in Buffalo. During an average shipping season on the Great Lakes, Buffalo receives more than a quarter of a billion bushels of grain, of which about 60 million are milled. The city ranks among the leading flour-milling centers of the world. (Fitzgerald Air Photo, Courtesy of Buffalo Chamber of Commerce.)

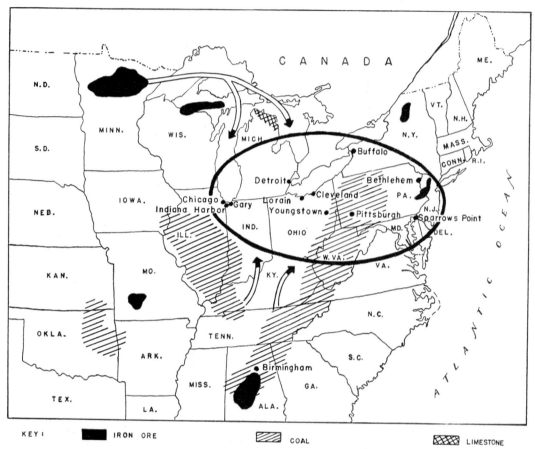

Figure 3–9. United States Steel-making Complex. At least 88.8 per cent of the iron and steel capacity of the United States is to be found in the area enclosed by the ellipse. With only about seven per cent of the people and seven per cent of the land area of the globe, the United States nonetheless produces more than half the steel and well over one third of all goods of the world. This achievement reflects the unique advantages of this region for industry. (Based on map by *The New York Times*.)

Hamilton, the leading center in this district, as well as in all Canada, enjoys the same geographical advantages for iron and steel fabrication as Buffalo.

Flour Milling. Buffalo is the world's leading flour-milling center, having displaced Minneapolis in 1930 (Figure 3–8). This is a reversal of the trend of early days when mills grew up in the wheat-growing regions, as in Rochester and Kansas City, or on the market sides of them as in Minneapolis. Buffalo's mills reap the advantages of cheap water transportation on the Great Lakes, nearness to the large consuming markets of

the East, low power costs, excellent transportation facilities for the product in all directions by canal, railway, and highway, and the milling-in-bond privilege.[13]

---

[13] The milling-in-bond privilege is one that is offered by the United States Government to any place that can economically make use of it. Unless a city is in the line of transportation followed by Canadian grain, it cannot economically make use of the privilege. The mill has to pay the salaries of government inspectors, and the plan can be operated only on a large scale. The milling of flour in bond simply means that the wheat is milled in transit and that the flour is bound for foreign markets. Flour that is milled in bond cannot be sold in the United States.

Electro-Chemical and Metallurgical Industry. The Niagara Frontier, with its tremendous resources of cheap hydroelectric power and its large consuming market, ranks as one of the world's leaders in the production of alloys and abrasives.

The Pittsburgh – Cleveland District

The Pittsburgh-Cleveland District is the continent's outstanding primary iron and steel-producing area. It also has a diversity of other industries — those making rubber tires, electrical machinery, motor vehicles, machine tools, airplane parts, paints and varnish, chemicals, clay products, clothing and textiles, glass, and countless others. The dominant centers, Cleveland and Pittsburgh, are followed closely by Youngstown, Akron, Wheeling, and others. This area supplies southeastern Michigan and most of Ohio and eastern Indiana with the raw and semi-finished steel used in secondary industries.

The area is strategically located for heavy industry, since it lies between Lake Erie on the north, over whose waters move the millions of tons of iron ore and limestone, and the productive Northern Appalachian coal field on the south (Figure 3–9). Here, too, is one of Anglo-America's leading markets for iron and steel.

Iron and Steel. A large part of North America's metallurgical industry is located in this area (Figure 3–10).

Through concentration of production the steel industry has been able to reduce its costs below what would have been possible if steel plants were scattered throughout the country with primary thought given to location of consumers' plants and secondary consideration to the costs of assembling raw materials.[14]

It would not be economical, for instance, to manufacture steel pipe in quantity at points in the great mid-continent oil province, nor tin plate for food containers near every canning center. The consumer's chief hope is for cheaper transportation costs. No one steel-producing area is ideally lo-

cated, all being affected by influences favorable and unfavorable, natural and artificial.[15]

Most iron and steel manufacturing is still carried on near or relatively near one or more of the raw materials. Though proximity to market is a factor of ever-growing importance, assembly costs are the more compelling. Unfortunately, nature seldom places raw materials in accord with consuming centers. The ideal location for iron and steel manufacturing is at that point where raw materials and markets for the finished prod-

Figure 3–10. Distribution of blast furnaces in the United States and Canada in 1951. Though many things are brought out on this map, the one most vividly portrayed is the great concentration of blast furnaces in the Chicago-Gary and Pittsburgh-Youngstown-Cleveland-Detroit areas, all in the American Manufacturing Belt. (Based on data from *Directory of Iron and Steel Works of the United States and Canada.* Map by Pierre Hathaway.)

ucts are available. No single steel center in Anglo-America combines these, although Chicago and Detroit approach this condition most closely.

In the United States iron ore usually moves toward the coal fields, the main reason being the presence in or near the coal fields of general manufacturing districts (the largest markets for most steel products). To produce 1 ton of pig iron requires about 1.7 tons of iron ore, .9 tons of coke, and .4 tons of limestone. The problem of fluxing stone is less

---

[14] C. E. Wright, "Geography of Steel: Factors Governing Location of Main Producing Areas," *The Annalist,* Vol. 49, No. 1269, May 14, 1937, p. 766.

[15] Marion Worthing, "Comparative Assembly Costs in the Manufacture of Pig Iron," *Pittsburgh Business Review,* Vol. 8, No. 1, January 31, 1938, p. 21.

important than that of ore and coal because limestone is widely distributed. Two states, Pennsylvania and Michigan, supply 62 per cent of the country's metallurgical stone. The world's largest quarries, those at Calcite on Lake Huron, provide 27 per cent of the steel industry's requirements (Figure 3–11).

So long as Lake Superior ores are in general use, the bulk of the American iron and steel industry will be located on or near the

By-product coke. No discussion of the iron and steel industry is justifiable without mention of the manufacture of coke — the chief fuel used in blast furnaces. Before the development of by-product ovens, coke was made in "bee hive" ovens from which the valuable volatile materials escaped into the open air. Coke, almost pure carbon, is made by driving off certain volatile materials.

The "bee hive" industry was virtually dead

Figure 3–11. Enormous limestone plant at Calcite, Michigan, with its own harbor on Lake Huron. In the center is the loading slip. (Photo by Abrams Aerial Survey Corporation, Lansing, Michigan, courtesy United States Steel Corporation.)

Lower Great Lakes, and the Pittsburgh-Cleveland area will occupy a prominent place (Figure 3–10). It is pointed out in Chapter 10, that high quality "Lake" ore is diminishing and that several new plants have already been constructed on the Atlantic Coast for utilization of Canadian, African, and Latin American ores. On the other hand, the big steel companies have already made investments exceeding half a billion dollars for getting iron economically from taconite.[16]

---

[16] "Taconite: Tomorrow's New Ore," *Monsanto Magazine,* Vol. 31, August, 1952, p. 10.

until the time of World War II. It then provided a reserve source of coke when by-product ovens could not meet the entire demand. The most famous "bee hive" coke center was Connellsville, southeast of Pittsburgh, where coal from the Pittsburgh seam made superior coke. Accordingly, myriads of ovens sprang up in its tributary area. "Bee hive" coke was made at the mines, since the by-products (gas, tar, oils, and chemicals) were not saved. By-product coke, on the contrary, is made in or near cities — manufacturing centers, where the by-products which are not used by the iron and steel industry itself are available to other industries. The largest by-product plant in the world is located at Clairton at the southern end of Pittsburgh on the Monongahela River.

The Rubber Industry. The rubber industry and Akron have long been synonymous to the average American. Rubber *made* Akron. In 1917–1918 it, together with nearby Barberton, employed 70,000 persons in its rubber factories and was probably the most highly specialized city in the nation. This city along with its suburbs still is the world's leading rubber-manufacturing center.

Akron's first rubber factory was established in 1870 — the result of sheer accident. B. F. Goodrich, dissatisfied with his business prospects at the close of Civil War, engaged in the oil business. Being unsuccessful, he went to New York and dealt in real estate. In his dealings he came into possession of a rubber factory at Hastings-on-Hudson. Handicapped by lack of funds, he was encouraged to go to Akron by a friend who lent him money. His small factory there became the nucleus of the great Akron rubber industry.[17]

Concentration of rubber manufacturing was a good thing during the industry's infancy, for buyers and sellers could get together conveniently. Akron was also a central spot for skilled labor. Now that the industry is mature, however, such concentration is no longer desirable. Mills have sprung up in Alabama, California, Maryland, Mississippi, New England, New York, and Texas, as well as in foreign countries. This decentralization is in large measure the outgrowth of serious strikes. As labor unions became increasingly powerful, the cost of labor soared and Akron's cost of production became high — the highest in the country. The companies then introduced more and more labor-saving machinery. To make such a change harmoniously is difficult and more strikes followed. Decentralization away from Akron followed. Another decentralizing factor has been the need for more economical distribution of the finished product.

The Clay-products Industry. This in-

[17] National Youth Administration in Ohio, *The Rubber Industry in Ohio,* p. 3. Columbus: 1937.

dustry whose products include brick, china ware, clay refractories, porcelain, terra cotta, tile, pottery, and vitrified sewer pipe is especially important in the Upper Ohio Valley of Pennsylvania and Ohio. The high degree of concentration, despite the fact that clays are widely distributed throughout Anglo-America, indicates that the raw material as a factor of location is less important than fuel, access to large markets, and skilled labor. The Ohio River area is especially well located with respect to fuel — both coal and natural gas.

The stoneware industry, centered at East Liverpool — the continent's leader in pottery fabrication, procures its clays from Georgia, Florida, and South Carolina (kaolin), Maine (feldspar), Kentucky and Tennessee (ball clay), and Illinois and Pennsylvania (flint). The clay refractories or heat-resisting products industry is located principally in the Allegheny Plateau of Pennsylvania, where the fire clay is interlayered with bituminous coal. This clay is procured underground rather than from surface pits. Clay refractories are in demand by the nearby iron and steel industry.

Because of America's high tariff on imported china, the Havilands, after much research on American clays, selected New Castle, Pennsylvania, on the Shenango River as the site for their United States factory.

The Glass Industry. For 5,000 years glass-making was a handicraft because the workers had to be highly skilled. About 1908, machines began to perform the operations and, except in the non-standardized and small-volume business, glass-making has become a mechanical industry. Glass is made by fusing sodium sulphate, calcium carbonate (pure limestone), and quartz sand. From 60 to 70 per cent of all the glass sand used in the country, and certainly the best in quality, comes from Illinois, Pennsylvania, and West Virginia.

Charcoal, the first fuel used, was later displaced by coal, and coal in turn by natural gas. At first glass-making was concentrated east of the Appalachians, but the adoption of the new fuels resulted in western Pennsylvania, southeastern Ohio, and northern

West Virginia becoming the chief centers. Natural gas is the ideal fuel because it is clean and inexpensive and produces very high and uniform temperatures. An immense amount of heat must be available to melt the raw materials. Glass sand and other materials invariably travel to where cheap fuel is located. Natural gas is thus the major factor contributing to the location of this manufacturing enterprise though nearness to market is also important. So fragile and bulky a product naturally takes high freight rates.

Machine Tools. The machine-tool industry came into being as a separate entity about 1870, when industralists were widely adopting mass-production methods. New England had been the source of most of America's machine tools. As manufacturing migrated westward, it had to have metal-cutting machines, and New England's factories were too far away to supply them. The first plant in Ohio was established in Cincinnati shortly after the Civil War. Cleveland, which today ranks next to Cincinnati, did not get started until the early 1880's. The principal locational factors in this industry are availability of highly skilled labor, proximity to markets, and availability of raw materials. Machine-tool plants producing parts used in the assembly of other machine tools are usually located in or near the regions producing the final product. Most of the factories in the United States are located in the American Manufacturing Belt and the Pittsburgh-Cleveland District ranks very high (Figure 3–6).

Electrical Equipment. The American Manufacturing Belt produces the bulk of all electrical machinery, and Pittsburgh is one of the largest centers. Here is located the enormous Westinghouse plant, which employs about one fifth of all the secondary metal workers in the city. Cleveland, too, ranks high, with Lincoln Electric (outstanding in the manufacture of electric welders and welding wire) and General Electric, with its world-famous laboratories at Nela-Park.

The Chemical Industry. A relatively new major chemical industrial area with an investment exceeding 200 million dollars since

1945 (half of it since the beginning of the Korean conflict), stretches for about 75 miles along the Ohio shore of Lake Erie from Lorain on the west to Ashtabula on the east, including, besides these two centers, Avon Lake, Cleveland, Barberton, Fairport, Painesville, and Perry. Most of the new plants are being located near existing works.

For convenience only, this area is included as a part of the Pittsburgh-Cleveland Dis-

Figure 3–12. Charleston, West Virginia, on the Great Kanawha River. This area, known as "Chemical Valley," ranks among Anglo-America's leading areas in the manufacture of chemicals. (Courtesy of Charleston Chamber of Commerce.)

trict; actually it has a personality all its own. This area, which makes basic chemical products as well as synthetic fibers, plastics, and detergents, possesses all the requirements for a successful chemical industry.

Great Kanawha Valley

In a 60-mile stretch of West Virginia's Great Kanawha Valley, stretching from Gauley Bridge on the east to Nitro on the west, lies a spectacular industrial district known far and wide as "Chemical Valley" (Figure 3–12). Large plants are closely spaced along the upper and middle valley. The manufacture of chemicals got started here during World War I in an effort to contribute to the country's emergency and it has been expanding and broadening ever since. The chemical industry was drawn to the valley by the natural advantages of coal, natural gas, petroleum, salt, vitreous clay, hydroelectric power, and water. Transportation facilities are well developed. Railroads, highways, and pipelines carry the bulk of the trade but the river also is used. Efficient transportation has been a basic factor in the concentration of industry.

Among the more important products made here are sulphuric acid, caustic soda, ammonia, chlorine, ethylene, chloroform, ether, glass, rayon-staple fibre and synthetic rubber and textiles. Ferro-alloys also are manufactured and this area supplies these key metals to one fourth of the American steel industry. Charleston with its suburbs of Institute, Nitro, and South Charleston, sitting in the middle of this industrial concentration, is the outstanding center; Belle and Glen Ferris also have giant plants. Approximately one eighth of West Virginia's total population resides in Kanawha County and of this number, one third resides in Charleston.

This valley is the original home of nylon and it still manufactures half the world output. It also produces the most famous brands of anti-freeze as well as many hydro-carbons for the manufacture of plastics.

Inland Ohio – Indiana

This district is distinctly removed from the Great Lakes, but is strategically located with respect to the Ohio River. It lies between the coal fields to the east and the productive farm lands to the west. Its industries are diversified — machine-tools, cash registers, electric refrigerators, soaps, meat, tobacco, iron and steel, beer, shoes, radios, and clothing. The most important part is the Miami Valley from Piqua or Springfield to Cincinnati. Indianapolis is the major center in the western part; Cincinnati, in the eastern.

Eastern Part. The eastern part of the Ohio-Indiana District, still is important for its agriculture. In the early days farm products were so low in price they were fed to cattle and swine, which in turn were driven over the Appalachian Mountains to Baltimore. Later — by the 1850's — Cincinnati had become so important as a meat-packing center (called "Porkopolis") that it put an end to droving.

The real stimulus to manufacturing here was the Miami & Erie Canal. Along its route developed a string of cities and towns which later became important centers of industry. Three stages distinguished the industrial evolution of the Miami Valley: (1) the days of the early river and canal, when mostly quasi-manufactured goods from the farms — flour, meat, leather, and wool — moved down the Ohio and Mississippi rivers to Southern markets; (2) the railroad period when the manufactured products — agricultural implements, tobacco, soap, paper, and machinery — moved to national markets; and (3) the present period of specialized industries — iron and steel, machine tools, all kinds of machinery, radios, aircraft, automatic and calculating machines, and many others.

This area is unique in that it lacks raw materials and power. It is strongly individualized by the high value of its manufactures, an emphasis upon precision machinery, and a widely ramified market. This area has become a reservoir of skilled labor.

Western Part. As in the eastern part of the Ohio-Indiana District, agriculture in the western part remains important. Nevertheless, manufacturing is outstanding. The leading products are agricultural implements, chemicals, glass, automobile parts, electrical machinery, steel forgings, pharmaceuticals, hosiery; airplane accessory parts, engines, and propellers; and wood products, particularly furniture. Flour milling, meat packing, and vegetable canning are especially outstanding. Indiana is a leader in vegetable canning, which began in Indianapolis as early as 1861. Madison County alone has 43 canneries. More than 100,000 acres are devoted to tomatoes in this state. At Elwood is held an annual pageant in honor of the tomato. Other vegetables that are canned include corn, kidney beans, pumpkin, and cabbage (sauerkraut).

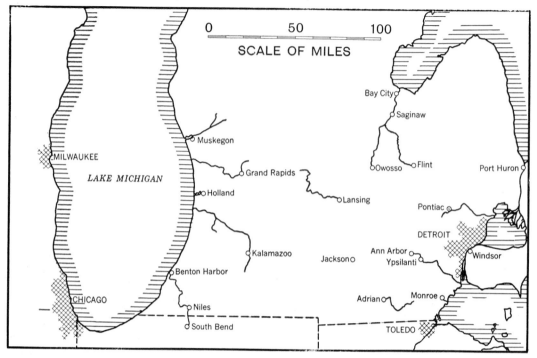

Figure 3–13. The Southern Michigan Automobile District. Although Detroit is the natural center, neighboring cities and towns in Michigan, Indiana, Ohio, and Canada produce many of the bodies and parts.

The Southern Michigan Automobile District

The automobile-manufacturing district, including besides the metropolitan area of Detroit and Windsor the "inner" and "outer" rings of cities (Figure 3–13), contains the heart of the world's automotive industry. The other products made here are definitely secondary.

Included in the semi-suburban inner ring are Mount Clemons, Pontiac, Ann Arbor, Ypsilanti, and Monroe. Included in the outer ring are eight cities definitely in the orbit of Detroit's great industry – Flint, Lansing, Owosso, Jackson, Adrian, Port Huron, Toledo and South Bend.

Despite this area's overwhelming importance in the automotive industry, which consumes more steel than any other, this district is not yet a major producer of primary iron and steel.

The Automotive Industry. The automo-

tive industry has made Detroit, more than any city on the lakes, an industrial city. Moreover, it is almost a one-industry city. Seven of the total 17 makes of passenger cars and 4 of a total of 50 makes of trucks and buses are assembled within the limits of metropolitan Detroit.

The making of motor vehicles is not, however, a single industry, for the automobile is an assembled product. The materials going into these parts are legion. Nearly every steel part is made of *alloy steels* — steels made by adding precise quantities of one or more of the ferro-alloys to the heat of steel in the furnace for imparting specific qualities — additional hardness, greater toughness, increased elasticity, and resistance to stain and to rust. Thus axles must be tough and shock-resistant and made from different steel than the spring and engine block. Several non-ferrous metals are utilized — aluminum, lead, copper, tin, and zinc — for electrical devices, pistons, and other vital parts. Glass, upholstery, rubber tires, paint and a host of other products must be purchased — purchased from thousands of concerns from all sections of Anglo-America, albeit the majority come from the area shown in Figure 3–13 whence most of the assembled cars are shipped. In no industry is there so much subcontracting. The automobile definitely should not be considered just a Detroit product.

Detroit became the first great motor car center "by the accident of being the hub of a circle within which were located the pioneers of the industry."[18] Ford developed

an automobile cheap enough for almost every family; he adapted the assembly line to the industry (Figure 3–14); and he introduced standardization and interchangeable parts to the industry, thereby making mass production possible. Ford was not the innovator, however, of modern mass production despite the fact that most engineers and production men believe he was.[19] The credit for this achievement goes to Eli Whitney.[20]

[18] John A. Piquet, "The Factor of Plant Location in Automobile Production," *Industrial Management,* Vol. 68, No. 5, November 1924, p. 297.

[19] Roger Burlingame, *Backgrounds of Power: The Human Story of Mass Production.* New York: Charles Scribner's Sons, 1949.

[20] Jeanette Mirsky and Allan Nevins, *The World of Eli Whitney.* New York: The Macmillan Co., 1952.

Figure 3–14. Windsor plants of Ford of Canada. Similar American models are made across the river in Detroit. Many small industries, making automobile parts and accessories, are located in the upper left of the photo. (Ford Motor Company of Canada, Ltd.)

Moreover, he raised the necessary capital among local bankers rather than on Wall Street. Ford and the alert local capitalists symbolize the rise of automobile manufacturing in Detroit.

Geographic and economic conditions have justified the selection of Detroit as the automotive center. The industry had to be strategically located with respect to steel. In the American Manufacturing Belt are concentrated 92.5 per cent of the finished-steel-producing capacity of the United States and 88 percent of the automobile-manufacturing plants. Detroit is well located for getting steel cheaply by water from South Chicago, Gary, Cleveland, Lorain, and Buffalo. If Cleveland's pioneer inventors—Stearns, Winton, and Gaeth—had gone in for mass production of inexpensive cars, and if Ford had done just the reverse, in all probability Cleveland and not Detroit would be the hub of the automotive industry today. And if Ford had started tinkering with clocks in Bismarck, North Dakota, and had remained there permanently, his fame would have been local and short-lived—"the visionary who didn't make good."

However, the motorcar industry is decentralizing—decentralizing toward both coasts, to Canada, and overseas, "following the twin principles of modern relocation: first, regional plants; and second, production in well-balanced communities where labor efficiency is high." [21]

The automotive industry is dominated by three large corporations which together supply nine tenths of the automobiles in Anglo-America and are among the world's leading industrial corporations in size and organizational complexity. Largest of the three is General Motors Corporation which, with its subsidiaries, contributes about two fifths of the total production. In order of size following General Motors are the Ford Motor Company and the Chrysler Corporation.

The Canadian motor-vehicle industry, which is mainly centered at Windsor and

Oshawa in Ontario, is this province's most important industry. As in the United States, however, factories in many widely scattered cities and towns provide the innumerable parts. Some of these devote so large a part of their total industrial output to the automobile that they may justifiably be termed "automobile cities."

Windsor is the "Detroit of Canada," as well as the outstanding automotive center of the entire British Commonwealth. Its advantages for automobile manufacture are: (1) the city is separated from Detroit by the international boundary; if there were no boundary Windsor would be a suburb of Detroit instead of a city with more than 100,000 inhabitants; (2) the city is just across the river from Detroit and parts of all kinds can be assembled easily and cheaply; (3) Windsor is close to the big American companies which have branch factories in Canada; (4) about 60 per cent of Canada's people live in the two provinces of Ontario and Quebec. This means that most of the Canadian market is easily accessible. Windsor probably is not so strategically located to market, however, as Toronto. In a scientific market study the Ford Motor Company of Canada found that 36 per cent of Canadian cars and trucks are sold within a 200-mile radius of Toronto. Hence this company has threatened to move its assembly operations to Oakville—20 miles from Toronto; Windsor also has easy access to iron and steel as well as to other metal materials.

In one very significant respect the Canadian industry differs from that of the United States: a manufacturer may, because of restricted market, turn on a single assembly line the engines for three or four makes of cars, whereas in the United States each make of car has its own engine-manufacturing plant.

The Chemical Industry. So important is the automotive industry in this area that the average person is completely unaware that the manufacture of chemicals is an impressive enterprise too. Most of the chemical plants, based upon huge deposits of salt which underlie the city, are located down the

[21] John A. Piquet, "Is the Big City Doomed as an Industrial Center?" *Industrial Management,* Vol. 68, No. 3, September 1924, p. 140.

Detroit River from the Rouge and just beyond the northern edge of the city.

Agricultural Implements. Canada's agricultural implement industry is centered in this district. When implements were made largely from wood, it was natural that their manufacture should have taken place in the lowlands where such hardwoods as oak and maple were available. Due to the early start here, the industry has remained despite the fact that iron and steel implements have replaced those made from wood, the prairie was opened up to agriculture, and farm implements acquire bulk in the process of manufacture. To save freight costs in shipping, of course, the implements are "knocked down" and reassembled near the market. In addition to the huge market for farm machinery in the Prairie Provinces a large demand is also near at hand in Ontario and Quebec. Finally this area is well located for exporting, the importance of which is indicated by the fact that about one third of the total Canadian output is shipped abroad.

The industry is comprised of a large Canadian company, Massey-Harris, and of branches of the largest American manufacturers.

Iron and Steel. Though Detroit is the largest steel-consuming center in the United States and though it enjoys every advantage of other Lower Lake centers for the economical assembly of raw materials at the blast furnaces with resulting low manufacturing costs, the city is not yet a major iron and steel producer. However, it will be only a matter of time until the automobile-steel market will compel the iron and steel industry, which now is sending steel from distant points, to construct plants in Detroit in order to make deliveries more quickly, give better service, and reduce prices.

Only two conditions may prevent Detroit from becoming the great iron and steel center that its economic and geographic conditions would seem to guarantee it: (1) security requirements and consequent dispersion of most industry and (2) the increasing decentralization of the automotive industry itself.

The Chicago – Milwaukee District

The Chicago-Milwaukee District occupies the western and southwestern shores of Lake Michigan from Gary to Manitowoc and includes satellite towns and cities extending a short distance inland. Heavy industry predominates; South Chicago and Gary constitute the best-balanced primary metallurgical district in Anglo-America and the one that threatens ultimately to displace the Pittsburgh district in production. The fountainhead of all manufacturing is thus the great primary iron and steel industry at the southern end of Lake Michigan from which fans out in all directions, though mostly to the west and northward, the many industries that utilize steel. The type of product made varies with the distance from the steel mills: heavy and relatively simple products obviously are fabricated closeby, lighter and more complicated articles farther away. This district, then, may well be considered to be the western outpost of both the great primary and secondary iron and steel industries of the continent.

Other major enterprises pack meat, refine oil, make corn products, machinery of many kinds, telephones, electric equipment, watches, airplane engines and accessories, agricultural implements, railway cars, automobiles and trucks, clothing, shoes, and cement.

Most manufacturing in Wisconsin and Illinois is confined to this area. Chicago is the economic capital of this district, as well as of the entire Middle West.

Iron and Steel. Chicago-Gary, comprising one of the outstanding manufacturing areas of the world, is strategically located for making iron and steel, for iron ore and limestone can be brought directly to the blast furnaces by lake carrier, and coal is not far distant in central and southern Illinois, though some coking fuel is brought in from West Virginia and Kentucky, partly by rail and partly by the combination of rail and lake carrier. This district has the best balance between production and consumption of any iron and steel area in the United States. With the removal of "Pittsburgh

Plus" in 1924 and of the multiple basing-point system in 1948, this district almost equals Pittsburgh in production. In fact it has equalled it in some years.

Gary is one of the outstanding examples of a scientifically planned industrial location. Not only can it assemble its coal, iron ore, and limestone economically, but it has near at hand possibly the largest market for steel. For 50 years its metallurgical industry has been built up step by step. In 1905 the United States Steel Corporation needed a new plant to serve the rapidly growing Midwestern market. What is now Gary was then an area of sand dunes and swamps. Its intermediate location between the Northern Appalachian coal fields and the Lake Superior iron-ore deposits enables this area to assemble these two raw materials economically, and limestone is available in Indiana and Michigan. Gary's location with respect to markets is unsurpassed (see Chapter 2).

Agricultural Implements. Until pioneers poured through the Appalachian barrier into what is now the Agricultural Interior, farming methods had changed little from earliest times. Even up to 1820 most farmers had only such equipment as a hoe, rake, ax, scythe, sickle, flail, and perhaps a plow. A combination of favorable conditions, however, stimulated the invention of remarkable machines that surpassed anything the world had previously known. Scarcity of labor in the newly settled region meant high wages. The machine was the answer to both problems.

The new implements made of iron and steel brought to agricultural tasks a degree of nonhuman power hitherto unknown and unattainable. The new machines inaugurated the modern age of agricultural technology. It once required 57 man-hours of labor to produce an acre of wheat yielding 20 bushels. Today technological advances make this same production possible from less than four man-hours of labor.

Though the American agricultural implement industry had its inception along the Eastern Seaboard, it migrated westward with the population via New York, Pennsylvania and Ohio. Illinois ultimately became the leading producing state and today turns out approximately one half the country's production. Chicago is the outstanding center. Since agricultural implements are bulky, this industry locates as near as possible to the farmers who use them.

Petroleum Refining. The Whiting-South Chicago industrial district, lying within the Chicago Metropolitan Area, is one of the three largest petroleum refining and storage centers in the American Manufacturing Belt. Whiting represents the *market-oriented* refinery location—today the most important of the five basic types of locations. More than two thirds of the refineries in the United States today are located with respect to concentrated markets, either in coastal areas or at strategic interior points. Obviously the Whiting market is one of the largest in all Anglo-America.

Many products are procured in the distillation process. Hence it is more profitable to refine oil near the market for these products than to ship them from refineries in or near oil fields and far from large consuming areas. Fifty per cent of the petroleum coke of the nation is produced in the Whiting area. Crude oil can be moved to inland refineries today by pipeline at very low cost.

Oil refining as now carried on is more of a chemical industry than a processing operation. The industry to be profitable must be conducted on a steady basis of operation and on a large scale.

Meat Packing. Prior to the development of big cities, slaughtering was a local enterprise. The first real concentration of slaughtering and meat packing took place at Cincinnati, which predominated as long as its tributary area led in the production of livestock. After cattle raising developed farther west, meat packing followed. The basic characteristic of the meat-packing industry is that about two thirds of the livestock of the United States are raised west of the Mississippi River, whereas about two thirds of the people live east of it. This separation of production and consumption means that livestock or meat or both must move considerable distances.

Meat packing in recent years has been

migrating still farther west into areas where range animals are sent for winter fattening, a response to the proximity of grazing lands, feedlots, and rapid transportation. This is an effort to avoid heavy freight charges on the waste material (actually by-products rather than waste) forming a large part of the weight of each animal and to prevent the animals from losing weight enroute to slaughtering centers. The refrigerator car, which was developed about 1880, has enabled the industry to overcome the handicap of geographical location. Since only 70 to 75 per cent of a hog is pork and only 50 to 60 per cent of a steer is beef, transportation costs are reduced when slaughtering houses are located near grazing and fattening areas.

The meat-packing industry is now one of the nation's largest, drawing about 127 million animals to it from 5 million farms and ranches and turning out in excess of 20 billion pounds of meat in an average year.

Though there is still considerable local slaughtering and though packers run the whole gamut in the size of their enterprises, it is the "Big Four" (Swift, Armour, Wilson, and Cudahy) who do the bulk of the business. They operate nationally and internationally. Each company operates from 8 to 50 plants. For the decade ending 1938 the "Big Four" handled 41 per cent of the hogs, 68 per cent of the sheep, 46 per cent of the calves, and 47 per cent of the cattle commercially slaughtered.

While Chicago still is the greatest single meat-packing center, it no longer dominates the industry as it once did. Chicago's fame as a slaughter center was based at first upon the packing of pork alone. It gained its great stature only after the development of the refrigerator car which enabled beef to be handled. Up to this time beef was slaughtered locally. Mass production methods could now be employed.

The packers purchase their animals in the livestock terminal markets and also in smaller markets. The development of good highways and the universal adoption of the truck have revolutionized the method of getting livestock to market (Figure 3–15). What it

Figure 3–15. Hauling livestock by truck. Since 1941 the number of trucks on farms has risen to more than two and one-half million. Nearly all livestock in the Agricultural Interior travel at least part of the way by motor vehicle (71 per cent was trucked to market in 1951). (Courtesy of Automobile Manufacturers Association.)

did primarily was to encourage selling to markets located close to home.

The Chicago packing plants are large, well-organized and extremely efficient (Figure 3–16). Many can handle up to 1,000 hogs per hour. One Chicago packer handles 250 cattle per hour.

Changes occuring in the Agricultural Interior which are affecting the packing industry are (1) the replacement of the lard type of hog by a dual-purpose animal because of the competition of vegetable oils with lard, and (2) the demand for baby beef, which is ready for slaughter within 18 months and which is fostering the breeding of cattle *within* the region at the expense of feeders from the Great Plains and Rocky Mountain regions. Decentralization of population also has affected the location of this industry. The growth of population in California, with its important market for fresh meats, has caused more and more western animals, which in past years moved to Chicago, to be shipped to California. Also, the new grasses introduced into the South have resulted in a shift in meat packing to that region, at the expense of Chicago and other packing centers in the Agricultural Interior. If Chicago still is to meat packing what Pittsburgh is to steel, it is for the same reason: industrial inertia and the huge and relatively durable investments there.

as grain. Little is fed to livestock. This proximity of the growers to the processors results in corn prices being generally 5 to 10 cents higher per bushel than on farms in the more distant corn-growing areas mostly west of the Mississippi River. A similar situation exists in northwestern Iowa and adjacent Nebraska and South Dakota within a radius of 150 miles of Omaha. The world's largest corn-refining plant is at Argo, on the south-

Figure 3–16. "Packing Town," Chicago — meat capital of the world. Such mammoth plants are imperative because all by-products are used and the utilization of some of these requires very expensive equipment which only larger companies can afford to install. (Courtesy of Armour and Company.)

Corn Products. About 85 per cent of the corn grown in the United States in an average year is fed to livestock on farms. A small amount, however, 80 million to 100 million bushels, serves as the raw material for a variety of prepared foods and industrial products—corn flakes, corn syrup, corn oil, corn meal, corn starch, dextrose-sugar, alcohol, paper, rayon, fiber board, and stock feed. Chicago is the center of this industry. Northeastern Illinois, within a radius of 100 to 150 miles of Chicago, sells almost all of its corn

west limits of Chicago. Decatur (Figure 3–17), Omaha, Battle Creek, Kansas City, St. Louis, St. Joseph, and Cedar Rapids also have important corn-processing plants.

The Industries of Rock Valley. An outlier on the fringe or near the western margin of the American Manufacturing Belt is the Rock Valley of southern Wisconsin and northern Illinois—one of the smaller industrial areas. It is included as a part of the Chicago District only for convenience.

The leading products are metal goods —

Figure 3–17. Corn and soybean products manufacturing plant in Decatur, Illinois. This industry needs much room: its buildings are massive and dispersed and its machines are immense. This plant is the second largest in the industry, and northern Illinois is the heart of the industry. (Courtesy of A. E. Staley Manufacturing Company.)

machinery, hardware, machine tools, and automotive equipment, although some furniture, textiles, and foods are also manufactured.

The cities which contribute most to production—Rockford, Beloit, Madison, Janesville, Sterling, and Freeport—constitute the core of the area.

Considering the Valley's prominence industrially, it is surprising to note the paucity of local raw materials, absence of an important local source of coal and hydroelectric power, lack of a substantial encircling market, and average transport facilities. The market deficiency is particularly significant,

resembling that in iron and steel making at Duluth.

The big advantages are a labor supply with disposition and talents for manufacturing, location near enough to Eastern markets to prevent prohibitive transport costs, early start (the factories were built to supply the local market based upon local water power and local timber resources) and the advantages inherent in small cities. Wages are slightly lower than those paid for the same work by Eastern competitors. The first of these factors is indisputably the most important; 25 of the 61 native factories can be traced directly to local inventions.

St. Louis District

The St. Louis District lies mostly in Missouri but partly in Illinois. The largest urban center between Chicago and the Pacific Coast, St. Louis is a city of national importance and one of the leading industrial centers in Anglo-America. It exerts strong influence in the Middle Mississippi Basin. The district's industries are diversified; there is no specialization such as was noted in Lynn, Akron, Detroit, and Pittsburgh. The largest of its industries—electrical goods—represents only about six per cent of the total product.

A strategic location on the high west bank of the Mississippi River a short distance below the mouth of the Missouri has enabled St. Louis since early days to dominate much of the river trade. The city later became an outstanding railway center and today ranks second only to Chicago. Despite its importance in manufacturing, St. Louis is essentially a commercial city. The metropolitan district, which includes East St. Louis, Alton, Belleville, and Granite City, contributes heavily to the nation's total output of shoes, beer, meat, electrical equipment, airplane engines and accessories, chemicals, drugs, alumina, glass, refined petroleum (the towns of Wood River and Roxana), and iron and steel. About 75 per cent of the factories and plants are in the city and its Missouri suburbs; the remaining 25 per cent are on the Illinois side of the river.

Montreal – Ottawa – Trois-Rivières District

This district, like the Great Kanawha Valley, is isolated from most of the other districts but can logically be considered a part of the American Manufacturing Belt. It is one of Canada's two leading industrial areas, the other being the Niagara Frontier, part of which lies across the international boundary in the United States. All but two of the nation's manufacturing cities and all of its distinctly industrial ones are located in these two districts (Figure 3–3). Located along the St. Lawrence and the lower Ottawa, St. Maurice, and Saguenay rivers, this district comprises the industrial heart of the St. Lawrence Valley.

Half the total trade of Canada passes through it and many exports and imports are processed or manufactured there. An abundance of cheap hydroelectric power, a plentiful supply of intelligent labor at a reasonable price differential, plenty of clear, cold industrial water, good transport facilities, ample room for the establishment of new and for the expansion of old industrial plants, and a rapidly growing market have made the area more interested in manufacturing than in agriculture or shipping. An additional factor contributing to this area's, as well as the nation's, rapid growth in manufacturing, is American investment. In 1950 and 1951 Americans invested nearly two billion dollars in Canadian industry, and their total investment in 1952 exceeded eight billion, most of it having been made in the two districts in the American Manufacturing Belt.

The area's principal industries are engaged in the manufacture of aluminum, lumber, pulp and paper, flour, textiles, shoes, sugar, chemicals, oil, railway and electrical equipment, farm implements, aircraft, and cement. Many of these industries, of course, could not exist if it were not for the tariff on products made south of the border. Only the cement industry needs coal and this is delivered cheaply by water.

While many industries are important here, only the two dominant ones are discussed: (1) pulp and paper and (2) aluminum.

Pulp and Paper. Canada leads the world in the production of pulp and produces much paper also. She produces more than 20 per cent of the total paper output of the world and supplies the raw material for three of every five newspapers. Altogether the nation has 110 pulp and paper mills widely scattered but it is the string of water-driven mills lining the southern edge of the forest along the lower St. Lawrence that is so noteworthy and with which we are here concerned.

The pulp and paper industry, the principal manufactural enterprise in the nation, has a larger capital investment than any other in Canada, and is first in employment, in wages paid, in export values, and in the net value of production. Moreover, it provides the principal and ofttimes the only industrial activity in many towns. Yet in spite of its importance, the industry utilizes only about 16.7 per cent of the annual forest consumption—considerably less than that used for fuelwood. The pulp and paper industry has been one of the major reasons for the huge development of water power in Canada; in fact cheap power is the major locative factor, for in order to produce a ton of newsprint 60 to 80 H.P. daily are required. The cost of transportation is equally important in the location of pulp mills. Since it is cheaper to transport the newsprint than the semi-finished material, the industry tends to cling to the source of supply of the raw material—the forest.

In this district, besides the tremendous supply of water power, are such location factors as propinquity to the great forest, rivers for stream-driving logs, and navigability of the St. Lawrence. Taking advantage of such a location is Trois-Rivières—the world's leading pulp-and-paper-manufacturing center (Figure 3–18).

Of the five and one-half to six million tons of newsprint manufactured by Canada, 95 per cent is exported. 85 per cent of the total exports go to the United States, and the rest to Europe and Latin America. Newsprint is admitted into the United States duty free. In a recent year the United States consumed 70 per cent of the world output of woodpulp.[22]

Canada much prefers to export newsprint than logs, for it is six times more valuable. The further the pulpwood is processed, the more revenue the provinces and the national government obtain and the more people find employment in the Canadian forest industries.

It would not be inaccurate to say that because of the lower costs for labor and raw materials, the United States industry has to a large extent migrated to Canada. However, Canada's potential supply of pulpwood is not unlimited; the Canadian forests are not as vast as many people in the industry once thought. Hence, the provincial governments are at present much concerned with the need for conserving the forests.

Aluminum. The aluminum industry, like that of pulp and paper, is dependent upon

[22] Klaus G. Scheye, "Analysis of Pulp and Paper Industry and the Raw Material Supply," *Paper Trade Journal*, Vol. 130, Feb. 16, 1950.

Figure 3–18. Part of the paper industry at Trois-Rivières, Canada, world's leading pulp and paper center. Three large companies have mills here. The relationship of the mills to navigable water is apparent. (Courtesy of Canadian International Paper Company and of Canadian Pulp and Paper Association.)

an *abundance of cheap power.* No other electro-metallurgical operation consumes so much electricity. To make 1 ton of aluminum requires electrical energy equivalent to that of 16 tons of coal; this amount produces 18 tons of newsprint. Moreover, power comprises a higher percentage of the total manufacturing cost than in any other industry — 16 per cent as compared with 2.8 per cent, the average for all industries. The aluminum

district and Kitimat in British Columbia. The plants in this district, with a total capacity of 350,000 tons per year, produce more than one-fourth of the world's aluminum.

Arvida. When the plant built at Shawinigan Falls on the St. Maurice in 1900 could no longer supply the needs of the industry and at the same time satisfy the demands of factories moving into the valley, it became nec-

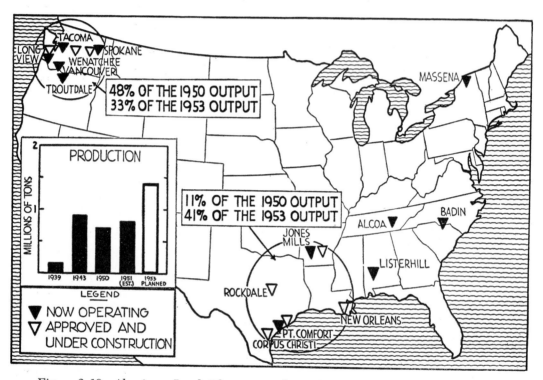

Figure 3–19. Aluminum Land. The center of our expanding aluminum industry has shifted to the Texas-Louisiana-Arkansas area. (Courtesy of *The Wall Street Journal.*)

industry then, "a hog for power," of necessity seeks out cheap electricity. The Canadian Shield, and its southern fringe, with its riches of water-power, has enabled Canada to rank among the first three world producers of aluminum despite the fact that all the raw materials must be imported (Figure 3–19).

Canada's reduction works are located at Shawinigan Falls and Beauharnois on the St. Maurice and at Arvida (Figure 3–20) and Isle Maligne on the Saguenay in this

essary to establish reduction works in another location. The valley selected was the Saguenay and the site chosen was the present city of Arvida, 400 miles northeast of Montreal.

The Saguenay Valley has been able to meet the three basic needs of the aluminum industry: (1) labor, (2) great quantities of low-cost electricity, and (3) cheap transportation for bringing in raw materials and exporting the fabricated product. The amount of raw materials actually consumed in mak-

Figure 3–20. Aluminum plant at Arvida, Quebec, largest aluminum factory in the world, uses hydroelectric power from the Saguenay River and bauxite from British Guiana and Jamaica. (Courtesy of Aluminum Company of Canada, Ltd.)

ing one ton of aluminum is staggering— about seven tons—including four tons of bauxite.

Huge amounts of electricity are generated in the 30-mile stretch in which the Saguenay, a raging torrent, drops 330 feet between Lake St. John and tidewater. A dam was constructed at Shipshaw several miles from Arvida in 1942 having a development of 1,500,000 H.P. and a total installed capacity in the Valley of 2,000,000 H.P. (Figure 3–21).[23]

Actually Arvida is not on navigable water, the terminal facilities being at Port Alfred, 20 miles from the head of navigation on the Saguenay, with which it is connected by railway. For 60 miles inland from the confluence of the Saguenay with the St. Lawrence, the river is a deep, quiet, mountain-flanked stream, offering ideal navigation during the ice-free months. Thus ocean-going ships from the far corners of the earth can dock within 20 miles of the plant at Arvida.

[23] B. J. McGuire, "Aluminum – The Story of Fifty Years of Growth by the Canadian Industry," *Canadian Geographical Journal,* Vol. 42, October 1951, p. 153.

Transportation

In a region where manufacturing is predominant, cities numerous, and population dense, transportation must be superior. The American Manufacturing Belt has an unsurpassed network of railways, highways, airways, and waterways that bind it together and link it with other regions.

Some significant changes in the relative importance of the several types of transportation took place during the depression of the 1930's. Railroad transportation declined in relative importance, whereas that by motor gained. That by pipeline declined while that by water gained, although this situation was completely reversed in 1942 as a result of the numerous sinkings of tankers by packs of German submarines.

Ocean Transportation. Brief reference must suffice for this topic since New York, Baltimore, Philadelphia, and Boston have already been treated and it was seen that as port cities they all excel. All are connected with the far corners of the earth and all have ready access to the food, industrial raw materials, and markets of interior Anglo-America.

The Great Lakes. The Great Lakes comprise the most valuable system of inland waterways in the world. For 1,700 miles they extend in an east-west direction, connecting the great raw-materials producing Central Northwest with the fuel, industries, and markets of the East. Few barriers to navigation now exist between Duluth and Montreal. The lakes seldom experience severe storms, but they are closed by ice normally from December to May. The shores of the lakes are dotted with great industrial and commercial cities.

Most of the traffic consists of bulky products—iron ore, coal, wheat, and limestone. These are handled economically by specially designed boats capable of carrying enormous cargoes. Speedy loading and unloading facilities have been installed at the ports (Figure 3–22).

The Great Lakes – St. Lawrence Seaway. For more than a third of a century this project has been widely discussed throughout the United States and Canada. It would link the Great Lakes and the St. Lawrence River with the Atlantic, permitting ocean-going vessels of considerable size to penetrate the continent 2,350 miles to Duluth. It also would provide an abundance of hydroelectric power estimated at 2.2 million H.P. near Massena, New York.

To complete the Seaway, specified channels would have to be dredged to a depth of 27 feet and locks would have to be constructed to by-pass certain sections (Figure 3–23).

Since the greater part of the Seaway is on the international boundary, Canada and the United States must agree on a plan before work is begun. The estimated cost is be-

Figure 3–21. Shipshaw power development on the Saguenay River provides abundant power for the industries of the region. Shipshaw Number One is in the background, Number Two in the foreground. Most of this power is used locally in the aluminum and pulp and paper industries. (Courtesy of Aluminum Company of Canada, Ltd.)

tween 800 million and one billion dollars. But the biggest question at the time this book goes to press is whether the United States and Canada will do the job jointly or whether Canada will do it alone. This decision will be made by Congress. It now seems probable, as a result of the powerful minority group in the United States, that Canada will have to "go it alone." The Canadian government, which has waited many years for the United States' decision, has at last become wearied of the vacillation. It has recently had the plans approved by the Inter-

Since 1897, the Seaway has been under consideration. At first, the argument for the Seaway was that it would speed the marketing of American grain. During the depression, it was discussed as a make-work project. During World War II, the Seaway would have been valuable as a safe inland waterway for transporting war materiel. Now, a leading reason for the Seaway is that it would facilitate the transport of high-grade iron ore and other base minerals from northeast Canada and other countries to the United States.

American opposition is aimed at the proj-

Figure 3–22. The Benjamin F. Fairless being unloaded at Conneaut, Ohio. This vessel made a world record in 1945 by hauling 18,543 tons of iron ore in *one trip* and nearly 525,000 tons in 30 trips. The big unloading machines seize from the vessel's hold as many as 20 tons at a single bite. (Courtesy of United States Steel Corporation.)

national Joint Commission—the body created by the two countries to work out solutions to problems involving mutual boundary problems.

World conditions have so changed since Pearl Harbor that the project now seems vital to the industrial and commercial welfare of both nations. Geography ordains that this be a joint operation. The United States has a common interest in every aspect of its development: the power, which would be shared equally, is badly needed by expanding industry, and shipping rights on the St. Lawrence are guaranteed to the United States by treaty in perpetuity.

Arguments for and against the Seaway.

ect from many directions. The railroads fear that they will lose business. Power companies in the Massena vicinity do not want competition from the government hydroelectric plant. The coal industry, selling to the power industry and to the railroads, feels that it would suffer if steam power were replaced by electricity. The Great Lakes shipping lines protest that they would be hurt by competition from foreign vessels that have a lower draft and pay lower wages to crews than do their vessels. Furthermore, Great Lakes harbors at present do not have channel or pier facilities to accommodate larger vessels. The big port cities on the Atlantic and Gulf coasts are afraid that their com-

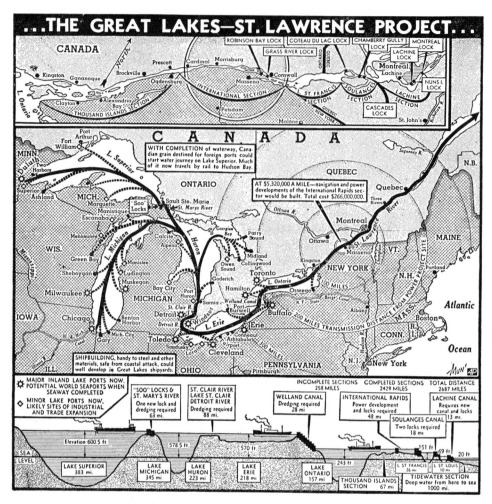

Figure 3–23. The proposed Great Lakes-St. Lawrence Seaway and Power Project. Presumably this should be a joint Canadian-United States project, but after two decades of fruitless negotiation resulting from blockading tactics by sectional interests in the United States, Canada has finally decided to build the Seaway alone. (Courtesy of Associated Press and the Hon. L. C. Rabaut of Michigan.)

merce will decline. The lake city of Buffalo also foresees an economic decline: now Buffalo unloads goods from lake steamers and transships them onto railroads and the barge canal to New York City. Some critics argue that since the Seaway would be closed for five months of the year, the project would be financially foolish. But during the seven months when the Seaway would be open, there is a tremendous demand for transport facilities. The St. Mary's Canal at Sault Ste. Marie, Michigan, has more tonnage passing through it in its seven-month season than the combined tonnage of the Suez and Panama canals during a twelve-month period. Fog has been cited as a hindrance, but the busy port of New York has more days of fog than does Montreal. Since the Seaway would be vulnerable to air attack, military strategists no longer uphold the building of the Seaway, as they did early in World War II. Moreover, some feel that the estimated cost of 818 million dollars, including 400 million dollars for the power project, may prove to be less than the actual cost.

However, there are strong arguments in favor of the project. Should a war emergency arise, the completed Seaway would hasten ship construction in the Great Lakes ports and would be conducive to decentralizing industry from the East Coast. The power plant would be a source of cheap power for a large industrialized area. According to Mr. W. W. Durrell, general manager of the Iron Ore Company of Canada, the Seaway is necessary if more than 10 million tons of iron ore are to be shipped economically annually from the Quebec-Labrador region into the Lower Lakes region. The Seaway would also save money. Mr. L. Chevrier, Canadian Minister of Transport, has said that the Seaway would eliminate the cost of an estimated 200 million dollar increase for the steel mills yearly. An additional 30 million dollars could be saved by not having to transship grain and other commodities because large ships could penetrate the Great Lakes. Furthermore, the cost of the project would be self-liquidating as tolls are collected from ships using the Seaway.

Rivers. Rivers were the great highways of colonial days, having been used whenever possible in preference to the hard and slow overland routes. Their chief advantages as highways were low cost and convenience. Many a stream that now seems too small or shallow to have served was very extensively used, and many a settlement would have died out had there been no stream over which to float products to market. All large western communities in the period 1800 to 1850 were located on the Ohio or the Mississippi.

The Detroit (a link in the Great Lakes system), Monongahela, Ohio, Great Kanawha, Hudson, Mississippi, and Illinois are the principal rivers of the American Manufacturing Belt and most important are the first three.

The Detroit River. The Detroit River, which drains Lake St. Clair into Lake Erie, is 28 miles long and one-half to three miles wide. A shoal that formerly blocked its entrance from Lake St. Clair has been cut through. About three fourths of the tonnage moving down the lakes passes through the Detroit River—more than moves through the Suez and Panama canals combined.

The Monongahela River. The Monongahela, a deeply entrenched river, is unique in two respects: (1) it is the most used in Anglo-America, averaging more than 30 million tons per annum, and (2) it is one of the few important streams flowing northward. Its valley is a land of chemical plants and coke plants, of glass-works and steel mills—and of coal.

Because the Monongahela, which flows through an area richly endowed in coal, focuses upon Pittsburgh, the world's leading iron and steel center, and because it was handicapped by annual drought and floods, it was the first river in the United States to be improved for navigation. Today it is navigable from Fairmont, West Virginia, to Pittsburgh.

Pittsburgh's principal competitive advantage in the iron and steel industry is the low-cost barge transportation on coking coal from river tipples to by-product coking plants without transshipment.

The Ohio River. The channel of the Ohio River was not navigable during the droughts of late summer until the federal government established a permanent nine-foot stage with a system of more than 50 movable dams which back the water into a succession of pools deep enough for navigation. Locks permit the boats to get around the dams.

The Ohio accordingly has become one of the continent's leading carriers of freight. Thousands of commodious barges, shackled in tows, are propelled over the river at all seasons, except for several days in spring when the water is too high or in winter when ice is objectionable. The tonnage is several times greater now than it was at the height of the steamboat period. Ninety-five per cent of the total freight consists of bulky products—coal, coke, ore, sand and gravel, stone, grain, pig iron, and steel. Increasing quantities of gasoline are being shipped. Most of the traffic is in the hands of contract and private carriers.

Canals. Space forbids adequate treatment of the fascinating and romantic subject of canals. Though most of them proved inadequate, particularly because they were closed by ice for several months each year, they did, nevertheless, play a vital role during the decades when people depended primarily upon inland water transportation. Canals were built to connect natural waterways.

The Welland Canal. Most important in this region is the Welland Canal, built to avoid Niagara Falls and connecting Port Colborne on Lake Erie with Port Weller on Lake Ontario. First built in 1829, it was a tortuous ditch with 25 locks. Nevertheless, it did a tremendous business and during the boom grain year of 1928 handled 131,531,000 bushels. Unfortunately, the large lake carriers, which constitute about 90 per cent of those on the lakes, could not navigate the canal; cargoes had to be unloaded at Port Colborne, the Canadian terminal harbor 25 miles west of Buffalo, and placed aboard smaller ships. These required about 16 hours to make the trip, against 8 hours today. The greater economy and efficiency attained by larger lake vessels led to a desire to enlarge the canal; the work was begun in 1913 and completed in 1931. The new Welland Canal can handle any ship on the lakes. Whereas the old canal had 25 locks, the new one has but 7. Though 30 miles long, it has few curves and no bad ones.

New York State Barge (Erie) Canal. This canal, which connects Lake Erie with the Hudson River was opened in 1825. It follows the only practical route through the Appalachian barrier—the Mohawk Gap and the Ontario Plain. Freight rates between Buffalo and New York immediately dropped from $100 to $5 per ton and the transit time was shortened from 20 to 8 days. The Erie Canal, probably more than any other single factor, made New York City the greatest port on the Atlantic Coast. Traffic from the interior poured into New York Harbor. The Erie was financially successful, and it was the busiest inland waterway in the world for many years.

In 1875, however, its traffic was surpassed by the railway. Tolls were abolished in 1883, but this was only a temporary solution. By 1895 the tonnage fell to 3,500,000 as against 19 million for its competing railroad. The solution appeared to be a larger canal—the New York State Barge Canal, which was completed in 1918. It followed the route of its predecessor most of the way. It is 353 miles long from Buffalo to Waterford (near Troy) on the Hudson. But the canal is a disappointment. It is used only by self-propelled vessels or tows propelled by them. Traffic has been increasing in recent years but only slowly.

The Illinois and Michigan Canal. As early as 1673 the explorers Joliet and Marquette spoke of the advantages of a canal that would connect the Illinois and Des Plaines rivers with the Chicago River. Construction on the Illinois and Michigan Canal was not begun until 1836, however, and it was not open for traffic until 1848. The waterway was 6 feet deep, 48 feet wide, and 97 miles long. Fed in part by Chicago River water, it also aided in solving Chicago's sewage problem, which had been critical, since no current could carry the waste away from the dead end of Lake Michigan. In 1871 Chicago deepened the summit level of this canal in order to reduce the pollution of the lake. In 1911 the Chicago Drainage Canal, which paralleled its predecessor to Joliet, was opened. Since it had a depth of 21 feet, it soon drew away all through traffic from the old canal.

In the 1920's the Lakes-to-Gulf Waterway, of which the Illinois-Michigan Canal is a part, was further improved, and the canal is now a nine-foot barge waterway from Lake Michigan to the Illinois River. Traffic is definitely increasing.

The Chesapeake and Delaware Canal. The Chesapeake and Delaware Canal, connecting the Delaware River on the east with an arm of Chesapeake Bay on the west, is 19 miles long and 27 feet deep. It was completed in 1829, thus providing an all-water route from Philadelphia to Baltimore. Tideless and toll-free, it constitutes an important link in the Intra-coastal Waterway, which has been owned and operated by the United States government since 1919. Accommodating all but the very largest ocean-going vessels, it shortens the route from Baltimore to Philadelphia by 316 miles.

Railroads. Though the United States has but seven per cent of the world's population and seven per cent of its area, it has nearly one-third of the railroad mileage. Most cities in the United States developed simultaneously with railroads; 73 per cent of all rail traffic terminates in urban areas. As early as the 1850's, far-seeing men felt certain that the West would be developed by railroads rather than by rivers and canals. By 1860 railroads had triumphed over inland waterways, and since then port rivalries have been expressed in the competition of the railroads serving them.

The American Manufacturing Belt has a real rail web—the most important in the United States. Its railways carry more than half the passengers and tonnage handled by all American railroads. This volume of traffic is attributable to the fact that so large a part of the total population dwells in the Manufacturing Belt that most of the products of the farm, the mine, and the factory must be consumed there. Most of the lines run east and west. In this region no one, be he an inhabitant of a city, town, village, hamlet, or farm, is more than a few miles from a railway.

Highways. The roads of the colonies were little more than cleared paths and were made mostly for local traffic. Toll roads were built by private companies between 1790 and 1840. The federal government began construction on the National Road in 1811, opening it in 1817. Since then this nation, but more particularly the American Manufacturing Belt, has been spider-webbed with roads, because hard-surface highways and heavy traffic are synonymous with dense population and high productivity. Without automobiles and motor trucks speeding over the roads day and night, urban dwellers would experience difficulty in securing food. Motor trucks benefit from low capacities and high speed and can, therefore, provide frequent shipments at low cost. They also have a distinct advantage over railroads in short hauls, and are competing successfully with railroads on intermediate and even long hauls.

Trucks have been a potent factor in decentralizing industry.

Unfortunately the highway system in the region under discussion is glutted with bottlenecks, especially in and around cities. By-passes, parkways, and turnpikes are, however, relieving some of the congestion.

Pipelines. *Crude oil, natural gas, and gasoline.* Petroleum, when first discovered, was transported in barrels by wagons, and somewhat later by railroads. As production skyrocketed, a new method of getting petroleum to market had to be found. The pipeline resulted. Pipeline routes are chosen with great care—often with the aid of aerial surveys. Sharp valleys, ridges, and rivers are avoided whenever possible, and even soil, climate, and vegetation are considered. The routes usually go directly to their destinations except when skirting urban centers.

The American Manufacturing Belt has attracted many of the trunk pipelines from the Mid-Continent and other provinces to refining and marketing centers on the Great Lakes, the Mississippi River, and the Atlantic Seaboard of both Canada and the United States.

Formerly only crude oil was shipped but now considerable quantities of gasoline move by pipeline.

Natural Gas. Few businesses have boomed in recent years as has that of production and transportation of natural gas. Production and sales tripled between 1936 and 1950. Much of this expansion must be attributed to the increasing use of long-distance transmission lines. Today the United States has more than 375,000 miles of natural gas pipelines; several of the individual lines exceed 1,500 miles in length. Most of these pipelines extend from the South into the American Manufacturing Belt.

Air Transportation. The great size of the United States and Canada, along with the demand for speedy transportation, stimulated the rapid growth of airways particularly after 1930. Most of the traffic is passenger but the amount of air freight is increasing.

Airline routes of the United States and Canada are confined to fairly well-defined lines of travel, since they connect leading cities and depend upon ground aids. The natural environment of the region over which planes fly has much influence on weather conditions and hence on safety. Especially is this true of mountains and of areas affected by fog, heavy rain and snow, thunderstorms, surface winds, and upper winds.

The Outlook. It has been pointed out that the American Manufacturing Belt contains a disproportionate share of Anglo-America's population, metropolitan areas, cities, manufacturing plants, and wealth. It is essentially a region of industrial cities and towns.

This region's future will undoubtedly be a continuation of its present. This seems to be well substantiated by the fact that during the decade 1940–1950 most of the industrial growth of the two nations occurred in those areas that comprise the American Manufacturing Belt. This situation, however, so far as the United States is concerned, is contrary to public opinion which assumes that most of the new industry sprang up in the South and Far West. During the rearmament program, the same region has benefited most.

The American Manufacturing Belt is a region of great cities. While cities will continue to grow and while most of the nation's population will remain urban, city growth in the future probably will be slower and more uncertain than in the past. The suburbs will continue to grow faster than the cities themselves. Continued mechanization of farms and the limited opportunities in rural areas will release more and more young people from the land and a large percentage — about 50 per cent — of these will gravitate to the cities. Thus farms and farm villages function as "seed bags" of our cities. Normally large cities with populations of 100,000 and more do not have a birth rate sufficiently high to maintain themselves. It is estimated that they would decline to one third of that population in three generations if forced to rely upon their own birth rate.

Economically and socially, the small towns and the suburbs of large cities, are better places to live; the cost of living is not so high and the comforts of life are greater for the masses. Hence, it would appear that many industries and their workers would do better to locate in small communities.

For some time there has been going on in the nation a form of decentralization, known as diffusion — a movement out of the centers of metropolitan areas to their peripheries. Decentralization has been going on for some years but only when companies could be sure it was to their economic advantage. Since the end of World War II and particularly since the middle of 1951 the federal government has been urging the dispersion of defense plants "away from congested areas" to places which are at least 10 to 20 miles outside target cities. In the sense that it grants or withholds financial aid to companies, the government is actually drawing a new industrial map of the nation. Pilot studies have now been made of all so-called "target areas." Whether the present plan of dispersal of industry is justifiable is unknown. After two and one-half years of aerial bombing of Germany, her aircraft industry produced two and one-half times as many planes as in 1942. Most companies to date have not been frightened by threats of atomic bombs and guided missiles and have accordingly as in the past put economic considerations first.

In the Canadian segment of the region, the same conditions prevail as in the United States. Nowhere else in the world, perhaps, is there so superb a combination of geographic, economic, political, and social conditions conducive to supporting manufacturing of the first order as in the American Manufacturing Belt of these two countries.

Selected Bibliography

John W. Alexander, "Manufacturing in the Rock River Valley — Location Factors," *Annals of the Association of American Geographers*, Vol. 40, September 1950, pp. 236-253.

Marvin J. Barloon, "Some Problems of Relocation Facing the Steel Industry," *Latin American Studies*, University of Texas, Vol. 9, 1950, pp. 31-49.

F. S. Blanchard, "Massachusetts Textile Decline Needs Drastic Steps for Cure," *Textile World,* Vol. 102, January 1952.

Chester Bowles, "New England is More Than a Museum," *New York Times Magazine,* March 19, 1950, pp. 14-15.

Council of Economic Advsiors, Committee on the New England Economy, *The New England Economy. A Report to the President,* Washington, D. C.: Government Printing Office, July 1951.

C. Hartley Grattan, "What Makes New England Go?" *Harper's Magazine,* Vol. 199, August 1949, pp. 35-42.

S. E. Harris, "New England's Decline in the American Economy," *Harvard Business Review,* Vol. 25, 1946-1947.

Ray M. Hudson, "The Proposed New England Steel Mill," *New England Water Works Association,* Vol. 65, June 1951, pp. 103-109.

Walter Isard and William M. Capron, "The Future Locational Pattern of Iron and Steel Production in the U. S.," *Journal of Political Economy,* Vol. 57, April 1949, pp. 118-133.

B. J. McGuire, "Aluminum — The Story of Fifty Years of Growth by the Canadian Industry," *Canadian Geographical Journal,* Vol. 43, October 1951, pp. 144-163.

Blake McKelvey, "The Erie Canal: Mother of Cities," *New York Historical Society Quarterly,* Vol. 35, January 1951.

Glenn E. McLaughlin, *Growth of American Manufacturing Areas: A Corporative Analysis with Special Emphasis on Trends in the Pittsburgh District,* Bureau of Business Research, Monograph No. 7, Pittsburgh: University of Pittsburgh Press, 1938.

Allan Rodgers, "Industrial Inertia — A Major Factor in the Location of the Steel Industry in the United States," *The Geographical Review,* Vol. 42, January 1952, pp. 56-66.

————, "The Iron and Steel Industry of the Mahoning and Shenango Valleys," *Economic Geography,* Vol. 28, October 1952, pp. 331-342.

Alfred J. Wright, "Recent Changes in the Concentration of Manufacturing," *Annals of the Association of American Geographers,* Vol. 35, December 1945, pp. 144-166.

4.

Northeastern Anglo-America

NORTHEASTERN Anglo-America is a region which lies partly in the United States and partly in Canada and it serves as an excellent illustration of a geographic region which is not limited by political boundaries. The region consists of several somewhat diverse parts which differ from each other in physical appearance as well as in economic responses, but when considered as a whole they show remarkable regional unity. Here in one way or another the majority of the people are influenced by the sea. Whether they are engaged in fishing, lumbering, pulp and papermaking, shipping wheat, mining coal, quarrying building stones, growing apples, or raising dairy cattle or foxes, their outlook is and must always be seaward.

To many regionalists the inhabitants of all six New England states are New Englanders: "Americans of the older stocks think of the words 'New England' as connoting not only a region but a group of traditions, institutions, and ways of living and of thinking." [1] In fact, much work has been done that would in a way justify New England as being considered a region.[2] The difficulty here, however, comes in drawing a boundary between the highlands of Vermont and the

Adirondack Mountains of New York, or of separating either the Canadian Maritime Provinces or the St. Lawrence Lowlands from the coastal areas or the highlands of New England. For that reason the authors feel that the entire Northeast should constitute one region (Figure 4–1), and that at least four subregions should be recognized. These subregions are: (1) Coastal New England, including the lowlands of the south and the immediate littoral northeastward through Maine, but not including the large industrial centers discussed previously in Chapter 3, (2) The Northeastern Uplands, including the Adirondack Mountains, (3) the Coastal Lowlands of the Maritime Provinces of Canada, and (4) The Lower St. Lawrence Valley.

Physiographically, the provinces of the United States extend into Canada, and no marked differences appear in the way of life of the two peoples except in French Canada. The Canadian population is confined largely to a narrow strip relatively close to the bor-

---

[1] American Geographical Society, *New England's Prospects: 1933*, p. 459, Special Publication No. 16. New York: 1933.

[2] National Resources Committee, *Regional Planning, Part III — New England*. Washington, D. C.: Government Printing Office, 1936; and Council of of Economic Advisers, Committee on the New England Economy, *The New England Economy: A Report to the President*. Washington, D. C.: Government Printing Office, July 1951 referred to hereafter as *The New England Economy*).

72

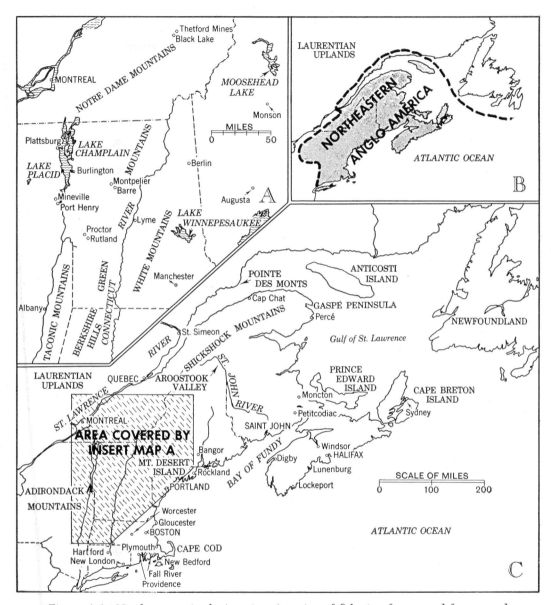

Figure 4–1. Northeastern Anglo-America. A region of fisheries, forests and forest products, quarrying and mining, dairying and specialized farming, commerce, and resorts.

der. The fact that each country, at the more important points of interchange, has resources which the other lacks has served to bring each country's railroads to important objectives beyond its border. It also helps to explain why Canada's railroads have been projected into the United States as a means of reaching strategic points — especially ports that are open to navigation during the winter.

The Physical Setting

Northeastern Anglo-America occupies North America's indented coastal ribbon from New York to and including the north bank of the St. Lawrence River. It comprises the littoral of Connecticut, Rhode Island, Massachusetts, New Hampshire, Maine and New Brunswick, all of Nova Scotia, Prince Edward Island, Cape Breton Island, and that part of Quebec on both sides of the river as far as the city of Quebec. It also includes the Adirondack Mountains, the Green Mountains, the Berkshire Hills and Taconic Mountains, the White Mountains, and the Notre Dame and Shickshock Mountains, and several lowland areas such as the Aroostook Valley, the Lake Champlain Lowland and the Connecticut Valley.

Surface Features. The coastal area consists primarily of low rounded hills and valleys. Most of the region is traversed by fast-flowing streams and much of it is dotted with small lakes. The coastal area has been slightly submerged; accordingly, ocean waters have invaded the lower valleys, giving rise to bays or estuaries. Often branch bays extend up the side valleys. The coast is characterized by innumerable good harbors. Superficially, the coasts of Maine and Nova Scotia appear to be fjorded, but, they are probably drowned normal river valleys and have been but little modified by ice action.

The Lower St. Lawrence Valley, which extends from the Isle d'Orleans to the constric-

tion in the river between Pointe des Monts and Cap Chat, is bounded by sheer cliffs which, in places, rise abruptly from the river bank. The escarpment is 1,500 to 2,000 feet high on the north side and 1,000 feet on the south side opposite Quebec, and 3,000 feet as it nears the Gaspé Peninsula. Coastal terraces mantled with marine soils provide the more important sites for settlement. The Lower St. Lawrence is really an arm of the Atlantic, for the submergence of the region has enabled ocean waters to penetrate to within 80 miles of Montreal. Below the Isle d'Orleans the river expands into a broad stream 10 to 20 miles wide.

All mountains of the upland area are geologically old and have been worn down by erosional agents. The Taconics, which border the western side of the Berkshires, are among the oldest in Anglo-America. The Green Mountains of Vermont have rounded summits (Figure 4–2) — the result of the great ice sheet which overrode ridges and valleys alike. The highest summits are less than 4,500 feet above sea level. The White Mountains are higher and bolder, particularly in the Presidential Range of central New Hampshire, where Mount Washington rises to an elevation of 6,293 feet. Northeastward the mountains become more rounded and less

Figure 4–2. The rounded summits and gentle slopes of the Green Mountains of Vermont are a result of continental glaciation. Compare this landscape with that of the Rocky Mountains in Figure 12–2. (Photo by Chandler.)

conspicuous, although their summits remain at an elevation of nearly 5,000 feet.

The mountains of eastern Canada are lower and more rounded, having been subdued through long periods of erosion. Their general elevation is slightly more than 2,000 feet above sea level. The Adirondacks, geologically an extension of the Laurentian Uplands, are also considered a part of this region because of similar human activities. Although an older upland mass, the Adirondacks underwent changes at the time of the Appalachian mountain-building movement, which caused a doming of the upper surface. Furthermore, they were eroded profoundly during glacial times. While not so high as the White Mountains, the Adirondacks cover more area.

The entire upland is composed of igneous and metamorphic rocks — granites, schists, gneisses, marbles, and slates — so valuable that this has become the leading source of building stones on the continent.

The stream courses of the upland area were altered by glaciation. Many water bodies such as Lake Placid, Lake Winnipesaukee[3], and Moosehead Lake characterize the region. They have been of inestimable value in the development of the tourist industry.

The Aroostook Valley, occupying the upper part of the St. John River drainage, is the result of stream erosion in softer rocks.[4] The Lake Champlain Lowland and the Connecticut Valley were eroded severely by tongues of ice that moved southward between the Green Mountains and the Adirondacks, and between the Green Mountains and the White Mountains.[5]

Climate. Climatically the region is not a unit. The littoral area differs from the uplands, from the Lower St. Lawrence Valley and also from Maritime Quebec.

[3] There are on record 132 different ways of spelling this name. *Sixth Report of the United States Geographic Board*, p. 822. Washington, D. C.: Government Printing Office, 1933.

[4] N. M. Fenneman, *Physiography of Eastern United States,* p. 367. New York: McGraw-Hill Book Co., 1938.

[5] Wallace W. Atwood, *The Physiographic Provinces of North America*, pp. 220-221. Boston: Ginn & Co., 1940.

Nearly every part of the littoral area lies within less than 35 miles of the ocean and hence is greatly influenced by it. Along the coast of Maine, New Brunswick and Nova Scotia, the marine influence results in a milder and more equable climate than would be expected in these latitudes. Nova Scotia's mean January temperature is about the same as that of central New York, despite its location two to five degrees of latitude farther north. Winters though long and cold, are not severe for the latitude. Temperatures, however, fall below zero nearly every winter. Snow covers the ground throughout most of the winter. Spring surrenders reluctantly to summer because of the presence of ice in the Gulf of St. Lawrence and because of the Labrador Current. Summers are cool — temperatures of 90 degrees being extremely rare. The growing season varies from 100 to 160 days in Nova Scotia.

Except in northern New Brunswick, the precipitation of 40 to 55 inches is well distributed throughout the year. Summer fogs characterize the coasts of New England, New Brunswick and Nova Scotia when southeast winds from the warm Gulf Stream blow across the cold waters between the Gulf of Maine and Newfoundland.

Maritime Quebec, the area comprising the Gaspé Peninsula and Anticosti Island, does not have a true maritime climate. Winters are long (November through April) but not severe for the latitude. As a result of proximity to the sea hot summers do not exist in the true sense.

The precipitation of about 30 inches is considerably less than in the littoral area; moreover, it varies from year to year. Though well distributed, the rainfall is greater in summer. Fierce gales are common in winter and are by no means unknown during the season of navigation.

The Lower St. Lawrence Valley has cold, long winters, though periods of mild weather are not uncommon. The river is closed to navigation normally from December to April. Summers are short and warm but the days are long. The growing season averages 135 days at Quebec.

The precipitation of 35 to 42 inches is not

heavy but is evenly distributed throughout the year. As would be expected, the snowfall is heavy. It remains on the ground all winter, for little of it thaws. Winter surrenders to spring, and summer to winter, with great rapidity.

The upland area lies within the humid continental climatic region, with the Atlantic Ocean exerting little influence. The growing season is short, averaging less than 120 days. Summers are cool, and winters extremely cold — temperatures dropping at times to 30 degrees below zero. The abundant precipitation is evenly distributed throughout the year, but in winter most of it falls as snow. Snow has been of great importance in the recently developed winter sports.

Natural Vegetation. It is extremely difficult to get an accurate word-picture of the forest in its primitive state. Probably nine tenths of the land included in this region was covered with forest. About the only treeless parts were the dunes, marshes, meadows, bogs, or some mountain summits (if ice-scoured or exposed to wind).

The composition of the forest was closely adjusted to land forms, soil, and climate. There was a great variety of species and a great difference in the ages and sizes of the trees. Between the pine forest of the valleys and the spruce forest of the mountains was a belt of hardwoods — maple, yellow birch, and beech — with occasional sprinklings of pine, hemlock, spruce, ash, and paper birch.

Coastal New Hampshire and most of coastal Maine contained white pine, spruce, hemlock, red oak, and white ash. White pine was the outstanding tree. Attaining a height of 240 feet and a diameter of 6 feet at the butt, it dwarfed even the tall spruce. It was sometimes called the "masting pine" because the larger trees were marked with the Royal Arrow and reserved for masts for the Royal Navy. Maine still is called the "Pine Tree State."

All of the upland area except the highest mountains, was originally clothed in a dense forest. The higher slopes had the typical fir, hemlock, and spruce of the northern forest; the lower ones had white pine and mixed hardwoods. As man cut the more accessible

timber for lumber and firewood and later cleared much of the land for farms, the primeval forests began to disappear. Rapid cutting, followed by forest fires, ruined much of the natural beauty of the upland, accelerated stream run-off, and caused floods and soil erosion. In recent years state and federal agencies have attempted to reclaim abandoned farmlands by reforestation. Forest reclamation has led to the establishment of several state forest preserves as well as the Green Mountain and the White Mountain national forests.

Soils. The soils are extremely varied, partly because of differences in the parent rock and partly because of widespread glaciation. Most of the farm land is on the sedimentaries. All the mature soils are pedalfers: gray-brown podzolic soils predominate in coastal New Hampshire and Maine, while podzols prevail in New Brunswick, Nova Scotia, and the Lower St. Lawrence Valley. The gray-brown soils which develop under a forest cover (chiefly deciduous) are less leached and less acidic than the podzols and are among the better pedalfers.[6] They are low in lime and are in need of continuous fertilization.

The podzols, on the other hand, comprise the light gray soils characteristic of climates with cool, moist summers and cold, long winters. Here the natural vegetation is coniferous forest, huckleberry, and fern — plants adapted to acid soils. Accordingly, this region has few good agricultural areas.

The uplands have thin soils which belong almost exclusively to the podzol group. The forests (largely coniferous) and the heavy year-round precipitation have together produced leached, acid soils of low productivity.

Settlement and Early Development

Northeastern Anglo-America was not settled by immigrants from a single country; the earliest settlers in the Maritime Provinces and Quebec were French, while those in New England were English.

---

[6] For soil terminology, see *Soils and Man, Yearbook of Agriculture, 1938.* Washington, D. C.: Government Printing Office, 1938.

The New England Segment. The first important settlement in what is now New England took place at Plymouth in 1620. All the early colonies, including those before and immediately after the landing of the Pilgrims, were planted on the seaboard. The coast was, then, the first American frontier. Its settlements were bounded by untamed hills on the west and by the stormy Atlantic on the east. Its shore-dwelling pioneers, beckoned alike by the soil and the sea, obeyed both, and their adjustments to the two environments laid the foundations for the land life and sea life of the nation.

As population became denser in maritime New England and Canada, the more venturesome settlers seeking new lands trekked farther into the wilderness. As long as the French controlled the St. Lawrence Lowlands, the Indians of the upland remained entrenched in this so-called "neutral ground," thus restricting white settlements to the seaboard. In the Adirondacks hostile Iroquois kept the English confined to the Hudson and Mohawk valleys until the close of the Revolutionary War. After the conquest of Canada by the British, pioneers from the older parts of New England penetrated the upland feeling that at last the power of the Indian had been broken. By the 1760's most of the lower valleys in New Hampshire and Vermont were occupied. Only forested slopes were therefore available to "newcomers" — slopes that never should have been cleared. Agriculture was of the subsistence type.

In New England . . . the colonial pattern of agriculture continued dominant until the second decade of the nineteenth century. Cultivation was extensive and exploitative, tools clumsy, systematic crop rotation and fertilizers generally absent, livestock neglected, and orchards and woodlands badly managed. . . . For the most part tools and clothing were made in the farm home.[7]

The clearing of the forest for farms led to an early development of logging and lumbering, which could be carried on in winter when farm work was not available. The logs, dragged on the snow to frozen streams, were floated to mills in the spring when the ice melted, thus providing a supplemental source of income for the pioneers, which continued to be important until the latter part of the nineteenth century.

Between 1800 and 1810 Merino sheep, imported from Spain, greatly improved the domestic flocks and gave a new industry to the upland farmer. Raising wool sheep became a leading activity for the next three decades, and was especially profitable during the 1830's. By 1840, Eastern wool growers owned 60 per cent of the country's sheep. The New England industry was confined almost exclusively to Vermont and the hills of western Massachusetts and Connecticut.

Because of remoteness and a more severe winter climate, the Canadian section of the Northeastern Uplands has remained largely a wilderness.

Maritime Canada. The first permanent settlement in North America, north of Florida was at Port Royal on the Bay of Fundy. Here the French found salt marshes which needed no clearing. This environment was attractive to men from the mouth of the Loire, whose forebears for generations had reclaimed and dyked somewhat similar land. These French called their new home Acadie (Acadia), and the Acadians converted the river marshes into productive farm land which characterized the cultivated area almost exclusively for a century.[8]

The French population grew rapidly after the Treaty of Utrecht in 1713. Louisburg was fortified to guard the mouth of the St. Lawrence and the fishing fleet.

Except during very brief intervals, they received little continuous aid or protection from their mother country. They were truly a self-made people, and by the opening of the eighteenth century they were native to Acadie. They conquered it to provide themselves with sustenance. They were almost independent of the outside world. They knew little of and cared

[7] Everett E. Edwards, "American Agriculture — The First 300 Years," *1940 Yearbook of Agriculture,* p. 205. Washington, D. C.: Government Printing Office, 1940.

[8] J. B. Brebner, *New England's Outpost: Acadia Before the Conquest of Canada,* p. 37. New York: Columbia University Press, 1927.

less for its problems and its politics. The only strong tie connecting them with Europe was their religion, kept alive and real by priests.[9]

Acadia thus became a backwater off the main stream of Anglo-American life.

The Acadians remained here until the outbreak of hostilities between the British and French preceding the Seven Years' War. Then more than 6,000 of them were rounded up and banished; they were scattered from Massachusetts to South Carolina. Some fled into the forests of what are now New Brunswick, Prince Edward Island, and Quebec; some made their way to Quebec City, the Ohio Valley, and even to Louisiana; others joined the French in St. Pierre, Miquelon, and the West Indies. Many starved. The reason most commonly given for their expulsion was the fear on the part of England that so heavy a concentration of French in this part of the continent was a menace to English safety.

This destruction and dispersal continued for eight years, ending in 1763. Then individuals and groups began to trickle back, and, though denied their old properties, they found abodes here and there in what are now called the "Maritime Provinces."

The first appreciable number of British to settle in the Maritimes arrived in 1749 at the site now occupied by Halifax. Shortly afterwards 2,000 Germans founded Lunenburg. Highlanders, who were to make Nova Scotia a Scottish province, did not arrive until 1828; then they came by thousands. Although the largest group of British Loyalists arrived after the close of the Revolutionary War, many came prior to 1776.

The Lower St. Lawrence Valley. The French colonized the Lower St. Lawrence Valley, occupying first the land along the river. As early as 1675 nearly all the ancestors of the present inhabitants had reached Canada. They practiced subsistance farming on terraces. Because of isolation, a culture became established that was picturesque in its retarded development and less affected than any other group in Anglo-America by ideas and customs from the outside.

[9] Brebner, *New England's Outpost,* p. 38.

The Present Inhabitants

The international boundary between the Canadian and United States portions of the region does not mean what it would in Europe; for, socially, the English-speaking people are one. There is a great difference, however, between them and the French Canadians.

The New Englanders. The original white settlers, of English stock, remained dominant until about 1840. For two and one-half centuries "during the period of poverty and struggle, the Yankees increased, beat down the forest, won the fields, sailed the seas, and went forth to populate Western commonwealths." [10] To them work was a virtue, idleness a sin.

The Yankees no longer dominate New England numerically, save in the rather isolated agricultural areas of the highland interior where there is a large proportion of old people. Yankee stock still contributes most of the bank directors, business executives, and college and university presidents — officials "not elected by popular vote."

The Inhabitants of the Maritime Provinces. The Maritime Provinces are not densely settled and the number of cities is small. The population is about equally divided between English and French, though other nationalities are represented. About one fifth are descendants of the Acadians.

This area has lost heavily through emigration to New England and to the Canadian Prairie Provinces. The rural population is less uniform than that of New England, because large blocks of immigrants settled together in groups. Thus most of northern New Brunswick is French, south-central Nova Scotia is predominantly German, western Nova Scotia is English, eastern Nova Scotia, eastern New Brunswick and Prince Edward Island are Scottish.

The French Canadians. The Lower St. Lawrence Valley is inhabited almost entirely by French Canadians, who have one of the highest birth rates in North America. They

[10] J. Russell Smith and M. Ogden Phillips, *North America,* p. 113. New York: Harcourt, Brace & Co., 1940.

have overpopulated their lands. Pressure of population has encouraged emigration to the United States and to the more western parts of Canada, as well as within French Canada itself. In order to stem the tide of migration and keep the people attached to the soil of the Province, the Roman Catholic Church and the Quebec Government are co-operating. They are creating a new Quebec in the Abitibi District in the western part of the Province (outside this region), where many thousands of farmers and miners have settled. The present generation is less conservative than most Americans picture it. Many of the young people especially are no longer attracted to the soil, feeling it will not provide them with an adequate livelihood.

The Decline of Agriculture

Farming naturally was the first occupation of the colonists in the Maritime Provinces, the Lower St. Lawrence Valley, and New England. It was on a small scale and with few exceptions on infertile soils. Moreover, the cool, cloudy summers and the long, cold winters retarded the development of a thriving agriculture.

New England. Those who originally settled New England arrived at the worst possible time for farming — the beginning of winter. At first they lived largely on corn and beans, which they obtained from the Indians. When they began their farming operations, they found that European cereals did not thrive. They accordingly grew more and more Indian corn, a pioneer crop with many advantages, including excellent keeping qualities and utility for food and feed. Not for some years were the Pilgrims successful in growing European cereals. Farming was very hard; it meant battling ceaselessly with the earth. A man had to spend a month removing stones from a single acre before he could plant his crops in it.

The rugged topography and the infertile soils necessitated small farms. It was impossible to accumulate capital in a small-farm economy — a circumstance that led New Englanders to turn to other occupations, especially fishing and trading.

In the early part of the nineteenth century, the level, more fertile, and more accessible lands of the Upper Mississippi and Ohio River valleys began to compete seriously with the stony hillside farms of New England. The Erie Canal, opened in 1825, brought a steadily increasing quantity of foodstuffs and wool to Eastern markets. The building of railroads west of the Appalachians opened up still larger farm areas in the Middle West. Meanwhile, because of its inability to meet this competition, the sheep industry declined. Besides, high wages in the mills of southern New England or the possibility of greater profits on new lands in the West attracted the more energetic farmers resulting in a widespread exodus of young people. Only the more conservative preferred to remain on the hillside farms.

So long as they were able to supplement their income by working in the woods in winter, they could remain but when the forest was cleared, the farmers either had to leave, or accept a lower standard of living because their small farms were definitely submarginal.

In describing the deserted town of Lyme, New Hampshire, James W. Goldthwait wrote:

... for almost a century deserted farms in New Hampshire have been growing up to blueberry pasture, woodland, and forest. The sturdy population that was once evenly distributed over thousands of square miles of the stony upland has slowly and steadily moved down from the hilltops, emigrating to distant places or lingering yet awhile in the valleys. Large tracts of land have been abandoned or have become the summer homes and playgrounds of well-to-do vacation seekers from the cities. . . . The eastern half of this (Lyme) township is deserted country, with scarcely an occupied house and very few traveled roads . . .[11]

Between 1920 and 1930, two thirds of Vermont's and half of New Hampshire's townships lost population. Between 1940 and 1950, however, only five of Vermont's fourteen counties, and only one of New Hamp-

[11] James W. Goldthwait, "A Town That Has Gone Downhill," *Geographical Review*, Vol. 17, No. 4, October 1927, p. 527.

shire's ten counties lost population, showing that the tendency toward depopulation is at least decreasing.[12]

The Maritime Provinces. Agriculture began in the Maritimes in the seventeenth century when, by dyking, the Acadians reclaimed the tidal marshes along the Bay of Fundy. Before their expulsion in 1755, some 10,000 Acadians were supported comfortably

wick, and Prince Edward Island, is characterized by low rounded mountain ranges, lakes, swamps, and forests, arable land always has been restricted. Most of New Brunswick still is in forest. Nova Scotia, though more favored, is not well endowed for agriculture; scarcely one third of its area is occupied as farm land. Its productive areas are confined primarily to the western coastal

Figure 4–3. The village of Ste. Germaine in Quebec. In this typical French-Canadian settlement, note the alignment of the village along the banks of the river. (Courtesy of Office Provincial de Publicite, Quebec.)

in Nova Scotia. It is estimated that they had put 100,000 acres of land into pasture, orchard, and garden. They got as many as twenty bushels of wheat to the acre, made their orchards of apples, pears, plums, and cherries yield remarkably well, grew luxuriant small fruits, and pastured their cattle in natural meadows.

Because much of Nova Scotia, New Bruns-

12 U. S. Census, 1950.

belt, the Atlantic Coast being an upland of crystalline rocks. The first successful farming colony was in the meadows around Port Royal — now Annapolis. Subsequent settlement was along the more extensive marshlands about Minas Basin, Cobequid Bay, and at the head of Chignecto Bay.

The Lower St. Lawrence Valley. The French Canadians in this area began as farmers. Settlement was in the form of large estates (seigneuries); that of Beaupré, for instance, was 48 miles long and 18 miles deep — the long side paralleling the river. The land was rented by the *seigneur* to vassals. The peasant holdings were laid out along the river bank in long narrow strips 2,600 by 260 yards. Thus each holding had access to the river highway, which for a long time was the only thoroughfare, while the narrow width promoted continuous settlement (Figure 4–3). The houses and outbuildings were placed close beside one another for miles and gave the impression of continuous villages. The same system was used with respect to roads, for it was easier to keep one road than several clear of winter snow. As time passed, holdings were subdivided. The long lots that extended back into the forest gave each family access to the river as well as property in each of the different zones — arable, grazing, and forest. The land devoted to pasturage increased with the clearing of the forest. The crops, with the exception of wheat, were mostly hardy ones, the same as those grown today. The agricultural technique was primitive; in the eighteenth century the two-field system was used, with alternation of wheat and fallow.

Present-day Agriculture

Today agriculture throughout Northeastern Anglo-America continues on a small scale.

New England. In coastal Maine and New Hampshire, Indian corn was the staple crop, and it continued to be so until large-scale agriculture was developed in the Middle West. Accordingly, the New England farmer, realizing that rough land surface discouraged extensive use of machinery in growing corn and wheat, turned to specialized crops — tree fruits, berries, vegetables, and dairy and poultry products.

Hay was and still is an important crop. It had great cash value when lumbering was at its height and large numbers of horses were used. But, when pulp cutting replaced logging and lumbering and machinery replaced horses, the market for hay was reduced. It

continues to be important, however, because of dairying.

Most of the crops of this area are grown for consumption in nearby urban areas although potatoes and cranberries are marketed nationally. The concentration of a large population in the nearby American Manufacturing Belt affords an important market for perishable foodstuffs. Unexcelled transport facilities permit enormous quantities of milk to be trucked daily into the cities.

In southern Maine, dairying has an adjunct, the important sweet-corn canning industry. The business of canning corn began here. The stalks and even the factory wastes — husks, shanks, silks, and cobs — are used for manure and silage.

In the uplands of New England, agriculture has continued to decline in importance except in areas such as the Lake Champlain Lowland and Aroostook County which specialize in dairying or potato growing.

The Maritime Provinces. In Nova Scotia the cultivated land, as a rule, lies in the northern lowland, settlement being discouraged by the granitic interior and the Atlantic Coast. Seventy-five per cent of the land is still in forest. The dyked lands of old Acadia, made famous by Longfellow in *Evangeline*, still are fertile, easily cultivated, and productive. Farm crops are primarily those able to mature in a short growing season — forage crops, potatoes, vegetables, and small fruits. The commercial production of apples is important also in the Annapolis-Cornwallis Valley. Nevertheless, the sea has influenced Nova Scotia's economic life more than has the land.

In New Brunswick the area in farms is about equal to that in Nova Scotia, but the area in field crops is nearly twice as great. That the Province is not outstanding agriculturally seems proved by the fact that forest still covers nine tenths of the land. Field crops are important in the central western and central eastern portions. Pasture is less important here than in Nova Scotia. Dairying is favored in southern New Brunswick by heavy summer precipitation and proximity to urban markets.

Prince Edward Island, with about 80 per cent of its inhabitants engaged in farming, sustains a prosperous agriculture. The principal commercial crop is potatoes. The island enjoys an international reputation for certified seed potatoes. When the soil becomes exhausted, mussel mud, consisting of the decay of oyster, clam, and mussel shells, is dug up from the bays and river mouths (though not within 200 yards of live oyster beds) and is spread over the land.

The Lower St. Lawrence Valley. Farming continues as the principal occupation of most of the French Canadians in this area. On the north shore, the crops consist of hardy small grains, hay, vegetables, and tobacco for home consumption. Except near Quebec, where milk, butter, and vegetables are produced for the urban market, cheese has long been the chief "money crop."

Farming practically terminates east of St. Simeon. On the south shore, where there is more lowland and the climate is somewhat milder than on the opposite shore, potatoes constitute the chief crop. Dairying is important, too, for it enables the farmer to work in winter in a climate where he would otherwise be idle. Winter feeding and housing, however, are costly.

Agricultural Specialization: Crop-specialty Areas

Cape Cod and Cranberries. Southeastern Massachusetts and Cape Cod lead the nation in cranberry output, accounting for more than all the rest of the country combined. Other producing areas include the coastal lands of New Jersey, the bog lands of Wisconsin, and the wet coastal areas of Oregon and Washington.[13] Cape Cod first grew cranberries in 1810 but did not begin commercial production until forty years later. This area, with hundreds of ponds, marshes, and swamps of glacial origin, grows its cranberries exclusively in bogs. These, averaging about an acre in size, have the necessary acid soils.

---

[13] "Cape Cod Cranberries," *Fortune,* October, 1946, pp. 144-149.

Figure 4–4. Harvesting cranberries in a Cape Cod bog. Pickers move on their knees through a bog in a "duck line," combing the bright red berries off the low-lying vines. (Courtesy Massachusetts Development and Industrial Commission.)

The growers clear the bogland and spread over it a layer of coarse sand about four inches thick, the purpose of which is to prevent the growth of weeds. Once the crop is planted, the growers watch the weather reports with great care. If frost is forecast, they flood the bogs as a means of protecting the crop.

Harvesting begins early in September and continues through October. Mechanical pickers are used to some extent but are not favored because their weight crushes and destroys many of the valuable berries. Most harvesting is done by Portuguese-American laborers using wooden-toothed scoops (Figure 4–4). Since thousands of the berries fall to the ground under the vines, a freshly harvested bog is usually flooded and the loose cranberries are floated to the surface. This fruit is used mainly for canning. Each acre yields on the average between twenty-five and forty barrels of fruit.

Washington County and Blueberries. Washington and Hancock counties along the eastern coast of Maine are in an area of leached, acid podzolic soils called "blueberry barrens." These counties produce most of the nation's crop, and can about nine tenths of the total pack. When the tree cover is removed, low-growing blueberry bushes take possession of the ground. To keep down brush and tree growth, the land is fired every two or three years.

Aroostook County and Potatoes. Northeastern Maine produces about one eighth of the total potato crop of the United States. The area lies in a narrow belt from one to three townships wide along the northeastern border of the state.[14] It has a short growing season and an easily cultivated silty loam glacial soil. Large-scale enterprises and highly mechanized production methods (Figure 4–5) have built up a sizable industry in this remote corner of the United States.

The crop is grown both for seed potatoes and for food. Seed potatoes are especially in demand by the truck-farming areas of the Atlantic Seaboard and the southern states, while for food purposes Aroostook potatoes supply the markets of almost all states east of the Mississippi River. Although commercial production in this area began in the 1870's, it did not become important until after the completion of the first railroad in 1895.

The Lake Champlain Lowland. Throughout its early agricultural develop-

[14] P. M. Lombard and Bailey E. Brown, *Potato Production in the Northeastern and North Central States,* U. S. Department of Agriculture, Farmers' Bulletin No. 1958, p. 38. Washington, D. C.: Government Printing Office, 1944.

Figure 4–5. Harvesting potatoes in the Aroostook Valley near Caribou, Maine. (Courtesy Maine Development Commission.)

ment, the Lake Champlain Lowland and tributary valley areas produced wheat, oats, and other small grains. But western competition forced much of the area to abandon the growing of cereals. The mild, moist summers, however, were highly conducive to the growing of forage crops. This lowland, in spite of its cold winters, provides an ideal environment for the dairy cow. With the coming of railroads and good motor highways, the area became connected with the large urban markets of New York and Boston, and developed into one of the major dairy regions of the country. While it has to compete with dairy regions to the west, nearby markets for fluid milk (which is 85 per cent water and hence is expensive to transport) gave it a decided advantage. The Champlain Lowland occupies the center of the great overlapping milksheds (areas from which cities draw their fluid milk) of New York and Boston. Vermont, dominating the major part of the Lake Champlain Lowland, ranks first among the states in per capita production of milk.

The agriculture and agricultural practices of the pioneer have vanished, except in the most remote localities. In the valleys and on the lower slopes of hillsides, the dairy cow is supreme. Fields of oats and hay occupy the fertile bottom lands, while apple orchards cover many hillsides. The newer and more scientifically located orchards occupy northward-facing slopes where blossoming is retarded until the danger of frost is passed.

The Connecticut Valley. The lower central part of the Connecticut Valley is a leading tobacco-growing area. Five sixths of the crop is of the cigar binder type and one sixth is Sumatra. The value of the latter, however, is almost equal to that of the former.

Binder types, as the name imples, are used mainly for binding the fillers into the forms of cigars. Good-burning qualities, aroma, and elasticity characterize binders of high quality. Sumatra tobacco is grown for wrappers, the best wrappers being thin, smooth and fine in texture. In order to obtain such qualities protection is needed against the sun and extremes of weather, and hence Sumatra tobacco is grown under shade at considerable expense. A permanent framework is erected

Figure 4–6. Tobacco field in the Connecticut Valley. Note the cheesecloth covering of the fields to protect them from the sun. (Courtesy of the Massachusetts Development and Industrial Commission.)

over which open-mesh cloth is tacked, enclosing large fields (Figure 4–6). The plants are set in rows and cultivation is carried on in the fields under the cover. The cloth overhead and on all sides diffuses the direct rays of the sun, minimizes wind movements, and affords some protection from overnight changes in temperature. Much of this type of tobacco is produced by large corporations under the most modern scientific methods. Because tobacco is grown on the same land continuously, liberal applications of commercial fertilizer (more than one and one-half tons per acre) must be used to insure satisfactory yields.[15]

In addition to tobacco, the Connecticut

Valley grows onions and other vegetables, and produces some hay. Dairying is also important, especially in the north.

Prince Edward Island and Fox Farming. Fox farming on Prince Edward Island began in 1894, when two farmers noticed that those black fox peltries having silver-tipped tails and scattered silver hairs, which gave them a silver sheen, brought especially high prices on the London market. They, therefore, experimented secretly to "fix" this silver strain, using wild foxes caught in traps for their breeding stock. The venture was highly successful, single pelts of extraordinary quality bringing as much as $2,600. Ultimately, of course, neighbors learned of the secret and established additional fox farms. In 1912 live foxes for breeding sold for $18,000 to $35,000 a pair. As

---

[15] Bureau of Agricultural Economics, U. S. Department of Agriculture, *Tobaccos of the United States*, p. 5 Washington, D. C.: Government Printing Office, 1948.

larger numbers of animals became available for sale, prices declined greatly.

Foxes reach maturity in eight months and are very prolific. The increased demand for furs and reckless destruction of wild life at the hands of its greatest enemy, man, restricted the regions of wild fur-bearing animals. Close settlement and trapping could not exist together. As the wilderness disappeared, so did the habitat of the fur-bearing animals. Accordingly an increasing proportion of the world supply of peltries began to come from fur farms.

The industry spread rapidly over Anglo-America, but Prince Edward Island, where it began, remained for many years the world's leader. Changing fur fashions, however, doomed this formerly lucrative industry, and although some of the larger fox farms are still operating, that activity now provides only about five per cent of the total farm income. Now, dairying and poultry raising are the chief agricultural activities on Prince Edward Island.

The Annapolis-Cornwallis Valley and Apples. About one-half of the commercial apple crop of Canada is produced in the Annapolis-Cornwallis Valley, the only area of outstanding commercial agriculture in Nova Scotia. This fairly level valley, 80 miles long and 10 to 15 miles wide, is sheltered from northwest winds and fogs by North Mountain, which lies along the Bay of Fundy.[16] Paralleling it is South Mountain. The valley trends in a general west-east direction from Digby to Windsor. Though apples are the main crop, hay and potatoes also are grown. This area, first settled by the French, is characterized by farms which are narrow strips of 20 to 120 acres having meadow and hay land in the bottom, orchard land midway, and pasture and woodland above. By growing their trees on slopes the farmers benefit both from well-drained soils and from air drainage. The latter especially is significant since there is danger to fruit trees from late spring frost.

Forest Industries

Lumbering. Northeastern Anglo-America, the continent's pioneer logging region, possessed an almost incomparable forest of tall, straight conifers and valuable hardwoods. Perhaps nine tenths of the region was forest-covered. For 200 years or more after the landing of the Pilgrims in 1620, the settlers continued uninterruptedly the removal of trees. At first they had reverence for the forest, since it supplied their fuel, game, and the timber for their homes; but it also harbored their enemies — Indians and wild beasts. Moreover, their agriculture had to be of the self-sufficing type. To make room for their crops they had to clear away the trees, hence, there grew up in their minds a hostility to the forest; they did not consider its destruction reprehensible.

Before long, logging became an enterprise prosecuted for export as well as for the home market. The straightest and tallest trees were felled and river-driven downstream to shipbuilding plants. The coast of Maine was pre-eminent in this industry. Bangor, on the Penobscot River, became the outstanding center specializing in the making and shipping of lumber. It had its own locally built fleet which carried lumber into far corners of the earth and brought back exotic products. Moreover, its loggers invented the snubber for handling sleds of logs on steep slopes, the log-branding ax, and the peavey,[17] "the greatest lumber invention since the saw." North of Bangor were two and one-half million acres of incomparable virgin timber in a solid block owned by a single individual. So impressed was the young Thoreau when, in 1846, he saw this now historic lumber town, that he wrote:

There stands the City of Bangor like a star on the edge of night, still hewing at the forest of which it is built, already, overflowing with the luxuries and refinements of Europe and sending its vessels to Spain, to England, and to the West Indies for its groceries — and yet only a few ax-

---

[16] A. W. Currie, *Economic Geography of Canada*, pp. 51-54. Toronto: The Macmillan Company of Canada, Ltd., 1946.

[17] A pointed iron lever fitted with a movable hook and used for handling logs.

men have gone up-river into the howling wilderness that feeds it.[18]

Maine is no longer of outstanding importance in lumber production, though this is a state where everybody said the timber would last forever. Were it not for its other economic activities, Bangor today might be a decaying ghost town.

Logging was and still is a winter activity. Cutting began in autumn and usually terminated before the first of January. As soon as the snow became deep and the ground frozen, tens of thousands of logs were hauled over iced roads by sleigh to streams, which in late spring and summer carried the logs to sawmills. The end of each log was marked with the brand of its owner.

Logging and lumbering have been important also in the Lower St. Lawrence Valley and especially in New Brunswick, where all other economic activities have been secondary. Trading in lumber in the Maritimes began as early as 1650. Mariners returning to Europe took cargoes of masts, spars, and ship timbers.

The entire upland area, with the exception of the highest peaks, was covered originally with a dense forest. At first the land-hungry settlers considered the forest an enemy in the same sense that they did the Indian. But with the Atlantic Seaboard's increasing

demand for timber for structural purposes and for shipbuilding, these same farmers soon found it profitable to cut logs in winter when they could not farm, and float them down the streams in the spring to tidewater mills. In some places in the region this supplemental source of income surpassed that from farming.

When iron and steel ships replaced those made of wood, New England's shipbuilding industry declined. Until the opening of the forests in the Upper Lakes states in the latter part of the nineteenth century, this region continued to provide the major part of the lumber for the United States. In a brief period of a little more than two hundred years, most of this great forest was destroyed. Lumbering today is relatively unimportant, though the cutting of pulpwood for paper is a major enterprise.

The Maple Sugar Industry. The highlands of Vermont and New York produce nearly two thirds of the maple sugar and maple syrup of the United States, and those of eastern and southern Quebec account for most of the Canadian supply. The sugar maple, the chief tree from which the sap is extracted, has a very long life. It is rarely suitable for tapping (Figure 4–7) until 40 years old, and it is twice that age before it reaches peak production.

The sap flow, which must be continuous and plentiful, is usually best when the change from winter to spring is slow, and when the days are warm and sunny and the nights frosty. The quality of sap that an individual tree yields is in direct relation to the size of its crown. Some sugar makers believe, however, that trees in a forest produce more sap than those in a grove.

Tapping maple trees is rugged outdoor work. A small hole is bored in the tree about four feet from the ground. It should be about two inches deep and slanting so the sap will take a downward course as it oozes from the cut tissue. A spout with a hook is then driven into the hole and a metal bucket is hung on the hook. The bucket is usually covered to prevent the sap from being diluted by rainwater. Tapping should be done at the beginning of the season since early runs of sap

---

[18] As quoted in S. H. Holbrook, "Historic Lumber Towns — No. I, Bangor, Maine," *American Forests*, Vol. 44, February 1938, p. 69.

Figure 4–7. Gathering sap from the sugar maple. (Photo by Chandler.)

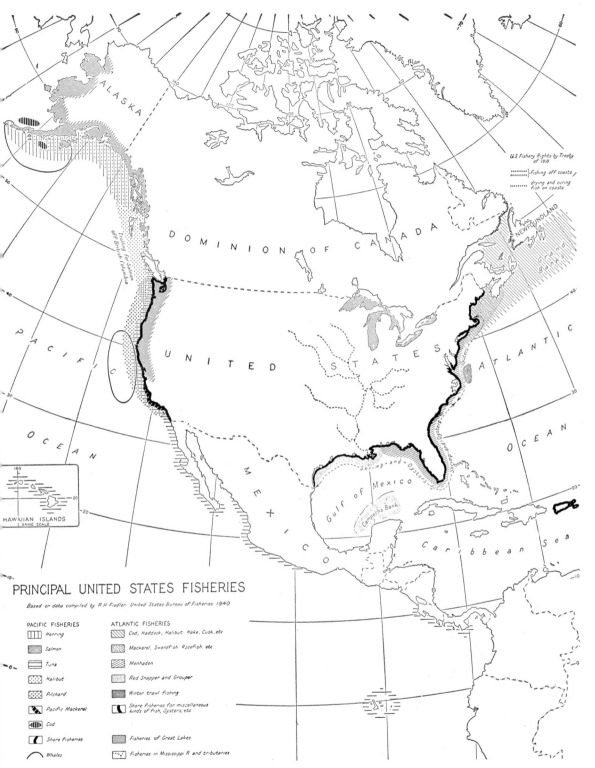

PRINCIPAL UNITED STATES FISHERIES

Based on data compiled by R H Fiedler, United States Bureau of Fisheries 1940

PACIFIC FISHERIES		ATLANTIC FISHERIES	
	Herring		Cod, Haddock, Halibut, Hake, Cusk, etc
	Salmon		Mackerel, Swordfish, Rosefish, etc
	Tuna		Menhaden
	Halibut		Red Snapper and Grouper
	Pilchard		Winter trawl fishing
	Pacific Mackerel		Shore Fisheries for miscellaneous kinds of Fish, Oysters, etc
	Cod		
	Shore Fisheries		Fisheries of Great Lakes
	Whales		Fisheries in Mississippi R and tributaries

U.S. Fishery Rights by Treaty of 1818
Fishing off coasts
drying and curing fish on coasts

HAWAIIAN ISLANDS
SAME SCALE

Figure 4-8.   Principal Anglo-American fishing areas. (Courtesy American Geographical Society of New York.)

87

are usually sweeter and better sugar producers. The season usually begins about the last of February when the days are becoming warm (temperatures going above 32° F.) and the nights are still cold. To gather the sap, a sled, on which is placed a large tub, is usually driven through the forest or grove and the sap from the individual buckets is dumped into it. Where the slope of the ground is suitable, pipelines are frequently used to carry the sap to the boiling house storage tanks. If more than two hundred trees are tapped a boiling house must be used. When the sap is brought to the sugar house and emptied into the sap containers, it is boiled to eliminate the water. The product thus obtained is maple syrup, which through further boiling may be reduced to sugar.[19]

Fishing

The first shore-dwelling settlers obeyed both the call of the land and of the sea. But the hard land environment yielded little more than subsistence farming, whereas the sea was rich in fish. The fish caught here in colonial days paid for imports of sugar and molasses. Cane sugar, brought back in payment for fish, was the basis for the refining and distilling industries; cacao the basis for the confectionery industries; hides for the shoe factories; and gold and silver for the southern New England jewelry industries. Also, the extensive New England brass industry started with a market for ship chandlery. All of these have been significant in New England's regional economic life.[20] Fish was the first export from the New World. From Newfoundland to Cape Cod lie the Grand Banks — one of the richest fishing areas in the world (Figure 4–8). These banks were frequented by Scandinavian, Portuguese, Dutch, English, and French fishermen before the period of colonization

in America. As early as 1504 Breton and Norman fishermen — men born to the sea — were catching cod in the western North Atlantic, and by 1577 France had 150 vessels, Spain 100, Portugal 50 and England 15 fishing for cod on the banks.[21]

Fishing is further aided by the fact that the entire coast is dotted with sheltered harbors, bays, and coves from which fishermen can operate with comparative ease and safety. The fisheries fall into two distinct divisions: (1) coastal or in-shore and (2) deep-sea — demersal (bottom) and pelagic (surface).

Coastal Fishing. Coastal or in-shore fishing is done usually within five miles of shore in small, swift motor boats carrying two or three men. The catch is brought into port each day. However, some "draggers" (inshore otter trawlers) from 30 to 50 tons in size may stay away from port as long as 48 hours. The fish caught are primarily cod, haddock, mackerel, and herring. Pollock, cusk, hake, and flounder also are important. Part of these are ground fish (cod and haddock) and part surface fish (mackerel and herring). Herring are used for bait. The bulk of the catch, after gutting and washing, is dropped into ice-packed chambers.

Deep-sea Fishing. For banks or deep-sea fishing, large vessels are used in the deeper waters over the 70,000 square miles of banks between Cape Cod and Newfoundland, where bottom fish such as cod, cusk, flounder, haddock, and halibut are sought. Both schooners and trawlers are used, the former still dominant in the Maritime Provinces. New England, on the other hand, has largely adopted the more efficient otter trawler.

The schooner, most efficient of all sailing craft, goes everywhere and sails in any kind of weather. The difficulties of operating dories in rough weather, however, confine activities of the line trawler to the summer season. It carries some fifteen or more dories (a type of rowboat), which are fitted one into another in nests. At sea, soundings are made until the right kind of bottom is found. The

---

[19] A. Hugh Bryan, William F. Hubbard, and Sidney F. Sherwood, *Production of Maple Syrup and Sugar*, U. S. Department of Agriculture, Farmers' Bulletin No. 1366. Washington, D. C.: Government Printing Office, 1937.

[20] Edward A. Ackerman, *New England's Fishing Industry*, Chicago: University of Chicago Press, 1941, p. 3.

[21] R. H. Fiedler, "Fisheries of North America," *Geographical Review*, Vol. 30, No. 2, April 1940, p. 201.

dories, manned by two fishermen, are then launched and may go miles from the mother ship. In each dory is a tub containing a trawl line a mile or more in length. This is stretched about three feet above the ocean floor and set with 400 to 500 hooks, about six feet apart and baited with herring or clams. The dorymen then move back and forth along the trawl, removing cod and rebaiting the hooks.

Banks fishing is dangerous. The region is foggy 40 to 50 per cent of the time, and it lies in the path of transatlantic liners, which occasionally run down the schooners. The stormy North Atlantic is infested with icebergs in spring and summer. Despite the danger, the men of Gloucester, Boston, Lunenburg, and the host of other ports, continue to fish on the Grand Banks. Today many of the vessels are equipped with auxiliary engines to keep them moving when the wind fails.

Trawlers permit exploitation of distant fishing grounds, are quite safe and seaworthy in even the roughest weather, operate throughout the year, and are speedy in delivering their cargo. They tow along the bottom a huge bag-shaped net, called an otter trawl, which, as it is drawn forward over the ocean floor, envelops the fish. Fishermen who operate other types of vessels claim that the trawlers are lowering the price of fish and are slowly destroying the fishing grounds. Since trawlers secure their fish from lower layers of water not fished by traditional methods, there is no evidence to support this claim. Whatever the advantages or disadvantages may be, trawlers are heavily taxed and only a few are operating in Canada.[22]

Part of the catch is dried, salted, and canned, but an increasing proportion is quick-frozen. Many vessels are equipped with complete refrigerating plants.

Banks are shallows in the ocean at or near the outer margin of the continental shelf. Occasionally they reach the surface, though ordinarily they lie about 240 feet below it. The banks considered here are those that extend from Cape Cod to Newfoundland

(Figure 4–8). Their surfaces, with cuesta-like ridges, are hummocky. Several theories have been advanced to explain their origin. There seems to be little doubt regarding their relation to glaciation, since great quantities of gravel and boulders are found on them at considerable depths far from land. Moreover, fishing trawlers report bringing up boulders weighing as much as three tons.

Banks are invaluable for fishing because they are shallow. The sun's rays thus penetrate to an adequate depth for the growth of algae, which are an abundant source of fish food. The banks thus serve as outstanding feeding grounds. The cold water favors the individual abundance of a small number of species, which aids in selling the catch to a single merchant. The banks also lie near the densely populated, highly industralized seaboard of the United States – a great market for fish.

Cod, Haddock, Halibut, Herring, and Mackerel. *Cod,* the most important species, feeds on the bottoms and is usually caught with long trawls to which are fastened hundreds of short lines with baited hooks. *Haddock* for many years were considered valueless when caught on codfishermen's hooks and were thrown back into the sea, but today haddock filet is popular. *Halibut,* usually inhabiting deep submarine gullies near shore or between banks, is caught from dories with hook and line. *Herring,* a cheap, appetizing, and nourishing fish which is also used for bait is captured by the million in fixed traps or in gill nets. *Mackerel,* an excellent food fish, schools in enormous numbers and eats at or near the surface.

Lobster Fishing. From Prince Edward Island to Massachusetts, some 30 million lobsters are caught annually in the Maritime Provinces and 3 million in Maine. Unfortunately, overfishing has badly reduced the catch; conservation for a long time was difficult because the laws of Canada and of the United States were not uniform. In Maine, fishermen were required to throw back small lobsters, though few did so. Artificial propagation is receiving considerable attention at the present time and progress is being made. The eggs are artificially hatched, and the

[22] Currie, *Economic Geography of Canada,* pp. 92-93.

young lobsters are permitted to grow in ponds along the shore before being turned into the sea. In 1947, New England lobstermen landed more than 23 million pounds of lobsters worth nearly nine million dollars. Maine accounted for 78 per cent of this total.[23]

Oysters, Clams, Quahaugs, and Scallops. These are important along the southern shore of New England and on Cape Cod. Since these are shell animals which live on the shallow sea floor or in beach muds, this has become more of a farming than a fishing industry. Individual ownership of the oyster beds is the rule. Some oysters are consumed locally in the shell, but because of costs most of them are "shucked" and marketed in a chilled or frozen form. Clams, quahaugs, and scallops are consumed in large quantities in New England.[24]

Fishing Ports. While almost every harbor where human beings live has its fishermen, there are only a limited number of outstanding fishing ports. The chief ones are Boston, Gloucester (Figure 4–9), Portland, Lunenburg, and Lockeport.

[23] *The New England Economy*, p. 191.

[24] Edward A. Ackerman, *New England's Fishing Industry*, pp. 243-259. Chicago: University of Chicago Press, 1941.

Figure 4–9. Gloucester Harbor with its colorful, stubby-masted fishing fleet of trawlers and draggers. Note the nets hoisted up the masts, drying in the sun. (Courtesy Massachusetts Development and Industrial Commission.)

The Value of the Fisheries. Despite continuous exploitation for more than four centuries, the western North Atlantic fisheries continue to provide a large and important supply of food — more than a billion pounds a year.

Unfortunately the continued prosperity of New England's fishing industry is threatened by: (1) the growing scarcity of key species of fish in North Atlantic waters causing increased production costs; (2) internal conflict between the Fishermen's Union and the fish dealers, hindering the smooth operation of the industry; and (3) increasing competition from foreign sources, particularly in the sardine industry.[25]

Recreation

Recreation as a business started in this region about the middle of the nineteenth century, but it was completely revolutionized later by the automobile. Large numbers of tourists began to invade the New England segment, many going to private homes. Catering to tourists has proved to be a salvation to great numbers of people, both in rural areas and in small cities and villages. In New England alone there are 1,600 resort hotels, 10,400 tourist homes and cabin groups, 700 boys' and girls' camps, and more than 165,000 seasonal dwellings.[26] Northeastern Anglo-America is highly attractive to tourists, for it has: (1) fine scenery of mountains, bold cliffs, varied coastline, glacial lakes, and fast-running streams; (2) cool, bracing summers and cold, snowy winters; (3) excellent fishing in both inland waters and the ocean; (4) yachting and boating with continuous shelter; (5) skiing and tobogganing; (6) famous historic shrines and other attractions.

In New England most farmers produce special crops for tourists. Many are not farmers in the same sense that they would be if they lived in the Dakotas or Iowa, since agriculture constitutes only a secondary element of income. New England alone in 1949 attracted visitors who spent about 850 mil-

[25] *The New England Economy*, pp. 191-193.
[26] *The New England Economy*, p. 195.

lion dollars. The vacation industry has excellent prospects for national and regional expansion because of (1) the rising standard of living, (2) the increasing proportion of people in the upper age groups, and (3) the increase in the paid-vacation movement.[27]

The upland areas are endowed with practically all of the natural factors necessary for the development of a large resort industry. The cool, moist summers are ideal for summer vacationists, and the snowy winters are popular with winter-sports enthusiasts. In addition, the region profits from proximity to centers of dense population. "One fourth of the people of the United States and Canada live within a day's drive . . . and over half of the largest cities of the two countries lie within 900 miles of Mt. Washington."[28] The ease of access by people living in the crowded urban centers of the Northeast makes this one of the most popular recreational lands of the continent.

The Adirondacks and the Green and White Mountains began to attract summer tourists by the middle of the nineteenth century. As railroads were constructed into the mountain fastness, more and more summer visitors came. Owing to the inconvenience of reaching the resort areas by train in those days, most tourists came for the entire summer, and there was a demand for large resort hotels. As the trade grew, many large summer hotels were built and equipped to provide every need of the visitor — swimming, boating, hiking, horseback riding, tennis, and golf (Figure 4–10), and were run on the American plan. Such hotels are expensive and appeal only to a wealthy clientele. Few facilities were provided for the low-income group because, before the days of the automobile, not many of that class of tourist reached the more remote places.

Until recently, the upland areas had confined the tourist business to the summer months, closing the hotels during winter. In many instances the manager of a large hotel in the White Mountains or in the Adirondacks operates a resort hotel in Florida dur-

ing the winter, moving seasonally from one to another with all of his domestic help, barbers, and bootblacks.

The automobile altered the summer resort industry considerably.

All-summer or month-long stays by a select few at a favorite hotel have tended to give place to short stops by nearly everybody in many hotels. Farmers and townsfolk who used to take in boarders now offer overnight accommodations to fleeting auto nomads. Villages still purvey groceries and meats, but they have added to the

Figure 4–10. A large resort hotel in the White Mountains of New Hampshire. (Courtesy of the Balsams Hotel, Dixville Notch.)

list ice cream and soda, gasoline and oil, and luncheon and tea.[29]

With the development of the automobile and good highways, the mountain country found itself at the crossroads between southern New England, French Canada, the Thousand Islands District, and the Maritimes.

State and national planning boards, park and forestry services have done much in recent years to develop the resort industry in this region. Several national forests have been established to preserve and restore the woods as well as to encourage summer re-

[27] *The New England Economy*, p. 195.

[28] National Resources Committee, *Regional Planning, Part III — New England*, p. 37.

[29] Derwent S. Whittlesey, in *New England's Prospects: 1933*, p. 455. New York: American Geographical Society, Special Publication No. 16, 1933.

sorts. Some of the recreational services for tourists now provided by the national forests include: (1) foot trails (more than 1,000 miles in the White Mountain National Forest alone), (2) youth hostels, (3) bridle trails, (4) canoe routes, (5) hunting and fishing facilities, (6) golf courses, (7) camps, and (8) winter sports. Today this subregion is a playground for all classes of people — those who spend their summers at large resort hotels as well as those who can stop only for the week end, traveling by automobile and spending each night at a tourist home, cabin, or one of the new motels. The latter type of traveler has made it possible for many of the all-but-abandoned farms to revive. Old farm houses and covered bridges add materially to the natural beauty of the region and attract large numbers of tourists. The Canadian section is gradually becoming a resort area, particularly toward the outer end of the Gaspé Peninsula, where the mountains approach the sea and French fishing villages add charm to the landscape. On Mt. Desert Island, off the coast of Maine, lies Acadia National Park, with its rocky cliffs, forested slopes, and beating surf. It is the oldest National Park east of the Mississippi River.

Winter Sports. Within the past few years, winter sports have developed rapidly, owing to (1) improved methods of clearing highways, (2) local promotion of winter sports, and (3) "snow trains" and "snow busses." The Northeastern Uplands are particularly favored for all types of winter sports, which attract rich and poor alike. People living in cities are learning that the sun does shine in winter in the great outdoor recreational areas, and are going to them by the thousands. The snowbound residents of the uplands keep roads open now that were never before plowed in winter. Also, some resort hotels stay open in winter and thereby increase their earnings.

Lake Placid, one of the best known areas in the Adirondacks is important as a resort center both summer and winter, but is particularly outstanding during the winter season. The village, located on the shores of Mirror Lake and Lake Placid, is surrounded

by some of the highest peaks in the Adirondacks. In 1932 this was the site of the International Olympic Winter Games.

The resort business in New England is highly seasonal. Despite the great amount of publicity which has been given to skiing, autumn foliage, and hunting and fishing, nearly 80 per cent of the annual tourist trade is still confined to the months of July and August.[30]

Maritime Canada is favored as a tourist center because it is near the densely settled centers of New England and New York, but it also suffers from this nearness because the American section of Northeastern Anglo-America has similar attractions and better roads. Some of the points of particular interest, however, in the Maritimes include: (1) the Reversing Falls at Saint John, (2) the tidal bore of the Petitcodiac, (3) sea cliffs and caves at Percé, (4) the Old World atmosphere of parts of Gaspé, (5) the rural serenity of Prince Edward Island, and (6) places of historical interest throughout the area.

Mining

Coal. While Nova Scotia has coal, the Dominion as a whole would benefit far more if these deposits were located in the more densely populated and industralized parts of the provinces of Ontario and Quebec, where it is now cheaper to buy American than Canadian coal. Some Nova Scotian coal, however, is transported economically by water to the cities of Quebec and Montreal during the season of navigation. Nova Scotia contains only one per cent of the Dominion's coal deposits, but produces one half of that mined.

Nova Scotian coal has been mined for more than a century. There are four fields — two on Cape Breton Island and two on the mainland. All of the collieries are on or within a few miles of the ocean, and more than one half of the coal is actually mined beneath the Atlantic. The coal seams extend for many miles under the ocean. Because of the dip of the strata the rock cover attains a thickness

---

[30] *The New England Economy*, p. 198.

of 4,000 feet at about six miles from the coast. This makes support of the roof so expensive in effort, labor, and material that it is not profitable to work the seams at a distance of more than about four miles from shore. Under-ocean mining has many difficulties not encountered in mines under land. Since no shafts can be sunk beyond the shore line, it becomes difficult to provide adequate ventilation, power and light for operation, and tramways to pull the mined coal to the base of the shaft.[31] The seams on Cape Breton Island vary in thickness from three to nine feet. The thickest seams, however, are in Pictou County on the mainland, where the principal seam in the Allan Shaft is 45 feet thick. The coal is of good quality and can be coked. Most of the coal which is not sent to the province of Quebec is used in the iron and steel industry at Sydney.[32]

Natural Gas. In the vicinity of Moncton some 80 wells produce natural gas of high heating value.[33]

Limestone. Limestone is quarried in Nova Scotia and at Rockland, Maine. Nova Scotian limestone is used for fluxing in open-hearth steel furnaces. The quarrying at Rockland constitutes the only mining activity of importance along the coast of New England. Limestone was first burned for lime here in 1732. The deposits are small and parallel the shore for several miles inland.

Gypsum and Salt. Gypsum, which is used in the manufacture of plaster and plasterboard and as a retarder in cement has been mined in Nova Scotia since 1770, that province accounting for four fifths of Canada's production.

Some rock salt is taken from the Malagash Peninsula in Nova Scotia where it is estimated 25 million tons are available at a depth of only 85 feet below the surface. As it is used mainly in the canning and curing of fish, production fluctuates with the fishing industry.

Asbestos. Southeastern Quebec contains the largest asbestos mining area in the world, the 1948 production representing about nine million tons with a value of more than 42 million dollars.[34] These vast deposits were discovered in 1876, and for many years were exploited only by open-pit mining methods. In recent times, however, most large producers are using underground methods. Although a small amount of asbestos is mined in northern Vermont, immediately south of the Canadian border, most of the production is concentrated in a narrow strip of territory extending northeastward from the international boundary almost to the St. Lawrence River. Thetford Mines is the major producing center. Other mining centers are Black Lake, East Broughton, Coleraine, Asbestos, and Norbestos (Figure 4–1).

Asbestos is used primarily for roofing materials, insulation for electrical equipment, and for automobile brake linings. Its chief properties are flexibility, incombustibility, and slow conduction of heat. The United States is the world's chief consumer of asbestos.

Iron Ore. Metalliferous deposits are widely scattered throughout the upland area, but they are of relatively small commercial value. Most important are the magnetic iron-ore deposits found on the flanks of the Adirondacks. At present five widely scattered areas are producing magnetic ores, which when concentrated into a sinter contain approximately 69 per cent iron, in contrast to the Lake Superior ores which have from 50 to 55 per cent iron. The active mines are: (1) the Mineville–Port Henry–Fisher Hill development on the west side of Lake Champlain, (2) the Lyon Mountain development, west of Plattsburg, (3) the MacIntyre development on the southern slopes of the Adirondacks, and the (4) Clifton Mines and (5) Benson Mines on the northwest slope of the mountains. All of these mines have been in operation for a century or more, although production has been suspended frequently because of the high cost of transporting the ores to steel centers in Pittsburgh or on the Great Lakes. With increased demands for

[31] Currie, *Economic Geography of Canada*, pp. 72-73.

[32] Currie, *Economic Geography of Canada*, p. 75.

[33] Currie, *Economic Geography of Canada*, p. 77.

[34] Dominion of Canada, Dept. of Commerce and Industry, *Industry in Action in the Province of Quebec*. Quebec: 1949.

Figure 4–11. Granite quarry near Barre, Vermont. The quarry covers more than 45 acres and is nearly 400 feet deep. The derricks of Douglas fir are 115 feet high with booms 100 feet in length. (Courtesy of the Rock of Ages Corporation.)

iron and steel at the outbreak of World War II, most of these properties were purchased by large companies such as Republic Steel Corporation, Jones & Laughlin Steel Corporation, and the M. A. Hanna Company, and with the aid of the Defense Plant Corporation, the properties were rebuilt and production increased.[35] At present it appears that the magnetic ores of the Adirondacks may be able to compete to some extent with the hematite ores of the Upper Lakes area, but with the development of the rich Labrador deposits, the Adirondacks mines may again be forced to curtail production in spite of the fact that great reserves of magnetite are still present.

Other Metallic Minerals. The Green and the White Mountains have little metallic

[35] Sven A. Anderson and Augustus Jones, "Iron in the Adirondacks," *Economic Geography*, Vol. 21, 1945, pp. 276-285.

wealth, but farther to the northeast in the Shickshock Mountains of Quebec and New Brunswick, small workable quantities of copper, lead, zinc, and gold are found.

Quarrying

The rocks that underlie most of Northeastern Anglo-America are dominantly igneous or metamorphic, consisting largely of granite, marble, slate, and others universally used as building stones. High-quality stone and nearness to large urban centers have made the region a leading producer in the building-stone industry. Although the Canadian part of the region is underlain with the same rock, its building-stone industry has not developed to any extent, no doubt the result of remoteness from markets.

During the war years the market for building stone was restricted. Since many stone fabricating mills were well equipped with planers, lathes, and other machines similar to those used in metal working, they were converted to make a variety of products essential to the war program. At the close of World War II, most of these plants reconverted their equipment to stone cutting so as to be ready for the post-war boom in building activities.[36]

Granite. Granite, a hard, massive, and durable stone is quarried extensively in central Vermont. The major producing area is in the vicinity of Barre, where the nationally famous "Rock of Ages" quarry is located (Figure 4–11). Because of its hardness and massiveness, granite is difficult to quarry. Drill holes are placed close together along a line in the bedrock, and into them wedges are driven. When the pressure from the wedges becomes sufficiently great, the granite block begins to crack along the line, and the stone is extracted in large blocks that are ideal for monumental and construction work. Small stones are used for paving or are crushed for road-building material. More than 100 plants for the manufacture of granite products are located in Barre, Montpelier, and adjacent Vermont towns. Numerous granite quarries have been opened in Maine, but their output is used chiefly for structural purposes. Since most of these quarries are located at or near tidewater, the stone can be shipped to Boston and New York City at a low cost.

Although Canada possesses one of the largest supplies of granite rock in the world, only an infinitesimal part is used, commercial development being confined to areas of southern Quebec near centers of population. The major granite quarries are located immediately north of the international boundary near the village of Beebe.

Marble. Vermont ranks high in the production of marble, although in recent years it has been surpassed by Tennessee and Georgia. Marble is a metamorphosed or altered limestone rock that has been hardened by heat and pressure. Although classed as a hard stone, it is much softer than granite,

and hence can be cut from the bed rock by powerful channeling machines. Blocks of quarried marble then go to the mills where they are sawed by smooth steel band saws into slabs and smaller pieces and are then sent to the finishing shops where they are carved and shaped for specific uses. The relative softness of marble makes it easy to work, but also keeps it from being a good building stone, particularly for exteriors. Nevertheless, it is quarried extensively, the chief producing centers being Rutland and Proctor. Vermont marble has the advantage of a wide variety of colors — pure white, red, gray, and green.

Slate. Slate, also a metamorphosed stone, can be split into thin sheets. Hence it is highly prized as roofing material, for electric panels, and for flagstones. Two of the more important slate-producing areas of the continent are in Maine, near the town of Monson, and on both sides of the Vermont-New York boundary. The slate from Monson is a black variety of high quality, used primarily in the manufacture of electrical panel boards and blackboards. The Vermont-New York product, occurring in several attractive colors, is used primarily for roofing. Some slate is quarried commercially in Richmond County in Quebec, but the industry there has declined in importance in recent years, and slate is being replaced by lower-priced fabricated building products or sheet metal.

Water-power Resources

This region possesses considerable water power — both potential and developed. The rocky north shore of the St. Lawrence below and including the Lower Saguenay has great power possibilities, but, except for the St. Lawrence itself, most power sites are on the border of the Laurentian Shield. The south shore with numerous short streams having sharp descents also is favored. Nova Scotia and New Brunswick, because of their heavy precipitation, high altitude near the coast, and good storage facilities, have considerable power. Most of New England's hydroelectric power is being generated in the upland of Maine, New Hampshire, and Vermont. Much

[36] *Mining and Metallurgy*, Vol. 27, 1946, p. 81.

of this power has been sent to industrial centers to the south in recent years.

Water power was an important factor in the early development of the upland, as the numerous small rapids and falls which characterize almost every stream were utilized by the early pioneers for power. Cheap hydro-power was the basis for the paper and pulp industry, which is concentrated along the north flank of the upland, particularly in the Adirondacks. The destruction of the forest cover over much of the upland area reduced the water-power possibilities considerably. There is a great need for a systematic survey and control of the power resources of the entire region, so that they may be utilized to their greatest capacity.

International Aspects. It is estimated that the power development of the St. Lawrence River could provide 700,000 kilowatts capacity for use in the United States. If made available, most of that amount would be consumed in New England.[37]

In the Canadian province of Quebec the numerous large and small hydroelectric plants have a total capacity of more than six million horsepower. Quebec's installation of approximately 1,580 horsepower per 1,000 inhabitants is nearly ten times that of the United States. Because of this the average price of electricity in the province was only 0.46 cents per kilowatt hours — the lowest in Anglo-America.[38] This has been of great value to the province, particularly to the St. Lawrence Valley and the area between the river and the United States boundary, in attracting many heavy industries which are large consumers of electricity, such as the titanium smelter at Sorel on the south bank of the St. Lawrence. This plant will separate titanium, slag and pig iron from the ilmenite ore of northeastern Quebec.

Manufacturing

The highly industralized areas of southern New England and of the Montreal district have been discussed in Chapter 3, *The American Manufacturing Belt.* As a result,

only the industries which are not located within those industrial areas are considered here, and hence *Northeastern Anglo-America* is not of outstanding manufacturing significance. It does, however, have several highly specialized industries.

Pulp and Paper. In the production of pulp and paper, few areas in the world surpass Northeastern Anglo-America. The distribution is largely a matter of geography: the pulp plants must be strategically situated with respect to the forest, cheap power, a dependable supply of soft, clean water, and good transportation facilities for the low-cost delivery of raw materials (sulphur, clay, soda). Fortunately, this region has large quantities of reasonably priced hydro-power close to great supplies of superior pulpwoods — spruce, hemlock, pine, poplar, and fir. One hundred tons of pulpwood yield less than 30 tons of pulp, but require the power equivalent of about 120 tons of coal. Consequently most pulp mills are located at convenient power sites close to the forest. Also, 100,000 gallons of water are utilized in the production of one ton of pulp. Paper mills, on the other hand, are located in or near centers of population where the bulk of the output is used. The Canadian part of the region contributes both pulp and paper, but the New England segment produces more paper than pulp.

When the United States tariff on newsprint was removed in 1911, much of the newsprint paper industry migrated from the United States to Canada, where the pulpwood could be made into pulp and paper at a saving of about ten per cent. In 1947 the pulp mills of New England consumed 2,300,000 cords of pulpwood, one fourth of which was imported.[39]

Pulp and allied products constitute an estimated 500 million dollar industry in New England, approximately 13 per cent of the national total. Formerly operations were confined to the use of softwoods, spruce, fir, and poplar, but recently the Brown Paper Company of Berlin, New Hampshire which owns and operates more than 500,000 acres of forests in Maine, New Hampshire, and

---

[37] *The New England Economy,* p. 116.
[38] *Industry in Action in the Province of Quebec,* pp. 16-23.

[39] *The New England Economy,* p. 189.

Vermont, has developed good pulp from hardwoods, so that they now constitute 60 per cent of the total used.[40]

Iron and Steel. Iron-making in the Maritime Provinces began in 1872 when the Sydney mills were built to supply steel rails for the rapidly growing Canadian railway system. Since 1918 the steel, coal, and related industries in the Maritimes have been administered by the Dominion Steel and Coal Corporation.

Sydney, the center of the industry, is a strategic locale for iron and steel manufacturing because: (1) it lies in the center of the coal area, (2) it has ample land on a commodious and well-protected harbor which is well suited to the manufacture of iron and steel, (3) it is the eastern terminus of the Canadian National Railways System, and (4) it can get Wabana iron ore cheaply from Bell Island, Newfoundland.

To operate profitably, the iron and steel industry must be able to assemble iron ore, coking coal, and fluxing limestone economically. Few places are better located with respect to coal than Sydney, where blast furnaces are within sight of the mine mouths. Not only is the quantity of coal enormous but the quality is good. Limestone and iron ore suitable for blast furnaces are obtained from Newfoundland. Despite the fact that the mines are 415 miles by steamer from Sydney, ore can be laid down economically at the steel mill.

Markets are probably less advantageous than raw materials and labor. Canada's steel has to pay a tariff to enter markets in the United States, and despite an excellent location on the Great Circle Route to Europe, it cannot invade that market. The district is well located, however, for shipping steel by boat to the industrial areas of Ontario and Quebec.

Recently, the Dominion Coal and Steel Corporation has installed 53 new coke ovens at Sydney, and is expanding its collieries and its steel plant at the cost of $23,500,000.[41]

[40] *The New York Times*, May 27, 1951.
[41] James Montagnes, "Canadian Steel Industry Boosting Annual Output," *Barron's*, February 19, 1951, p. 6.

Transportation

As the pioneers pushed farther into the wilderness, they naturally used the Indian trails, which for the most part followed the streams. When wheeled vehicles (ox carts) came into use, trails were widened where possible. Although the streams pointed the way through the forest, they seldom provided means of transportation. The same rapids and falls that aided the development of power hindered navigation. In the 1840's railroads penetrated the wilderness and caused some of the wagon roads to fall into disuse.

From the days of Cabot, Cartier, and Champlain, the St. Lawrence River has offered unique opportunities for water transport. Much of the trade of Canada moves in and out over this waterway.

River transportation was of considerable importance in the early settlement of New Brunswick, when the St. John and its tributaries were widely used. It is unimportant now, however, since there are few navigable streams. The Maritimes have not benefited from St. Lawrence traffic.

The New England railways are distinctive in that they serve directly only New England. More than in any other area in North America, tonnage consists of high-grade manufactures. Aside from forest and quarry products, the outbound movement of raw materials is almost negligible. Furthermore, food and industrial raw materials are carried eastbound into New England, but empty cars characterize much of the westbound traffic.

Prior to Confederation in 1867 which resulted in the construction of the first transcontinental railway, the Maritime Region had little railway mileage. The Maritime Provinces were more interested in the Intercolonial Railway than in the Confederation. They felt that this railway from the interior would greatly stimulate their ocean trade and their ports, especially in winter when the St. Lawrence could not be used. Prince Edward Island was the only part of the Maritimes to be indifferent, for it realized that such a route would not solve its local transportation problems. The extensions to the Maritimes are "weak thongs" in summer, but they become vital parts of the transcontinental systems in winter.

Railways have been constructed for some distance on both sides of the St. Lawrence east of Quebec, but they are important only in winter.

The uplands profit from railroad development outside the subregion. The first railways were built from the Atlantic ports of Boston, New York, and Portland to tap the resources of the interior. The Champlain Lowland, however, which had always been a highway for traffic between New York and Montreal, soon secured through lines. Later Canadian railways, seeking ice-free ports on the Atlantic, built several main lines across the uplands. The Adirondacks, northeastern Maine, and the highlands of eastern Canada were largely avoided, leaving many localities remote from rail connections.

The original settlements in Quebec were placed on the banks of rivers; those of the Maritimes and New England were along the coast. Everywhere they benefited from water transportation.

No roads were built in Acadia prior to the English conquest in 1713, and even by 1750 there were none fit for wheeled vehicles. In Canada, however, the French had built some. The earliest French adopted the methods of the Indians using canoes and trails; in winter they used snowshoes, and sometimes frozen rivers instead of trails. The change came when the French introduced the wheeled vehicle, which demanded roads.

The building of roads in the Lower St. Lawrence Valley entailed many difficulties. The forest was almost continuous, so that cutting and removing of stumps was necessary. The rivers required bridges. The severe climate induced deep frost which, in spring, raised humps and broke holes in surfaced roads and caused "the worst form of mud" on soft roads.

In New England, as population increased and farms wore out, the need for new lands became imperative. The migration which followed utilized streams or Indian trails. These paths were first widened into pack trails and subsequently to wagon roads. Thus arose a system of trails radiating from the seacoast.

Roads for wheeled vehicles came into existence during the turnpike era, which began in 1795 and reached its climax between 1830 and 1850. Turnpikes declined with the advent of the railroad.

Although many of them fell into disuse, they survived better in the upland area than elsewhere. With the advent of the automobile, many old roads were improved and new ones constructed. The ever-increasing automobile traffic through the highlands has created a demand for good roads. Except in the most remote places the region is well served by modern highways. The automobile highway has penetrated the mountain fastness to a greater extent than has the railroad.

The sea-level Cape Cod Canal, 17.4 miles long and 32 feet deep, was built to enable mariners to avoid the hazardous section southeast of Cape Cod and to shorten the distance between northern and southern New England. It is now operated by the United States Government, toll-free, as a link in the intracoastal waterway from Maine to Florida.

Commerce

So attractive were trade and shipping that, during colonial and Revolutionary times, maritime commerce became a leading activity. New England and Nova Scotian sea captains and sailors were recognized as among the ablest and most fearless to be found on the oceans.

Then came wars, followed by privateering and piracy. Speed in ships was imperative. Accordingly, the schooner became a clipper ship, and with it New England and Maritime Canada experienced the golden age of their salt-water activity. During this era — the first half of the nineteenth century — clipper ships dominated the seven seas, carrying the name of New England and of Nova Scotia to almost every port in the world. This continued until the advent of the iron ship. In 1860 United States vessels carried about two thirds of the country's foreign trade; by 1890 the amount had fallen to one tenth. Americans all but abandoned the sea — a situation attributable to (1) steamships made of iron, which displaced wooden sailing vessels, (2) national legislation whereby protection to American shipping was removed, (3) the Civil War, and (4) the development of the natural resources in the interior.

It might seem that the Maritimes should throb with trade, yet such is not the case. Commercially considered they are to a very real extent a land "that has been passed by."

The Outlook

Agriculture in Northeastern Anglo-America should not change greatly; its fishing may decline but certainly will not disappear; its pulp and paper industry should persist; its mining may increase; its shipping should hold its own.

Economically, the Maritime Provinces will suffer as a consequence of (1) isolation from the real center of Canadian activity and (2) political separation from their neighbor, New England. Agriculture cannot be greatly expanded because of the dearth of arable land, and mining, manufacturing and commerce all are definitely restricted in their possibilities for expansion.

As for the Lower St. Lawrence, agriculture will dominate, but will be mostly a self-sufficing patch type. Man must battle with nature to wrest even a bare living from the infertile soils. This part of the region will continue to be the land of the French Canadian.

The New England section has undergone repeated economic readjustments. Though forced to shift constantly to different types of economic enterprise, it has always done so successfully and promises to continue to do so.

For the most part the highland areas have been either (1) exploited and largely abandoned or (2) left as an unexplored wilderness. The steeper lands that were exploited by the farmer, the sheepman, and the lumberman never should have been cleared of their virgin forests, and accordingly are now being returned in many cases to national or state forests and wild-life preserves. The more inaccessible forest areas that, because of remoteness, have been spared destruction will probably remain in permanent possession of the general public.

Water power might be further developed, and pulp and paper manufacturing should continue to be important. The building-stone industry, though not likely to expand, should hold its own.

The activity with the brightest prospect is tourism. With an ever increasing number of tourists visiting the region in summer and winter, and with the rapid increase in the number of summer camps for boys and girls, Northeastern Anglo-America will continue as one of the major playgrounds of the continent.

Cities

The cities of Anglo-America are listed for each region in this volume by means of tables which give the population for (a) the urbanized area and (b) the political city, as delineated in the 1950 census of the United States and the 1951 census of Canada. The cities in each table are arranged in alphabetical order and only the more important ones which lie within the region under consideration are included. Where a city is located on or near the border between two regions it is arbitrarily placed in only one region, but it is marked with a footnote to show that it might belong also in another region. This is particularly true of all cities of the American Manufacturing Belt and

for that reason no table follows Chapter 3.

The 1950 census of the United States defines an "urbanized area" as "an area that includes at least one city with 50,000 inhabitants or more in 1940 or later according to a special census taken prior to 1950 and also the surrounding closely settled incorporated places and unincorporated areas." As this selection is based on the 1940 census, several urban centers which are larger than the 50,000-inhabitant minimum, appear only in the second column of each table but these are listed exactly as given in the census. Since the "urbanized areas" present a more accurate picture of the large urban agglomerations than the new "standard metropolitan areas" given in the 1950 census, they are used in these tabular classifications.[42] The Canadian census lists "greater cities" which correspond roughly to the "urbanized areas" of the United States, and hence they are given in the first column of each table.

Because of space limitation, the tabular method of treating the cities of each region was considered advisable. For the reader who wishes more detail on each city, however, two modern reference works, available in most libraries, are recommended: (1) *Webster's Geographical Dictionary,* and (2) *The Columbia Lippincott Gazetteer of the World.* A description of Bangor, Maine (Northeastern Anglo-America) is given below exactly as it appears in each volume.

Bangor. Commercial and industrial city of Penobscot Co., E. cen. Maine, at head of navigation on Penobscot river 60 m. NE of Augusta; pop. 29,822; lumbering, pulp and paper mills.

[42] For a detailed discussion of this topic see Robert M. Klove, "The Definition of Standard Metropolitan Areas," *Economic Geography,* Vol. 28, 1952, pp. 95-104.

Bangor Theological Seminary (1816; Congregational); Dow Air Force Base.[43]

Bangor. City (pop. 31,588), Penobscot co., S. Maine, on W. bank of the Penobscot, at head of navigation, at mouth of Kenduskeag Stream, opposite Brewer; alt. 100 ft.; 44°48′ N 68°46′ W. Third largest city in Maine; mainly a commercial center with varied industries supplementing once-dominant lumber and paper milling; printing, lumber processing, mfg. (shoes, dental supplies, tools, machinery, furniture, clothing, food products). Port of entry. Ships lumber, woodpulp, paper. Gateway to Mt. Desert Isl. and to an extensive resort area of many lakes. Seat of Bangor Theological Seminary and Northeastern Conservatory of Music. Settled 1769 on site probably visited (1604) by Champlain; town inc. 1791, city 1834. Developed in 19th cent. as flourishing shipping center handling lumber, furs, fish, ice.[44]

[43] By permission. From Webster's *Geographical Dictionary,* p. 101, copyright, 1949, by G. & C. Merriam Co. Springfield, Mass.

[44] *The Columbia Lippincott Gazetteer of the World,* p. 157. New York: Columbia University Press, 1952.

Table 1

SELECTED CITIES AND TOWNS OF NORTHEASTERN ANGLO-AMERICA

City or Town	Urbanized area	Political center	City or Town	Urbanized area	Political center
*Albany		134,995	Dartmouth		15,037
*Albany-Troy	291,897		Drummondville		14,341
Auburn		23,134	Edmundston		10,753
Augusta		20,913	Everett		45,982
Bangor		31,558	*Fall River	118,120	111,963
Barre		10,922	*Fitchburg		42,691
Berlin		16,615	Fredericton		16,018
Beverly		28,884	Glace Bay		25,586
Biddeford		20,836	Gloucester		25,167
*Boston	2,233,448	801,444	*Gloversville		23,634
*Bridgeport	237,435	158,709	Granby		21,980
Bristol		35,961	Halifax		85,589
*Brockton	92,116	62,860	*Hartford	300,788	177,397
Burlington		33,155	*Haverhill		47,280
*Cambridge		120,740	*Holyoke		54,661
Cap de la Madeleine		18,667	*Lawrence	112,309	80,536
Charlottetown		15,887	Levis		13,162
Chelsea		38,912	Lewiston		40,974
*Chicopee		49,211	*Lowell	106,661	97,249
Concord		27,988	*Lynn		99,738
Cranston		55,060	Malden		59,804

* Also in the American Manufacturing Belt.

City or Town	Urbanized area	Political center	City or Town	Urbanized area	Political center
*Manchester	84,918	82,732	Rutland		17,659
*Medford		66,113	St. Hyacinthe		20,236
*Melrose		26,988	St. Jean		19,305
*Meriden		44,088	St. John		50,779
Middletown		29,711	St. Laurent		20,426
Moncton		27,334	*Salem		41,880
*Montreal	1,395,400	1,021,520	*Schenectady	123,273	91,785
*Nashua		34,669	Sherbrooke		50,543
*New Bedford	125,495	109,189	Somerville		102,351
*New Britain		73,726	Sorel		14,961
*New Britain-Bristol	123,079		*Springfield		162,399
*New Haven	244,836	164,443	*Springfield-Holyoke	356,908	
*New London		30,551	*Stamford		74,293
*Newport		37,564	*Stamford-Norwalk	173,536	
*New Rochelle		59,725	Sydney		31,317
*Newton		81,994	*Taunton		40,109
*New Waterford		10,423	Thetford Mines		15,095
*Northampton		29,063	Torrington		27,820
*Norwalk		49,460	*Trois-Rivières		46,074
*Norwich		23,429	*Troy		72,311
*Pawtucket		81,436	Truro		10,756
*Pittsfield		53,348	*Utica	117,424	101,531
*Portland	113,499	77,634	Verdun		77,391
Portsmouth		18,830	Victoriaville		13,124
*Poughkeepsie		41,023	*Waltham		47,187
*Providence	583,346	248,674	Warwick		43,028
*Quebec		164,016	*Waterbury	131,707	104,477
*Quincy		83,835	Watertown		34,350
Revere		36,763	Westmount		25,222
Rimouski		11,555	*Woonsocket		50,211
*Rome		41,682	*Worcester	219,330	203,486

* Also in the American Manufacturing Belt.

Selected Bibliography

F. J. Alcock, "The Isles of Fundy," *Canadian Geographical Journal*, Vol. 39, 1949, pp. 92-107.

Sven A. Anderson, "Trends in the Pulp and Paper Industry," *Economic Geography*, Vol. 18, 1942, pp. 195-202.

Sven A. Anderson and Augustus Jones, "Iron in the Adirondacks," *Economic Geography*, Vol. 21, 1945, pp. 276-285.

Marius Barbeau, "Maple Sugar," *Canadian Geographic Journal*, Vol. 38, 1949, pp. 176-189.

Will R. Bird, "Nova Scotia's Highland Cape Breton," *Canadian Geographic Journal*, Vol. 38, 1949, pp. 78-91.

Albert Carlson, "Ski Geography of New England," *Economic Geography*, Vol. 18, 1942, pp. 307-320.

Charles B. Fobes, "Historic Forest Fires in Maine," *Economic Geography*, Vol. 24, 1949, pp. 269-273.

Roland B. Greeley, "Part Time Farming and Recreational Land Use in New England," *Economic Geography*, Vol. 18, 1942, pp. 146-152.

Lyn Harrington, "The Cabot Trail" (Cape Breton Island), *Canadian Geographical Journal*, Vol. 36, 1948, pp. 204-221.

Edward C. Higbee, "The Three Earths of New England," *Geographical Review*, Vol. 42, 1952, pp. 425-438.

Karol J. Kucinski, and Walter S. Eisenmenger, "Sand Dune Stabilization on Cape Cod," *Economic Geography*, Vol. 19, 1943, pp. 206-214.

Lorne Manchester, "Harvest of the Waters," *Canadian Geographic Journal*, Vol. 39, 1949, pp. 3-17.

———, "Science in Fisheries," *Canadian Geographic Journal*, Vol. 41, 1950, pp. 189-209.

Fred H. Phillips, "New Brunswick: Varied Vacationland of the Maritimes," *Canadian Geographic Journal*, Vol. 40, 1950, pp. 12-43.

Richard S. Thoman, "Portland Maine: An Economic-Urban Appraisal," *Economic Geography*, Vol. 27, 1951, pp. 348-367.

5.

The Atlantic Coastal Plain
and the Piedmont

THE Coastal Plain and the Piedmont is here considered as a single geographic region because the pattern of settlement and development is somewhat similar throughout. Differences in utilization of the unconsolidated sediments of the Coastal Plain, and the residual soils of the Piedmont, are of enough contrast, however, to establish two distinct subregions: (1) the Atlantic Coastal Plain, and (2) the Piedmont. Because of climatic differences it seems desirable to subdivide the Piedmont into three areas (Figure 5-1). The entire region possesses a degree of unity, however, in that types of economic activities are similar even though local variations exist.

The Coastal Plain Subregion, which occupies a belt 50 to 100 miles wide along the Atlantic Seaboard from the eastern end of Long Island through northeastern New Jersey to central North Carolina, owes its economic life to the huge market for fruits and vegetables created by the dense population between Norfolk and Boston. The southern boundary is drawn where cotton culture becomes dominant. The western boundary of this subregion, on the other hand, is marked by the Fall Line, which separates the crystalline rocks of the Piedmont from the Coastal

Plain. This "line" is most pronounced along the streams where falls or rapids have developed but in the interstream areas it becomes difficult to trace. The Fall Line is best shown, however, by the string of cities, which have grown up to utilize the power resources of the streams and because they are at the head of ocean navigation on those same streams.

Inland from the Atlantic Coastal Plain between the Blue Ridge and the Fall Line Zone, lies the Piedmont, a long belt of foothills averaging about 100 miles in width. Extending from southeastern New York to Alabama, it reaches its greatest width in southern Virginia and North Carolina. It differs from its neighbors to the east and west. Although not homogeneous throughout, it possesses considerable unity. The subregion may be divided into:

1. The Northern Piedmont (from southeastern New York across Maryland to north-central Virginia) — an area of general farming and dairying.

2. The Central Piedmont (central and south-central Virginia and north-central North Carolina) — especially noted for the production of tobacco and apples.

3. The Southern Piedmont (south-central

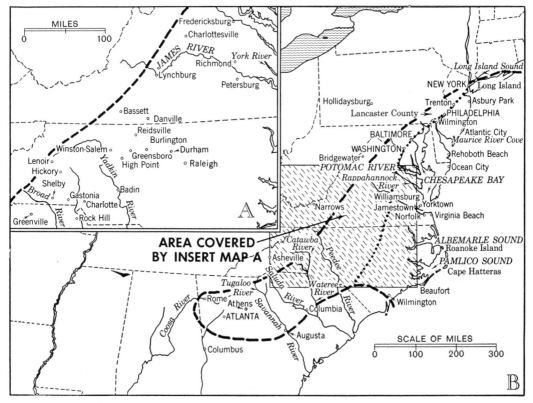

Figure 5–1. The Atlantic Coastal Plain and the Piedmont. A region of general farming, truck farming, tobacco growing, fishing, specialized manufacturing, and resorts. The dotted line is the *Fall Line* which separates the Coastal Plain from the Piedmont.

North Carolina, western South Carolina, northern Georgia and northeastern Alabama). Regionally this segment may be included also in the Cotton Belt, since the growing of cotton is the leading enterprise. However, it seems to be so definitely a part of the Piedmont that it is discussed in this chapter.

The Physical Setting

Surface Features. *The Atlantic Coastal Plain* was formerly a portion of the continental shelf that was raised above the sea without essential deformation. It is level to gently rolling. In relatively few places does the land rise more than 100 feet above sea level, though some of the long interstream areas rise to nearly 400 feet. Most of the cultural features, including roads and residences, are on these higher lands.

Poor drainage over much of the area is the principal surface condition limiting its use by man. Especially is this the case along the marshy coast of Virginia and North Carolina. In the embayed section of the Chesapeake Bay area, however, much of the land is rolling. The marsh and swampland is a breeding place for myriads of mosquitoes whose presence definitely discourages settlement.

The coast is broken by numerous peninsulas which are generally "splintered into smaller tongues." The lands of Tidewater Virginia lie along four major rivers — the York, the James, the Rappahannock, and the Potomac. The head of tidewater on the last three lies at the Fall Line. The coastline is one of submergence, so that stream valleys are drowned and form broad tidal estuaries.

The seaward margin is fringed with an

almost continuous succession of beaches and bars, the work of wave action. Incoming waves do not reach the shore, but break some distance out to form sand bars known as barrier beaches. Lagoons, varying in width from one-half to as many as eight miles, lie between these bars and the mainland. Most lagoons have been filled or are being filled by streams from the mainland or by sand blown from the beaches. Eventually the barrier beaches become so large that they prevent even the highest waves from washing over them. They are separated one from another by narrow inlets through which the tide enters.

The Piedmont, a rolling, hilly area at an elevation of 100 to 1,500 feet, differs considerably from the lower level-to-undulating lands of the Coastal Plain. While called an upland, it is really an erosional plain with a few hills rising above its otherwise gently rolling surface. The divides, with few exceptions, rise to an even skyline. It is smoothest along the interior border close to the Blue Ridge, where the full erosive power of the streams has not been felt. All the rivers are muddy and they fluctuate considerably in volume.

The Fall Line traverses the numerous rivers which flow from the Blue Ridge to the Atlantic. Where they pass from the older and harder rocks of the Piedmont onto the younger unconsolidated sediments of the Coastal Plain, there is a zone of rapids — the Fall Line. This Fall Line Zone has played a significant role in American history, since it determined the sites of a string of important cities from New York to Columbus, Georgia. Frequently rapids marked the head of navigation for sea-going craft; here bulk had to be broken. Moreover, water power was available for manufacturing.

Climate. The mild, semi-marine climate is the *Coastal Plain's* most important environmental factor. Its warm spring makes the early maturing of vegetables and small fruits possible. The Gulf Stream, which moves northward along the coast, ameliorates the range of temperature. The insular or marine climate is due partly to the numerous bays which seam the land.

Average annual precipitation varies from 40 inches in the north to 55 in the south, with the maximum in late summer and the minimum in autumn.

The long growing season, a result of proximity to the ocean, ranges from 190 days in the north to 240 in the south. Thus as many as four truck crops can be grown regularly on the same piece of land within a year.

Climatically the *Piedmont* is a sort of transitional area between the North with its long, cold, snowy winters and the South with its short, mild ones. Obviously an area extending over so much latitude could not have an identical climate throughout. It is mostly on the basis of climate and the resultant land use, that the Piedmont is divided into subregions. The growing season varies from an average of 160 days in the north to more than 230 in the south. The Southern Piedmont in winter averages 15° F. warmer than the Northern Piedmont.

Few agricultural areas in the United States receive so much annual precipitation; relatively few stations get less than 40 inches and some receive as many as 50. Maximum rainfall, in the form of thundershowers, comes in summer when crops need it most. These heavy downpours cause much soil erosion in a region where clean-tilled crops prevail. Hardly a week passes without a good rain, though this region, like most others, does have its occasional dry spells.

Soils. Despite the fact that agriculture occupies a high percentage of the land locally, the soils of the North Atlantic Coastal Plain, *are not fertile.* This condition is not altogether the result of man's failure to rotate crops, fertilize the soil, and employ a scientific system of farming. Nature herself had 'robbed' the soils long before the first colonist set foot upon the continent.[1] In this subregion soil is considered primarily a medium through which to feed the crops. All soils require manure or commercial fertilizer to produce cash crops.

Viewed regionally, the soils of the Piedmont vary in quality from good to bad. Soil

[1] L. A. Wolfanger, "Abandoned Land in a Region of Land Abandonment," *Economic Geography,* Vol. 7. No. 2, April 1931, p. 168.

is, nevertheless, the most potent single natural environmental factor distinguishing this subregion. Lancaster County, Pennsylvania, is a notable exception, its fertile limestone soils being world-famous. All Piedmont soils are pedalfers — gray-brown podzolic soils or red and yellow soils. From north to south they vary in texture from light to heavy. They are *residual;* that is, they are derived from the long disintegration in place of granites, gneisses, and schists — which underlie most of the region. Pedologists estimate that nature requires nearly 1,000 years to build one inch of topsoil. The only transported soils are confined to the valleys and are immature, having no relation to the underlying bedrock.

In colonial days, sandy loams seven to fifteen inches deep predominated, but these are now mostly gone, having been eroded from exposed slopes. Piedmont soils, never high in humus, have been depleted both by erosion and by leaching.[2] Leaching, especially in the Southern Piedmont, occurs throughout the year; in the Northern Piedmont, however, the ground is frozen during much of the winter and hence does not suffer.

Generous applications of commercial fertilizer must be used in this region to make the soil productive. The Southern Piedmont is said to be the most heavily fertilized part of the United States.

Natural Vegetation. Originally, except for the coastal marshes and sand dunes, virgin forest of conifers or of deciduous species or a mixture of the two, characterized the coastal plain.

More than one half of the area is still in forest and brush (not virgin), despite its early settlement by white men and its nearness to the great cities of New York, Philadelphia, Baltimore, Washington, and Norfolk. Some 1,200 square miles in southeastern and south-central New Jersey have almost no farm settlements. In these "pine

barrens" dwell the "pineys," who have attracted much attention from sociologists and historians. On hidden trails and beside dismal swamps live many illiterate people, despite the fact that they are within easy walking distance of modern communities and within two hours by train from Philadelphia and New York. At the outset the people who occupied the pine barrens were the same stock as those who settled on what later proved to be the better lands. The more energetic and able emigrated, however, resulting in a depreciation of the stock that remained.

The Piedmont, at the time of the first settlements, was an almost continuous expanse of forest — largely hardwoods. Into this pristine wilderness pushed the white man with his ax and fire, plow and seed. Soon, the original forest disappeared, being removed at a rate never before equaled in world history. Unfortunately, most of it went up in smoke, since only a small part could be used for fuel, fences, and dwellings. The forest seemed inexhaustible. Furthermore, it was a barrier in the way of agricultural progress and hence was considered by the settler as an enemy which should be destroyed.

Today, much of the Piedmont is again in forests, but the trees are inferior second-growth stock. In spite of this, however, numerous small sawmills dot the landscape showing an economic use of the forest that was not originally practiced. The forests of the present occupy old fields which have been abandoned.

Settlement

The Atlantic Coastal Plain. The Coastal Plain, especially Tidewater Virginia, was one of the cradles of Anglo-America. Colonial life centered in the plantation, rather than in the town, as in New England. The local isolation and economic self-sufficiency of the plantation were antagonistic to the development of towns. Prior to 1700, Jamestown was the only settlement in this region that really could be called a *town,* and it was actually nothing more than a village.

---

[2] Land that is cultivated loses fertility through the draining away of those mineral elements which dissolve in water. Some leaching is inevitable, but it is increased by practices which leave the land bare throughout much of the year. It can be retarded by growing grass and cover crops.

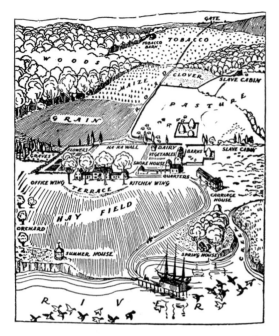

Figure 5–2. A typical eighteenth century tide-water plantation. With miles of shoreline available but with trackless forests inland, settlers located their plantations on the waterfront, relying almost wholly upon water transportation. (Courtesy Ginn & Company and the Maryland State Planning Commission.)

Nearly all settlements were located on navigable streams, and every planter owned a wharf which could be reached by the small ships of that day (Figure 5–2); in fact, one of the strongest reasons for which the planter selected his land was that it fronted on a water highway.

Plantations were governed geographically by the streams; counties were governed by the plantations; men thought in terms of plantations. ... The growth of towns and cities was simply not a part of the scheme of society. When late in that first century men bethought themselves of the need of towns, it was too late. The rural system was so well established that it was impossible to overcome its influence.[3]

Within twelve years after the founding of Jamestown, plantations had spread 70 miles

---

[3] A. B. Hulbert, *Soil: Its Influence on the History of the United States,* pp. 111-112. New Haven: Yale University Press, 1930.

upstream, extending inland for several miles from either bank. Nowhere was there between rivers a land-reach greater than 20 miles, and frequently it was five miles or less. It would be wrong, however, to believe that colonial Tidewater Virginia and Maryland were entirely lands of plantations, slaves, and beautiful mansions.

There were several strata of society, but only the great landowners and the yeomen will be considered here. The wealthier and more intelligent planters occupied the more productive lands. Yeomen, for the most part poor, operated the medium-size farms in the less productive areas. They found it both difficult and irritating to compete with Negro slaves. So powerful had the large plantation owners become that the yeomen experienced great difficulty in obtaining even small holdings. Hence the ablest migrated westward.

The Introduction of Slavery. Slaves were first introduced because the tobacco growers of Tidewater Virginia and Maryland demanded them. Slaves could be used only where the work was set in simple and continuous tasks, where the winters were mild so that they could work out of doors twelve months in the year, and where the cost of living was low. In fields growing tobacco and corn, slaves working in gangs could be supervised easily. Women and children also worked. Slavery never really prospered in this region, however, as it did in the cotton and sugar areas to the south. It is thus apparent that the distribution of slavery throughout the United States was based on geographical conditions and not on sentiment. By 1840 it was declining in both Maryland and Virginia.

The Piedmont. The American Indians, who had occupied the Piedmont for a long time before the coming of the white man, were primarily hunters and hence had not changed the primeval character of the landscape. They had divided the hunting grounds into family-size portions and never trespassed unless forced to do so. Each family killed only the game it actually consumed. This system of occupance put no scars of exploitation on the land.

The Piedmont was settled from the older

sections to the east — from the Chesapeake Bay and Albemarle Sound country and from Charleston, South Carolina — by people one, two, or three generations removed from the earliest settlers. It also received large numbers of Germans and Scotch-Irish who had followed the Great Valley southward and entered the Piedmont from the west. By 1750 most of the Piedmont had been occupied by white people.

Agricultural Activities of the Coastal Plain

Early Agriculture. From the time of the earliest settlement, farming has been the predominant occupation. In colonial days it was assumed to be the necessary employment of all, and nearly everyone considered the ownership of tillable land the acme of "human earthly desire." Even those who were classed as merchants, fishermen, and manufacturers were really part-time farmers.

The colonies composing the North Atlantic Coastal Plain were not entirely self-sustaining; they had to produce something for exchange. They planted the European grape, but it failed; they introduced the mulberry and the silk worm, but unsuccessfully; they tried to rely on furs, but the supply was neither permanent nor plentiful. Something had to be found that was in demand and had high value per unit of weight or bulk. *Tobacco proved to be that product.*

Tobacco. The commercial production of tobacco began in 1612, and within a few years it was the leading crop. In fact, it was grown almost to the exclusion of foodstuffs. The continuous growing of a single crop on a given area, however, is soil robbery, and the history of early agriculture here is the history of land exploitation. Tobacco had not long been cultivated before planters found it necessary to acquire additional land. As soon as the soil showed signs of exhaustion, it was allowed to grow up in grasses and trees, and new fields were cleared. For this reason the large plantations came into being. The tobacco planter had to have enormous acreage on which to grow this crop, since it was necessary to reclaim new land from the forest as the soil lost its fertility. It was soon

found that the soils were becoming depleted at so rapid a rate that few fields could produce more than three consecutive crops. To make matters worse, the neglect of the old fields encouraged washing and gullying. Thus tidewater counties were suffering from soil depletion as early as the First Census of 1790. About that time some planters began to move to the Piedmont. Though there was an agricultural revival during the 1850's when farm journals and soil chemists pointed out the value of commercial fertilizer,[4] deep plowing, and improved seed, Tidewater Virginia and Maryland were losing their Southern characteristics. The plantation was giving way to the small diversified farm, in which slavery had a steadily declining part. The truck farms were in sharp contrast to the large old-fashioned plantations from which they were carved.

Present-day Agriculture. Since the earliest settlement, a selective process has been going on in the Coastal Plain — the best lands continuing productive, the bad ones reverting to wilderness. Tobacco no longer is important except in southern Maryland west of Chesapeake Bay and the Inner Coastal Plain of North Carolina, where it is a major cash crop. Wheat, corn, and hay occupy a considerable part of the land under cultivation. If proper rotations are maintained and moderate amounts of commercial fertilizer used, the yields are satisfactory — the average wheat yields compare favorably with the average for the United States.

The growing of vegetables, however, is profitable in many parts of the region. Vegetable consumption in Anglo-America has increased greatly since 1920, largely as a result of (1) dietary research — especially as regards the value of vitamins — and (2) the development of refrigeration, which per-

---

[4] The use of chemical plant food in the United States probably dates from 1830, when the first Chilean nitrate was imported. Production of mixed fertilizers was started in Baltimore in 1850, and the establishment of other factories along the Atlantic Seaboard followed. It is estimated that production in 1856 was about 20,000 tons and in 1868, 50,000 tons. (H. Willett, *Fertilizer Consumption in the United States,* Washington, D. C.: The National Fertilizer Association, August 1937, p. 3.

mits perishable products to move great distances in season.

Every urban dweller, exiled from the soil, consumes an average of more than a half-pound of fresh vegetables each day. Only a fraction of the land available for truck crops is actually utilized in the North Atlantic Coastal Plain, which is the world's foremost producer of commercial vegetables. Moreover, truck farming is so intensive that it is not profitable, ordinarily, to work a large farm, since vegetables require 5 to 20 times as much labor as wheat. Ordinarily, as fast as one vegetable is harvested, the field is plowed, fertilized, and planted to another. Vegetable production nearly always is ahead of consumption.

The area is favored geographically for vegetable production by its long growing season, its level terrain, and its light, easily tilled soils that warm rapidly in the spring.

Figure 5–3. Harvesting tomatoes for a canning company. Most of the tomatoes grown in the Atlantic Coastal Plain are processed into soups, tomato juices, and other tomato products. (Courtesy of the State of New Jersey and the Campbell Soup Company.)

A superb location with respect to the nation's outstanding markets for truck crops, along with almost unexcelled transportation facilities — rail, boat, and truck — add to its advantages.

The crops. Potatoes and sweet potatoes are among the outstanding crops. Potatoes appear on the Northern market from late June to early August — after the peak of the season in the Carolinas but before the arrival of the Long Island crop. For the most part, potatoes are grown close to large population centers; in fact, maps of population and potatoes usually coincide remarkably well.

Sweet potatoes, tropical or subtropical in origin, have been grown here since 1650. Favorable conditions are the sandy loam soils, long growing season, warm nights, and relatively high temperatures. Since 1909, commercial production has been concentrating in New Jersey, the Eastern Shore of Maryland and Virginia, and northeastern North Carolina.

Other commercial crops include sweet corn, cucumbers, cabbage, peas, peppers, onions, greenbeans, lettuce, celery, asparagus, tomatoes, and spinach. Some of these are sold as they ripen, while others are grown for canneries. When truck farmers grow fresh vegetables for sale, they make the most money by getting their crops to market early; hence they try to settle in the warmest part of the area.

In summarizing, it may be noted that (1) potatoes are exceptionally important on Long Island, in central New Jersey, the southern part of the Eastern Shore of Virginia, and northeastern North Carolina; (2) sweet potatoes are found in northeastern North Carolina, on the Eastern Shore of Virginia, and in Maryland, Delaware, and New Jersey; (3) tomatoes are dominant in southern New Jersey, Delaware, eastern Maryland (Figure 5–3), and Virginia.

On the inner coastal plain of North Carolina, west of Pamlico Sound, lies an important tobacco area known as the New Bright Tobacco Belt. It has been settled for about three hundred years but has produced tobacco on a commercial scale only since about 1890. The landscape is monotonous and much of it is uncultivated, but on the small areas under cultivation, intensive production of bright cigarette tobacco is dominant, despite the fact that the soils have to be fertilized heavily.[5]

Peanuts are important, especially in southeastern Virginia and adjacent North Carolina, which grow the large-podded variety for human consumption. This crop requires a long summer and a light-textured soil. Although a legume, peanuts do not add nitrogen to the soil if the nuts are harvested. Hay from the peanut plant is fully as valuable as alfalfa and clover. The peanut has helped to terminate the one-crop system of farming so long prevalent here.

Long Island is outstanding for its production of potatoes and cauliflower, and it ranks high in many other truck crops. It has a great advantage of nearness to the largest urban market in the United States. It is also famous for its "Long Island ducklings" and as a producer of nearly half of the ducks of the United States, it ranks high in poultry raising.[6]

Watermelons, cantaloupes, strawberries, blackberries, and raspberries are important locally. Delaware, Maryland, and Virginia are notable for strawberries and southern New Jersey for cranberries.

Dairying. The North Atlantic Coastal Plain generally is of minor importance in dairying, despite large nearby markets for fluid milk. Where vegetables thrive one seldom sees a dairy farm.

A notable exception, however, is to be found on the Eastern Shore of Maryland where, because of insect pests and diseases, the fruit industry failed. Proximity to large cities and improved transport facilities enabled it to market fluid milk, much of which is sold by co-operative organizations. A city ordinance in Baltimore requires that milk come from a distance not to exceed 50 miles.

The marketing of vegetables. Large-scale commercial production of truck crops be-

came possible only in proportion to the availability of rapid and efficient transportation. The region everywhere is well served by rail, water, and highway. Moreover, within or adjacent to it is a long line of cities reaching from Boston to Norfolk whose inhabitants comprise an amazingly large part of Anglo-America's total population. Probably no other region on earth possesses such an enormous and immediate city market for its products. The great resorts are an additional market; tourists in New Jersey alone number millions annually. The Hampton Roads district is more important than its population figure indicates, because of its military posts and naval bases, and because many commercial vessels replenish their supplies there. The importance of proximity can not be overestimated — 75 per cent of the vegetables sold in New York City come in season from farms within 100 miles.

Agriculture of the Piedmont

Agriculture employs more people than any other industry on the Piedmont, though from Lynchburg to Atlanta manufacturing made great strides after 1930.

As already noted, the Piedmont was settled by farmers from the tidewater region and from the Great Valley. Upon clearing the forest, many of them planted tobacco, a row crop, successively for three, four, or even five years. When tobacco was no longer profitable, they grew corn until it would not pay for the labor expended. Then they abandoned the fields, cleared new land, and repeated the process.

The central and southern parts of the Piedmont are essentially areas of small farms. Many so-called "problem farms" have an average of only 18 acres in harvested crops. Much of the land is marginal or submarginal. Production is directed largely toward such cash crops as cotton and tobacco, whose prices fluctuate widely and occasionally bring misfortune to the farmer. Nowhere else in Anglo-America is tenancy increasing more rapidly; in fact, 68 per cent of the farms in the Southern Piedmont are operated by

[5] Parnell W. Picklesimer, "The New Bright Tobacco Belt of North Carolina," *Economic Geography*, Vol. 20, 1944, pp. 14-19.

[6] *The Counties of New York State*, p. 22. New York: New York Telephone Company, 1948.

tenants.[7] Nowhere else do livestock, milk, and home-grown vegetables play so small a part in the farming enterprise. There are, however, local exceptions, especially around cities and towns, because of manufacturing and commerce.

The Northern Piedmont. Lying north of the James River in the states of Pennsylvania, Maryland, and Virginia is an important dairy section. The farms, averaging 50 to 100 acres, are usually smaller than those in any other geographic region of their respective states. Dairying is so organized as to supply fluid milk to nearby cities; some goes as far as New York City. A secondary factor is that the soils are not sufficiently fertile nor the topography sufficiently flat for most successful general farming practices. Proximity to great markets has enabled the farmers to rise above the minor deficiencies of soil and topography. Probably nowhere in America is there an area better suited to dairying. Nearly all crops are grown with reference to it. Much wheat is grown, not for its cash value, but for the protection it offers against excessive soil erosion and leaching and for the straw it supplies for bedding dairy cattle. Barley is planted as a winter cover crop for the same reasons. Corn, grown for grain and silage, also is a major crop. The land, after it is laid by, is planted to winter wheat or barley. The hay crop is invariably a legume, either alfalfa or red clover.

Nearly all the farmers are white, because the plantation system never was important in Pennsylvania and did not extend beyond the Coastal Plain even in Maryland. Farmers of German descent, who follow scientific practices are numerically important, especially in Pennsylvania, and the high standard of the dairy industry is in no small measure attributable to them.

Lancaster County, Pennsylvania. Lancaster is one of the most scientifically farmed counties in the United States, and it merits separate treatment.

For the most part this area is a broad undulating plain lying southeast of all the

mountain ridges of Pennsylvania. The climate is highly favorable for farming. The growing season of 160 to 175 days is adequate for most middle-latitude crops. Winters are mild and summers hot. Precipitation averages about 40 inches, nearly two thirds of which falls from April to September, inclusive, when the crops need it most. The fertile limestone soils — those that have developed from a residue resulting from the decay of limestone — are, undoubtedly, the best in the state.

Lancaster County has one of the most advantageous locations in the entire country with respect to large consuming markets, because it is near Philadelphia, Baltimore, and Pittsburgh, and has excellent transportation facilities, both railway and highway.

Swiss Mennonites, followed later by Germans, were the original settlers. Today Lancaster County and Pennsylvania Dutch (German) are synonymous; three quarters of the people in the county are of German ancestry. It is indeed significant that this area was settled by immigrants from western Germany whose ancestors for many centuries had cultivated one of the richest wheat-growing regions of Europe. They were used to soils with a high lime content, and Lancaster County appealed to them. The Scotch-Irish, on the other hand, having learned from experience in their homeland that limestone soils are dry and given to heaving, selected the hills to the southwest or pushed into York County.[8] Since settlement, these thrifty and diligent Pennsylvania Dutch have transformed the region into a highly fruitful one (Figure 5–4). Unlike farmers in other regions, generations pass through the same homesteads, sons followed their fathers on the same soil.

Lancaster County is above all an agricultural land. More than 90 per cent of it is in farms, and in some townships more than 80 per cent is in crops. There is little waste land. Farms are relatively small — averaging only 53.3 acres — and are well cared for. Houses are well built but not ostentatious; barns are large and in excellent condition; all outbuild-

---

[7] Rupert Vance, *Human Geography of the South,* p. 33. Chapel Hill: University of North Carolina Press, 1935.

[8] Hulbert, *Soil: Its Influence on the History of the United States,* pp. 135, 142-144.

Figure 5–4. A Lancaster County farm. Few areas in Anglo-America have been so richly endowed by nature and so well handled by man as Lancaster County. The Pennsylvania Dutch, predominant element in the population, have brought their lands to a high degree of productivity. (Courtesy Lancaster Chamber of Commerce.)

ings and fences are painted. Roads everywhere are good and railroads numerous. The whole cultural landscape reflects prosperity.

Corn, winter wheat, hay, potatoes and tobacco are the major crops. Tobacco, which fits into the system of diversified farming in Lancaster County, is the money crop. Nevertheless, the smallest acreage is given to it because it is a "robber" crop, draining fertility from the land, and it requires an abundance of labor from planting through harvesting and marketing.

A three-, four-, or five-year rotation is scrupulously followed. The four-year is the most common: (1) tobacco, (2) wheat, (3) clover or alfalfa, and (4) corn. Lancaster County tobacco, mild in aroma and flavor, is used primarily for cigar fillers, of which it contributes about two thirds of the nation's supply. The county produces about 90 per cent of Pennsylvania's tobacco, and its per acre yield is high. In order to procure this high yield, the crop is grown only on the better soils — especially the silt and clay loams — and these are generously fertilized. Few areas have solved their fertilizer problem so well. This is done with the manure of steers and dairy cattle.

Dairying is not as important as one might expect, because its labor requirements are heavy and would compete with tobacco for the farmer's time. It is for this reason that the county has gone in for fattening steers. Stockers come mostly from western Virginia, an area growing insufficient corn to fatten them. In recent years, however, increasing numbers of cattle are being brought in from Texas and other western ranching areas. The extensive southeastern Pennsylvania holdings of the King Ranch of Texas is a notable example of this. Here the "Braford" (*brahma* and *hereford*) strain of beef cattle forms a conspicuous feature of the cultural landscape.

Hay, corn, and straw are fed to the steers and concentrates are purchased in addition. Not more than ten per cent of the land is in pasture.

Wheat shares with tobacco the distinction of being the principal cash crop, being widely distributed and grown on all soils. At least half is used within the county for livestock and human consumption. Corn, like wheat, is widely distributed. Since corn cannot stand shipment because of its low value, most of it is fed to steers and poultry. Potatoes, low in value and perishable, are grown by nearly every farmer. The excellent location of this area with respect to large consuming centers favors commercial production of potatoes. Probably no other area in this country gets larger per acre yields — about 600 bushels. Hay is an important rotation crop. Timothy, alfalfa, and clover all are grown. Legumes yield well everywhere. Nearly all the hay is fed on the farms where it is grown.

Mushrooms. In the southeastern corner of the Pennsylvania Piedmont lies the leading mushroom producing area of the United States. The actual acreage devoted to the crop is negligible, since it is grown in beds within mushroom sheds. The chief observable forms of the industry are the rows of ventilated sheds with large piles of horse-manure compost alongside. This area produces from 70 to 80 per cent of the country's mushroom crop, the product being sent to Philadelphia, New York, and other large urban centers by truck or express.[9]

The apple area of the Virginia Piedmont.

[9] Raymond E. Murphy and Marion Murphy, *Pennsylvania: A Regional Geography*, pp. 211-212. Harrisburg: 1937.

Bordering the Blue Ridge from the James to the Rappahannock is one of the leading apple districts in the eastern United States. The belt, with Charlottesville as the center, is approximately 45 miles wide and extends in a northeast-southwest direction. The industry began some 75 years ago when farmers planted apple orchards in the small, moist, fertile valleys (*coves*) at the foot of the mountain ridges. Location on slopes enabled them to benefit from air drainage. Many of them are on rough land and are called "mountain orchards."

In the Piedmont the Winesap makes up two thirds of the entire planting. The Albemarle Pippin (Yellow Newtown) is most widely cultivated in Albemarle County to whose granitic soils, rich in feldspar, it is especially adapted.[10] It is an export apple largely because of its good keeping qualities.

The Central Piedmont — Land of Tobacco. The Central Piedmont, one of the

[10] According to W. B. Alwood, apple grower, Greenwood, Virginia.

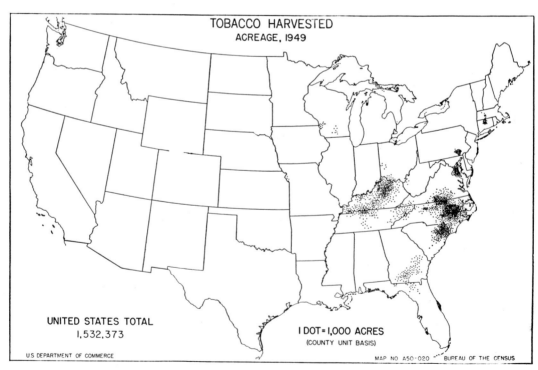

Figure 5–5. Tobacco harvested. Note the heavy concentration on the Piedmont and the Inner Coastal Plain of Maryland, Virginia, and the Carolinas.

continent's major tobacco-growing areas (Figure 5–5), grows dark fire and air-cured leaf in Virginia and bright flue-cured in Virginia and the states south of it.

By Revolutionary times, tobacco had nearly exhausted the "second bottoms" of Tidewater Virginia and was moving up the valleys of the Virginia and North Carolina Piedmont. Tobacco was the staple and every attempt to produce other export crops such as silk, grapes, flax, hemp, and cotton failed. But not everyone on the Piedmont grew tobacco. Those who came from the Great Valley were opposed to slavery and hence did not grow tobacco, and the poor whites who migrated from the Coastal Plain were non-slaveholding.

Dark fire-cured and air-cured tobaccos. These types are grown on the heavier soils of the Virginia Piedmont — the former in the central part, the latter in the north-central portion. The fire-cured type is identical with that grown in early days of Jamestown, and the method of treatment is fundamentally the same as that employed by the Indians. The cured leaf of these types is dark in color, thick, tough, oily, and high in nicotine. Dark tobaccos are used for pipe-smoking mixtures, snuff, and chewing. The fire-cured types have been grown primarily for export and the air-cured types for domestic manufacture. The demand both in foreign and domestic markets is decreasing.

Bright flue-cured tobacco. In 1852, near Durham, North Carolina, two farmers broke away from tradition and set their plants in light, sandy, siliceous, infertile soil. They heated some of the yield over hot flues and got a clear, rich gold leaf that was mild and sweet to smoke. Thus was revived the social economy of the wornout soil, and the lands that had been abandoned jumped in value many-fold. Flue-cured tobacco now is the most important cigarette variety in the world and has a money value nearly six times that of dark tobacco.

Land used for tobacco is carefully selected, since soil is the dominant environmental factor contributing to aroma, flavor, and thinness of leaf. On any given farm, only a small acreage is planted in tobacco and but a fraction of this grows the highest quality. Light-colored and light-textured soils, with little clay and organic material in the subsoil, are best for cigarette and pipe tobacco. Most farmers devote from two to ten acres of highly prized land for tobacco and use it year in and year out. This type of farming has so ruined the land that virgin soils are now at a premium. Legumes dare not be used to build up the soils, and manures must be used sparingly. The grower prefers to put his crop on almost sterile soil, to which he then may add plant foods in the right amount. It is little wonder then that this area is one of the largest consumers of commercial fertilizer (Figure 5–6).

Only a small acreage per farm is in tobacco because it is a back-breaking, highly technical crop to grow. It requires so much labor that little time is left for other crops. There is the seed bed, the preparation, the fields, transplanting, cultivating, topping (to prevent the growth of seeds), worming, suckering, spraying, harvesting, curing, stripping, and marketing. Tobacco is a crop that wears out men as well as the land.

Tobacco is now grown largely by tenants, white and colored, many of whom are very poor. The monetary returns do not by any means compensate them for their time and hard work. Since tobacco growing is not profitable to most of the growers, many people wonder why Piedmont farmers continue to produce it generation after generation. The reason is that they have been reared in a tobacco atmosphere and through experience have learned the intricacies of its cultivation. Moreover, they know nothing of any other system of farming and hence are reluctant to change.

Tobacco is hard on the soil because its root system tends to suck rather than to grasp and hold the soil. Moreover, it is a clean-tilled crop that induces erosion. The rows are kept scrupulously free of weeds during the growing season. There is no scientific rotation; if any exists at all, it consists of corn, tobacco, and corn. Finally, open winters and torrential summer rains on steeply sloping fields mean only one thing — soil loss.

Tobacco in the Central Piedmont is meet-

Figure 5–6. Field of southern bright tobacco on the Piedmont. (Courtesy of Cunningham & Walsh, New York.)

ing some competition, especially from dairying, poultry raising, and beef fattening. The Central Piedmont is now running large numbers of beef cattle on its lush pastures. On the large estates in the Virginia section the preference is for the Aberdeen-Angus breed, and today these sleek, black cattle form an integral part of Piedmont economy (Figure 5–7).

Corn is the outstanding crop in acreage and almost every farmer grows it. It yields best in river and creek bottoms but is grown also on steep hillsides. Like tobacco, it is a row crop that facilitates soil erosion. It is made into corn meal for human use and is used as feed for livestock.

The Southern Piedmont — Land of Cotton and Corn. From central North Carolina to Alabama, cotton replaces tobacco as the principal cash crop. This area lying south of the July isotherm of 78°F. has a growing season of 200 days or more. Its soils are heavier than those in the tobacco area to the north. Cotton, outstanding since 1820, was an excellent pioneer crop in the pre-railroad era because high value enabled it to stand transport changes. It could also employ Negro slaves.

The Southern Piedmont is one of the oldest cotton-growing areas in the United States but is no longer one of the best. It is finding it increasingly difficult to compete with the less humid cotton districts in Texas and Oklahoma. Unable to grow long-staple cotton, it produces the short-staple variety and hence is competing with such countries as China, India, and Brazil, which have much cheaper labor.

The natural environment in the Southern Piedmont is satisfactory for growing cotton. Rainfall is light in spring and early summer when cotton requires little moisture and great heat, and low in autumn when precipitation would discolor the lint in the opening bolls and retard picking. Since 1926, the decrease in cotton acreage in North Carolina has proceeded at a very rapid rate. More than a million acres have been taken out of cotton production in recent years.[11]

Cotton has been hard on the land. Tens of thousands of ruined acres have returned to forest.

Corn, a subsistence and not a cash crop like cotton, is grown for farmers and mules. Like cotton, however, corn is a clean-tilled crop which facilitates sheet and gully erosion and hinders systematic rotations. It also draws heavily on the life-giving soil nutrients. Many farmers over-crop with corn against their better judgment because low labor-income and tenant status offer no alternative. Corn and cotton have made much of the Southern Piedmont a problem area — a large portion of which should not be farmed at all.

Lespedeza, a deep-rooted perennial, is revolutionizing agricultural practices in the Southern Piedmont. It affords an excellent protective cover, makes the soil more absorbent, is a popular forage and, when plowed under, increases the yields of subsequent crops.

[11] Franklin C. Erikson, "The Cotton Belt of North Carolina," *Economic Geography*, Vol. 20, 1944, p. 5.

Soil Erosion. Few areas have been so manhandled (Figure 5–8) as the Piedmont. Soil erosion occurs on practically every acre of slope land, and the prevailing system of farming has not encouraged soil conservation. Hence nearly one third of the Southern Piedmont has lost 75 per cent or more of its topsoil. Over large areas crops are being grown on subsoil. Considerable land has been abandoned because it is submarginal — cannot produce crops at a profit.

The washing away of soil is the great problem of much of the Piedmont. In the central and southern sections, thousands of farmers operating on slopes now stripped of topsoil cannot make a satisfactory living. Their families are "ill-fed, ill-clad, and ill-housed."

Conservation. A national objective is to pass on to future generations a soil as nearly unimpaired as possible. The Soil Conservation Service is attempting to improve both the Piedmont and its people: little can be accomplished without considering both. Some of the conservation practices being employed are: [12]

1. *Contour farming.* The farmer plows around the hill rather than up and down the

[12] Guy-Harold Smith, editor, *Conservation of Natural Resources*, pp. 79-83. New York: John Wiley & Sons, 1950.

Figure 5–7. Aberdeen-Angus cattle on a blue-grass pasture near Gordonsville, Virginia. (Courtesy of C. T. Neale and the Virginia Aberdeen-Angus Association.)

slope. Each small ridge and furrow helps to hold back rain water.

2. *Strip cropping.* Strips of close-growing crops alternating with rows of clean-tilled crops are grown on the contour. The strips of close-growing crops filter out the soil particles from the silt-laden water moving

4. *Cover crops.* Close-growing crops are planted on steep slopes and bare ground to protect the land from erosion. One of the best crops for the Piedmont is _lespedeza,_ which is grown on hillsides, gully slopes, and road cuts, to reduce run-off and resist erosion. On an experimental plot this crop lost only about

Figure 5–8. Soil erosion on the Piedmont. Prior to the Civil War this was rich, productive land, but in less than a century after Appomattox the topsoil has been carried away and deep gulleys are tearing through the subsoil. (Courtesy Soil Conservation Service.)

downhill. The water is obstructed, its velocity is checked, and the load is dropped. The water then has more time to soak into the ground and prevents washing.

3. *Terracing.* Terraces act as impediments to the flow of water, thereby reducing its erosive power. They let surplus water run from the field in an orderly manner.

one ton of soil per acre as against 28 for bare plots, 18 for cotton, and 7 for corn. Another cover crop which has been successful on the better-drained soils of the Piedmont is the perennial _kudzu,_ a deep-rooted, leguminous vine with a dense broad-leafed foliage. Its rapid growth, as much as 50 feet in a single season, makes it especially desirable for protecting steep slopes from erosion.[13]

Topsoil contains the bulk of the life-giving humus and nitrogen. Since subsoil is only one fourth to one half as productive as topsoil, the need for conservation is obvious.

Rural Depopulation

Despite the importance of truck farming, fewer people in the Coastal Plain are engaged in agriculture today than a century ago. In fact, the more southerly part of the subregion passed the climax of its prosperity on the eve of the War for Independence. It suffered still more in the War of 1812. From 1820 to 1840 there was a heavy exodus. The principal cause of emigration was the opening of the cheap land and extremely fertile soils of the Middle West, with which Tidewater Virginia and Maryland could not compete. An additional factor was that the plantation system was so lacking in democracy that the family of small means could make little headway socially or economically, and the New West loomed as a beacon of hope.

The population in Tidewater Virginia and Maryland is only about half of what it was in 1810. The same is true in New Jersey which has 400,000 acres of deserted farms; here, however, the urban pull is strong and suburbs occupy much former farm land.

Tenancy

The Central and Southern subregions are capital examples of man's misuse of the land. Throughout the United States there is unmistakable correlation between tenancy and erosion. Tenancy had its inception after the Civil War. Planters with land and experience lacked funds for paying wages to their former slaves, and hundreds of thousands of newly freed Negroes were poor but knew the routine of caring for cotton under rigid direction. The tenant system brought these two interdependent groups together. The former slaves were given a share of the crop

13 R. Y. Bailey, *Kudzu for Erosion Control in the Southeast*, U. S. Department of Agriculture, Farmers' Bulletin No. 1840. Washington: Government Printing Office, 1944.

(usually half) for their part of the labor. At first only Negroes were croppers, but now there are almost as many white tenants as there are colored. White croppers dwell mostly in the Southern Piedmont and are cotton growers. Some also occupy the tobacco lands of the Central Piedmont. Nearly all emanate from the adjacent mountain areas or from patches of poor land which were scattered between plantations before the Civil War.

Most croppers are little more than *peons* — many are poorly nourished. Hookworm and malaria are common. Dwellings, of two or three rooms, are poorly constructed, weather-beaten and unsightly. In spite of the presence of the anopheline mosquito, doors and windows are rarely screened. Few tenants remain on the same piece of land for more than a year or two; in fact, one out of every three moves each year. Under such a system there is little incentive to conserve the land, which each year becomes more depleted and eroded. What this area needs more than anything else is to reform its agriculture — to break away from the one-crop system and attempt to feed itself, so far as meat, bread, fruits, vegetables, and dairy products are concerned.

Present Inhabitants

South of Delaware Bay on the Coastal Plain, the farmers are of old American stock and 35 per cent are colored. North of Delaware Bay, especially in New Jersey, the farmers are largely of foreign origin: German, Irish, English, and Italian. European immigrants have long shunned the lands south of the Mason-Dixon Line because their higher standard of living would prevent them from competing with the Negro and because the social status of the agricultural laborer is unattractive.

The difference in the composition of the population north and south of Delaware Bay affects the tempo of life. To the north the manner of living is typically Northern, to the south typically Southern. In the latter area farming is not as scientific, and the standard of living is low.

In Maryland and Virginia Negroes generally occupy better lands than white farmers, for they work parts of former plantations which had to be sufficiently productive to support both the landlord and his slaves. Many of the white farmers attempt to farm sandy soils that were never very good.

Estates of the Piedmont

Settlement of the Piedmont followed that of the Coastal Plain. This was due in part to the fact that the better lands of the Coastal Plain were filled at an early date and also to the realization on the part of the colonists that the soils of the Piedmont were more fertile. So long as settlement was confined to the Coastal Plain plantation homes were erected with their front doors facing the water — their chief contact with Europe. In the Piedmont section, however, the spread of people did not hinge so definitely on stream patterns. Homes occupied the higher and more attractive interstream areas.[14]

To this rolling and fertile Piedmont country came the Quakers and later the "Pennsylvania-Dutch" Mennonites to settle in Lancaster County; the English aristocracy to establish manor houses in Lord Baltimore's colony of Maryland; and the Cavaliers to the Virginia Piedmont. The type of settlement made by the German Mennonites in Lancaster County, Pennsylvania has been discussed. The settlement of the Manor Counties of Maryland, and the appearance of that area today is vividly described in the following quotation:

The Manor Counties of Maryland form one of the most distinctive and gracious communities in America. There the climate is hospitable, terrain comfortable, soils fertile and highly productive, resources varied and adequate, and the countryside peaceful and attractive. There, in the midst of plenty and prosperity, folks have learned long since the art of living abundantly and graciously, of entertaining delightfully, and enjoying to the fullest the loveliness and bounty of the land in which they live. There, American citizenship and patriotism have achieved a perfection that might well be envied and emulated throughout our country.

From the deep, fertile soils of the farms on the rolling terrain of the lower Piedmont, farmers take heavy yields of wheat, and corn, and alfalfa; on the luxuriant pastures they raise prize-winning cattle, swine and sheep; in their productive orchards all kinds of luscious temperate fruits flourish and yield heavily and trustworthily; in their gardens they can grow any and all healthful vegetables; from the shallow, mild waters of the neighboring bay, they take varied fishes and oysters and crabs; from the streams they get shad and smelt and other finfish; wild fowl throng the marshes and bays, quail and pheasant find cover in the broomsedge and cut-over woodlands, squirrel, and rabbit and raccoon haunt the brush and groves.

It is a land of rich and abundant living where tournaments, races, and riding after the hounds, enliven the days of toil. It is a land of fun and recreation as well as of industry and application to business. It is a land of superior transportation facilities, of capacious homes, of flourishing agriculture, and alluring landscape. It is a land of content and charm, as well as of vision and achievement. Men and women who dwell there, or who have been born and nurtured there, have made deep impress upon the institutions and history of America. The Manor Counties of Maryland grace America's rural life.[15]

The Virginia Piedmont closely resembles the Manor Country of Maryland. Monticello, the plantation home of Thomas Jefferson, is a classic example of the "gracious living" practiced by the landed aristocracy in the "land of the FFV's." In recent years, many of these old plantations have been purchased by urban dwellers from Washington, Baltimore, Philadelphia, New York, and other large metropolitan centers. Low property taxes have in part attracted these large investments, and as a result many old plantations have been modernized and revived. Today, as one drives through the Piedmont, between long rows of white fences one wonders how land that is not particularly fertile can support such magnificent and costly estates. The answer is, in most cases, that the estate is being supported by money

---

[14] Henry J. Warman, "Population of the Manor Counties of Maryland," *Economic Geography,* Vol. 25, 1949, pp. 34-35.

[15] Editorial in *Economic Geography,* Vol. 25, No. 1, 1949

supplied from the industry and commerce of the cities and not from farming. In Virginia a common statement is that "farms" have ordinary fences and "estates" have white painted fences. The result, however, is a very pleasing landscape such as could be found only in a land with great natural beauty, upon which outside wealth has been spent in a lavish manner.

The Piedmont of the Carolinas and Georgia was either developed under the cotton culture of the antebellum South or was left largely in the backwoods. With the collapse of Southern economy following the Civil War, little new money flowed into the area and the old estates were abandoned. Modern development has come largely in the form of manufacturing industries.

Mineral Resources

The Piedmont ranks low in minerals, though it does have several building stones of economic value. The first coal to be mined in the United States was dug near Richmond, Virginia, and, until the Gold Rush to California in 1849, Georgia was the country's leading source of gold. But no part of the Piedmont is important today for metallic minerals.

Most of the rocks are crystalline and are among the oldest in the world — granites, gneisses, schists, marbles, and slates. Granites of high quality are quarried widely throughout the region and are used in a number of Eastern cities as building and monumental stones, curbing and paving blocks. Broken-up granite is used as an ingredient of concrete, as railroad ballast, and as artificial sand. In the hilly Piedmont of northern Georgia is a narrow belt some 60 miles long and a few miles wide, where one of North America's more important marble-working areas is to be found. Pure-white and pink marbles of high quality are quarried. Asbestos, chromite, copper, corundum, feldspar, gold, mica, serpentine, and talc are also produced.

Limestone, quarried in Pennsylvania, Maryland, and Virginia, is used for cement, burnt lime, building stones, and as a flux in the iron industry.

Water Power

Water power is one of the leading resources of the Piedmont. The natural factors responsible for it are:

1. A heavy rainfall well distributed throughout the year.
2. Land mostly in slopes.
3. Forested watersheds.
4. Room for dam sites and storage reservoirs.

The Piedmont possesses more than 20 per cent of the developed hydroelectric power of the country, though it has within its boundaries only 7.6 per cent of the potential supply.

The principal part of the Piedmont's water-power development includes the Catawba-Wateree, the Yadkin-Pedee, the Broad, the Saluda, and the Tallulah-Tugaloo rivers. The Catawba, a remarkable stream, drops 1,058 feet in a distance of only 300 miles. One of the most interesting features of the hydro development in this stream is the use of dams and pools. So well planned is it that at many places the tailrace of one pond flows into the head of the next. Unfortunately, careless farming methods have resulted in silting up many of the reservoirs, thereby reducing the amount of water power available.

Manufacturing on the Coastal Plain

Away from the Fall Line Belt, the Coastal Plain has had merely "crossroads," "stores," and "courthouses." Even today a county seat may consist of little more than a courthouse. The coast has few harbors capable of accommodating large ships and hence has not developed an industrial and commercial population.

Canning. The Atlantic Coastal Plain is the greatest vegetable-canning area in the world, and Baltimore is one of the few large American cities ranking high in that industry.

Canning does not depend on the surplus produce of the area — that which would otherwise spoil because of glutted markets. In Maryland 90 per cent of the tomatoes, sweet corn, and peas are sold to some 400 canneries. More than 90 per cent of the requirements of the canneries is grown and sold on a contract basis. In spring a contract is made whereby the farmer agrees to grow a specified number of acres of crops for a definite price. He guarantees that he will deliver only his own produce and that this will be all he raises except for his own consumption. The best canneries watch their farmers closely, keeping inspectors constantly on the job, estimating yields and advising on scientific production. The farmer normally contracts with a cannery located nearby, to simplify the problem of transportation. Growers who produce without a contract must sell wherever they can and for whatever price they can get.

The tendency in the past was toward regional specialization in the growing of crops for canning. Only the market gardens, which lie close to great cities, grew a large variety of vegetables. Recently, however, the trend in truck farming has been toward greater variety.

From the growers' standpoint, the canning industry is a form of insurance. In years of glutted markets, they are saved by the canneries. Canning communities are invariably prosperous.

Quick-freezing. In quick-freezing, which has become important in the truck-growing areas of the Coastal Plain, vegetables are reduced to a temperature of about zero degrees Fahrenheit in an hour or less, and they must be kept at a sub-freezing temperature until ready for use. New York (Long Island), New Jersey, and Maryland are among the more important states in this new method of food preservation.[16]

The canning industry has given rise to many subsidiary enterprises, for example; the making of crates, baskets, and boxes. The only other industries of importance are fertilizer-making, shipbuilding, vegetable-oil processing, and cleaning and roasting peanuts.

Manufacture of Fertilizer. The Coastal

---

[16] *Crops in Peace and War, Yearbook of Agriculture,* 1950-1951, pp. 218-219. Washington, D. C.: Government Printing Office, 1951.

Plain, strategically located with respect to large local markets for fertilizer and to ports that import fertilizer ingredients, ranks high in this branch of the chemical industry. In fact that region has been important in the manufacture of commercial fertilizer since the middle of the nineteenth century. Fertilizer materials rank first in the import trade of several cities, such as Norfolk.

Shipbuilding. Newport News has one of the largest and best equipped shipbuilding yards in the world. It has constructed many of the nation's most powerful and formidable battleships as well as an imposing list of merchant vessels.

Heavy Industries. Steel mills, locomotive works, chemical and explosive plants, refineries, and other shipbuilding yards, are found in the Fall Line cities of Baltimore, Wilmington, Philadelphia, Trenton, and New York. These were discussed in the sections on the Metropolitan New York and the Southeastern Pennsylvania Subregions in Chapter 3 (Figure 3–3).

Piedmont Manufacturing

Until the early 1800's, manufacturing on the Piedmont was confined to the Fall Line cities, which benefited from advantageous location at the head of river navigation and from water power. Immigration and industry were not attracted by the Piedmont in the early decades of the nineteenth century at the time northeastern United States was booming industrially. At heart the Piedmont was agrarian, and it had few incentives for manufacturing. In the 1880's Richmond added to its iron works cotton-textile mills, flour mills, and factories making boots and shoes, fertilizer, and tobacco products.

Since then the manufacturing of cigarettes, furniture, paper, cotton textiles, rayon, knit goods, and chemicals has increased, replacing agriculture to a considerable extent.

The Cigarette Industry. Cigarette manufacturing is the most notable industrial enterprise entirely created and owned in the South. It is rooted geographically in propinquity to the raw material — bright tobacco. Manufacturing on a large scale began in the

Figure 5–9. In vast modern warehouses, scattered over the Piedmont of North Carolina and Virginia, are stored millions of pounds of tobacco for aging, before being manufactured into cigarettes. (Courtesy of Cunningham & Walsh, New York.)

period 1890-1900. North Carolina and Virginia together account for most of the cigarettes produced each year, and pay enormous taxes to the Collector of Internal Revenue. The entire industry, confined to the Piedmont between Richmond and Winston-Salem, includes also Durham, Reidsville, and Petersburg.

The Central Piedmont is the logical place for cigarette-making, since, for the past 80 years, thousands of men have studied and solved the intricate problems connected with the production of bright leaf tobacco. There is little likelihood of any drastic relocation of this industry (Figure 5–9).

A unique feature of the cigarette industry is the great disparity between the cost of raw material and the price (including taxes) of the finished product. Even so, the industry pays attractive wages. The answer, of course, is large-scale production by machinery. This industry is practically immune to depression.

The factories invariably occupy the hearts of their cities (Figure 5–10), since they were

[17] S. T. Emory, *Bright Tobacco in the Agriculture, Industry and Foreign Trade of North Carolina*, p. 120. Chicago: University of Chicago Press, 1939.

there first.[17] The highly mechanized processes require little labor.

The Furniture Industry. Although the furniture industry of the Piedmont began with the "Industrial Revolution of the South" in the 1880's, it was not until 1911 that the

Figure 5–10. Large cigarette factories occupy the centers of many Piedmont towns. This is the new Chesterfield factory at Durham, North Carolina. (Courtesy of Cunningham & Walsh, New York.)

first meeting of the Southern Furniture Manufacturers' Association was held. Thus the industry is relatively young.

The major producing area lies on the Piedmont of North Carolina and southern Virginia, with Bassett, Lenoir, and High Point the chief manufacturing centers. Within this area lies more than 75 per cent of the region's manufacturing and at least four of the country's largest furniture factories. Most

Figure 5–11. Interior of a furniture factory in High Point, North Carolina. Most of the work is done by highly skilled hand labor. (Courtesy of North Carolina News Bureau.)

manufacturing, however, is done in small factories (Figure 5–11) scattered throughout the region in cities of less than 25,000 population. Recent growth of this industry is shown by the fact that in the vicinity of Lenoir some 75 new companies have been formed.[18]

Some advantages offered by the region to the furniture industry are: (1) an abundant supply of reasonably priced labor, (2) cheap hydroelectric power, (3) good transportation facilities, and (4) an abundant supply of hardwood timber in the Piedmont and in the adjacent Appalachian Uplands.

Originally the industry supplied only the Southern market which was at first small but which has grown at an amazingly rapid rate in recent years. As early as 1921, however,

[18] *Fortune*, January 1947, p. 111.

Southern furniture was shipped to the North. At first only cheap merchandise was made, but now high quality furniture is manufactured along with the medium priced products.

Today the leading furniture companies own and operate their own forests, practicing efficient reforestation as they cut. They engage in every phase of the industry from logging to the shipping of the finished product.

An interesting adjunct to the industry is the recently organized four-year curriculum in Furniture Manufacturing and Management at North Carolina State College. The course is being sponsored by the various manufacturers through the establishment of the Furniture Foundation, Inc. It is designed to train personnel (technicians and managers) for the rapidly growing industry. The natural advantages of the region such as the supply of hardwood timber and the abundance of cheap labor are no longer as significant as formerly. Hence, the industry now provides technical and managerial resources through this training program.

The Pulp and Paper Industry. The manufacture of pulp and paper has become an important industry throughout the South and a number of mills have developed in or near the Piedmont. One of the earliest to be established was the pulp mill of the Champion Paper and Fiber Company which was built at Canton, North Carolina, in a mountain cove a short distance west of the Piedmont boundary. Originally it secured its pulp logs from the mountain area but now much of its supply comes from the Piedmont of South Carolina and Georgia.

Another type of paper mill recently established in the nearby Appalachian Region, is the Ecusta Paper Mill near Asheville. This mill is devoted entirely to the manufacture of cigarette papers; the raw material, flax, from which the paper is made is produced in the Agricultural Interior Region or along the Southwest Gulf Coast. This industry owes its location to an abundance of pure water from mountain streams, cheap hydroelectricity, and especially to the large nearby markets of the cigarette factories of the Piedmont.

Numerous kraft-paper mills are found throughout the Piedmont, and recently a large newsprint mill was opened at Coosa River, Alabama. This new 32 million dollar plant is the South's second newsprint mill, the first being established in the Cotton Belt at Lufkin, Texas in 1940. The Coosa River mill is now producing 300 tons of newsprint daily, and in addition is equipped to turn out 146 tons of bleached kraft and 74 tons of semibleached kraft.[19]

The Cotton-textile Industry. The South has become the center of the nation's cotton-textile industry and the Piedmont is the heart of it. The principal advantages of the South over the North have been the price differential and the longer working hours of labor. The price differential, however, is fast disappearing and the differential of working hours (of the individual worker) already has disappeared.

Piedmont mill workers are mountain whites and former croppers. Formerly, most of the mills occupied villages on the outskirts of towns, many lying only a short dis-

tance from the fields. However, the mill village is beginning to disappear from the textile scene. Older mills are finding it desirable to sell the houses to their employees on an easy-payment plan, and the newest mills (Figure 5–12) are making no attempt to construct villages for their employees.

Labor unions had little influence upon these workers before the New Deal, but since then unionization has made some progress, wages have been raised, and hours shortened. The labor supply is abundant, and it can subsist at less expense than that employed in Northern mills. The textile worker usually has a garden which supplements his income from the mill, and though he receives smaller wages than the New Englander, his dollars go further.

Nearness to raw cotton is not the chief location factor. Most of the bales used by the North Carolina textile mills are brought in from other states, largely from west of the Mississippi. Thus Piedmont manufacturers, getting their raw cotton from the same sources as the New England mills, have but a slight advantage if the product moves all the way by rail.

---

[19] *The Blue Book of Southern Progress*, p. 64. Baltimore: 1950.

Figure 5–12. A modern textile mill near Lancaster, South Carolina. The newer mills of the Piedmont make no attempt to build villages for employees as was formerly the custom. (Courtesy of South Carolina Research, Planning and Development Board.)

As regards power, the Piedmont is as favored as New England. Moreover, its power is considerably lower in cost. Mills are free to locate anywhere as the result of the transmission of electrical energy over long distance power lines. Atmospheric conditions of the Piedmont originally were less favorable than those of New England, but air conditioning in the new ultra-modern factories has changed this.

The Piedmont is not hampered by tradition or obsolescent power establishments, and its mills are located strategically. Most of them are close to the main line of the Southern Railroad, which has direct outlets to the North, the South, and the Middle West. The Piedmont differs from New England in that its mills are *scattered* and not *concentrated*. The *position* factor is of slight importance in the Southern Piedmont, one choice being about as good as another. It is the *site* factors that count, and they will play an increasingly important role in the choice of industrial locations in the future.

The Synthetic Fiber Industry. The South is the center of the rayon industry — Virginia alone accounting for a large part of the total production. Some of the plants are located on the Piedmont, which shares the following advantages with the Southern Appalachians: (1) a copious supply of soft water, (2) access to an ample supply of local labor capable of being quickly trained, (3) nearness to markets, (4) ready access to an abundant supply of raw materials, (5) sufficient level land for factory sites, and (6) efficient transport facilities and favorable freight rates.

Most of the factories are located in agricultural areas rather than in or near large cities where they would have to compete for labor.

One of the leading producers of synthetic fibers is the Celanese Corporation of America. It operates a number of textile mills in the Appalachian Region and in the Piedmont, including (1) the cellulose acetate yarn and staple-fiber plant at Narrows, Virginia, (2) a mill for the manufacture of warpknit jersey fabrics at Bridgewater, Virginia, (3) a new mill at Rock Hill, South

Carolina for making cellulose acetate yarns, and (4) a viscose process filament yarn mill at Rome, Georgia. These mills, either on the Piedmont, or in the adjacent Valley area of the Appalachian Highlands, serve the large and rapidly growing apparel industries of the Piedmont. The source of their chemicals for the manufacture of the fibers and yarn, however, is the large chemical plant owned by the company at Bishop, on the Texas Gulf Coast near Corpus Christi. These synthetic yarn and fiber plants, together with the cotton-textile mills of the Piedmont provide the basic materials for the wearing apparel industries which include a wide variety of products.

The Wearing Apparel Industries. Factories making women's cotton dresses, men's dress and work shirts, overalls, and novelties of cotton cloth dot the landscape of the Southern Piedmont from Virginia to Georgia. The center of the fabrics industry, however, is around Burlington, North Carolina, where women's underwear fabrics, men's rayon summer suiting, home-furnishing fabrics, and ribbons are produced.[20] In this same area are found the major hosiery-producing mills of the United States. These are scattered throughout the many small towns of the Carolina Piedmont, although the chief concentration is in the vicinity of Burlington and High Point.

Other Industries. The chemical industries of the Piedmont include a wide variety of manufactured products, with plants scattered throughout the region, but an important type is the fertilizer factory which produces plant food for the depleted soils of the Southern Piedmont. Since the chemical industry is more highly developed in the Subtropical Gulf Coast Region, a detailed description of it will be considered in Chapter 8.

At Badin, North Carolina, is located one of the smaller electrometallurgical plants of the Aluminum Company of America for reducing alumina, a powdery compound of aluminum and oxide, to metallic aluminum. Although geared to a capacity of more than

---

[20] *Fortune*, May 1948, p. 32.

100 million pounds of aluminum at the close of World War II, it did not expand with the rapidity of many of the other aluminum plants in the post-war period.

Fisheries

The Atlantic Coastal Plain Subregion leads all others in Anglo-America in the production of shellfish. Most of the world's oysters are removed from the coastal waters between Cape Cod and Cape Hatteras, the outstanding areas being in Chesapeake and Delaware bays, Long Island Sound, and Maurice River Cove (Figure 4–8).

The favorable geographic conditions of the region are its many bays, estuaries, coves, and tidal flats, and its relatively warm and shallow water. Chesapeake Bay is the choice fishing ground; its waters have the ideal salinity, its tides are weak, it is relatively free from mud and shifting sands, and it lacks such pests as screw-borers, black-drums, and starfish. It also is close to the great markets of the industrial East.

The Indians taught the white man to catch oysters with a forked stick. This method was too slow for the white man, however, and he soon used a boat and a pair of tongs. Later came the dredge and suction methods for extracting oysters. The oyster industry boomed from 1870 to 1890, when between 800 and 900 dredges sailed the Chesapeake region, scooping up oysters from the bottom of the bay and stripping the beds. In 1880 the catch in Maryland alone exceeded that of all the rest of the world. As a result of overfishing and pollution, the rich Chesapeake beds were nearly destroyed in two decades.[21] Thereupon oyster farming was begun, and it is hoped that this will insure a continuous supply. The industry's future depends on whether oystermen can change their viewpoint from that of "hunters" to that of "farmers." Thousands of acres of useless bottom have been transformed into valuable food-producing areas. The oyster is readily cultivated.

Under favorable conditions the shell re-

mains ajar. Water passes through the gills, bringing oxygen and food. It is said that an oyster pumps more than 15 gallons of water through its gills daily. A single female may produce millions of eggs at one spawning and several hundred million in a summer. The development of the oyster from the egg to the setting stage requires 13 to 16 days. The eggs, after being laid, float through the water and hatch in the drifting current. The ideal temperature for spawning and propagation is 68°F. or above. For a short time the young oyster is a free swimmer. After about two weeks it cements itself to some clean, hard, submerged object — an old tin can, bottle, automobile tire, tree, loose rock, or oyster shell and begins to develop its own shell.

The blue crab is also very important in the Chesapeake Bay Area. Shad, sea trout, flounder, butterfish, alewives (river herring), and menhaden all are important commercially in the region. In the spring millions of fish ascend the streams to spawn. Menhaden, despite its importance, is one of the least-known fish of American waters. It is used primarily as a source of oil and meal for the livestock and poultry industries, and it also plays an important role in the commercial fertilizer industry. The menhaden catch from the entire area amounts to about 250 million pounds, or 68 per cent of the catch of all species of fish and 43 per cent of all fish and shell fish combined. Beaufort, North Carolina, is one of the chief menhaden fishing centers.[22]

Recreation

The coast, one of the leading summer playgrounds for the great industrial East, is dotted with scores of beach resorts including, among the better-known, Asbury Park, Atlantic City, Rehoboth Beach, Ocean City, Virginia Beach, and the numerous beaches of North Carolina. The warm water and white sand make bathing far more pleasant here than in New England.

[21] "The Oyster," *Fortune*, Vol. 2, December 1930, p. 72.

[22] Rachel L. Carson, *Fish and Shellfish of the South Atlantic and Gulf Coast*, p. 31. Conservation Bulletin 37, Department of the Interior, Washington, D. C.: Government Printing Office, 1944.

Atlantic City is the most famous. Its site was formerly low-lying, sandy, mosquito-ridden, and uninhabited. With more than 1,000 hotels, many of which are elegant, it can accommodate in excess of 500,000 overnight guests. It is reached by magnificent motor roads and fast railways.

This coast eventually may become almost solidly lined with cities and cottages as workers in manufacturing plants put in shorter hours and have more leisure.

What Atlantic City is to the northern part of the region, Virginia Beach is to the southern. In addition to the incomparable bathing characterizing the entire coast, Virginia Beach is near many of the nation's top-ranking tourist attractions such as colonial Williamsburg, Jamestown, and Yorktown, as well as Kitty Hawk, where aviation history began in 1903, and Roanoke Island the site of the "Lost Colony" of 1585–87.

The Piedmont, with all the charm of its rural landscape, does not offer those inducements to tourists which require the establishment of large resort centers such as those along the coast. The long and colorful history of the area, however, has made it a tourist mecca for millions. Practically all Piedmont states have capitalized upon selling "history" to tourists, but Virginia with its hundreds of permanent historical markers along its highways has done the most complete job. Some areas of particular historical interest are the Gettysburg Battlefield, the battlefields associated with Fredericksburg and the Wilderness Campaign, and those that served in the defense of Richmond, Petersburg, and Appamatox Court House.

Perhaps the greatest tourist attraction in this subregion, however, is Washington, D.C. and its National Capital Parks, which embrace 750 reservations totalling about 42,000 acres of land in and near the District of Columbia.[23] These include The Mall, the Washington Monument, the White House, the Lincoln and Jefferson memorials, the Chesapeake and Ohio Canal Parkway, the Mount Vernon Memorial Highway, and oth-

ers. While figures are not available, the number of tourists visiting the National Capital is enormous, greater, perhaps, than the number visiting any city in the United States with the possible exception of New York.

Transportation

Because of the excellent water transportation and the difficulty and cost of north-south railroad construction in an area deeply cut by large rivers and estuaries, waterways provided the only means of transportation on the Coastal Plain for more than 150 years. Hence most north-south railroads and highways are on the Piedmont west of the Fall Line. Also, in Tidewater Virginia and Maryland, the dominant population living on large estates did not wish its culture disturbed by an influx of outsiders attracted solely by economic motives. These people were by no means certain that the railroads would be financially successful and since they possessed the bulk of the wealth, they did not wish to back a doubtful investment. They were fairly well provided with transportation, considering that each plantation was largely self-sustaining so far as the necessities of life were concerned and that English merchantmen brought other items to their very wharves (Figure 5–2). Much later, railroads were discouraged because of the fear of competition from the hinterland.

In the Eastern Shore country, between Chesapeake and Delaware bays, conditions were substantially the same until the modern demand for rapid transportation caused the building of railroad lines between the truck farming areas and the large urban markets to the north. Fortunately, no large rivers or estuaries offered barriers to railroad and highway construction here as they did in Tidewater Virginia and Maryland. In recent years, the Eastern Shore country (known also as the Del-Mar-Va Peninsula) has developed an excellent system of railroads and highways to speed the movement of truck crops to market.

Compared with the Coastal Plain, the Piedmont in colonial days was retarded economically and socially because its rivers were

---

[23] *National Capital Parks*, p. 3. Department of the Interior, Washington, D. C.: Government Printing Office, 1949.

not navigable. It did not come into its own until the advent of railroads, canals, and hard-surfaced roads.

The railroads which were built (1) to supplement canal and river transportation, (2) to haul agricultural products from the Piedmont to the Northeast in exchange for manufactured goods, (3) to deliver agricultural products to the Middle West in exchange for grain and manufactured goods, (4) to move coal to nearby ports, and (5) to transport cheap commercial fertilizers to the farmers, broke down the barriers of distance and isolation in the Piedmont.

All east-west railroads were located on interstream divides except the Chesapeake & Ohio, which follows the James River and thus has the advantage of easier grades and the disadvantage of less speed and greater distance. From north to south the leading east-west railroads are the Pennsylvania, the Philadelphia & Reading, the Baltimore & Ohio, the Chesapeake & Ohio, the Norfolk & Western, and the Virginian. The last two have their termini at Hampton Roads, the others at Philadelphia and Baltimore. There is no east-west trunk railroad in North Carolina, although the Southern operates trains across the Appalachians via Asheville and the French Broad Valley to Knoxville and beyond.

The important north-south railroads are the Atlantic Coastline, the Seaboard Airline, and the Southern — the last serving nearly every community of importance.

Until the 1880's there was considerable traffic on the canals of the Piedmont. The West was being opened up and prosperity beckoned to those able to tap its resources. New York led the way in 1825 with the Erie Canal; Pennsylvania, Maryland, and Virginia answered the challenge, but theirs was a poor reply.

The canals that were built during this period were:

1. The *Pennsylvania Canal,* opened in 1834, in an attempt to secure some of the trade then using the Erie Canal. Its route consisted of a railroad from Philadelphia to Columbia, a canal from there to Hollidaysburg, another railroad over the abrupt rise of the Allegheny Front to Johnstown, and a canal from there to Pittsburgh.

2. The *Chesapeake & Ohio Canal,* started in 1828 but completed in 1850, was 186 miles long and connected Washington (Georgetown) with Cumberland, Maryland. For decades this canal was an important link between the Ohio Valley and the Atlantic Seaboard. It had locks, aqueducts, and tunnels.

3. The *James River Canal,* the first one built in the United States, extended westward from Richmond, on the Fall Line, to Lynchburg, the route being along the James River. It was further extended to Buchanan in 1851, but never got beyond that point because of the mountain barrier. The canal was abandoned after a damaging flood in 1877.

Although land transportation was expensive, by 1758 there was a continuous road connecting Philadelphia with Pittsburgh. The turnpike, a privately financed toll-road, was introduced about that time to remedy this situation. In 1806, the "National Road" was authorized and provided for by federal funds. It was covered with crushed stone and was completed as far west as Wheeling by 1818. Except in the Northern Piedmont, however, there were very few good roads until after 1925. Today all is changed. Isolation and inaccessibility, with their attendant provincialism, have been broken down by good roads. One of the most spectacular highways of the United States is the *Pennsylvania Turnpike* which was opened in 1940. This highway extends eastward across the Piedmont to the outskirts of Philadelphia, and westward to the Ohio border. It is a four-lane speedway, built largely on an abandoned railroad grade. It has no grade crossings, and being a toll road, can be entered only at specified gates.

The Outlook

Possibly no other region in Anglo-America has an outlook so difficult to forecast. The part of the Coastal Plain being farmed will continue, perhaps for a century or more, to specialize in the commercial production of vegetables and fruits for the large urban markets. Most of the subregion, however, will probably remain in forest, with the area under cultivation actually declining, because sandy soils are not well suited to staple crops and pasturage and because truck crops demand but small acreage.

The tourist business should increase. The New Jersey portion will become more highly industrialized. The Coastal Plain might be suitable for the type of community being strongly recommended by some regional planners — one combining farm work with factory work.

The Piedmont will continue to be important agriculturally. The growing of tobacco and cotton will decline, whereas dairying and its supporting crops should increase. Farming will necessarily become more scientific and intensive. Stock raising, particularly the fattening of beef cattle, should become increasingly important. Soil erosion should be reduced because too many farms have been melting away. Man has been practicing level-land farming on rapidly eroding hills. For centuries he has been growing gully-stimulating crops — corn, tobacco, and cotton. Slope lands plus summer torrential rains, plus clean-tilled crops constitute an ideal triad for erosion. Moreover, land destruction is worse in the Southern Piedmont since turf does not thrive in hot humid areas. In the future, man must cultivate intensively only the level to gently rolling areas, terrace and strip-crop the more sloping fields, and place the remainder in pasture and trees.

Much of the Piedmont, however, is rapidly developing into a major manufacturing region. Especially is this true of that portion between Lynchburg and Atlanta, where factories literally dot the landscape. In fact there are some areas — the Hickory, Greensboro-High Point, Charlotte-Gastonia, Shelby, and many others — where mills seem to run along for twenty miles at a stretch. In this subregion there is a close balance between manufacturing and agriculture.

The future of the cotton-textile industry of the Piedmont seems assured, though as the wage differential between Northern and Southern mills is narrowed, as a result of new federal laws and the growth of unionism in the South, the Piedmont's chief location factor — the price differential in labor — may no longer be important.

Although cigarette manufacturing may not expand, it should not relocate. The furniture industry will become more important now that the forests are being conserved. Forestry systems are evolving whose purpose is to effect proper cutting and to treat trees as a crop. Manufacturing is becoming more varied, as numerous new industries making a variety of products such as synthetic yarns, nylon yarns, plastics, paper and paper products, and chemicals build large plants within the region.

Since few parts of the country have so many attractive small towns where labor, power, and efficient transportation are satisfactory, numerous new industries will be attracted.

Table 2

SELECTED CITIES AND TOWNS OF THE ATLANTIC COASTAL PLAIN AND THE PIEDMONT

City or Town	Urbanized area	Political center	City or Town	Urbanized area	Political center
Alexandria		61,787	Bethlehem		66,340
Allentown		106,756	Bloomfield		49,307
Allentown-Bethlehem	225,962		Camden		124,555
**Athens		28,180	Charlotte	140,930	134,042
Atlanta	507,887	331,314	Charlottesville		25,969
Atlantic City	105,083	61,657	*Chester		66,039
Augusta	87,733	71,508	Clifton		64,511
*Baltimore	1,161,852	949,708	**Columbia	120,808	86,914
*Bayonne		77,203	Danville		35,066
Bellville		32,019	Durham	73,368	71,311

* Also in the American Manufacturing Belt.
** Near the Cotton Belt.

City or Town	Urbanized area	Political center	City or Town	Urbanized area	Political center
Easton		35,632	Norfolk		213,513
*East Orange		79,340	Norfolk-Portsmouth	385,111	
*Elizabeth		112,817	*Passaic		57,702
Fayetteville		34,715	*Paterson		139,336
Greensboro	83,412	74,389	Petersburg		35,054
Greenville		58,161	*Philadelphia	2,922,470	2,071,605
High Point		39,973	Portsmouth		80,039
*Hoboken		50,676	Raleigh	68,743	65,679
*Jersey City		299,017	*Reading	154,931	109,320
Lancaster	76,280	63,774	Richmond	257,995	230,310
Lynchburg		47,727	*Trenton	189,321	128,009
Montclair		43,927	Union City		55,537
*Newark		438,776	Washington	1,287,333	802,178
*New Brunswick		38,811	*Wilmington (Del.)	187,359	110,356
Newport News		42,358	Wilmington (N.C.)		45,043
*New York		7,891,957	Winston-Salem	92,477	87,811
*New York-Northeast-			*York	78,796	59,953
ern New Jersey	12,296,117				

* Also in the American Manufacturing Belt.

Selected Bibliography

Samuel T. Emory, "North Carolina Flatwoods," *Economic Geography,* Vol. 22, 1946, pp. 203-219.

Franklin C. Erickson, "Tobacco Belt of North Carolina," *Economic Geography,* Vol. 21, 1945, pp. 58-61.

L. C. Gottschalk, "Effects of Soil Erosion on Navigation in Upper Chesapeake Bay," *Geographical Review,* Vol. 35, 1945, pp. 219-238.

Parnell W. Picklesimer, "New Bright Tobacco Belt of North Carolina," *Economic Geography,* Vol. 20, 1944, pp. 14-19.

Parnell W. Picklesimer, "Agglomerated Settlements in the New Bright Tobacco Belt," *Economic Geography,* Vol. 22, 1946, pp. 38-45.

K. M. Seitz, "Wheat in the Southeastern States," *Economic Geography,* Vol. 24, 1948, pp. 170-173.

L. Le Mar Stephen, "Peanut Producer in South Eastern United States," *Economic Geography,* Vol. 21, 1945, pp. 183-191.

Henry J. Warman, "Population of the Manor Counties of Maryland," *Economic Geography,* Vol. 25, 1949, pp. 23-40.

6.

The Appalachians
and the Ozarks

THE Appalachian Highlands and the Ozark-Ouachita Uplands are two disconnected segments of a single region, separated by the broad expanse of the Mississippi Valley (Figure 6–1). This region has three outstanding characteristics: (1) it is dominantly hilly or mountainous, (2) it is everywhere surrounded by broad, flat lowlands, and (3) it presents a great variety of adaptations by man from densely settled lowlands of modern, progressive agricultural, and industrial communities, to sparsely settled, isolated, and backward mountain communities, which only recently have begun to feel the impact of modern civilization.

The Appalachian Highlands extend from central New York State, south of the Mohawk Valley, to central Alabama, where they terminate on the Gulf Coastal Plain. The general trend of the mountains and their intervening valleys is northeast-southwest.

Geographically the eastern boundary of this subregion is the contact between the low, rolling Piedmont and the Blue Ridge–Great Smoky Mountains. The western boundary is the western edge of the Appalachian Plateau where the upland gives way to the Central Lowlands. The subregion (Figure 6–2) is divided into (1) an eastern mountain province – the Blue Ridge–Great Smoky Mountains, (2) the Ridge and Valley country, and (3) the Appalachian Plateau, which is further separated into a northern part called the Allegheny Plateau and a southern part known as the Cumberland Plateau. The Allegheny also contains a glaciated portion in New York, Pennsylvania, and northeastern Ohio, and an unglaciated area in southwestern Pennsylvania, southern Ohio, West Virginia, and eastern Kentucky.

The Ozark-Ouachita Highlands represent in many respects a smaller replica of the Appalachian Area. They are completely surrounded by lowland plains and are also subdivided into (1) the Ouachita Mountains, (2) the Arkansas Valley, and (3) the more extensive Ozark Plateau (Figure 6–2). The total area of this subregion is more than 50,000 square miles, and like the larger Appalachian Highlands, it represents densely settled lowlands with modern agricultural and industrial culture and sparsely settled mountain areas where the older culture of the mountain folk is still dominant.

Although the two parts of this region are separated by extensive lands which do not

Figure 6–1. The Appalachians and the Ozarks. A region of mining, farming, hydroelectric power development, manufacturing, and resorts. The two parts of the region — the Appalachian Highlands and the Ozark-Ouachita Uplands — are separated by the Mississippi Valley. The subregions are shown in Figure 6–2.

belong within the regional boundaries, it seems desirable to consider them as forming one region because of their remarkable similarity both in physical appearance and in agricultural responses.

This is one of the most highly diversified regions in Anglo-America — topographically, climatically, and economically. Nevertheless, a thread of internal unity holds the several parts together, making them one major geographical region. The most densely settled areas, those with more than 100 persons to the square mile, are the valleys while the sparsely settled areas, with less than ten inhabitants per square mile, are those of broken relief. The opportunities available to the inhabitants are closely associated with the distribution and utilization of natural resources. Considerable discrimination is shown in the

selection of places for settlement, especially regarding the suitability of the land for crops. Since most of the population consists of farmers and miners, the inhabitants of the Appalachian Uplands are everywhere conscious of their dependence upon nature.

The Natural Environment [1]

The Blue Ridge — Great Smoky Mountains. The Blue Ridge consists largely of crystalline rocks of igneous and metamorphic origin — granites, gneisses, schists, diorites, and slates. Extending from Pennsylvania to Georgia (Fig. 6–2) the Blue Ridge exceeds all other mountains in the East in altitude:

[1] Based largely on Nevin M. Fenneman, *Physiography of Eastern United States*, pp. 163-342, 631-689. New York: McGraw-Hill Book Co., 1938.

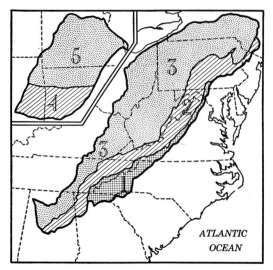

ATLANTIC
OCEAN

Figure 6–2. The subdivisions of the Appalachian-Ozark Region. (1) The Blue Ridge — Great Smoky Mountains. (2) The Ridge and Valley Area. (3) The Appalachian Plateau. (4) The Ouachita Mountains. (5) The Ozark Plateau.

north of Roanoke it consists of a narrow ridge cut by numerous gaps; south of Roanoke it spreads out to form the Great Smoky Mountains a tangled mass of mountains and valleys, more than 100 miles wide. The mountains are steep, rocky, and forest-covered. The highest peak in eastern United States is Mount Mitchell in North Carolina (6,684 feet).

Some of the gaps through the Blue Ridge enable railroads to penetrate the barrier; outstanding is the one at Harper's Ferry, through which the Baltimore & Ohio passes.

Because of heavy rainfall, the Blue Ridge was clothed with magnificent forests, the original covering consisting of hardwood trees, especially oak, chestnut, and hickory. In luxuriance only the *selva* of the Rainy Tropics surpassed it. The greater part of the original forest was logged years ago, much of it being converted into charcoal for iron furnaces in the nineteenth century. Much of the area has been cut repeatedly and a great deal has been badly burned.

The Ridge and Valley. This subregion consists of the Great Valley, which is made up of several broad longitudinal valleys such as the Shenandoah Valley and the Valley of Eastern Tennessee, and the Ridge and Valley Section, which is a complex folded area of parallel ridges and valleys, well developed in Pennsylvania and southwestern Virginia (Figure 6–3).

The Great Valley, a nature-chiseled groove that trends northeast-southwest from the Hudson Valley of New York to central Alabama is one of the world's longest mountain valleys (Figure 6–2). In no sense a rugged area, it is broad and relatively flat-bottomed. The divides between its several streams are rolling.

The Great Valley has numerous segments. Near the Delaware, it is called the Lehigh Valley; north of the Susquehanna, the Lebanon Valley; south of the Susquehanna, the Cumberland Valley; in northern Virginia, the Shenandoah; in Virginia as a whole, the Valley of Virginia; and in Tennessee, the Valley of East Tennessee.

It has long been the great north-south highway in the Appalachian barrier as well as one of the most productive agricultural areas in the East. For the most part it has never been of outstanding industrial importance, though several of its cities, particularly

APPALACHIAN PLATEAU   VALLEY RIDGES   BLUE RIDGE

GREAT VALLEY

HORIZONTAL SEDIMENTARY ROCKS   FOLDED SEDIMENTARY ROCKS

Figure 6–3. Cross section of the

in Pennsylvania and Tennessee, have important manufacturing establishments.

The eastern and western confines of the Great Valley are definite: the knobby wooded crest of the Blue Ridge towers above the valley floor on the east; the wild, rugged, though less imposing Appalachian ridges bound it on the west.

Gray-brown podzolic soils prevail over all but the southern part where red and yellow soils rule. The most productive are the transported soils of the larger flood plains and those derived from limestone. Having developed largely under a forest cover, they contain little humus and are acid in reaction. Some leaching has occurred.

The Ridge and Valley Section of this subregion (Figure 6–2) consists of a belt of land between the Great Valley on the east and the Appalachian Plateaus on the west. It is characterized by a series of roughly parallel ridges and valleys, variable in width and in number of component ridges. From an airplane the forested ridges show up as dark parallel bands and the cleared valleys as light ones.

The ridges are not everywhere the same, some are low and narrow, others high and fairly broad. For the most part the valleys are narrow, flat to undulating, and cleared. Gaps appear in all of the ridges. South of Knoxville the Appalachian Ridge and Valley Section merges with the Great Valley.

Since more land is in sandstone, shale, and conglomerate ridges than in limestone and shale valleys, most of the soils are infertile.

Climatically this area gets less rainfall than other parts of the Appalachians — about 40 inches. This difference is due to the sheltering effect of the Blue Ridge on the one side and the Allegheny-Cumberland Escarpment on the other. The seasonal distribution is quite even, though autumn is somewhat drier than spring; about half the precipitation falls during the growing season, the average length of which varies from 176 days in the north to 200 days and longer in the south.

The natural vegetation of the valley lands consisted primarily of oak and hickory with sycamore, elm, and willow near the streams. On the ridges it was similar to that found on the Blue Ridge Mountains to the east. There were also areas of grassland in the broader river valleys — the result of annual burning by the Indians. The greater part of this magnificent forest was destroyed by the pioneers who settled in the area.

The Appalachian Plateaus. The western division of the Appalachian Highlands is a broad belt of land known as the Appalachian Plateaus. It has a bold, high escarpment along its eastern edge, the Allegheny Front, which is so steep that roads and railroads ascend it with extreme difficulty. Most of the layers of rocks comprising the plateaus lie flat one upon the other. This subregion extends from the Catskill Mountains to north-central Alabama, and from the Allegheny Front to the Interior Lowland. The plateau is everywhere dissected, but not identically throughout. Geographically this area is divided into (1) the Allegheny Plateau (glaciated and non-glaciated sections) and (2) the Cumberland Plateau (Fig. 6–2).

The Glaciated Allegheny Plateau. Rugged topography puts its stamp on most of this area which on the north is bounded by the Mohawk Valley and Ontario Plain. The nearly flat-lying sandstones and shales are much dissected by streams that have cut

PIEDMONT

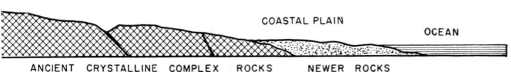

ANCIENT CRYSTALLINE COMPLEX ROCKS   NEWER ROCKS

Appalachian Highlands (after Atwood.)

down and back into the plateau. In the northern part, the Finger Lakes country, six slender north-south trending lakes occupy the valleys of preglacial streams that were modified by ice erosion and blocked by ice deposition. Here is an area of rolling terrain. In northeastern Ohio and adjacent northwestern Pennsylvania, the plateau was modified by the ice, and the relief is gentle with broad divides. Northeastern Pennsylvania consists of a hilly upland with numerous streams, lakes, and swamps.

Gray-brown podzolic soils characterize the entire area. These are mostly derived from sandstone and shale, are acid in reaction, and are not outstanding in fertility. Locally, limestones and calcareous shales occur and their soils are more fertile.

The Unglaciated Allegheny Plateau. Topographically this plateau is more rugged than its glaciated neighbor to the north. Most of this area might properly be regarded as hill country, for the plateau has been maturely dissected. In the Kanawha Valley, the streams are from 1,000 to 1,500 feet below the plateau surface. Some of the valleys are so narrow and canyonlike as to be uninhabited; some have inadequate room even for a railroad or highway.

Gray-brown podzolic soils prevail here, but in the eastern portion, near the Allegheny Mountains, the soils are infertile and stony. All have developed from sandstone and shale, are light in color, are classed as sandy and silt loams, and are deficient in lime and humus. Along the larger streams lie patches of sandy alluvium.

The Cumberland Plateau. This plateau is mostly rugged hill country, which is so maturely dissected that practically none of its former plateau characteristics remain except locally as in parts of Tennessee. It is reached only with great difficulty — from the east by relatively few gaps through the steep Cumberland Front and from the west by tortuous and labyrinthine valleys from the Blue Grass Area and the Nashville Basin. No sharp boundary separates it from the Allegheny Plateau to the north. In fact, the boundary is arbitrary. Thus the Cumberland Plateau is regarded here as beginning in southern Ken-

tucky (the upper reaches of the Kentucky River) and extending to the Gulf Coastal Plain. It includes parts of southeastern Kentucky, eastern Tennessee, and northern Alabama.

The northeastern part of the Cumberland Plateau is less dissected than the Unglaciated Allegheny Plateau to the north. Streams have etched it into an elaborately branching system of steep-sided valleys separated by narrow, winding ridges. There is a dearth of level upland, especially in the northern part, and not a great deal of level lowland except narrow strips along the streams. To the northwest a belt 40 miles wide and 300 miles long, extending from Kentucky to Alabama, is in sharp contrast to the maturely dissected northeastern part. This area, a true tableland, is undulating to rolling, and is crossed and cut into by V-shaped valleys. The southern part of the Cumberland Plateau, which lies entirely in Alabama, is rolling to hilly, with here and there roughly dissected parts. Its physiographic character is like that to the northwest except that the bluffs are lower and hence less effective barriers.

The Ozark-Ouachita Uplands. The Ozark-Ouachita Subregion (Fig. 6–2) is composed of three major subdivisions: (1) the Ozark section, by far the largest, consisting mainly of plateaus, including the Salem and Springfield plateaus, along with two hilly areas, the St. Francois Mountains in Missouri and the Boston Mountains in Arkansas; (2) the Arkansas River Valley, a broad structural trough corresponding to the Ridge and Valley Section of the Appalachians; (3) the Ouachita Mountains, a lens-shaped, compressed ,and faulted upland. The Ouachita Mountains reach their highest elevation — about 2,800 feet above sea level, near the Arkansas-Oklahoma border.

Settlement of the Appalachian Highlands

Most of the people who live in the Blue Ridge and Great Smoky Mountains are of old colonial stock. Their ancestors were crowded out of the tidewater by slave labor and plantation management. The pressure of population in the Great Smoky Mountains is so great that every arable spot is now pre-empted, and in many areas the once productive soil has become depleted by overcropping or hopelessly ruined by sheet erosion and gullying. Much of that being cultivated should be in forest.

In the maturely dissected area the people are very poor. Their houses are crude, bathrooms are practically absent, and, in most instances, water is carried from nearby springs. The standard of living is low and inbreeding common. Yet there is something to be said in favor of their way of life.

They do not make elaborate preparations to enjoy life but begin at once, and if their scheme of things is simple, it is no less satisfying. Mountain man will hardly slave through a sunny spring day when he longs to enjoy the weather in order that he may take a vacation in the same sunshine somewhere else later on. His affairs are not so pressing. As soon as he thinks of it, he will probably pick up a chair, tilt it back against the sunny side of the house, tip his hat down over his eyes, and start in on the business of enjoying the day.[2]

Since the small mountain farms of the Blue Ridge cannot be subdivided indefinitely, children from the large families find it necessary to migrate to the lowlands. Sometimes the entire family moves onto the Piedmont to work in textile mills.

The Ridge and Valley Area was settled largely by English, Scotch-Irish, and Germans. Because of their craving for independence, the Scotch-Irish particularly made admirable frontiersmen. The Germans chose the rich limestone soils, the Scotch-Irish the slaty hills. Hostile to the Virginian and North Carolinian way of life, the Germans and Scotch-Irish made the Valley one of relatively small holdings, diversified farming, and free labor. Slavery never was so important here as in the valley areas to the east and south.

The Allegheny Plateau was settled in the latter part of the 18th century and the early part of the 19th century by colonists from eastern Pennsylvania or from overseas. At first, settlement was confined to the fertile valleys although some pioneers chose upland localities in order to utilize grazing and forest lands. The uplands contained salt licks, fish, and game and therefore provided an almost ideal habitat for a self-contained culture. Although coal was discovered in the Allegheny Plateau as early as 1750, it seemed to have had little effect on localizing the original settlements.[3] Unlike the Cumberland Plateau, the Allegheny served as a route for land-traffic flowing through the deeply entrenched river valleys to the more fertile lands of Ohio. Settlements in the uplands, therefore, did not become dominant and did not develop the type of culture found in the Cumberland. With the industrialization of the valley areas, as around Pittsburgh (Chapter 3), isolation was broken down in this part of the Appalachian Plateau at an early date.

The Cumberland Plateau has been isolated because of the influence of its topography upon the transportation pattern. Most of the main railroad lines avoid it by going north and south of the Appalachian barrier. Roads and truck transportation, however, are doing much to overcome its isolation.

Even before the Revolutionary War, the frontier was moving westward. Some of the pioneers migrated through the gaps in the Appalachians. Large numbers continued on their way, but many dropped like seeds into the coves of the Appalachians.

The first settlers occupied the valleys, where they built cabins and grew crops. Isolation forced upon them a subsistence type of agriculture. They combined farming with stock raising, hunting, and fishing. As their numbers increased they found it necessary to work back into the hills. The forests are now largely gone, most of the game has been destroyed, and the topsoil has been swept from the steep cultivated slopes by torrential rains. As a result, poverty has settled down upon the people, hope has departed, and they have been cast into a mold of helpless inactivity. They see no way

[2] Muriel Earley Sheppard, *Cabins in the Laurel,* pp. 157-158. Chapel Hill: University of North Carolina Press, 1935.

[3] Ralph H. Brown, *Historical Geography of the United States,* p. 184. New York: Harcourt Brace and Company, 1948.

whereby they can, through their own efforts, shake off the forces that have rendered them helpless. The only possibility for improvement lies in government aid through geographic planning.

The hill folk are not inferior. They are of Anglo-Saxon and Celtic stock and as intelligent and resourceful as the people elsewhere in Anglo-America, but nature denied them

Living Conditions. Many of the farm homes are unlivable according to present standards, and many are in a pitiable state of disrepair. Most of them are small, one-storied, log cabins or simple board shacks of one or two rooms (Figure 6–4). Seldom is one painted. The chimney is made of rough stones and mortar. In some parts of the area conditions are changing. Log cabins are

Figure 6–4. A run-down hill-country farm, wasted by the ravages of erosion. On these acres farmers can hardly make a living and pay taxes to support schools and other public services. (Courtesy Tennessee Valley Authority.)

nearly all means of making a livelihood except by farming.

Considering the type of terrain, the Appalachian and Ozark highlands include some of the most densely populated parts of Anglo-America. Many valleys in this area, devoted almost entirely to farming, contain more than 200 persons to the square mile. Frequently such valleys are hemmed in by slopes having no resident population whatsoever. Population pressure here is a grim reality.

being replaced by plain board shacks and by small frame houses. Some of the houses are covered with a false-brick sheathing and the "brown-brick appearing" shack is now somewhat common. Some small houses are also painted white. The cheap electricity of the TVA is reflected also in the presence of the washing machine on the front porch of many rural homes.

Language and Music. Until about 50 years ago the Southern Appalachian highlanders in hundreds of isolated communities had a vocabulary that was colloquial and provincial. It had remained so for 150 years. In some of the more isolated and inaccessible coves, this situation still holds. With improved rural education, however, the youth of the region are giving up their lingual Scottish and English heritage and are using the speech of the lowlanders.

Ballads centuries old have been handed down from generation to generation. The culture represented by them is dying out and soon will be a thing of the past.

Changes Through Improved Transportation. For generations the Southern Appalachians were a sort of land-locked island, isolated from the rest of the country. For the most part the rivers were too swift to be used for transportation, and the rugged terrain caused railroads and highways to avoid it. Even today most of the railways are branch lines built solely to exploit the coal and timber resources. Until lately, highways were dirt roads and some, mere trails hewn from the forest. Recently the Tennessee Valley Authority and other federal and state agencies have built highways in an effort to break down isolation and make this unique region available to people throughout the nation.

In Kentucky, which probably had the most "back-woodsy" areas in the plateau, were many counties where pioneer culture and primitive living persisted for a long time. The most striking changes came to the area when WPA money was used for building "farm to market" roads, and today change is coming rapidly. Thus with improved highways, better agricultural methods are being introduced by farm agents. Home demonstrations in canning, sewing, and household management, along with "4H" Clubs, are bringing better living conditions. The handicrafts of the hills are now being sold in Asheville, Gatlinburg, Berea, and Spruce Pine, as well as in many large stores in the metropolitan centers of the North. Improved roads are leading to the consolidation of schools. Mail-order catalogues (the "wish-books") are making the people, especially the women, fashion-conscious.

Settlement of the Ozark-Ouachita Uplands

The earliest white settlements in the Ozarks-Ouachita Uplands were those of the French along the northeastern border in Missouri. They were only feeble attempts and were based on the presence of the minerals — lead and salt. Since silver, the one metal they wanted, was lacking, the French did not explore systematically or try to develop the subregion. The first recorded land grant was made in 1723. The French, who never penetrated far into the Upland, were reduced to a minority group by English-speaking colonists toward the close of the eighteenth century. After the purchase of this territory in 1803 by the United States, settlement proceeded rapidly.

The Upland was occupied before settlements were made in the lowland prairies to the northwest, west, and southwest. The area immediately to the west was set aside by the United States government between 1820 and 1837 as the Indian Territory and was not opened to white settlement for many years. The Kansas-Nebraska prairies to the northwest and the Texas prairies to the southwest, however, could have been occupied by these pioneers had they wished to settle there. Several factors attracted them to the Upland: (1) the climate was more humid and the winters less severe than on the adjacent plains; (2) the plateau was timbered, thus providing the pioneer with wood for construction and fuel; (3) the soils were believed to be more fertile; (4) hillside springs were abundant and supplied good potable water; (5) wild game was plentiful; and (6) Indians were less numerous here than on the plains. After the first settlements in the Missouri, Mississippi, and Arkansas river valleys, succeeding pioneers entered the rougher and more remote sections of the Upland and remained there. The hilly forested habitat that provided so amply for the needs of the pioneers later retarded their development by isolating them from the progress of the prairies.

Hunting is no longer dominant. Subsistence farming and the raising of livestock, particularly sheep and low-grade cattle, are the principal occupations in the more rugged areas, supplemented by such household handicrafts as weaving, basketry, pottery, and furniture-making. Before the middle 1920's when the Missouri and Arkansas state highway systems were constructed, the mountaineer of the Ozarks was truly a backwoodsman, largely living out of touch with the outside world. Even today his life is simple and his wants few. His farm consists of a few acres of bottomland in which he grows corn and other food crops, and timbered hillsides which furnish pasturage for cattle, sheep, and hogs. His house, usually in a valley bottom but occasionally on a ridge, is a one- or two-room cabin made of roughly hewn logs or roughly sawed boards.

Soon after the Anglo-Saxon pioneers entered the Upland, other settlers came from Germany. They occupied the northeastern borders of the Upland, particularly in the Missouri section; later they moved down into the valleys and into the cities. The Germans developed a better type of agriculture, partly because of their inherent skills and partly because of the fertility of the valleys in which they settled. Agriculture in these border sections has kept pace with the modern development on the prairies beyond the Upland. The farmsteads of the Springfield Plain resemble those of the Kansas Prairie or the Missouri River Lowlands.

World War I was an important factor in the breakdown of isolation in this subregion. The draft and the appeal for volunteers caused many ridge dwellers to leave the hills to join the armed forces. High wages during the War also enticed them away from their mountain fastnesses. After the War, those who returned brought back new ideas. The depression following 1929 had the opposite effect, for many who went to the cities lost their jobs and returned to the Upland. With the development of various relief agencies under the New Deal, a large part of the plateau population went on relief. World War II, repeated the effect of the first World War — Selective Service and high wages attracting many of the younger persons away from the hills. Most of these persons are still

in the cities and will probably remain there unless economic conditions should cause them to return to the upland farms as in the 1930's. Since much of the land still is in timber, soil erosion has been less serious than in the Southern Appalachians. The pioneer Anglo-Saxon who came into this Upland a century ago succeeded in establishing a home and making a living, and his descendents, too, will no doubt work out their destiny in this environment that they understand and love.

As in the Southern Cumberland Plateau, modern highways and the automobile are influencing the lives of the people more than any other thing; they not only bring in outsiders, especially to the resort areas, but also make it possible for the mountaineer to get into the village or town with comparatively little effort. Some of the products of home industry, particularly pottery and baskets, find their way with ease to crossroad stores or to resorts on through highways, where they are sold to tourists.

Agriculture

Blue Ridge–Great Smoky Mountains. While agriculture is the most important economic activity in the Blue Ridge and the Great Smoky Mountains, the area does not favor commercial farming. Much of the land, both in the north and south, is rugged and stony and should be forever the stronghold of the forest. In the southern Blue Ridge, small patches of arable land called locally "coves" or "hollows" are given over to growing corn, apples, and sorgo (sweet sorghum for syrup). The coves vary in size from those able to support only a single family to those capable of sustaining 40 to 50 families. Commercial apple orchards were started in this area near Afton, Virginia, as early as 1890. Most of the orchards of Virginia, Maryland, and Pennsylvania are confined to the gravelly loams on either side of the Blue Ridge, primarily to guard the trees against spring frosts — the slopes assuring good air and water drainage. Access to both the Great Valley and the Piedmont enables the crop to be delivered without difficulty. In the more isolated sections, large quantities are converted into applejack. Corn, the leading crop, is grown by agile farmers on amazingly steep slopes or in the narrow valley bottoms. Though grown mainly for subsistence, when made into whiskey, the corn becomes a cash "crop." The value of corn in proportion to its bulk is so low that the mountain farmers cannot economically deliver the grain to market, but by converting it into whiskey, only one thirtieth as bulky, they can sell it at a profit. Moonshining, "the hidden industry of the hills," has been important in this region since colonial times.

The Ridge and Valley. Most of the Great Valley is in crops or pasture, and the majority of the people make their living from agriculture. General farming predominates, though dairying is important near cities and towns.

The Shenandoah Valley is Virginia's leading agricultural area and it vies with Pennsylvania's Lancaster County in importance. In this valley, one of the best general farming areas in the entire Appalachian Highlands, the density of the population is considerably lower than in the less fertile and more rugged neighboring subregions. This means that general farming requires more capital and smaller units of labor than subsistence farming.

Crops such as wheat, corn, hay, and apples predominate from Pennsylvania to Alabama. For a century after the Shenandoah was occupied it was a leading wheat-growing section. Wheat was well-suited to the fertile limestone soils, and most farmers made it their chief crop, but as cheap, fertile, and relatively level land was put under the plow in the Middle West, the valley farmers were forced out of competition. Nevertheless, winter wheat still is an important rotation crop, and helps in equalizing the seasonal distribution of labor.

Corn fits into every rotation system. Though grown on both level and rolling terrain, it is more concentrated on alluvial bottom lands where the highest yields are procured.

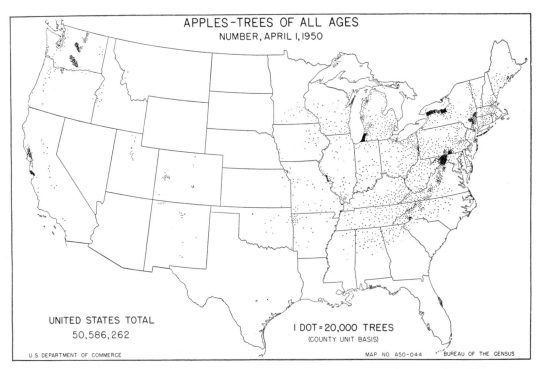

Figure 6–5. The Northern Appalachian Region, particularly the Shenandoah Valley, is one of the most important apple-producing areas of the United States.

Hay provides feed for livestock, supplies fertility by adding humus and nitrogen to the soil, needs little labor as compared with apples and other clean-tilled crops, and provides excellent fall pasturage.

The Shenandoah Valley is one of the country's outstanding apple-growing sections. In it people think and talk in terms of apples. Though apples have long been grown, commercial orcharding has been important only during the past five or six decades. While some failures have occured where air drainage was poor or where soil was not suitable, the soil, climate, topography, and access to market make the area well-suited to this crop. Orchards are found along mountain slopes and foothills, and on level and rolling land (Figure 6-5). The most famous area is "Apple Pie Ridge" which extends through Frederick County, Virginia, to Berkeley County, West Virginia — an almost unbroken series of apple orchards — for a distance of 25 miles. New York City, rather than Hampton Roads, is the exporting port because of faster rail service.

With splendid pastures during six to eight months of the year and with large urban centers not far away, dairying has become an outstanding activity, and is growing rapidly in importance.

Beef cattle are raised in large numbers in the Virginia-Tennessee portion — on lands too steep for crops. Formerly large numbers of beef cattle were exported alive to Europe; now, however, they are shipped to local markets and to Lancaster County and other areas of the Piedmont for winter fattening.

In the minor valleys and ridges of this subregion about one half of the land is in farms, but of this only a small part is actually under the plow. The broken surface insures wooded slopes and abundant pasture land; hence the raising of livestock is important. Settlements are scattered along the valleys and lower slopes. The ridge farms, as well as those in many extremely isolated canoe-shaped valleys, are definitely submarginal and should be replaced by forest.

Often the valleys are so narrow that farmers find it difficult to make room for even a small field. Where limestone valleys occur they are wider and more fertile, a few of many examples being Burkes Garden in Virginia, Greenbrier Valley in West Virginia, and the Central Limestone Valley in Pennsylvania. In Pennsylvania the large, fertile Nittany and Kishacoquillas valleys, floored with limestone, reach in places as high a degree of productivity as Lancaster County. Some of these valleys are miniatures of the Great Valley.

By and large, however, the Ridge and Valley does not constitute an area of big barns and well-kept homes such as characterize the Shenandoah Valley, but rather one of small farms and poor homes and barns. Erosion has been robbing the farmers of their richest topsoil, and scarred fields characterize most holdings.

In an area with rugged terrain, with soils of only fair fertility, with cool, moist conditions favoring luxuriant grass, and with limited transportation, the production of livestock is an outstanding economic activity. Where the land is not too steep for pasture and yet too rugged for growing crops, beef cattle predominate. Over much of this area natural blue grass clothes the slopes as soon as the timber is removed. On slopes too steep for cultivation and the grazing of heavy cattle, sheep are being raised in increasing numbers. Sheep are effective destroyers of weed seeds and demand little labor.

The Appalachian Plateau. General farming prevails over much of the glaciated section but fruit, truck, dairy, livestock, part-time, and self-sufficing farming also are common.

The Finger Lakes District of New York is nationally famous for its fruits, vegetables, and dairy products. A large grape industry is supported here, especially on the slopes of Lake Keuka. The care of the vines is a year-round job, for there are about 680 individual vines on a single acre. A large part of the crop consists of the Concord variety. Along the shores of the lakes are also fine orchards of apples and peaches.

In the northern part of the Finger Lakes District is one of the few truck farming areas in the East comparable with that of the North Atlantic Coastal Plain. It produces two fifths of the cabbage and a large part of the beets, beans, peas, asparagus, and sweet corn of New York State. Many of these are grown for canning factories. Phelps (north of Geneva) is the center of the nation's sauerkraut industry.

In southern New York and adjacent northwestern and northeastern Pennsylvania, as well as in northeastern Ohio, is an outstanding dairy section. Hay, oats, winter wheat, corn, and potatoes are grown. Potatoes and fresh milk are in demand in Cleveland, Buffalo, Rochester, Syracuse, Pittsburgh, New York City, and Philadelphia. This area also is the country's leading buckwheat producer. The crop does well here because it is quick-growing and hence can do well even with a short frost-free season. It matures if sown as late as July.

The farmland of the rest of the Allegheny Plateau is much like that in the glaciated area to the north except that it is more rugged and the soils are less fertile. More than one half of the land is in forest, about one fifth is in pasture, and only one fifth is in crops. Much of the land is too hilly or too infertile for growing any crops. General farming prevails; the chief crops are winter wheat, corn, oats, and hay. Much land is impoverished by long cultivation, the owners failing to realize that inch by inch the topsoil has been slipping away.

Throughout the Unglaciated Subregion, many of the farm buildings are falling into disrepair and taxes are becoming delinquent.

Sheep have their greatest and almost their last stronghold in the East in western Pennsylvania, southeastern Ohio, and northern West Virginia, mostly, though by no means exclusively, in the unglaciated parts of this area. Steep slopes and soils derived largely from sandstone and shale discourage agriculture. Thus the eastern boundary of the Corn Belt halts abruptly upon reaching the Allegheny Plateau. Sheep thrive better on steep slopes than do cattle. Moreover, the climate favors sheep; winters are relatively mild and only a small amount of feed is necessary. Most of the sheep are of the dual-purpose type, suitable either for meat or wool, depending upon market price.

In the northeastern part of the Cumberland Plateau farming is the predominant occupation. In spite of the fact that nearly all the arable land is in use, it is incapable of supporting the large population. Much of the area is submarginal — sterile and very steep. Level land is lacking except along the larger stream courses. Fields, accordingly, extend around the steep hillsides. A cornfield on a 55 per cent slope is not unusual (Figure 6–6). Most of the hillsides are too steep for wheeled implements, and homemade sleds must be used. After several years of this type of farming, the land is eroded beyond repair and must be abandoned. Yet many a barren field continues to be doggedly tilled as the only means of family subsistence.

Poor land is farmed because it is cheap land, and this is the only kind poor people can acquire. Fertile land is so expensive as to be beyond their reach. In southeastern Kentucky the average hill farm has about ten acres in crops, three quarters of which is in corn.

In the northwestern part of the Cumberland Plateau, where the surface is not deeply dissected by rivers and creeks, farming encounters few physical obstacles. Though machinery may be used, the area is poorly developed agriculturally and only about one fourth is in farms. This situation is hard to explain. Some attribute it to shallow, rocky soils, but isolation appears to be the dominant factor. Roads, now penetrating the highland, eventually will make it more accessible.

In the southern section of the Cumberland Plateau, agriculture is more advanced. Warmer weather permits the growing of cotton. Since cotton farms are small, owing to the restricted acreage of cultivated land, the population is dense. Within the past two or three decades, this section together with the adjacent Tennessee River Valley, has become the leading cotton-producing area of Alabama. In 1945 the two areas produced 45 per cent of the cotton of the state.[4] This area (Figure 7–3), although included within the

[4] J. Allen Tower, "Cotton Change in Alabama, 1879-1946." *Economic Geography*, Vol. 26, 1950, p. 10.

Figure 6–6. Suicidal agriculture in the hills of Tennessee. Slopes as steep as these should not be cultivated but should be kept in forests or in permanent pasture. With almost no level land, however, hillsmen are forced to cultivate these steep slopes in their effort to make a living. (Courtesy of the Soil Conservation Service.)

Appalachian-Ozark Region, has the economy of the Cotton Belt, and hence will be considered further in Chapter 7.

The Ozark-Ouachita Uplands. The agriculture of this subregion consists of two distinct types: (1) subsistence farming as practiced by the mountaineers on the upland ridges or in the narrow valley bottoms, and (2) modern commercial farming in the Arkansas Valley and the Springfield Plateau. In the latter peripheral areas, crops are grown for outside markets and sold for cash. Most farms are prosperous and resemble farmsteads in better localities elsewhere. The same contrasts exist here as between those of the Blue Ridge and the Great Valley in the Appalachians.

Because of climatic conditions and nearness to the great cotton-producing lowlands of southeastern Arkansas, the Arkansas Valley could be considered an extension of the Cotton Belt. Although there is some diversity, cotton in normal times constitutes the principal cash crop. Good transportation by railroad and highway facilitates marketing this crop at Little Rock and other Cotton Belt

cities lying along the eastern border of the region.

North of the Boston Mountains the open land resembles the rolling terrain of the Virginia Piedmont more than the hilly areas of the Ozarks. This Springfield Upland or Southwestern Ozark Plateau has developed into an important fruit-producing region, the leading crops being grapes, apples, strawberries, and tomatoes.

In recent years the rolling hill country of northwestern Arkansas and southwestern Missouri has become the fifth ranking grape district of the continent. Production for years was confined to fresh grapes for the city markets in the surrounding territory. Nevertheless, there are many small wineries in this part of the region.

This portion of the Ozarks is one of the few places in the South able to grow a good table apple. Like the grape industry, however, apple production suffers from a lack of large nearby markets.

Strawberries also are important. It is estimated that one seventh of the nation's crop comes from here. Recently strawberries have returned a yearly cash income of more than $600,000 to the highland growers. Parts of southwestern Missouri specialize in shipping early high-quality strawberries to the large Northeastern markets.

Canning of tomatoes for local consumption, began in northwestern Arkansas and adjacent counties of Missouri about forty years ago, but until recently only tomatoes were processed. In the 1930's diversification became important and today there are more than 30 kinds of canned items coming from the area, although green beans, spinach, and tomatoes, in the order named, still dominate the industry.[5] Springdale, Arkansas, is the chief canning center.

The Ozark-Ouachita Uplands have long produced wild game and semi-wild hogs (razorbacks), but until recently few domestic animals were produced for the outside market. In some areas sheep have been raised largely for wool to be sold in urban markets. More recently cattle and poultry have been introduced. Cattle fed on native grasses are shipped as stockers and feeders into the Kansas City area of the Corn Belt, where they are fattened before being slaughtered. Those fattened on corn from the better farms in the valleys go directly to packing plants in Kansas City, East St. Louis, or Chicago. Poultry and dairy cows have taken the place of sheep and cattle in some of the more favored districts and, for the subregion as a whole, rank next to meat animals as a source of farm income. In areas near St. Louis and Springfield, however, dairying has become a major enterprise.

Logging and Lumbering

Although practically all of the Appalachian Highland Area was forested and at some time or other supported logging and lumbering activities, the last great area to fall before the woodsman was in the southern highlands, within the confines of the present Great Smoky Mountains National Park. Hence, it seems desirable to describe the

logging activities in that area as illustrative of that type of activity throughout the Appalachians.

Logging and lumbering came late in the Great Smoky Mountains area because the roughness of the terrain made it too expensive to build roads and logging railroads as long as timber could be secured on the more accessible lowlands. The increase in demand for hardwoods, however, and the depletion of the supply in the Great Lakes area, caused commercial logging to begin in the Great Smokies in the 1890's. At first only the precious cabinet woods (walnut and cherry) or the choicest construction timbers (basswood, yellow poplar, and white pine) were cut. Portable saw mills, some of them cutting up to 100,000 board feet a day, were erected near timbered tracts. By 1905 the finest of the cabinet woods and the soundest of the construction timbers had been culled and throughout the area logging and lumbering began to decline. The establishment of the Great Smoky Mountains National Park and the several national forests in the area have caused logging to be restricted severely in recent years in the Southern Appalachians.[6]

The pulp and paper industry is reviving woodworking in the Southern Appalachians as revealed by the establishment of a large paper mill at Charleston, Tennessee, in the Ridge and Valley Area. This mill will secure its pulpwood from the Great Smokies, from the Cumberland Plateau, and from the woodlots of the farms of the Tennessee Valley. Because of this new development, pulpwood is becoming a leading crop of the valley farms.

The tanning industry has been important in the Pennsylvania section of the Appalachian Highlands since Civil War times, the bark from the hemlock and oak being used to produce tannic acid. In recent years, however, most of the tanning industry has concentrated in Philadelphia, where it secures imported tannic acids from such remote areas as the quebracho forests of Paraguay.

In the Ozark-Ouachita Uplands lumbering

[5] Irene A. Moke, "Canning in Northwestern Arkansas: Springdale, Arkansas," *Economic Geography,* Vol. 28, 1952, p. 153.

[6] Edwin J. Foscue, "Gatlinburg: A Mountain Community," *Economic Geography,* Vol. 21, 1945, p. 197.

never has been important commercially except in a few restricted areas because of the difficult terrain over which logs have to be transported and because of nearness to the important lumber-producing Cotton Belt. Cutting, however, has taken place over most of the forests, the timber being used for railway ties, firewood, and barrel staves. Much of the area still is in forest — mostly second growth. The chief lumber mills are located in the small valleys of the Ouachita Mountains, up which logging roads have been built to secure hardwood trees for flooring mills and furniture factories.

A considerable part of the timbered lands, having been secured by the federal government, are now included in two large national forests.

Mineral Industries of the Appalachians

Copper and Zinc. The output of mines and quarries is important, though less so than that of farms. Numerous small deposits of metallic ores yielding copper, zinc, and small quantities of other metals are worked along the western flanks of the Great Smoky Mountains. In the Copperhill-Ducktown District of southeastern Tennessee are located the mines and the smelter of the Tennessee Copper Company. This area produces blister copper and zinc concentrate.

Iron Ore. Large deposits of both brown ores and red hematite ores underlie portions of the southern part of the Valley in Alabama. These form the basis of the iron and steel industry of Birmingham, and their extraction places Alabama in third place among the iron producing states of the nation.[7]

Cement. Widespread limestone deposits have encouraged industrial development, especially the manufacture of cement. In 1910 the Lehigh Valley produced more than 70 per cent of the total output of the United States, but by 1949 in spite of a much larger local production, this was reduced to 16 per cent of the nation's total. The cement industry is now decentralized, since the market is nationwide and the product of relatively

[7] Norwood B. Melcher and Jachim M. Forbes, "Iron Ore," *Minerals Yearbook, 1949*, p. 615.

low value and great weight. Freight rates accordingly set a definite limit on the distance a given area can serve.

The Lehigh Valley, with about 20 plants, still ranks first in this industry. Since cement-making requires much fuel, its location close to coal is advantageous. Cement-making, however, is not confined to the Lehigh Valley; it characterizes numerous towns and cities throughout the entire extent of the subregion.

Slate and Marble. Additional stone-working enterprises include the quarrying of slate in the Lehigh Valley, which produces almost one half of the total of the United States, based on value; and marble in the Knoxville District of East Tennessee.

Anthracite Coal. In the extreme northern end of the Ridge and Valley country in northeastern Pennsylvania lies the great anthracite coal field of Anglo-America. It is unique in being engaged almost exclusively in mining; it is not a farming area merely interrupted by sporadic evidences of mining. The anthracite region, characterized by narrow valleys, is clogged by large mine buildings, enormous piles of waste, and many railroads. Though only 480 square miles in extent, this area produces almost 100 per cent of the anthracite of the United States. The Northern Field, one of three, is the most important, contributing more than half the tonnage and employing more than half the labor in the entire industry. The mines and mining towns are located in the valleys and are huddled so close together that the whole seems to be a single urban center.

Anthracite is metamorphosed bituminous coal — soft coal that, as a result of geological changes, has lost most of its volatile material. As the earth's crust in eastern Pennsylvania folded, the horizontal coal beds were elevated, distorted, compressed, and fractured to such an extent that the volatile materials were squeezed out.

As a result of folding and faulting as well as of the presence of much earthy material, anthracite is neither so easily nor so cheaply mined as the bituminous coal of western Pennsylvania (Figure 6–7). Accordingly, more labor is required in mining and separat-

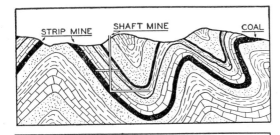

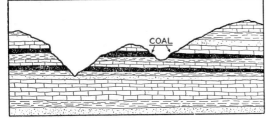

Figure 6–7. Cross section of anthracite and bituminous coal beds. Mining is difficult and costly in the highly folded coal beds (*above*) of the Pennsylvania Anthracite District, while it is much more simple and economical in the horizontal beds (*below*) of the Appalachian Plateau.

ing it from slate. Both strip and underground mining are carried on, but the latter is more important.

The first record of the practical utilization of anthracite was for blacksmithing in 1768. Until the use of Connellsville coke and the establishment of Pittsburgh as the center of iron making, the American metallurgical industry was concentrated in the anthracite region. The area lost this, its chief market, after 1875. Anthracite, because it is smokeless, was long in great demand for domestic heating. It is at present suffering from intense competition, however, with natural gas and petroleum, particularly the former.

The anthracite industry has passed its peak and is definitely declining, but not because of exhaustion of deposits. Despite Pennsylvania's monopoly of this valuable resource, the anthracite district is not prosperous; in fact it is poor and the future is far from bright.

Bituminous Coal. Most of the Appalachian Bituminous Coal Field, greatest in the world, lies in the dissected Allegheny Plateau. Nearly the entire area is underlain by bituminous coal, which is interbedded

with layers of sedimentary rocks. The seams vary in thickness from a few inches to more than ten feet. The bulk of the mining is carried on in beds four feet thick or more.

When the plateau was being formed, there was so little deformation of the strata that neither the coal beds nor the rock between them were disturbed. Over much of the area, streams in cutting toward base level have exposed the seams on the sides of the valleys (Figure 6–7), making possible the low-cost drift type of mining, where the miners tunnel into the out-crop at the side of a hill.

In traveling over the area, one is not always aware of the importance of coal mining, since scores of mines are tucked away in the hills and are thus invisible from the main highways.

The coal for the most part is of high quality. The Pittsburgh bed in western Pennsylvania, eastern Ohio, and West Virginia is the world's largest deposit of high-volatile gas and coking coal. So excellent was much of this fuel that it set the standard for coke-making. The bulk of the high quality coking coal of the continent is here, as well as most of the so-called "smokeless coals."

Seventy-five per cent of the mining is done by machinery. As the coal is cut, it is placed in cars, which are brought to tipples at the mine mouths. Here it is sized and dumped into railway cars or river barges. When the distance to market is not great, trucks may be used. At present an increasing amount of coal is being taken from strip mines. Stripping, however, makes the country a sort of "no man's land" — largely unfit for farming or anything else.

The Unglaciated Allegheny Plateau is the source of most of America's coal (Figure 6–8). Pennsylvania and West Virginia alone contribute about one half of the total bituminous coal output.

Petroleum. Petroleum has long been important in Pennsylvania, Kentucky, and Ohio; in fact the first oil well sunk, the Drake Well, was put down near Titusville in northwestern Pennsylvania in 1859, and that state led all others in the production of crude oil until 1895. Before the Drake Well, petroleum, which had been called "Seneca Oil," was gathered from the surface of springs with blankets. Following the completion of the first well, land values soared; land formerly valued at $5 an acre became worth $50,000 or more. Pennsylvania reached its peak about 1891 when it produced 31,424,000 barrels of petroleum. Though still productive, the area is outstanding more for high-quality lubricants than for the quantity of production. Production of crude petroleum has declined steadily in Pennsylvania from 12.5 million barrels in 1945 to 11.3 million barrels in 1951. The total number of wells drilled in the state in 1951 was 1,738 which was considerably less than the 5,626 drilled in Oklahoma or the 16,655 drilled in Texas during that same year.[8]

Despite that fact that the discovery well for the world was located in the Allegheny Plateau, it is today one of Anglo-America's

[8] Philip C. Ingalls, "Well Completions Climb to New Record High," *The Oil and Gas Journal*, Vol. 50, No. 38, 1952, pp. 208-211.

minor oil-producing areas. For that reason a more detailed discussion of petroleum production will be considered in chapters 7, 8, 11, and 14.

Mineral Industries of the Ozark-Ouachita Uplands

For an upland area, the Ozark-Ouachita Subregion is poor in minerals. The northeastern section, one of the oldest mining areas of the United States, however, is a major producer of lead. It was worked by the French in the early eighteenth century. In the northwestern plateau lies the famous Tri-State (Missouri-Kansas-Oklahoma) Zinc and Lead District, one of the major zinc producers of the country. Aside from these two metals, however, there are few valuable minerals. In the western part of the Ouachita Mountains are some small deposits of anthracite coal that were worked profitably in the past. Some coal is still mined near McAlester,

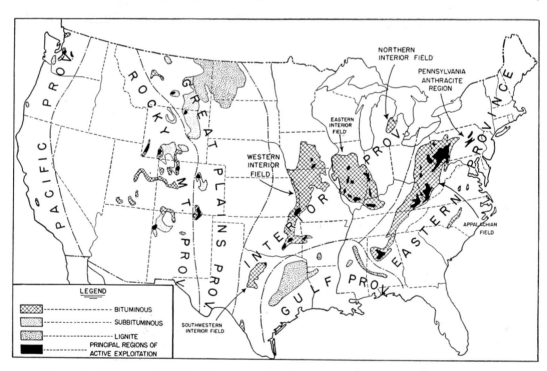

Figure 6–8. Major coal fields of the United States. (From Nels A. Bengston and William Van Royen, *Fundamentals of Economic Geography*, 3rd Ed., p. 356. New York: Prentice-Hall, Inc., 1950.)

Figure 6–9. A combined mine and tailing mill in the Tri-State Zinc-Lead District. Note the great amount of waste material. (Courtesy of the American Zinc Institute.)

Oklahoma. The great production of petroleum and natural gas in the region surrounding the Upland leaves little demand for coal as a fuel. In the southeastern part of the Ouachitas, near Hot Springs, is a small but unique whetstone industry that quarries Arkansas novaculite. Since it must compete with artificial abrasives, this enterprise has declined in importance.

The Lead District of Southeastern Missouri. Lead was discovered here by French explorers in the early part of the eighteenth century. Except for spasmodic interruption during the early years, production has been continuous since 1725. It is the largest single lead-mining area in the United States, supplying 31 per cent of the total domestic output in 1949. Prior to 1869, nearly all the lead was obtained from shallow workings in solution pits and caves, but with the perfection of the diamond drill, ore was procured from greater depths. Since then the output has increased greatly.

The low metallic content of the ore necessitates large-scale operations. When conditions are normal, nearly 29,000 tons of ore are handled each day. In recent years the mines have been consolidated, two companies now producing almost the entire output.

In the vicinity of Flat River, about 60 miles south of St. Louis, are located the major lead-producing mines of the United States, and the third-largest in the world. The properties of the St. Joseph Lead Company are surpassed in production only by the great Sullivan Mine in British Columbia and by mines at Broken Hill, Australia. Practically all workings of this mine are deep under ground; only the few buildings around the mine shaft and the large piles of ore waste (tailings) give any indication of the magnitude of the subterranean activities. Below ground no mine props are used and no timber is visible; the roofs of the vast chambers, ranging up to 200 feet in height, are supported by huge limestone columns.

The Tri-State Zinc-Lead District. Lying along the northwestern edge of the Ozark Plateau, is the Tri-State Zinc-Lead District of southwestern Missouri, southeastern Kansas, and northeastern Oklahoma. Although its presence has been known for a long time, large-scale production has been carried on only during the past half century. The district, mainly a producer of zinc, has yielded from 50 to 80 per cent of the total for the United States and nearly 30 per cent of that for the world. Production is confined to small units of varying size, separated from each other by relatively barren ground. Hence the entire district is pitted with mine shafts (Figure 6–9) and presents an unusually barren appearance. While zinc is the chief

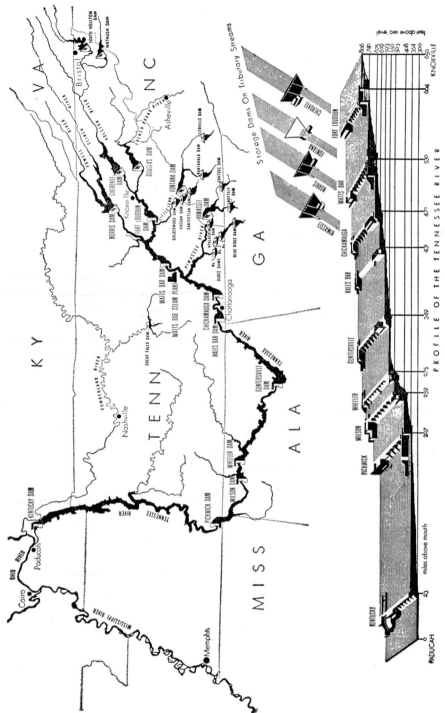

Figure 6–10. The Tennessee Valley Authority. (Courtesy of the Tennessee Valley Authority.)

metal mined, lead, which was worked first, is also produced in sizable quantities. Nearly all the zinc and lead ores are shipped to Joplin for further processing. Zinc production in the Tri-State District has been decreasing steadily in recent years, being lower in 1948 than in any year since 1896, despite the critical shortages of the metal. Future mining will probably concentrate on low-grade ores.

Other Minerals. Small quantities of copper and silver are recovered from working the lead and zinc ores, but the iron-mining district in southeastern Missouri, where production began in 1845, is of only minor importance today.

In southwestern Missouri and south central Arkansas are located the nation's two chief producing areas for barium sulphate (barite). This white, inert mineral is used in sludge for oil wells and it replaces white lead in paints.

In the east-central Missouri Ozarks, is a major producing area for diaspore aluminum, which is used in the manufacture of the high-grade refractory clay products of the St. Louis industrial area.

The Tennessee Valley Authority

The TVA is the greatest experiment in socio-economic planning and development thus far carried out by the federal government.[9] It was created in 1933 to aid in controlling, conserving, and utilizing the water resources of the area. It deals with such diverse problems as flood control, power development and distribution, navigation, fertilizer manufacturing, agriculture, afforestation, soil erosion, land planning, housing, and manufacturing.

The TVA (Figure 6–10) consists of the watershed of the Tennessee River and its tributaries and embraces an area of more than 40,000 square miles. It lies in seven states and contains 2 million people in its watershed and an additional 4 million in adjoining territory. This area was selected

[9] The TVA is not confined to the Valley, but since the most important part lies within it, this seems the most logical place to discuss the project.

because of its relation to navigation, flood control, and power production. Except that it is a drainage basin, the TVA is not a unified region because land utilization, agriculture, manufacturing, transportation, and the economical distribution of hydro-power all cut across the drainage boundary.

Nevertheless the TVA has many of the things necessary for a well-developed economy: hydro-power, coal, petroleum, metals, chemicals, pigments, abrasives, ceramic materials, fertilizer ingredients, lumber, and farm lands.

Power. In potential water power the TVA is one of the richest areas in eastern United States. For example, in the vicinity of Muscle Shoals, prior to the building of Wilson Dam in 1916, the river dropped 134 feet in 37 miles. Generating plants are now located at the foot of each of its dams. The water flows through raceways against the blades of giant turbines, which generate electricity for the transmission lines. Behind the dams are artificial lakes, some more than 70 miles long, for storing water.

So large is the area, so sparse the population, and so unimportant the manufacturing, except in the Knoxville and Chattanooga areas, that a major economic problem faced by the government is the lack of major local markets for power. The great power market — that consuming two thirds of the nation's supply — lies east of the Mississippi River and north of the Ohio. A considerable part of TVA electricity must be marketed, therefore, outside the delimited area. This energy can be transmitted economically a distance of some 250 miles. In the early 1940's a tremendous step-up of power was required by the war industries — aluminum, munitions, chemicals, and others.

The TVA markets power by underselling private corporations, yet it is claimed by some who are disinterested that the government does not know the *exact cost* of this power, since part of the expense is charged to flood control and navigation.

In recent years the TVA has developed a number of steam plants to supplement hydroelectric power. Three of these have been completed at Watts Bar, New Johnsonville, and Kingston, Tennessee. Although these new installations have caused considerable controversy over TVA policies, it seems to point to the fact that the limit of water power development is being approached and that future industries locating in the Tennessee Valley may have to depend upon steam power.

Navigation. The Tennessee River connects southeastern United States with the Mississippi Valley. Existing navigation facilities on which commerce may move now include nine reservoirs and navigation locks to connect them (Figure 6–10). With the completion of the nine-foot navigable channel to Knoxville, a large amount of traffic is moving over the river — the volume in 1949 being fifteen times as great as that in 1933. Commodities being shipped include petroleum products, grain, coal and coke, iron and steel, phosphate fertilizer, forest products, and automobiles. High-grade traffic increased tenfold between 1933 and 1949, as is shown by the fact that Guntersville, on the Tennessee River in northern Alabama, has become a major point for distributing automobiles by barge. During 1949 more than 25,000 automobiles moved through that river terminal to destinations in the southeastern states.[10]

Soil Erosion and Conservation. More than one half of the two million people in the TVA live on farms. Man has cut down the forest and farmed steep slopes as though they were flat land. Hill-country agriculture is bad in many areas since farmers are working steep and eroded acreages and are becoming poorer each year. There has been too much dependence upon the one-crop system; diversification must now be practiced. Another major aim of the TVA is to conserve soil, first as a means of giving the farmers a higher standard of living, second as a means of retarding the filling-in of reservoirs behind dams. Much remains to be done to assure soil conservation and optimum sustained productivity. Changes in land-use

are also needed which will reduce the acreage of row crops and increase the amount of land in legumes, small grains, and pastures.

Flood Control. A major purpose of the TVA is to control floods that formerly destroyed millions of dollars of property, took many lives, and left desolation and poverty in their wake. It is alleviating flood damage not only in the Tennessee Valley but in the Mississippi Valley as well.

The TVA in National Defense. Wilson Dam and the two nitrate plants at Muscle Shoals were built under the National Defense Act of 1916, but the war ended before production was started. Except for some electricity generated and sold to the Alabama Power Company the properties remained virtually idle until 1933. The development of the TVA between 1933 and the outbreak of World War II, made possible a vast expansion in hydroelectric power which was needed by the aluminum industry at Alcoa and by other war industries which were being established in the Appalachian Subregion. By 1941 electric furnaces were ready to produce phosphorus for tracer bullets, incendiaries, and other war uses as well as for fertilizer. By 1943 when aluminum production had reached its peak a new demand for electric power was placed upon the TVA through the location of the famous Oak Ridge atomic fission plants in the Tennessee Valley. Despite this rapid development of hydroelectric power for war purposes, the TVA was able to reconvert to peace-time schedules in about ten months. The power needed to serve the economy of the region today is greater than that of the wartime peak, yet additional hydroelectric power must be secured to meet any emergency.[11]

Power Developments in the Ozark-Ouachita Uplands

The federal government has spent large sums of money in hydroelectric power development along the White, Arkansas, and Ouachita rivers which flow through this subregion. Several large dams have been completed recently in the White River Basin of

[10] *Ten Rivers in America's Future: The Tennessee* (Report of the President's Water Resources Policy Commission), pp. 718–720. Washington, D. C.: Government Printing Office, 1950.

[11] *Ten Rivers in America's Future*, pp. 732–733.

northwestern Arkansas, including the Bull Shoals Dam which was dedicated by the President on July 2, 1952. The total power which might be developed in this upland subregion, however, will not compare with that of the TVA because there is no comparable stream which serves the area in that respect. The Arkansas Valley, which includes large areas to the west of the Ozark-Ouachita uplands, has been made the basis for a regional planning study,[12] but it has not progressed to the place where it could be included among the ten major rivers and river basins of the nation. Navigation, and other facilities which were important in the TVA development would be of minor significance here.

Manufacturing

Manufacturing is less important in the Blue Ridge–Great Smoky Mountains Area than in the neighboring Southern Piedmont. Some textile mills, rayon and paper mills, and furniture factories are situated in those localities where timber, labor, power, and transportation are available. Copper smelting, one of the few industries based upon Blue Ridge mining, is carried on at Ducktown, Tennessee. Handicraft industries, such as weaving, woodworking, and pottery, are typical of mountain areas. Until recently revived in the Southern Appalachians by settlement schools and other philanthropic organizations they were an almost forgotten art. Schools of the type established in Gatlinburg, Tennessee, in 1911, not only revived these native arts and crafts but aided the mountaineers in marketing their products throughout the nation. Gatlinburg, today a famous resort center, provides thousands of tourists who support these handicraft industries. While perhaps the best known of the southern Appalachian handicraft centers, there are numerous others which produce the manufactured products of the mountains.

In the Ridge and Valley province, the dominant industrial development is asso-

[12] Natural Resources Planning Board, *Regional Planning, Part XII-Arkansas Valley.* Washington, D. C.: Government Printing Office, 1943.

ciated with the TVA and its hydroelectric power. The TVA has the following resources for industrial development:

1. Fuel — coal, lignite, petroleum, natural gas.

2. Light metals — bauxite and magnesium.

3. Heavy metals — iron ore, chromium, copper, and manganese.

4. Raw materials for making cement, ceramics, chemicals, and fertilizer.

5. Low-cost hydroelectric power.

6. Improved transportation — water, rail, and highway.

As a result of careful planning, industrial progress is being made. The TVA has a Division of Land Planning and Housing (for making an inventory of the natural resources) and a Division of Social and Economic Studies. These determined the new industries which would be best adapted to the area and precisely where they would be most scientifically located. They can and do give advice. Those in charge believe that the TVA will be a better place for human beings if industry is decentralized and its factories scattered among the small rural communities. Plants, small in size, employ members of farm families, who live on their farms. These families at least have food and shelter should the shops be forced to close down during a depression.

Among the more important industries already established are those making cheap fertilizer, which is badly needed to restore the worn-out soils. Synthetic nitrogen compounds also are being made for explosives. Textile mills are springing up where power, labor, and transportation are favorable.

In the anthracite area of northeastern Pennsylvania, every town of more than 5,000 inhabitants has some manufacturing. Scranton is the dominant center.

In the extreme south, at Birmingham, Alabama, is an important iron and steel industry. This is the only district in the United States that lies astride all three raw materials for iron making; on the east is red hematite ore; on the west good coking coal; in the valley bottom, dolomite and limestone. About one fourth of the mined ore is self-fluxing —

carrying 38 per cent iron oxide and 20 per cent lime. This district is reputed to have the lowest assembly costs in the country, though it uses larger quantities of both iron ore and coal than other districts. Gaps through the ridges give ready access to and from the rest of the country. Though Birmingham is not actually on navigable water, it lies only 18 miles from Birmingport on the Black Warrior River, over which the Federal Barge Line operates. The two are connected by a short railroad, owned by the federal government, which functions (so far as freight rates are concerned) as though the channel of the Black Warrior extended to the Birmingham mills. Despite these many advantages, Birmingham has not rivaled Pittsburgh, the Chicago area, or even Youngstown because it is considerably removed from the major markets for iron and steel. Hence its advantage in assembly cost is partially offset by the expense of marketing when it sells pig iron and steel north of the Ohio River. Birmingham is strategically located, however, for supplying structural steel and oil-field equipment to the rapidly growing industrial South, for shipping to the Pacific Coast, and for engaging in the export business. Moreover, its largest mills are owned by the United States Steel Corporation, which gives it many market advantages.

Manufacturing in the Appalachian Plateau Subregion is highly developed in the northern (Allegheny) section around the great industrial centers of Pittsburgh, Youngstown, Wheeling, Charleston, and Parkersburg, but these industrial developments have been discussed in Chapter 3, *The American Manufacturing Belt* (Figure 3–3, subregions G and H) and will not be considered further here.

In the southern Cumberland Plateau of Kentucky and Tennessee, handicrafts constitute the dominant industry in the same manner as in the Blue Ridge–Great Smoky Mountains Area. Although not so well-developed as around Gatlinburg or Asheville they present a similar picture.

Manufacturing in the Ozark-Ouachita Uplands is confined largely to handicrafts, or food processing such as the canneries and wineries of northwestern Arkansas. In the Tri-State Area the lead and zinc industries are dominant. As more hydroelectric power is developed in this subregion manufacturing will increase in importance but the area will never become outstanding industrially.

Transportation in the Appalachians

The Blue Ridge offered a partial barrier to the westward movement of the pioneer from the Coastal Plain and the Piedmont, but the numerous water gaps through the mountains made it possible for him to cross into the Ridge and Valley Area and beyond at an early date.

A Great Highway. Pioneers westward-bound had to find a way across, through, or around the Appalachian Uplands. The most famous early route was through the Great Valley. Prior to the Revolutionary War it was used by the English Quakers and German colonists from eastern Pennsylvania in their migrations southward. Some pioneers left the Great Valley near Shippensburg, Pennsylvania, and went over the mountains to Pittsburgh. Most of those from Maryland, Virginia, and North Carolina, en route to the Kentucky Blue Grass, followed the Great Valley to the headwaters of the Tennessee to a notch in the Cumberland Mountains, the Cumberland Gap. From here on was the famous Wilderness Road.

During the Civil War the Valley was the roadway by which the Southern Army moved north and the Northern Army marched south. The Confederate Army reached its most northerly point in the Great Valley at Carlisle, a few miles south of Harrisburg. It was following the line of least topographic resistance. The Valley's strategic location with reference to objective points of both armies is well known: Richmond, capital of the Confederacy, was the goal of the Army of the Potomac, while Washington was the goal of the Army of Virginia.

Few areas saw so much fighting or devastation as the Shenandoah Valley. Winchester was taken and retaken 72 times during the conflict.

Interesting indeed is the fact that the present "Valley Pike" (the old Indian Road) was the first macadamized highway in Virginia, having been built between 1830 and 1840. For decades it was the main line of travel for farmers of this and adjacent areas.

Rugged land presents many obstacles to transportation in the Ridge and Valley Area. In the pioneer period travel was by horse and wagon and followed the valleys. The chief barriers to transportation were not broken down until the advent of railroads which came to exploit the coal, iron ore, and lumber. Main lines invariably follow the transverse stream valleys.

The Wilderness Road. Roads, which were the first improved means of transportation, were scarcely better than trails hewn from the forests. Most famous of the early ones was the Wilderness Road blazed by Daniel Boone in 1775. This road led from the Valley and Ridge province through the Cumberland Mountains to the Cumberland Plateau. For about 30 years it served as the main link connecting the new settlements in Kentucky with the Atlantic Seaboard. The rise of the Wilderness Road was attributable to the fact that the easiest and best route, the Mohawk Valley, was blocked by the powerful and hostile Iroquois. That through Pennsylvania to the Ohio led to a stream that was uncharted and hence dangerous. The country south of the Appalachian barrier was controlled by the warlike Cherokees. Because Kentucky was a neutral ground, the first important settlements west of the mountains took place there, and the Wilderness Road, the only feasible route to the west, was followed. From 1775 to 1800, 300,000 people went through the Cumberland Gap and over the Wilderness Road through the long miles of mountainous desolation. The importance of the Road declined when the power of the Indians was broken and better routes could be utilized.

Modern Roads. Today there exists a comprehensive network of all-weather roads. Those in Pennsylvania and Virginia are especially good. Many of the highways follow the prevailing northeast-southwest trend. One of the most notable highways in Anglo-America, the Pennsylvania Turnpike (Figure 6-11), traverses the Appalachians between Harris-

burg and the western boundary of Pennsylvania. It has two wide lanes in each direction separated by a central plot of grass, and has not a single traffic light or cross-road. It follows a route laid out for a railroad in 1881, at a time when a great battle was being fought between the New York Central and the Pennsylvania railroads.

The physical contrast between the northern and southern parts of the Appalachian Plateau had a profound effect upon the

Figure 6-11. The Pennsylvania Turnpike as it winds through the ridges of the Appalachian Mountains. (Courtesy of the Pennsylvania Turnpike Commission.)

building of highways and railroads. The northern (Allegheny) portion, with its through-flowing streams such as the Ohio, provided easy grades for highways and railroads, while the southern (Cumberland) portion, lacking large streams, presented a great barrier to transportation. In addition, the Allegheny Plateau lay between the major port cities—New York, Philadelphia, Baltimore — and the rapidly growing Agricultural Interior south of the Great Lakes, while the Cumberland Plateau was located between Charleston, South Carolina, on the Atlantic Coast, and the Nashville Basin and Lower Mississippi Valley on the west. Traffic from the Mississippi settlements could move easily to the Gulf Coast or go around the southern end of the Appalachian Mountains (Figure 6-1).

Transportation in the Ozark-Ouachita Uplands

While parts of this subregion continue to present a picture of remoteness, isolation is gradually being broken down. Soon after the middle of the nineteenth century railroads, built primarily to tap important lead mines or to connect St. Louis with the rapidly growing prairie lands to the west and southwest, began to penetrate the subregion. The mining roads were usually short and did not reach far into the hills. The through railroads were built around the upland area and for the most part avoided the hill country. The Arkansas Valley, however, provided a good westward route from Memphis between the Ozarks and the Ouachitas (Figure 6–1). In recent years highways have been built into some of the remote areas which were never reached by railroads.

Resorts and Recreation

The Blue Ridge–Great Smoky Area. From north to south the Blue Ridge is becoming famous for its resorts. Hotels, camps, and summer homes are springing up in Pennsylvania's Blue Ridge which is relatively near New York, Philadelphia, Baltimore, and Washington.

In the South the national parks attract large numbers of tourists. Shenandoah National Park, with its beautifully timbered slopes and valleys, attracts about a million visitors annually. The picturesque Skyline Drive is a paved highway extending along the crest of the Blue Ridge between Front Royal and Waynesboro. Farther south it connects with the Blue Ridge Parkway. The southern segment of the Appalachian Trail, which extends from Maine to Georgia, follows the crest of the Blue Ridge. One of the country's leading regional planners, Benton MacKaye, who conceived the Appalachian Trail, has called it "the backbone of a primeval environment, a sort of retreat or refuge from a civilization which was becoming too mechanized."

The establishment of the Great Smoky Mountains National Park in 1926, with its lofty mountains clothed with dense forests of spruce, fir, and hardwoods (Figure 6–12), transformed a relatively remote part of the country into one of the most accessible and most popular resort areas in eastern United States. The completion of a paved highway across the mountains between Gatlinburg and Asheville, diverted many tourists through the area and across Newfound Gap for the first time. Gatlinburg, designated as park headquarters, was the most logical settlement to profit from the tourist trade, and it began immediately the construction of hotels, motels, gift shops, and all other features of a typical resort town. Today it is perhaps the best known tourist center in the Appalachians.[13]

The Ridge and Valley Country. The Valley is a great highway connecting the North and the South. It is rich in limestone wonders such as Natural Bridge and numerous famous caverns, is one of the country's most historic areas, and is productive agriculturally. Possibly nowhere else in Anglo-America are historical episodes presented so clearly and accurately to the traveler.

Figure 6–12. One of the larger resort hotels in Gatlinburg, gateway to the Great Smoky Mountains National Park. (Courtesy of the Greystone Hotel.)

[13] Edwin J. Foscue, "Gatlinburg: A Mountain Community," pp. 200-205.

The Appalachian Plateaus. Until the establishment of the TVA, there were relatively few resorts developed either in the Allegheny or the Cumberland plateaus, because of inaccessibility and the lack of tourist facilities. With the completion of the Norris Dam and similar structures in the TVA area forming large lakes, and with the construction of picnic grounds, shelter houses and over-night accommodations, the tourist is being attracted to the plateau. It is doubtful, however, if this area will be able to compete in the tourist trade with the loftier and more scenic Great Smokies.

The Ozark-Ouachita Uplands. The recreational possibilities of this subregion were recognized by Congress as early as 1832, but the resort industry as it exists today is a recent development. Although Hot Springs and other centers became important locally in the 1890's, the present development had to wait until better railroads and highways were built into the mountains and until the urban centers in surrounding regions attained sufficient size to support a large nearby resort industry. Both of these goals have now been achieved, and the Ozark-Ouachita Uplands today occupy the unique position of being the only hilly or mountainous area within a day's drive of such populous urban centers as Kansas City, St. Louis, Memphis, Little Rock, Monroe, Shreveport, Dallas, Fort Worth, Oklahoma City, and Tulsa. The most remote of these lies less than 300 miles from the center of the subregion.

The climate being only reasonably favorable for resorts, tends to offset the advantages of location and mountain scenery. Winter temperatures are cold and there is considerable snow on the higher slopes, but not enough for winter sports. Summers experience spells of hot, humid weather that are far from desirable in a resort area.

The establishment of the Ouachita and Ozark national forests has greatly improved conditions for the resort industry, because the Forest Service has not only opened up much inaccessible territory through the construction of good secondary roads but has also built recreational facilities in various scenic parts.

The Outlook for the Appalachians and the Ozarks

With the exception of the valley areas and the Glaciated Allegheny Plateau, which have satisfactory environmental conditions for farming or for certain types of manufacturing and whose future promises to be a continuation of the present, the rest of the Uplands is largely a problem region. As thousands of acres were destroyed by soil erosion, much of the land became submarginal and the standard of living of the inhabitants fell. The majority of these people have never known prosperity in any form.

Most of the mineral resources of the Allegheny Plateau — coal, petroleum, and natural gas — are used in the American Manufacturing Belt. While they enrich outsiders, they have done little to ameliorate the living conditions of the hillsmen. Eventually most of the coal-mining settlements will become "ghost towns," since they have nothing to sustain them once the coal is gone. Exhaustion locally is already resulting in abandoned communities hopelessly stranded. Despite enormous reserves, the coal is disappearing at a rapid rate. The peak of production in both petroleum and natural gas has long since been passed.

While the struggles of the people in the Blue Ridge, the Unglaciated Allegheny Plateau, and the Cumberland Plateau have made a brave human story, it is a story that violated all the rules of careful stewardship of land. For the most part the outlook is dark. The region is now definitely overpopulated. The problems facing these people today are beyond their individual wills or efforts and call for careful regional planning. To improve their lot, whether they be miners or farmers, is a big task, and the solution is not easy. This problem is not one to be solved in the next few centuries but one to be handled now, because the saturation point has already been reached over a wide front. The one outstanding example of geographic and social planning is the TVA, where the federal government has undertaken a comprehensive development of the entire watershed of the Tennessee River. It is not yet possible to

The Appalachians and the Ozarks

forecast with assurance the result of this experiment, but it is an attempt to keep an area viable and may ultimately serve as the model for the whole nation.

In spite of modern commercial and industrial developments in some areas, much of the Ozark-Ouachita Uplands will likely remain in a somewhat backward and wild state. Some of its timbered areas are now in national forests.

The mineral industries of southeast Missouri and of the Tri-State District will continue to produce for some years, since the reserve of lead and zinc ores appears large. There is little likelihood, however, of this industry increasing markedly in importance; in fact, zinc mining is on the decline.

Commercial agriculture offers little opportunity for further development. Most of the area is not suited to it and, save for the small "scratch" farms on the ridges, only the most favorable localities in the larger valleys can be utilized for cash crops. The growing of fruits and berries should be increased year by year as better marketing facilities are perfected, but the subregion has no particular advantages to make it an outstanding national producer. The demand for beef cattle and dairy products in nearby cities will increase but it is doubtful if it will become large.

Tourism is the industry whose future seems brightest. This area has natural scenic beauty and is easily accessible to a number of large urban centers. Only in a few places are hotels and recreational facilities up to the standards of other resort centers. However, improvement is being made in this respect.

Table 3

SELECTED CITIES AND TOWNS OF THE APPALACHIANS AND THE OZARKS

City or Town	Urbanized area	Political center	City or Town	Urbanized area	Political center
*Akron	366,765	274,605	*Huntington		86,353
*Altoona	86,614	77,177	*Huntington-Ashland	156,288	
Anniston		31,006	*Ithaca		29,257
Asheville	58,437	53,000	Jamestown		43,354
*Ashland		31,131	Johnson City		27,864
*Binghamton	144,011	80,674	*Johnstown	93,354	63,232
**Birmingham	445,314	326,037	Joplin		38,711
Bristol		32,725	Kingsport		19,571
*Canton	173,917	116,912	Knoxville	148,166	124,769
*Charleston	130,914	73,501	*Massillon		29,594
Chattanooga	167,764	131,041	Oak Ridge		30,229
Clarksburg		32,014	*Parkersburg		29,684
*Corning		17,684	*Pittsburgh	1,532,953	676,806
Cumberland		37,679	Roanoke	106,682	91,921
*East Liverpool		24,217	Rome		29,615
*Elmira		49,716	*Scranton	236,076	125,536
Fayetteville		17,071	Spartanburg		36,795
Florence		23,879	Springfield	75,549	66,731
Fort Smith	56,046	47,942	*Steubenville		35,872
Frederick		18,142	*Syracuse	265,286	220,583
Gadsden		55,725	**Tuscaloosa		46,396
Greenville		58,161	*Wheeling	106,650	58,891
Hagerstown		36,260	*Wilkes-Barre	271,589	76,826
*Harrisburg	169,646	89,544	Williamsport		45,047
Hazelton		35,491	*Youngstown	298,051	168,330
Hot Springs		29,307			

* Also in the American Manufacturing Belt.
** Near the Cotton Belt.

Selected Bibliography

William W. Burchfiel, Jr., "Land of the Smokies," *Journal of Geography*, Vol. 45, 1946, pp. 297-308.

Robert M. Crisler, "Cities of Central Missouri," *Economic Geography*, Vol. 23, 1949, pp. 72-75.

————, "Recreation Regions of Missouri," *Journal of Geography*, Vol. 51, 1952, pp. 30-39.

Leslie M. Davis, "Economic Development of the Great Kanawha Valley," *Economic Geography*, Vol. 22, 1946, pp. 255-267.

Loyal Durand and E. T. Bird, "The Burley Tobacco Region of the Mountain South," *Economic Geography*, Vol. 26, 1950, pp. 274-300.

Edwin J. Foscue, "Gatlinburg: A Mountain Community," *Economic Geography*, Vol. 21, 1945, pp. 192-205.

Leslie Hewes, "Cultural Fault Line in the Cherokee Country," *Economic Geography*, Vol. 19, 1943, pp. 136-142.

————, "The Oklahoma Ozarks as the Land of the Cherokees," *Geographical Review*, Vol. 32, 1942, pp. 269-281.

E. Willard Miller, "Economic Geography of the Bradford Oil Region," *Economic Geography*, Vol. 19, 1943, pp. 177-187.

————, "The Industrial Development of the Allegheny Valley of Western Pennsylvania," *Economic Geography*, Vol. 19, 1943, pp. 388-404.

————, "Penn Township — An Example of Local Governmental Control of Strip Mining in Pennsylvania," *Economic Geography*, Vol. 28, 1952, pp. 256-260.

————, "Strip Mining and Land Utilization in Western Pennsylvania," *Scientific Monthly*, Vol. 69, 1949, pp. 94-103.

Irene A. Moke, "Canning in Northwestern Arkansas; Springdale, Arkansas," *Economic Geography*, Vol. 28, 1952, pp. 151-159.

Raymond E. Murphy and Hugh E. Spittal, "Movements of the Center of Coal Mining in the Appalachian Plateaus," *Geographical Review*, Vol. 35, 1945, pp. 624-633.

John L. Rich, "A Bird's Eye Cross Section of the Central Appalachian Mountains and Plateaus: Washington to Cincinnati," *Geographical Review*, Vol. 29, 1939, pp. 561-586.

7.

The Cotton Belt

For many years the Cotton Belt has been considered to be that part of southeastern United States where, largely because of a suitable climate, cotton has been the principal cash crop and a dominant factor in the lives of the agricultural population. To some extent this is still true, but instead of a virtually continuous belt of cotton from the Carolinas and Georgia to western Texas, several disconnected areas of intensive cotton production stand out (Figure 7–1). Cotton is grown in the intervening areas, but is of secondary importance to other crops. Acreage reduction has obliterated the old Cotton Belt in the sense of a vast continuous cotton-producing region (if it ever existed in that form), but increasing yields and increasing prices have offset acreage decreases to the extent that the gross regional income from cotton is approximately the same as it was 25 years ago.[1]

The regional boundaries of commercial cotton production are largely climatic, though areas of intensive production within these boundaries are primarily responses to superior soils (Figure 7–2). The northern limit coincides roughly with the line of a 200-day growing season — the time between the last killing frost in the spring and the first

killing frost in autumn. Cotton production north of that line is speculative. The western boundary is located where cotton must be irrigated. This boundary is a transitional zone between the cotton and the range areas although, as more drought-resisting varieties have been developed, cotton has been produced farther west. Cotton grown by well-irrigation on the High Plains of west Texas and New Mexico, and in the irrigated valleys of New Mexico, Arizona, and California, is discussed in Chapters 11, 13, and 14.

The southern boundary is drawn approximately on the 10-inch autumn rainfall line. Where more than this amount falls, cotton may be beaten down and discolored and picking seriously hindered. This rainfall boundary, paralleling the coast 75 to 100 miles inland, separates the Cotton Belt from the Subtropical Gulf Coast.

The eastern boundary is indefinite. The boll weevil has rendered much of the South Carolina – Georgia coast unproductive to cotton and much of this land has reverted to wilderness. In recent years, however, small areas here have been returned to production through the growing of truck crops and rice.

The Physical Environment

Except for the Red Prairie of Texas and Oklahoma, the Cotton Belt lies wholly within

[1] Merle Prunty, Jr., "Land Occupance in the Southeast: Landmarks and Forecast," *Geographical Review*, Vol. 42, 1952, p. 443.

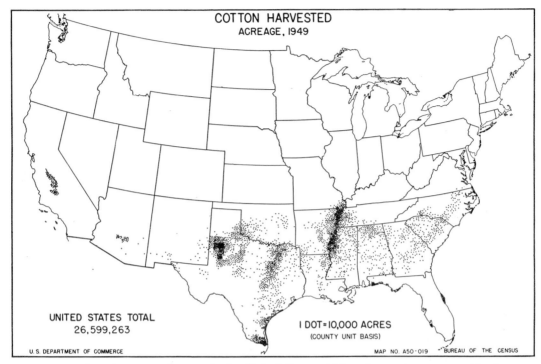

Figure 7–1. Cotton production in the United States. Although certain areas outside the boundary of the Cotton Belt Region produce large quantities of cotton, notably the Lower Rio Grande Valley, the High Plains of Texas, and the Great Valley of California, the older cotton-producing areas are still of prime importance.

the physiographic province known as the At-lantic-Gulf Coastal Plain (Figure A–1).

Most of the Cotton Belt is a broad plain composed largely of sedimentary materials brought down by streams from the Appalachian Mountains or the Ozark-Ouachita Highlands. The rivers cross through low-lying and even swampy areas, particularly in the southern section. Flowing southward and dividing the region almost equally is the Mississippi River.

Climate. The rainfall of the Cotton Belt, largely of the convectional thundershower type, varies from 20 inches on the west to more than 50 on the east. A mild spring with light frequent showers and a moderately moist summer, warm both day and night, is followed by a dry, cool, and prolonged autumn. The growing season ranges from 200 to 260 days.

Soil. Except in northwest Texas and southwest Oklahoma, Cotton Belt soils are pedalfers. By far the largest part of the region is covered by red and yellow soils. Red soils occupy areas of good drainage where the water table lies many feet below the surface, whereas yellow soils lie in flat areas where ground water comes near the surface. These are all forest soils.

The soils of the Black Belt of Alabama-Mississippi and of the Black Prairie of Texas are also pedalfers, but are derived largely from marl or limestone. In the Black Belt of Alabama, however, the prairie soils are no longer black, having lost their dark color through excessive sheet erosion.

The dominant soils along the Mississippi River and its tributaries are of alluvial origin, rich in organic materials, and are usually dark in color, having been derived from materials transported in part from the northern prairies or the Great Plains. Cotton is grown on almost every type of Cotton Belt soil but yields are greatest on the dark colored types.

Natural Vegetation. The Cotton Belt was originally a timbered region characterized by southern pines (longleaf, loblolly, slash) and southern hardwoods (gum, oak, cypress); exceptions were the prairies of Alabama and Texas, which later became two of the most productive cotton districts of the South.

Historical Geography of Cotton Production

When this region was first settled, the colonists thought they were in a tropical country, where it was assumed that white men could do little physical labor. Accordingly, Charleston and Savannah became great slave-importing cities. The first crops raised with the help of slave labor were rice, indigo, sugar cane, tobacco, and some cotton. In 1786, long-fibered Sea Island cotton was introduced and was successfully grown along the coastal lowlands.

In 1793, Eli Whitney invented the cotton gin, which soon revolutionized the cotton industry. Until then cotton had been one of the more expensive vegetable fibers because its separation from the seed was so difficult a task that large scale production was impossible. The textile industry in northwest Europe began to demand increasing quantities. Southern planters (of the Carolinas and Georgia), having had little success with crops previously grown, then saw new opportunities in cotton. More acreage and more slaves were needed, and the plantation system began to expand rapidly in this region.

Westward Movement of Cotton. Westward expansion of cotton growing was blocked temporarily by Indian tribes in western Georgia, Alabama, and eastern Mississippi. At the beginning of the nineteenth century the white settlements that composed the "cotton" South were confined to a relatively narrow strip along the Atlantic Coast

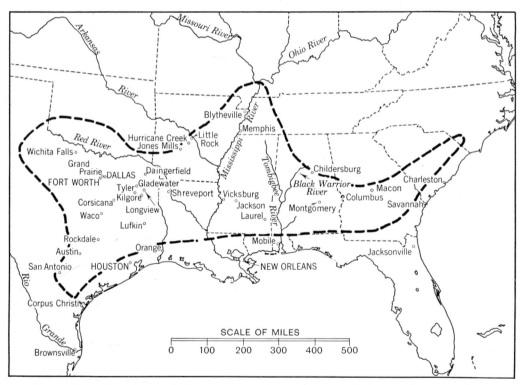

Figure 7–2. The Cotton Belt. A region of cotton, corn, livestock, forest products, minerals, and manufacturing.

and to the Southern Piedmont. Acquisition of Louisiana and the opening of the bottom lands along the Mississippi and its tributaries, however, made large areas available for the establishment of the plantation system. The intervening areas were also thrown open to settlement. It was at this time that the Black Belt of Alabama became the heart of the Old South. With the separation of Texas from Mexico, the establishment of the Republic, and its annexation to the United States in 1845, cotton migration continued westward until it reached the treeless prairies of central Texas, where it halted, owing to (1) the pioneer's distrust of grasslands, (2) the heavy soil that was difficult to till with the iron plow then in use, and (3) the lack of protection from nomadic, warlike Indians. Thus during the first half of the nineteenth century cotton became "king" in the area between the Atlantic Ocean and the Texas prairies.

The Civil War and Its Effects. By the time of the Civil War many southern planters realized that slavery was doomed, that it was no longer economical. Had some practical method been suggested at that time for compensating the owners in part for their heavy investments in slaves, secession might have been averted. However, the strong agitation of the radical abolitionists of the North caused these planters to resolve to hold their slaves, even at a financial loss. At that time most planters had many more laborers than were needed in the fields or as domestic servants. Another cause of the Civil War, incidentally, was the growing protective tariff that increased the cost of all manufactured goods the southern planter had to purchase while it did not favor his commercial crop — cotton.

In 1860 the United States shipped more than four million bales of cotton to Europe as against 779,000 supplied by the rest of the world. By 1864, federal blockade of all Southern ports and decreased production due to the war reduced exports to 241,000 bales (most of these smuggled out), while foreign regions supplied 2,300,000.[2] Thus began foreign competition in the production of cotton. It did not become serious, however,

for nearly fifty years, and immediately upon the resumption of normal trade after the Civil War, the South again became the greatest cotton-producing area in the world.

Two other factors must be considered as consequences of the war: (1) the freeing of slaves, and (2) the abandonment of many plantations in the southeast which resulted in a second westward movement. The southern planter, as soon as he became reconciled to the fact that he no longer owned slaves, set about rebuilding his farm economy. If his land had not become worn out by continuous cotton cultivation, he subdivided the plantation into small plots to be tilled by former slaves who refused to leave even though free. This led to sharecropping, a system still common in many parts of the South. It was a natural outgrowth of the former plantation-slavery system. Throughout much of the Old South it was the only solution. The Negro farmer had no experience in planning for himself nor did he have land and the financial backing necessary for independent farming.

In many cases, however, the old plantation was so completely ruined and the planter's family so broken up that he could only move westward to make a new start. Some planters settled in unoccupied lands of east Texas, some moved to the Black Prairie and with the help of exslaves again planted cotton, while still others went farther west where they engaged in the cattle business on the High Plains.

The Boll Weevil and Its Effects. Another westward shift in cotton production took place in the early twentieth century with the invasion of the boll weevil. Since the weevil thrives under the more humid conditions of the eastern Cotton Belt, many areas were abandoned in favor of the dry lands to the west and northwest. The boll weevil, a native of the plateau of Mexico and Central America, first appeared in the United States in 1892 near Brownsville, Texas. By 1894 it had spread through southern Texas. By extending its range annually from 40 to

---

[2] E. J. Kyle, "Cotton Farmers at the Crossroads," *Cotton Trade Journal, International Edition,* 1938, p. 158.

160 miles, it had reached virtually every part of the Cotton Belt by 1921.

When the boll weevil first appeared, it damaged as much as 50 per cent of the crop, creating panic among cotton planters. Later, this loss was reduced considerably by the use of insecticides and by burning or plowing under, in autumn, cotton stalks which otherwise would be used by the weevils as hibernation shelters.

The pink boll worm, also a native of Mexico, first appeared in Texas in 1920. Its effect on the cotton industry, while not so severe as that of the boll weevil, has brought about the division of infested areas into districts with varying regulations for its control. Cottonseed is treated as it is ginned and both the fiber and seed are shipped under regulation.

The Decline of the South's Supremacy in Cotton Production. When Southern farmers first began growing cotton more than 100 years ago, they had the best natural conditions for the crop and hence became the world's most important producers. Nature favored a prosperous agriculture, but economic factors such as exorbitant interest rates, high ginning costs, and high transportation and marketing costs took a heavy toll.

During the Civil War, Southern cotton growers were cut off from foreign markets, a situation that greatly stimulated foreign production. At the close of World War I, as prices of farm products collapsed, cotton farmers, hoping to offset low prices, increased their plantings. But the financial positions of the United States and Europe were reversed, and Europe, as the debtor, experienced difficulty in purchasing cotton. The years after World War I were marked not only by economic difficulties, but by the ravages of plant diseases and insect pests, particularly the boll weevil.[3] Moreover, the widespread effects of soil erosion were felt throughout the Cotton Belt. During the economic depression of the early 1930's, cotton prices were so low that the financial return

hardly justified the investment. In 1933 government controls limiting acreage planted and controlling prices were established which lasted until after the beginning of World War II.[4] One important effect of this period was the Soil Conservation Service's program to institute better agricultural practices through incentive payments, farmers being subsidized when they adopted recommended practices. The great demand for cotton along with competition from foreign areas, forced farmers to improve methods of production. The United States is still one of the leading cotton-producing countries, but it no longer dominates the world picture. The trend of cotton production is still westward with more than half of the crop now being grown west of the Mississippi River.

Areas of Intensive Cotton Production

Cotton has been grown on practically all the better drained lands of the Cotton Belt, but owing to better soils certain areas have been outstanding (Figure 7–3). Some of these areas now have importance which is merely historical.

Areas of Historic Importance Only. The Sea Island District of Georgia, South Carolina, and northern Florida was the first important cotton-growing area in the United States. Both the coastal islands and the mainland grew the long staple "Fancy Sea Island" variety which commanded a high price because of its superior quality. Because of the boll weevil, very little cotton is grown in the South Atlantic coastal area today; in fact little of anything is grown there.

The Black Belt of Alabama and Mississippi is no longer one of the South's important cotton districts. The dark calcareous soils formerly produced heavy yields, but as a result of soil erosion and depletion, boll weevil ravages, unstable markets, and high cost of production, there are few counties in central Alabama where cotton occupies as much as five per cent of the cultivated land.

With the decline of cotton, the mainspring of Black Belt agriculture, the area suffered a

[3] Merle Prunty, Jr., "Recent Quantitative Changes in the Cotton Regions of the Southeastern States," *Economic Geography*, Vol. 27, 1951, pp. 189-207.

[4] Franklin C. Erickson, "The Broken Cotton Belt," *Economic Geography*, Vol. 24, 1948, pp. 263-268.

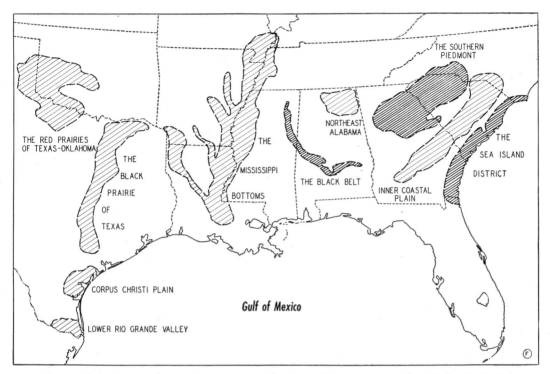

Figure 7–3. Areas of intensive cotton production of importance today (light shaded),
and those of historic significance only (dark shaded).

severe blow. The readjustment problem has not yet been completely solved, but the raising of livestock has become an important activity and in certain areas the growing of truck crops, watermelons, and peanuts has provided a partial solution.[5]

Areas of Present-Day Importance (Figure 7–3). *The Inner Coastal Plain of the Carolinas and Georgia,* an old cotton-producing area, has suffered greatly from soil erosion and the ravages of the boll weevil. Nevertheless, it is still an important producer of cotton, principally because nearness to the textile mills of the Southern Piedmont gives it an advantage in the marketing of the crop. The use of much fertilizer on the old depleted soils has enabled the area to rank high in per-acre yield.[6]

[5] J. Allen Tower, "Cotton Change in Alabama, 1879-1946," *Economic Geography,* Vol. 26, 1950, pp. 6-27.

[6] Merle Prunty, Jr., "Recent Quantitative Changes in the Cotton Regions of the Southeastern States," pp. 198-200.

The Mississippi Bottoms, which include the floodplains of the master stream and its tributaries, form a belt of alluvium in Arkansas, Mississippi, and Louisiana. The better-drained soils, rich in lime and organic matter, are devoted to cotton, the highest yields being obtained in the Yazoo Valley and in the Mississippi River bottom lands of Tennessee, Missouri, and Arkansas. Flat bottom lands, fertile soils, and heavy rainfall permit this area to lead in the production of upland long staple cotton.

The Black Prairie of Texas, an area of heavy cotton production, is about 300 miles in length from north to south, and from 40 to 70 miles wide. It is nearly twice as large as the State of Maryland and throughout is composed of black calcareous soil, well suited to cotton production. Practically the whole area is arable, and the heavy black soils are reputed to be the most fertile of the entire trans-Mississippi region. The climate favors cotton production because of (1) rainfall which varies from 30 to 40 inches, (2) a growing season ranging from 230 days in the north to 260 days in the south, and (3) long, hot summers. Cotton still is an important crop in the Black Prairie but corn, wheat, and livestock are competing for acreage.

The Red Prairie of Texas and Oklahoma owes its importance largely to the ravages of the boll weevil in the more humid sections of the South. Its semi-aridity makes it an unfavorable habitat for this pest.

In the western part are some rough, badly-eroded areas, locally known as "breaks," which are unsuited to cultivation. The brown and red soils are of fair fertility. The annual rainfall of 23 to 30 inches is offset by high summer temperatures, high wind velocities, and low humidity. Production is limited by frequent summer droughts. The cotton plant can stand drought better than many crops because it stops growing during dry periods, resuming growth and putting out new bolls only after a good rain.

Other cotton producing areas border the Cotton Belt. In these districts cotton is important but of secondary significance in the total economy of the adjacent regions (Figure 7–1).

The Southern Piedmont and Northeastern Alabama, important cotton-growing areas because of their proximity to southern textile mills are considered parts of the Atlantic Coastal Plain–Piedmont Region and the Appalachian-Ozark Region. The Corpus Christi

area and the Lower Rio Grande Valley lie in the Humid Subtropical Coast Region. These areas, however, place their major emphasis on subtropical fruits and vegetables. The irrigated cotton of the High Plains of Texas and New Mexico form a relatively new producing area which lies outside the Cotton Belt and within the Great Plains Region.

The Production of Cotton from Seed to Bale

Although mechanization has made inroads in recent years, much of the cotton grown in the Cotton Belt is still produced on farms that follow traditional methods involving much back-breaking labor. Plowing is followed by bedding the land into ridges, usually three or four feet apart, and several days later the cottonseed is dropped into the furrows. In some backward areas planting is still done by home-made planters which are operated by hand.

Cotton begins to come up from four to six days after it has been planted, depending upon the warmth and moisture of the soil. The plants then have to be thinned, generally with hoes. "Cotton chopping" is followed by almost two months of weeding and cultivating. At about the end of June or early July the cotton plant begins to bloom. In three days the flowers fall off and a pea-sized boll is left which will develop within the next forty or fifty days into a mature boll with its cotton fiber and seed. There must be no delay in picking the cotton for the plant is sensitive to sudden changes in the weather and one rain may seriously injure the quality of the fiber and materially lower its market value. Cotton picking is still done mostly by hand (Figure 7–4), however, on the larger farms in the Mississippi Bottoms and in the western areas of the Cotton Belt a large percentage of the cotton is being picked by machine.

After the cotton has been picked it still is not ready for the market until the seeds have been removed at the gin (Figure 7–5). The cotton comes out of the gin in a bale weighing about 500 pounds gross. For every 500 pounds of cotton baled, about 825

Figure 7–4. Although the mechanical picker is becoming more important each year, much of the Cotton Belt is still picked by hand. (Courtesy Waco Chamber of Commerce.)

Figure 7–5. Interior of a cotton gin. In these large machines the fiber is actually sawed away from the seed. The fiber is then blown through large pipes to a bin for bailing, while the seeds drop down into another conduit and are transported to a seed house. (Courtesy of the Murray Company of Texas.)

pounds of seed remain to be processed later in the cottonseed and cottonseed-oil industries. The small farmer usually sells his cotton in a nearby town to a buyer who makes the highest bid.[7]

Plants known as "compresses" reduce the size of the bale and are usually located at interior markets or railroad concentration points. The standard 500 pound square bale (density 12 to 15 pounds per cubic foot) is so bulky as it comes from the gin that only 30 to 35 can be loaded into a box car. In

order to be shipped, they are compressed to a density of 22 to 24 pounds per cubic foot, enabling 65 to 75 bales to be loaded into a box car. Some exporting ports have "high density" compresses that make the bale still smaller, giving it a density of 35 pounds or more per cubic foot.

Mechanization of Cotton Picking

Cotton is one of the few major crops which has not been completely mechanized. Most planting is done by machinery, and weeding, although still a hand process, is being me-

[7] Victor Schoeffelmayer, *White Gold*, pp. 28-47. Evanston: Row Peterson and Co., 1941.

chanized through the use of new herbicides applied by machine. Picking, however, offers several drawbacks to mechanical processes, mainly because cotton, unlike the grains, has a protracted season during which both green bolls and ripe bolls appear on the same stalk. Since much of the crop is grown on small farms cared for by the farmer and his family, the expense of buying and maintaining machinery is often prohibitive. In the last decade, however, mechanization has proceeded at a rapid rate on the larger farms of the region.

Many types of mechanical pickers have been used with varying degrees of success. An early type involved a series of mechanical fingers or whirling nozzles attached to a suction tube which was applied to the individual cotton bolls. Another machine sucked off the open fiber in the manner of a huge vacuum cleaner. Pneumatic pickers, however, failed because of the great amount of power required to operate them, and because of the leaves, trash, and dirt sucked in by the vacuum, and because they had to be applied directly to the individual cotton boll by hand, making them about as slow as hand picking. Some years ago the High Plains of northwest Texas had a large crop of cotton going to waste because pickers could not be secured. Late in the season a farmer experimented with a piece of picket fence which he dragged through his field to snap off the bolls. While his experiment was crude and he gathered a mass of cotton burrs, stalks and dirt along with the cotton, it was the forerunner of the cotton sled that has been used extensively on the High Plains. Many improvements have been made in the machine now called the "stripper-harvester" and two implement manufacturing companies have developed types that are successful. Several agricultural-implement houses have recently developed various spindle-type pickers mounted on tractors and they have been used very successfully (Figure 7–6). These machines pick approximately an acre in an hour and 15 minutes and are almost as careful and efficient as hand picking, taking the lint from 95 per cent of the open bolls but leaving the trash in the field. Furthermore they do not harm growing plants and unopened bolls.

Figure 7–6. This one-row machine picks an average of 95 per cent of the open bolls without damaging the plants and unopened bolls. In the diagram, the mechanism of the picker is shown. (Courtesy of the International Harvester Company.)

The Future of Cotton

Soil Erosion and Depletion. For the past one hundred and fifty years cotton has dominated the agricultural picture as the most important cash crop of the American farmer. In the last quarter of a century, however, certain factors have gradually been forcing changes upon the cotton economy.

With the growing of intertilled crops such as cotton and corn year after year soils have deteriorated here more rapidly than in any other part of the nation. The natural factors — rolling lands, open winters, and heavy rainfall — are conducive to soil erosion; but if fewer intertilled crops were planted, erosion could be reduced.

The South averages more than twice as many thunderstorms as the North. Moreover, in the North, nearly all thunderstorms occur in late spring and summer, while in the South they occur throughout the year. Most Southern stations have received at some time or other more than eight inches of rain in 24 hours; twenty-nine stations have received more than 15 inches; and there are seven which have received more than 20 inches in 24 hours.[8]

These intense rains cause serious damage to the soil. Upon even slightly sloping land, the waters run off in torrents that carry away large quantities of soil. Already much sloping land that was once farmed has been abandoned or rendered unproductive by soil loss. Level land, too, is injured by excessive rainfall, which in sandy areas leaches out the mineral plant food. Thus the South uses more fertilizer than the North. River bottoms are flooded and covered with mud or other sediment. It has been assumed generally that such land is made more fertile, but as a rule the reverse is true because the runoff often carries not only fertile topsoil but also infertile subsoil and even sand and gravel.

The Cotton Belt has become accustomed to the gully and has accepted it as the symbol of erosion, but the process that precedes gullying — sheet erosion — went unnoticed in most places for a long time. At a Soil Conservation station in east Texas, it was found during a four-year period of experimentation that a farm planted continuously in cotton lost 105 times more soil than one planted in grass and 237 times more than one planted in trees.

Thus it may be seen that the torrential

[8] S. S. Visher, "Torrential Rains as a Serious Handicap in the South," *Geographical Review*, Vol. 31, 1941, pp. 644-652.

rainfall and the traditional system of farm economy, with two dominant row crops occupying most of the cultivated land, conspired to accelerate soil erosion and soil depletion in the Cotton Belt. Millions of acres in this region, no longer fit for cultivation, are being changed to pasture and forest.

Conservation. Since 1933 the Soil Conservation Service and various other government agencies have made great progress in introducing better agricultural practices to the South. Many types of measures are used including terracing, contour plowing, strip cropping, and the planting of cover crops to be plowed under for fertilizer. Many crops introduced either for soil conservation purposes, or to provide the farmer with a commercial product, have been found to fit into the cotton economy and their production has continued.

The trend during recent years has been toward more effective land use. Livestock grazing is more important today than at any other time in the history of the Cotton Belt. Much needs to be done to effect a balance between prevailing agricultural practices and better farm management, but considerable progress has been made in regard to soil-erosion control and the use of fertilizers.

The Market. With present world conditions, cotton is in abnormally high demand, but the sharp decline of the export market for American cotton and the development of competition in the domestic market from paper and from synthetic fibers are bringing new problems which may become more acute when world economy is stabilized. In recent years cotton acreage has been curtailed in an attempt to limit production but suitable crop replacements have not yet been found. Consumption of cotton has remained somewhat stationary while the yield per acre has increased.

To meet the loss of the export market and to meet domestic competition, production costs must be reduced and quality of the product improved. While mechanization is proceeding at a rapid rate in some areas, in large sections of the Cotton Belt the cost of equipment to the small farmer is prohibitive. In addition, much of the land is rolling terrain on which heavy machinery operates with difficulty. Further mechanization and the inability of the small farmer to maintain himself if cotton prices should fall materially, will cause a shift of a part of the farm population. To some extent this has already begun, and to date the exodus has affected proportionately more Negroes than Whites.[9]

This would seem to indicate that the Cotton Belt is today in a definite state of flux. If the cost of cotton production can be lowered to meet foreign competition and the increasing domestic use of synthetics, and if some adjustments can be made to offset the shift in population, then the Cotton Belt should be in a more stable economic position than ever before in its history.

Other Crops and Agricultural Products of the Cotton Belt

Corn. The principal system of farming in the Cotton Belt has been based on two crops, cotton and corn, practically every farmer growing both. Since 1938, however, total corn acreage has decreased almost 25 percent;[10] this decrease has been greatest in the western areas where corn has been largely replaced by grain sorghums. During the same period the yield per acre has increased materially and further increase on an even more reduced acreage seems to be the trend for the future. While a large percentage of the corn now produced in the Cotton Belt is grown for commercial use, the South still imports grain and feed and could easily absorb local increases in corn production.

Wheat. In the western part of the Cotton Belt wheat tends to replace corn as the second crop. In Oklahoma and the northern part of the Black Prairie of Texas wheat occupies almost as much land as cotton. In terms of the major crop, much of this border area might be considered as a part of the Great Plains Region growing cotton, rather than as a part of the Cotton Belt growing winter

wheat. The grain elevator shares with the cotton gin the cultural landscape of many Oklahoma and north Texas towns.

Grain Sorghums. In the drier parts of this region in Oklahoma and Texas the grain sorghums — kaffir corn, milo maize, feterita, and hegari — also share acreage with cotton. These drought-resisting crops serve as stock feed in an area that is too dry for corn.

Soybeans. The soybean became significant in the Mississippi Valley during the early 1930's when its introduction was encouraged by the Soil Conservation Service as a legume soil building crop.[11] Yields per acre were low and the soybean was not in any way considered a rival to cotton. Faced with a shortage of labor during World War II cotton farmers, attracted by the adaptability of soybeans to mechanized farming and by their value as a cash crop, began to increase acreage. Continued research to improve the quality and productivity of the bean and to extend its utilization has resulted in such an increase in areal distribution that the Mississippi Valley today is the second largest soybean-producing area in the United States. In certain parts of the valley the supremacy of cotton was threatened and has resulted in a soybean-cotton cultivation adjusted to the prevailing land tenure system.[12] The Mississippi Valley has been, and is primarily a cotton producing area; however, it seems probable that because of the many advantages that this dual cultivation offers, it can be expected to continue.

Other Legumes. Several important legumes grown throughout the Cotton Belt are used for green manure, stock feed and for human consumption. The production of *peanuts*, a legume that is frequently classed a nut because of its flavor, was nearly trebled between the years 1929 and 1948. The increased demand for vegetable oils during World War II brought about the displacement of prevailing crops in the sandy lands

---

[9] Tower, "Cotton Change in Alabama, 1879-1946," pp. 26-27.

[10] Prunty, "Land Occupance in the Southeast: Landmarks and Forecast," pp. 448-449.

[11] Alvin A. Munn, "Production and Utilization of the Soybean in the United States," *Economic Geography*, Vol. 26, 1950, pp. 227-234.

[12] Merle C. Prunty, Jr., "Soybeans in the Lower Mississippi Valley," *Economic Geography*, Vol. 26, 1950, pp. 301-306.

of the Cotton Belt; this was particularly true of cotton districts in Georgia, Alabama, and Florida which today produce more than half the nation's crop of peanuts. Former cotton-growing lands of central Texas form another important producing area. Research into the utilization of peanut hulls, nuts, and oil is continuing and plants are being constructed near all the leading growing centers to process these products. *Cowpeas* are grown largely for stock feed and as a cover crop. The areas of major production lie in the inner coastal plain of South Carolina and Georgia, and in Arkansas, Louisiana, and Texas. *Velvet beans* are grown for green fertilizers and stock feed, in southern Georgia and Alabama.[13]

Sweet Potatoes and Yams. Although these crops are grown principally in the South, they extend as far north as Iowa and New Jersey. They are grown in the South chiefly as a food, but recent experimentations in dehydration have proved that they can be turned into valuable stock feed. The dried vines have about as much feeding value as alfalfa. A sweet potato starch factory was established at Laurel, Mississippi, to provide sizing for textiles and adhesive for stamps. Other uses doubtless will be found for this interesting root crop that grows so prolifically in the Cotton Belt.

Tree Crops. Peaches lead all other fruits in importance. Georgia, "The Peach State," is an important producer, and, with South Carolina and California, accounts for more than one third of the country's total. Another typically southern tree crop is the pecan. Although native pecans are grown throughout the Cotton Belt, large commercial orchards are restricted to east Texas, Louisiana, Arkansas, and Georgia. While these two tree crops have brought a good revenue to many growers, the total amount of land planted to each is limited by market demand.

Truck Crops. Although the Subtropical Gulf Coast produces the major part of the truck crops of the South, a wide variety is grown in the Cotton Belt. The most important crops are tomatoes, onions, and water-melons. The area of greatest tomato production is in northeastern Texas. Onions are grown widely for local use, but in the northern part of the Black Prairie of Texas a large commercial industry has developed. Watermelons are grown intensively in small areas throughout the South with Georgia and Tennessee as the chief producers.[14] Central Texas also ranks high with Parker County, in the west Cross-timber Belt of the area, famous throughout the Southwest for the quality of its melons. One of the major forces involved in the creation and expansion of these specialized truck areas is the influx of the frozen-food and canning industries.

Rice. The leading crop of this region during colonial times was rice. Today most of the nation's rice is grown outside the Cotton Belt in the coastal areas of western Louisiana and southeast Texas as well as in central California. Although ranking far below Louisiana and Texas, an area in southeastern Arkansas within the Cotton Belt is also important. With 345,000 acres under cultivation, it produced 7,975,000 bags of 100 pounds each in 1950.

Roses. Rose growing in East Texas has become a unique and a highly successful agricultural enterprise. With Tyler as its center, the area in a normal season will ship from 15 to 20 million plants all over the country. While the marketing of rose bushes is the principal source of revenue, the sale of cut flowers has potentialities for greater expansion. Freezes sometimes cause great damage but recovery in the past has been rapid.

Livestock. Although cotton farms in the Cotton Belt have always maintained a small number of work animals, milk cows, and chickens, it is only in recent years that the raising of livestock has become important commercially. The Black Belt of Alabama led the way when it was forced to abandon much of its cotton acreage because of boll-weevil infestations and soil erosion. During World War II high prices for beef accentuated the trend in other areas and more recently advances in mechanization have released acreage previously devoted to sus-

---

[13] *Agricultural Statistics, 1951,* p. 322. Washington, D. C.: Government Printing Office, 1951.

[14] *Agricultural Statistics, 1951,* p. 268.

taining work animals. While in some ways the entire South has gone into the cattle business, and no particular section is outstanding, cattle raising seems best developed in the following portions of the Cotton Belt: the Black Belt, the alluvial Mississippi Valley from Baton Rouge northward, and the northern Black Waxy Prairies of Texas.

Poultry. In the past, poultry raising — particularly chickens — has been of importance for home consumption and local market only, however, there are certain areas in the South today where the raising of poultry for commercial consumption dominates farm activities. Two of the areas lie within the Cotton Belt in southeast Texas and in the Guadalupe-San Marcos Valley.

Dairying. Dairying is a new but growing activity in the Cotton Belt. Small dairies for years have supplied the needs of southern cities and in many cases large milk-products plants developed in the cities as urban markets grew. Urban population has increased greatly in the past decade and production of dairy products has also increased but not enough to satisfy the demand. No part of the Cotton Belt is comparable to the dairying areas of Wisconsin or Vermont; however,

with the climatic advantage of mild winters and long frost-free seasons this activity should increase until it adequately meets the demand.

The Processing of Agricultural Commodities

Agricultural by-products, which were once considered of little importance, are today providing industry with a large proportion of its raw materials. Agriculture is dealing more and more directly with the processing plant and the field of chemurgy, now in its primary stages, offers with continued research almost limitless possibilities.

Cotton Fiber. One of the purest forms of cellulose is found in cotton fiber, but the stalks and hulls also contain large amounts. Cellulose, when partly refined, is used in the manufacture of paper, of building- and insulating-board, and of absorbents. When freed of impurities and converted into cellulose compounds, it is used in the making of rayon, lacquers, plastics, cellophane, explosives, and many other products.

Cottonseed Products. Before the Civil War period cottonseed was considered a

Figure 7–7. A typical cottonseed oil mill in the Yazoo Delta area near Clarksdale, Mississippi. Throughout the Cotton Belt, mills of this type produce linters from the coarse fiber left on the seed by the gin, livestock feed from the hulls removed from the seed, and oil from the cooked kernels of the seeds for use in making shortening, margarine, and other food products. (Courtesy National Cottonseed Products Association.)

waste product and those seeds not needed for planting the next season's crop were destroyed. During the Reconstruction Period large quantities of seed were used in the South for fertilizer and stock feed.

Although the extraction of oil from cottonseed began before the Civil War, the industry did not become important until 1879 when it was learned that the oil could be made edible by a new purifying process using fuller's earth. As cottonseed deteriorates rapidly in storage, the industry is of necessity highly seasonal, coinciding with that of ginning. Oil mills operate as near to capacity as possible so as to offset the large overhead cost of the mill, which remains idle for the greater part of the year. With the expanding use of cottonseed oil as food, and with the increase in the number of mills, intense competition for seed has developed. Manufacturers and refiners, to protect themselves on the supply, price, and quality, bought out and combined many of the crushing plants, and also acquired control of many gins in an effort to assure themselves sufficient seed. Soon the industry became concentrated in the hands of several large companies (Figure 7–7) that operated chains of mills throughout the entire Cotton Belt. During the first World War there was a great inflation in cottonseed prices ($65.59 per ton in 1919) and an overexpansion of the industry. The deflation that followed ruined many oil plants and necessitated a complete reorganization of the industry. A second price collapse came in the depression years of the early 1930's when cottonseed reached an all-time low of $8.98 per ton.[15] Since then no agricultural product has fluctuated in price more than cottonseed.

Cottonseed yields four primary products — oil, linters, hulls, and cake or meal. Oil, the most valuable, is a base for vegetable shortening, salad oil, sardine packing, and soap. In 1950 cottonseed oil provided 56 per cent of the vegetable oils used in making oleomargarine, which is becoming increasingly important in the American home. Linters, the residual fibers left on the seed after ginning, are used in making absorbent cotton, felt,

and rayon. The hulls and other solid material left after oil extraction, are pressed into a cake, ground into meal, and sold as stock feed and fertilizer. With further development of chemurgy, additional uses will be found for cottonseed products.

Plastics. Within recent years the manufacture of plastics, one of the fastest-growing industries of the United States, has become important in the South. It utilizes a great number of waste products from both farm and forest.

The plastics industry is probably the best example of man's ability to improve on nature. Many of these products leave the mould finished, not requiring further treatment such as varnishing or painting. The bulk of organic plastics can be made from forest and farm products.

As yet this industry in the South is small, but expansion seems assured because of the great variety of raw materials available.

In 1934 a small sweet potato starch plant was established at Laurel, Mississippi, to ensure a market for sweet potatoes in that area and to provide an income for farm families. This plant provided needed opportunity for research and the results formed the basis for the designing of new plants. The Laurel plant continued to manufacture starch and byproduct pulp until 1944, when operations were suspended because the high cost of growing sweet potatoes made the production of starch unprofitable.[16]

Soybean Products. The processing of soybeans usually results in two products: soybean oil and the residue called oil meal or cake. The oil is used in the production of shortening, oleomargarine, and salad dressing. Flour, animal feed and fertilizer are made from the residue. In industry soybean oil is used as a semi-drying agent in paints and varnishes (the paint and varnish industry used 150 million pounds in 1949), in the making of soap, and in many other ways.

Forest and Forest-Products Industries

The Cotton Belt lies largely in the south-

---

[15] *Agricultural Statistics, 1951*, p. 122.

[16] *Crops in Peace and War, The Yearbook of Agriculture 1950–1951*, pp. 165–167. Washington, D.C.: Government Printing Office, 1951.

Figure 7–8. A wood-products plant in southeastern Arkansas. In addition to its sawmill, the Crossett Lumber Company also operates a chemical plant (foreground) and a paper mill (background). (Courtesy of the Crossett Lumber Company.)

ern part of what was once the greatest stretch of timber in the world — the eastern forest. With the exception of the prairie areas, every part of the Cotton Belt was originally forested. Demand for cotton land, coupled with reckless burning, reduced the standing timber long before lumbering began. It is becoming increasingly evident to land owners that forests produce a valuable crop and the forest industries today are second only to agriculture in their contribution to the economy of the South.[17] In 1944 the Forest Service estimated that southern forests were producing roughly 42 per cent of the nation's lumber and timber, 53 per cent of its fuel wood, 44 per cent of its pulp, and virtually all of its naval stores.[18] More attention is being paid to better cutting practices, and restocking is proceeding more rapidly than formerly. Too much of the forest, however, is still being mined rather than farmed. Only a very small portion of the forest lands

of the Cotton Belt, or of the South as a whole, is publicly owned. Since most of the land is in the hands of private corporations or on small farms, it is difficult to improve forest conditions. Softwoods make up about 90 per cent of the commercial wood grown in the Cotton Belt, although, during World War II, the use of hardwoods expanded. The hardwood forests, particularly in the bottom lands of Arkansas, Louisiana, and Mississippi have been more completely destroyed than the softwoods, and since they grow more slowly, they cannot restock themselves rapidly.

Lumbering. The lumber industry removed the better timber first in the Upper Lakes District and then in the South. Its traditional policy has been to cut the best timber as fast as possible and then to abandon the location. This policy was followed throughout most of the Cotton Belt, which today is scarred as a result of destructive lumbering. The system of taxation based on standing timber was in part to blame, since it encouraged cutting the timber as soon as possible and moving it from the land.

The South is favored, however, over other lumber-producing sections of the country in

[17] J. Herbert Stone, Charles F. Evans, and W. R. Hine, "Forestry on Large Ownerships in the South," *The Yearbook of Agriculture, 1949*, p. 280. Washington, D. C.: Government Printing Office, 1949.

[18] Merle Prunty, Jr., "Land Occupance in the Southeast: Landmarks and Forecast," p. 440.

that a long growing season and heavy rainfall assure rapid tree growth. New growth from voluntary seedlings and reforestation has maintained a large lumber industry although the Forest Service has estimated that trees are being cut much more rapidly than they are being replaced. Many wood-products industries are installing trained personnel to improve forest management practices. The South, primarily the Cotton Belt, in 1947 produced 39 per cent of the board lumber in the United States (Figure 7–8). Many of the mills are small, with 82 per cent producing less than one million board feet a year.[19] Some of the larger mills also produce wood-pulp and plastics.

The Hardwood Industries. A considerable part of the southern forest consists of hardwoods such as oak, hickory, cypress, and gum. These hardwoods have been in great demand for furniture, veneers, and shingles. Since the best stands were in the Mississippi bottoms, Memphis, the largest nearby city, became the leading hardwood center in the nation. At first the industry cut only choice large trees that were suited for furniture. The railroad cross-tie industry has used many smaller and less desirable hardwood trees, but as a result of creosoting, pine cross ties now can compete. Although most southern pulp mills use pine, some pulp is being made from hardwoods: in papermaking the long fibers are preferred for strength, but the short fibers of the hardwoods give smoothness and opacity, and are often mixed into the papermaking formula.[20] Despite the increased use of hardwoods during World War II, in proportion to the total pulpwood consumption, the use of hardwoods has not changed greatly since 1939.

Naval Stores. Before the advent of iron and steel ships, tar and pitch from the South Atlantic coastal states were used to calk seams and preserve ropes of wooden vessels. Tar and pitch products therefore became known as "naval stores." When it was discovered that turpentine and resin could be dis-

tilled from the gum of longleaf and slash pine, many new uses were found for these products in no way connected with ships — paints, soaps, shoe dressing, and medicines. Until 1900 the South produced about 80 per cent of the world's naval stores; since that time the percentage has dropped materially as petroleum by-products are competing seriously with pine turpentine. Naval stores are still of major importance in the South — the volume of business in 1947-48 being 39 million dollars. The major naval-stores area today, in southern Georgia and northern Florida, lies in the Humid Subtropical Gulf Coast Region which produces more than 90 per cent of the total.[21]

The Pulp and Paper Industry. The manufacture of pulp and paper in the South has grown with amazing rapidity in recent years. The Cotton Belt, particularly, gives promise of becoming the nation's great future source of pulp and paper. With its copious rainfall, abundant sunshine, and long growing season, conifers grow four or five times as fast as does the spruce of New England, the Lake States, or Quebec. In 1911 a small mill — the first in the South, was established at Orange, Texas, to produce sulphate pulp for wrapping paper. Today one half of the pulp and one third of the paper of the United States is produced in the South as a whole, and the industry is still expanding. These industries have stimulated business in their surrounding areas; they have invested more than a billion dollars and have manufactured products that add 500 million dollars to the income of the region. The mills employ an estimated 100,000 persons directly in the production, transportaton, and manufacture of wood pulp.[22]

Today most kraft paper made in the United States comes from southern pines and southern mills; only since 1939 has the manufacture of paper for newsprint and other light paper gained a foothold. For a long time sulphate pulp, because of the resin

[19] Stone, Evans, and Hine, "Forestry on Large Ownerships in the South," p. 281.
[20] "Champion Paper," *Fortune*, January, 1949, pp. 80-85.

[21] Jay Ward, "Naval Stores: The Industry." *The Yearbook of Agriculture, 1949*, p. 287. Washington, D. C.: Government Printing Office, 1949.
[22] Stone, Evans, and Hine, "Forestry on Large Ownerships in the South," p. 281.

problem, was thought impossible to bleach and was made into bags and wrapping paper. Ultimately it was discovered that large amounts of resin occurs in the older trees — those more than 25 years old — it being a pathological substance produced by nature to heal cuts or wounds in trees. It is significant that most trees in this region are less than 25 years of age, the older ones having been removed by the lumber industry some years ago. This means that the best supply of trees for pulp in the whole nation is to be found in the South.

Bleached pulp has become an important southern product. In 1940 the South's first newsprint mill was opened at Lufkin, Texas. During its first year of operation this plant manufactured, sold, and shipped more than 31 million tons of newsprint. Since that time the plant has greatly increased production capacity. In 1949 a second plant went up when a southern newspaper group raised 32 million dollars to build an ultra modern plant at Childersburg, Alabama, called the Coosa River Newsprint Company.[23] In addition to producing 300 tons of newsprint daily, this plant is equipped to turn out 146 tons of dried bleached kraft and 74 tons of semi-bleached kraft.[24] A third plant is now being built and with its natural advantages for production, the South seems destined to dominate the paper pulp industry in the future.

Minerals of the Cotton Belt

Geographic regional boundaries which seldom are determined by mineral distribution, frequently cut across mineralized areas. Thus many minerals of the South such as iron ore, phosphate, sulphur, salt, and coal lie largely, if not entirely outside the boundary of the Cotton Belt and hence are not considered in this chapter. In fact the only ones of major importance in this region are those hydrocarbons — petroleum and natural gas — that are found largely in the trans-Mississippi

portion. In addition some lignite, iron ore, bauxite, and salt are mined.

Iron Ore. In recent years the development of the iron ore deposits of East Texas has given added impetus to the increasing industrialization of the Southwest. From the beginning of the settlement of East Texas, the obvious existence there of a large quantity of easily available iron ore encouraged the belief that an iron and steel industry could be developed. Before the Civil War there was some production of pig iron from small furnaces, but all of them were closed by 1910. The building of two large blast furnaces at Houston and at Daingerfield, in the Cotton Belt, brought about a revival in production of Texas iron ores in 1943. While the plant at Houston primarily utilizes imported ores and scrap, the Lone Star Steel Company at Daingerfield is using the brown iron ores, mined from open pits, in its immediate vicinity. The East Texas ores exist in large quantities, although no definite estimate of tonnage can be made, and usually occur in strata forming the cap rock of low hills.

Lignite. Prior to the discovery of the great abundance of oil and natural gas the lignite deposits of Texas were worked extensively. Lignite is widely distributed in two formations which extend from the Rio Grande into Arkansas and Louisiana. The recent announcement of the Aluminum Company of America that it plans to use lignite as a source of power for its plant near Rockdale, in central Texas, for the manufacture of aluminum has aroused great interest. In 1949 the reserves near Rockdale were estimated to possess about 200 million tons. The easy availability of lignite, often by the strip mining process, and its proximity to centers of industry, are factors which indicate that the future development of these reserves will be extensive.

Bauxite. Although the major portion of the bauxite ores used in the United States still is imported, largely from Surinam, British Guiana, Haiti, and Jamaica, domestic production is also important. All domestic supplies now being worked lie within the boundaries of the Cotton Belt Region. Two coun-

[23] Lawrence P. Lessing, "Research Rebuilds the South," *Fortune*, March, 1952.

[24] *The Blue Book of Southern Progress*, 1950, p. 64.

ties in Central Arkansas, near the boundary of the Ozark-Ouachita Subregion, accounted for 95 per cent of domestic production in 1949; three counties in Alabama and Georgia supplied the remainder.

In the Arkansas district only about 16 per cent of the bauxite is mined underground and 84 per cent is strip mined. In 1949 imports constituted a larger proportion of the total supply than in previous years owing in part to the increasing costs of mining domestic ores and to the competition of higher-grade foreign ores.

Most bauxite is consumed in the aluminum industry, although an increasing amount is being used for abrasives, chemicals, and oil refining. It is replacing fuller's earth for decolorizing lubricating oils.

Petroleum and Natural Gas

Commercial petroleum production in Anglo-America began with the discovery of the Drake Well in northwestern Pennsylvania in 1859. It soon spread westward into Ohio and Indiana, and later into most parts of the United States and to many foreign countries. Oil from numerous seeps was used locally throughout the country. One such locality, Nacogdoches County, in the southwestern part of the Cotton Belt, procured oil from an open pit as early as 1867. It was used on harness leather. The development of the large Mid-continent Oil Province, which lies partly in the western Cotton Belt and partly within the Great Plains Region began in Kansas, later spreading to Oklahoma, Texas, Arkansas, and Louisiana.

The first commercial production in the Southwest began in the 1890's with the discovery of oil in a well being drilled for water near Corsicana, Texas. Within a short time Texas production had climbed from 50 barrels in 1895 to nearly 66,000 in 1897. In the following year it reached 546,000 barrels and the great oil industry of the Southwest was under way. Although numerous small fields were brought in during the next decade, no important development took place within the Cotton Belt until 1911, when the Electra Field, near Wichita Falls, Texas, was

discovered. Many large fields were then discovered in rapid succession, including such famous producers as Ranger, Burkburnett (the field that caused the Red River boundary controversy with Oklahoma), Mexia, and Powell in Texas; numerous fields in southern Oklahoma; Smackover and El Dorado in Arkansas; and some important ones in Louisiana. Although each presented new problems of overproduction, the industry in the Southwest and the nation as a whole continued to postpone the "evil day" when oil wells would have to be prorated and production limited. Such conditions might have continued had not the East Texas field, the largest in the world, been developed in the early 1930's. Its enormous potential production threatened to wreck the entire petroleum industry. The size and importance of this field warrants a more detailed description.

The East Texas Oil Field. Some time before the discovery well was brought in, geologists had condemned the area as an oil producer because it did not show any of the common structures present in other developed fields. Accordingly no major companies had leased large tracts of land, and the whole area was in the hands of small land owners. A veteran "wildcatter," C. M. (Dad) Joiner, brought in the discovery well (3,592 feet deep) in the southern part of the field in Rusk County on September 8, 1930. It was the third well he had drilled, the other two having been dry holes. Since it produced only about 300 barrels per day, it all but discouraged further drilling in that section. On December 28, 1930, the second well was brought in yielding between 10,000 and 15,000 barrels a day (Figure 7–9). This started the boom in the East Texas field. Table 4 indicates the rapid rate of well drilling in the next decade.[25] Since most of the land in East Texas was privately owned, almost everyone owning property within the field drilled a well if he could secure financial backing. Ultimately the boundaries of the producing area were determined by the marginal dry holes. At its maximum extension, the field

[25] *Kilgore Oil Carnival.* Kilgore, Texas: October 1940.

Table 4

WELLS DRILLED BY YEARS IN EAST TEXAS FIELD

Year	Oil Wells Completed	Gas Wells Completed	Dry Holes
1930	5	0	0
1931	3,299	0	41
1932	5,723	6	64
1933	2,424	6	27
1934	3,696	6	60
1935	3,999	4	121
1936	2,509	1	117
1937	2,380	2	84
1938	1,765	0	41
1939	417	0	8
Total	26,217	25	563

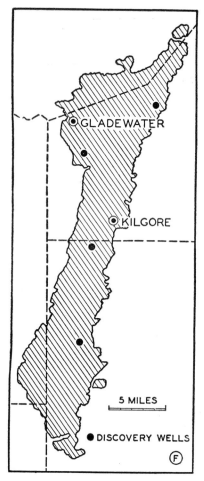

Figure 7–9. The East Texas oil field showing the discovery wells. (Adapted from map in *The Oil Weekly,* October 7, 1940.)

proved to be about 42 miles long and nearly 9 miles wide. Within an area of about 300 square miles, more than 27,000 producing wells were drilled. Small cities, such as Gladewater or Kilgore, had more than 300 within their boundaries. Although production has been severely curtailed almost from the beginning, this field easily leads the nation.

So great was the production from these many wells in the East Texas field that soon the market was flooded with oil and prices declined. Oil that brought $1.10 a barrel when the discovery well came in dropped to ten cents by the following spring. The Texas Railroad Commission (the controlling agency) provided a total allowable of 70,000 barrels a day for April, 1931, but by the time the order became effective, the field was producing 140,000 barrels per day. On April 9th, it increased the daily allowable to 90,000 barrels, but the field was then producing 195,000 barrels daily. On May 7 the allowable was placed at 160,000 barrels daily, but

Table 5

PRODUCTION OF AMERICA'S SIX LEADING OIL FIELDS[26]

Field	State	Production since Discovery (barrels)	Estimated Reserves (barrels)
East Texas	Texas	2,877,058,000	2,222,942,000
Midway Sunset	California	772,759,000	157,241,000
Long Beach	California	759,844,000	80,116,000
Oklahoma City	Oklahoma	681,570,000	88,430,000
Wilmington	California	557,879,000	422,121,000
Sante Fe Springs	California	538,646,000	51,354,000

[26] *Oil and Gas Journal,* Vol. 50, No. 38, 1952, pp. 264–272.

a week before the field was producing 340,000 barrels daily. The average price of oil by that time was between ten and fifteen cents per barrel. The entire American petroleum industry faced ruin. Finally on August 17, 1931, the Governor of Texas called out the State National Guard and completely closed the field until September 5th. During that period the Railroad Commission conducted hearings to determine the best method of proration, since it definitely had been proved necessary for the future welfare of the industry. These first proration orders considered among other things the proper spacing of wells and the limitation of production per well. Unfortunately, through the ignorance of some and the greed of others, this first attempt at control was unsuccessful. Many people were determined to get their oil to the refineries at all costs and thus began a new development —"hot-oil running."

Influence of Oil on the Cultural Landscape. The sandy lands within the East Texas oil field that previously had little value suddenly became almost priceless. The new industry was purely extractive and had no interest in community betterment. Its workers came with a single motive — to exploit the oil resources.

The conservation laws in Texas which were enacted to remedy conditions in the East Texas field have since proved of great value to the entire oil industry and to the nation by increasing recovery of oil and preventing waste. In the light of the present world situation this is daily becoming more important. East Texas, still the largest oil field in the nation in total production, has settled down to a normal existence, although more than 300 new wells were drilled in 1951 — twenty-one years after the discovery well came in. Many towns in and near the East Texas field, however, still bear the marks of the early oil boom days.

Kilgore, in the heart of the field, illustrates the remarkable development of an oil-boom town. Before oil was discovered, it was a small rural business center in a cotton-farming district of low productivity. It was unincorporated and hence was not listed in the 1930 census; estimates placed its total

population at a few hundred.[27] The community had been hard hit by the depression and its economic outlook was far from bright. By the close of 1930, however, when the East Texas field was definitely established, the quiet conservative spirit of Kilgore had disappeared almost overnight, and in its place had grown an ugly, dirty oil camp, overrun by a multitude of strangers whom the town was ill-equipped to serve. Since Kilgore was on productive property, oil wells were drilled on almost every lot (Figure 7–10). As the boom subsided and the oil-workers moved on to other parts of the field, the town began to spend its newly acquired wealth on new buildings, street paving, and beautification. Though Kilgore today is a modern small city, it still retains the forest of steel derricks that represent its lifeblood. Nowhere else, save in a town dependent upon minerals, logging activities, or fishing, can one find a

[27] William T. Chambers, "Kilgore, Texas: An Oil Boom Town," *Economic Geography*, Vol. 9, January 1933, pp. 72-85.

Figure 7–10. A forest of oil derricks in the heart of the business district of Kilgore, Texas. (Courtesy of the *Kilgore News Herald*.)

single industry dominating the life of such a large proportion of the population.

Natural Gas. Although most oil wells contain gas, its presence after lifting the oil to the surface has, until recently, been a liability.

In many old oil fields, large gas flares told the story of man's waste of this valuable natural resource. As a result of legislation, oil operators must send it to market by pipelines, utilize it in drip gasoline plants or put it back into the ground. Many long gas pipelines from southwestern fields serve communities at a great distance, but much gas still remains below ground.

Pipelines. When the oil industry was first developed in the Southwest, most petroleum was shipped in tank cars. Some oil still moves by rail, and a large part of the refined gasoline is transported by motor truck; however, the bulk of the crude petroleum, natural gas, and gasoline today flows to refineries and markets by pipelines. Texas, the point of origin for a great number of pipelines, serving most parts of the United States, had, in 1950, more than 86,000 miles of pipeline within the state.

Other Manufacturing Industries of the Cotton Belt

In the past, the Cotton Belt has been primarily an agricultural region with certain localized manufacturing industries. During World War II the process of decentralization from the vulnerable eastern and western coastal areas accelerated industrial development in the region. Its location midway between East and West and nearness to the deep waters of the Gulf of Mexico were partially responsible. Since the war many industries have expanded and new ones have entered the region. Textile, rayon, and garment manufacturing industries have long had a foothold in the Cotton Belt but heavy industries such as steel mills, aluminum plants, and aircraft factories constitute the more recent development.

Textiles and Rayon. Cotton textiles are manufactured throughout the South and many large mills lie within the bounds of the Cotton Belt. The same holds true for the rayon industry although as yet most of the mills are in the Piedmont and Appalachian regions. Since these industries have been discussed, no further consideration of them is given here.

The Garment Industry. The garment industry's greatest point of concentration, Dallas, has almost doubled production in the past decade. Near the end of 1951 there were 192 factories operating in the Dallas area producing a wide range of clothing from work clothes to fashionable dresses, suits and coats for women. These are gaining nation-wide recognition and the opportunity for future expansion is favorable.

The Aluminum Industry. One of the most spectacular industrial developments in the Cotton Belt during recent years has been the expansion of the aluminum industry. In Arkansas, the Reynolds Metals Company leased the Government owned alumina works at Hurricane Creek and also the nearby smelting plant at Jones Mills. The company also bought from the Government the alumina works which it had operated during the war. The Aluminum Company of America by 1953 will have three aluminum plants operating in Texas, one of these at Rockdale in the Cotton Belt Region. The Rockdale plant will be the first aluminum smelting works in the United States to use electric power generated by lignite.

Iron and Steel. The iron and steel industry in the Cotton Belt is in its infancy, but the recently completed Lone Star at Daingerfield and LeTourneau at Longview in northeast Texas, utilizing the iron ores of adjacent areas are, new and interesting developments.

The Aircraft Industry. Dallas, Fort Worth and surrounding towns now are among the foremost aircraft manufacturing centers of the nation. During World War II the adaptability of Texas climate to flying and proximity to large military airbases stimulated the growth of the industry. The close of the war saw a reduction in output of many of the plants and the closing of others. The renewal of the Federal Government's military program brought production again to a high level by the end of 1951. The largest aircraft factory in the area is the Consolidated Vultee Aircraft Corporation at Fort Worth with an estimated yearly payroll of 75 million dollars. Its principal product is the B-36, the largest of the bombers. The Chance Vought Division of the United Aircraft Corporation at Grand Prairie, manufacturing the Corsair and a newer jet plane, the Cutlass, and the Bell Aircraft Corporation at Fort Worth are other important manufacturers. The concentration of aircraft manufacturing in this area has attracted some satellite industries.

Transportation

Rivers and Canals. Prior to 1811 there was considerable downstream traffic on the Mississippi by flat-boat and by raft, but real trade developed with the appearance of the first steamboat. The use of steam power made possible the upstream journey and ushered in a period of heavy steamboat traffic which lasted until the 1859's when the railroads began to offer serious competition. From the close of the Civil War to the beginning of the twentieth century, traffic on rivers almost vanished.

The creation of the Inland Waterways Commission in 1907 marked the approach of a new era in river transportation. Yet even with the improvements that have been made on the Mississippi and its tributaries (including TVA work on the Tennessee) the traffic moving by water cannot compare with that by rail or motor truck. Shipments by water benefit from cheaper rates, but they are also much slower. No other water transportation of significance is found today in the Cotton Belt except on the Tombigbee and Black Warrior rivers of Alabama.

Flood Problems on the Mississippi. For many years the building of levees along the banks of the stream was the only means of preventing floods in the lowlands. For most high water stages, these winding levees served well but an unusually heavy flood occasionally broke the levee at some weak point — usually on the outside of a bend — and flooded extensive bottom lands. The banks of the river lay in six states — Missouri, Arkansas, Louisiana, Kentucky, Tennessee, and Mississippi — and with no unified federal action, these states could not agree on a plan. The severe flood of 1927 showed the necessity of federal aid and plans were soon made to treat the flood problems of the lower Mississippi as a unit. Many factors were involved in this new plan, but probably the most significant was the establishment of major emergency floodways to carry off excess floodwaters and to reduce the level of the main stream. Another method of protection has been the straightening of the river by dredging cutoff channels. These cutoffs, navigable at all times, have not only reduced distances, but have also increased the velocity of the stream thereby reducing flood hazards. The success of these methods in the years since their inception has demonstrated the effectiveness of the plan.

Other Methods of Transportation. With the decline of river traffic at the close of the steamboat era (largely produced by railroad competition), industries demanded better rail transportation. Southern railroads (in the Cotton Belt and in the Subtropical Gulf regions) have developed rapidly within the last fifty years and today no part of the area lies far from the railroad. The last three decades have seen also the establishment of a network of modern highways throughout the Cotton Belt. With the expansion of commercial aviation to provide excellent connections with all major points of the United States and Latin America, transportation facilities are keeping pace with the industrial and population growth of the region.

The Outlook

The Cotton Belt is no longer the one-crop region it has been in the past. Instead of a more or less continuous cotton field as it might have appeared in earlier times, the region today is marked by areas of intensive cotton production and areas where cotton is secondary to other crops.

For the entire region, cotton yields have increased steadily while the total acreage in the crop has declined. In some of the older cotton-producing areas, cattle grazing is replacing cotton in the major use of the land. This may be particularly noticeable within the next few years in the inner Coastal Plain and the Black Waxy Prairies. As livestock production increases, small grain production undoubtedly will expand eastward across the Cotton Belt.

Dairying will increase in importance around the major cities, but no part of the region is likely to become dominantly a dairying area. Oilbean crops, particularly peanuts and soybeans, will expand as the national demand for vegetable oil increases. Specialty crops, such as truck crops, fruits, roses, and other flowers, will be produced intensively in local areas, but none will become dominant for the region. With the perfection of the mechanical cotton picker, larger cotton farms will develop, particularly in the extensive bottom-land areas of the Mississippi River Valley. These will continue to be some of the major cotton producing areas of Anglo-America. Here the trend will be toward larger farms, with larger fields, more mechanization, and a smaller total force of farm labor.

The gross forest acreage will decrease, but with the establishment of new pulp and paper mills and other wood-working plants, and with the further development of scientific forestry in the South, continued growth of these industries seems assured.

Although the Cotton Belt will remain primarily an agricultural region, manufacturing is becoming increasingly important. Processing of agricultural and forest products will expand, industries dependent upon petroleum and natural gas will increase in importance, and new industries producing iron and steel, aluminum, and perhaps other metals will be built as the supply of cheap fuel — both natural gas and lignite — and essential raw materials are discovered and developed.

City growth has been rapid during the past decade, and with it has come a variety of manufacturing industries including large automobile assembly plants, farm machinery plants, and airplane factories. While the Cotton Belt will never become an industrial rival of the American Manufacturing Belt or even the Humid Subtropical Gulf Coast, it should continue to derive a constantly increasing amount of its total income from manufacturing.

This region is rapidly retreating from its former classification as the nation's "number one problem area" to one of the nation's most progressive regions where the opportunities for future development are very promising.

Table 6

SELECTED CITIES AND TOWNS OF THE COTTON BELT

City or Town	Urbanized area	Political center	City or Town	Urbanized area	Political center
Albany		31,155	Little Rock–		
Alexandria		34,913	North Little Rock	153,643	
Austin	135,971	132,459	Longview		24,502
Columbus (Ga.)	118,485	79,611	Lufkin		15,135
Columbus (Miss.)		17,172	Macon	93,499	70,252
Dallas	538,924	434,462	Marshall		22,327
Denison		17,504	Memphis	406,034	396,000
Fort Worth	315,578	278,778	Meridian		41,893
Greenville (Miss.)		29,936	Monroe		38,572
Greenville (Tex.)		14,727	Montgomery	109,468	106,525
Hattiesburg		29,474	Natchez		22,740
Jackson (Miss.)	100,261	98,271	North Little Rock		44,097
Jackson (Tenn.)		30,207	Paris		21,643
Jonesboro		16,310	Pine Bluff		37,162
Little Rock		102,213	San Antonio	449,521	408,442

City or Town	Urbanized area	Political center	City or Town	Urbanized area	Political center
Selma		22,840	Tyler		38,968
Sherman		20,150	Vicksburg		27,948
Shreveport	150,208	127,206	Waco	92,834	84,706
Temple		25,467	Wichita Falls		68,042
Texarkana		40,638			

Selected Bibliography

William T. Chambers, "Shopping Areas of the Near Southwest," *Economic Geography*, Vol. 17, 1941, pp. 121-129.

Franklin C. Erickson, "The Broken Cotton Belt," *Economic Geography*, Vol. 24, 1948, pp. 263-268.

J. Sullivan Gibson, "The Alabama Black Belt: Its Geographic Status," *Economic Geography*, Vol. 17, 1941, pp. 1-23.

Leslie Hewes, "Indian Land in the Cherokee Country of Oklahoma," *Economic Geography*, Vol. 18, 1942, pp. 401-412.

Clyde F. Kohn, "Development of Dairy Farming in Mississippi," *Economic Geography*, Vol. 19, 1943, pp. 188-195.

Walter M. Kollmorgen, "Agricultural - Cultural Islands in the South," *Economic Geography*, Vol. 19, 1943, pp. 109-117.

————, "A Reconnaissance of Some Cultural-Agricultural Islands in the South," *Economic Geography*, Vol. 17, 1941, pp. 409-430.

Merle Prunty, Jr., "Land Occupance in the Southeast: Landmarks and Forecasts," *Geographical Review*, Vol. 42, 1952, pp. 439-461.

————, "Recent Quantitative Changes in the Cotton Regions of the Southeastern States," *Economic Geography*, Vol. 27, 1951, pp. 189-208.

————, "Soybeans in the Lower Mississippi Valley," *Economic Geography*, Vol. 26, 1950, pp. 301-314.

J. Allen Tower, "Cotton Change in Alabama 1879-1946," *Economic Geography*, Vol. 26, 1950, pp. 6-28.

J. Allen Tower and Walter Wolf, "Ethnic Groups in Cullman County, Alabama," *Geographical Review*, Vol. 33, 1943, pp. 276-285.

Wilbur Zelinsky, "The Changing South," *Focus*, Vol. 2, No. 2, October 1951.

8.

The Humid Subtropical Coast

THE production of early vegetables, citrus fruits, and other subtropical crops, as well as a phenomenal industrial growth in recent years, characterizes the Humid Subtropical Coast, which extends from the Atlantic Coast of the Carolinas, Georgia, and Florida to the Mexican border in the Lower Rio Grande Valley (Figure 8–1). Although it includes the southern part of the Atlantic Coast, it is largely dominated by the Gulf of Mexico. Most of the region is bounded on the north by the Cotton Belt; on the southwest it borders the southern Great Plains, the boundary being drawn where ranching becomes dominant. The Atlantic and the Gulf of Mexico determine the eastern and southern boundaries.

The Physical Setting

Relief of the Land. Since this region represents the outer portion of the South Atlantic and Gulf Coastal Plains, its physiography is similar to that of the Cotton Belt, except that its terrain is definitely flatter. No part of the region lies more than 500 feet above sea level; some large areas along the Gulf side of the peninsula are only a few feet above high tide. Interior swamps, coastal marshes and lagoons occupy a considerable part of the region, giving it the largest per-

centage of wet lands needing drainage within the United States. Much of the coast line is bordered by barrier beaches. North-central Florida, a gently rolling area with underground drainage, rises to about 100 feet above sea level. Elsewhere, except on the Mississippi Delta, the land gradually increases in elevation toward the interior.

Climate. The humid subtropical climate of the region is characterized by a heavy rainfall and a long growing season (from 260 days on the north to the almost frostless areas of southern Florida and the Lower Rio Grande Valley). The total precipitation decreases from more than 60 inches in southern Florida and along the east Gulf Coast to less than 30 inches in the southwest. Over most of the region the rainfall is evenly distributed throughout the year, but the maximum comes during the summer and early autumn — the hurricane season. These tropical storms usually bring excessive rains and cause considerable crop damage. The torrential rains (most stations in this region have experienced more than 10 inches of rain in a 24-hour period) coupled with winds of high velocity have wrought great destruction to many communities at some time or other. Weather forecasting is now so efficient that people can learn of coming storms in ample time to protect themselves and, to some ex-

182

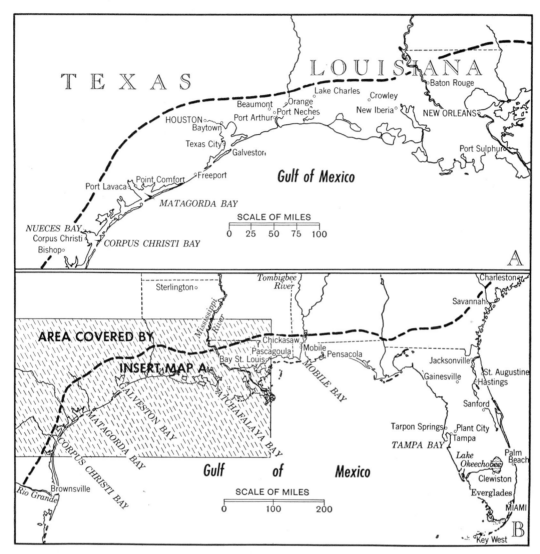

Figure 8–1. The Humid Subtropical Coast. A region of sugar cane, rice, citrus fruits, truck crops, stock raising, minerals, manufacturing, commerce, fishing, and resorts.

tent, their property. From the psychological standpoint, mild, sunny winters largely offset the hurricane menace and thus enable this region to capitalize on climate in its agriculture and resort business.

Soils and Vegetation. The Subtropical Gulf Coast is characterized by infertile, sandy soils which predominate everywhere except in the muck lands of the Florida Everglades and other marshy areas, the rolling lands of the Florida lakes area, the Missis-

sippi Delta, and the Rio Grande Delta.

Because of heavier rainfall, the eastern part of the region is covered largely with forests, mainly slash or longleaf pine, the chief exception being the grasslands of the Everglades. West of the Mississippi Delta, coastal marshes appear; the inland areas there, however, are dominated by pine forests. Still farther west, along the coast of Texas is a prairie that has long been important in the raising of cattle.

Sequent Occupance in the Region

The Subtropical Atlantic-Gulf Coast was one of the first regions explored and settled by Europeans. (The oldest city of the United States, St. Augustine, was founded by the Spaniards in 1565.) However, except in a few favored localities such as Mobile and New Orleans, little progress was made until modern times. In fact, this region represents one of the nation's last frontiers.

In colonial times, the entire region was controlled by either Spain or France — neither one a good colonizing nation. Florida and West Florida belonged to Spain, Louisiana to France (although for a period it was Spanish territory) and the Texas coast to Spain and later to Mexico. Except for a few settlements such as St. Augustine, Pensacola, and Mobile, the eastern part of this region remained almost unoccupied by white men until it was acquired by the United States. Furthermore, in spite of its several major ocean ports today, few if any good natural harbors existed. Agriculturally the Cotton Belt to the north was far superior. Since cotton could not be grown successfully, the coastal areas were not desired by colonists.

Because of their commercial significance, New Orleans and the Mississippi Delta became important at an early date. French colonists, supplemented later by Acadians, began the cultivation of sugar cane during the eighteenth century. Except on the southwest coastal plain where a few Spaniards had established large *ranchos,* the Texas Gulf Coast remained largely unoccupied.

The Anglo-Saxon trek to Texas came almost entirely by land, colonization being confined to the inner margin of this region. After the establishment of the Republic of Texas in 1836 many Mexican (formerly Spanish) settlers abandoned their holdings on the Texas coast and allowed their cattle to run wild. Then followed a period in which Spanish cattle (longhorns) multiplied rapidly. Before the Civil War, people in this remote coastal area hunted wild cattle, taking only the hides and allowing the carcasses to become carrion. Later there grew up along the Texas coast some 32 cattle ports that shipped

animals "on the hoof" to New Orleans, Havana, and New York.

With the opening of the Great Plains following the Civil War and the building of railroads into the frontier, the Texas coast became the chief source of cattle. In time, the great cattle drives began — records showing that between 1866 and 1880, 4,223,497 cattle were driven northward from Texas.[1]

When the western ranges proved to be superior for cattle, ranching decreased in importance along the Gulf Coast. The introduction of the hardy Brahman cattle, however, has revived interest in ranching. From Florida to Texas large numbers of cattle now graze on the grasslands scattered throughout the timbered areas and on the coastal prairies.

The major development of the Subtropical Coastal Region came, however, after the beginning of the twentieth century, as a result of a number of factors including: (1) improvements in transportation facilities and ports, (2) increasing demands for early vegetables and subtropical fruits and other crops, (3) the discovery of oil, gas, salt, sulphur, phosphate, and other minerals, (4) the development of the petrochemical industries, and (5) the location of many new industrial plants on the coast to benefit from cheap freight rates and cheap fuel. Other advantages include the mild subtropical climate and the relatively remote location making this perhaps the least vulnerable coastal region in the event of an air attack. The stupendous industrial growth of this region during the past decade (1942 – 1952) is equaled by few other regions of Anglo-America.

Agriculture

Cotton. Some cotton is grown in this region (Figure 7–2), but it is of minor importance except in limited areas along the coast of Texas. Heavy autumn rains make the crop highly speculative, for an entire year's work may be destroyed in a single

---

[1] Clarence Gordon, "Report on Cattle, Sheep, and Swine," *Tenth Census of the United States, 1880,* Vol. 3, p. 975. Washington, D. C.: Government Printing Office, 1880.

rain storm. Since cotton cannot be important, staple crops — sugar cane, rice, grain sorghums, and flax replace it on the Louisiana and Texas coasts.

Sugar Cane. Sugar cane growing in the delta country of Louisiana began in 1751 when Jesuits introduced the crop from Santo Domingo. The first successful sugar mill, built on a plantation near New Orleans in 1795, inaugurated the industry in that area.

The Acadians who came to Louisiana in 1757 took up the cultivation of sugar cane and spread its production westward. After the decline of indigo in the Carolinas and Louisiana, cane became the leading crop, though little was grown outside the delta for more than 100 years. Toward the close of the nineteenth century production spread into the Texas coastal prairies and into the Lower Rio Grande Valley. Cane cultivation was discontinued in the latter area, however, during the first World War, because of remoteness from markets and because fruits and vegetables became more profitable. In the Sugarland area near Houston, it remained an important crop until about 1923, when production was discontinued because the large refinery there found it cheaper to import Cuban raw sugars.

In recent years, there has been a considerable development of sugar cane in the Florida Everglades. In 1931 the United States Sugar Corporation acquired and expanded the properties of a small producer near Lake Okeechobee, constructing its large mill at Clewiston. The Everglades area with a longer growing season than that of the Louisiana district can more effectively rival Cuba as a sugar producer than can any other part of the United States. In this area it is unnecessary to replant each year as must be done in Louisiana, where killing frosts occur almost every winter. In Cuba and other tropical cane-producing regions, from 10 to 12 crops may be cut from a single planting; in the Everglades, from six to seven crops may be secured; while in Louisiana the crop must be replanted each year. In 1950, Louisiana produced 5,037,000 tons of cane sugar on 276,000 acres, and Florida produced 1,169,000 tons on 37,400 acres.[2]

In recent years there has been a tendency toward consolidation of many small mills into larger mill-plantation units, which have proved to be economical, since most of the small mills were obsolete. This type of consolidation has made it possible in the Louisiana delta country for many small, run-down plantations to operate today at a profit. The day of the small cane-sugar producer in the United States is definitely at an end; only large well-organized companies can hope to compete with the foreign cane and domestic beet sugar production.

The refining of sugar yields several useful by-products, including molasses and bagasse. Molasses is one of the basic sources of industrial alcohol. It is also mixed with feedstuffs as a fattener for livestock. Celotex, a construction material made from bagasse or waste sugar cane stalks after the juice has been extracted, has proved satisfactory as insulating material. Recent experiments with bagasse as a source of cellulose for pulp and paper show that as yet the cost of separating high-grade from low-grade cellulose, is too great to allow it to compete with wood and other low-cost sources.

Rice. In colonial times the coastal areas of South Carolina and Georgia produced large quantities of rice. Although grown in Louisiana for more than a century, rice did not become an important commercial crop until after 1880, when the introduction of harvesting machinery permitted large-scale farming on the prairies of southwestern Louisiana and southeastern Texas.

When the Acadians spread westward along the coast of Louisiana, they occupied first the higher, lighter, and more easily drained lands along the streams, leaving unoccupied the heaver prairie soils of the interfluves. These prairie areas, where the surface was underlain by an impervious claypan, were covered by thousands of shallow ponds that held water after each rain.[3] When these were drained by ditching, they made ideal areas

---

[2] *Agricultural Statistics, 1951*, p. 89. Washington, D. C.: Government Printing Office, 1951.

[3] Lauren C. Post, "The Rice Country of Southwestern Louisiana," *Geographical Review*, Vol. 30, 1940, pp. 574-575.

for the cultivation of rice. The flat relief permits subdivisions of the fields by small levees (Figure 8–2), a necessity since the field must be covered with about six inches of water during much of the growing period. Heavy rainfall supplemented by artesian wells and surface streams provides ample water. With proper drainage the water can be taken from the fields when mechanical equipment is ready to harvest the crop, or when heavy rains flood the area.

When railroads were built across the prai-

Mills, concentrated largely in Crowley, Lake Charles, and Beaumont, are equipped with complicated machinery for drying, cleaning, and polishing the rice and for utilizng its by-products. Favorable geographic conditions and complete mechanization enable this region to grow rice at a low per acre cost.

Between 1940 and 1945 the acreage in rice increased markedly particularly along the Texas coast as far southwest as Matagorda Bay (Figure 8–3). This increase in acreage,

Figure 8–2. An irrigated rice field in the Gulf Coast Region. Note the flatness of the land and the contour levees in the field. (Courtesy Beaumont Chamber of Commerce.)

ries in the 1880's, they began advertising the value of the land for growing rice. Many of those who came were Middle Western grain farmers, accustomed to using farm machinery. Harvesters, similar to those used in the wheat regions, were employed with great success. First they were drawn by draft animals, later by tractors. The rice is harvested in late summer or early autumn. When cut with a binder it is automatically tied into bundles and placed in shocks to dry before threshing. If the weather is fair the grain can be threshed in about two weeks. Combines, which cut and thresh the rice in one operation, are replacing the binder and thresher in many parts of the coastal plain.[4]

together with high prices has brought prosperity to rice growers in the Gulf Coast region.[5]

Grain Sorghums. Before World War II, grain sorghums were used largely for feed, but in recent years they have become a source of industrial raw materials such as protein and cornstarch. The major grain sorghum area of the United States, which lies on the Great Plains, will be considered further in

[4] G. A. Collier, *Rice Production and Marketing in the United States*, U. S. Department of Agriculture, Misc. Pub. No. 615, pp. 11-13. Washington, D. C.: Government Printing Office, 1947.

[5] William A. Faught, "The Rice Industry of Texas," *Monthly Business Review*, Vol. 32, No. 11, 1947, p. 161.

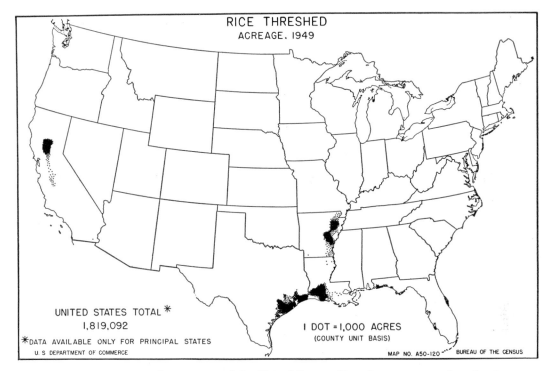

Figure 8–3. Rice-producing areas of the United States. Note the concentrated production along the Texas-Louisiana coast, with secondary centers in the Arkansas part of the Cotton Belt, and in the Sacramento Valley of California.

Chapter 11. However, the heavy producing area along the Gulf Coast in southwest Texas (Figure 11–5) is favored by transportation advantages in reaching important domestic and foreign seaboard markets, and this led to the building of the Corn Products Refining Company's plant in Corpus Christi to process millions of bushels annually.[6] This plant is so unique in its operation and so revolutionary in its architectural design, that a brief description seems desirable.

The Corn Products Refining Company completed its ultra modern factory at Corpus Christi in June, 1949, at a cost of 20 million dollars. It manufactures dextrose, starch, edible oils, and gluten feeds by a wet process (similar to the ones used in making the same products from corn) from milo maize

grown extensively on the adjacent coastal plain. The architectural design of the plant is revolutionary in that the buildings are constructed without walls and without windows (Figure 8–4). Since the machinery is sealed, walls are not required and the open sides of the building make air-conditioning machinery unnecessary. Only during the occasional short cold spells in winter is shelter needed around the areas where the few technicians work, and these places are protected by temporary walls. Being without sides this type of plant design also minimizes the damage from hurricanes by reducing resistance to storm winds.[7]

Flax. A new crop in the Subtropical Gulf Coast Region is flax. It has developed rapidly in the past few years in southwest Texas. Grown as winter crop, it can take advantage

---

[6] John H. Martin and M. M. MacMasters, "Industrial Uses for Grain Sorghum," *Crops in Peace and War, The Yearbook of Agriculture, 1950–1951,* pp. 349–352. Washington, D. C.: Government Printing Office, 1951.

[7] Edwin J. Foscue, "Industrialization of the Texas Gulf Coast Region," *The Southwestern Social Science Quarterly,* Vol. 31, 1950, p. 10.

Figure 8–4. Aerial view of the Corn Products Refining Company plant at Corpus Christi, Texas. The buildings, constructed without walls, make this a well-ventilated, blast-proof plant. It is well adapted to the subtropical climate of the Gulf Coast. (Courtesy Corn Products Refining Company, Photo by Sammy Gold.)

of rainfall and soil moisture, and can be produced on the same land which is planted in cotton or grain sorghum in the summer. Production in southwest Texas has increased from 1,000 acres in 1938 to 273,000 acres in 1949. Flax provides three commercial products: (1) linseed oil for paints, varnishes, oil cloth, patent leather, etc., (2) linseed meal for stock feed, and (3) fiber from flax straw for making cigarette papers and fine writing papers.[8]

Truck Farming. With increasing demands for fresh vegetables, the Subtropical Gulf Coast has become one of the major early truck-farming regions of the continent. Aside from parts of southern California and the gardens under glass in the North, most of the nation's winter vegetables grown for sale come from this region, Florida alone supplying about one fourth. Other vegetable-producing areas are found along the east Gulf Coast and the southwest Gulf Coast, particularly the Lower Rio Grande Valley of Texas. Climate is the dominant factor af-

[8] A. C. Dillman, *Flax, A Winter Crop for South Texas,* Texas Flax Improvement Association, Bulletin No. 9, 1949.

fecting the growth of early vegetables, and soils help to determine the specific locations. In Florida, the best truck crops are produced on muck or other lands having a higher organic content than the sandy soils which characterize much of the state. Vegetable growing in the Lower Rio Grande Valley is confined largely to the alluvial lands of the delta.

Climatically, most of the region is suited to the production of early vegetables. In the southern parts of Florida and Texas, some winters have no killing frosts. However, even here an occasional cold spell or "norther" may sweep down from the interior and kill the more sensitive vegetable crops. Production is limited by economic rather than geographic conditions. Winter markets can consume only a limited amount of truck crops. Therefore, the growing of winter vegetables even in the most favored places, is highly speculative, although sometimes highly remunerative.

Green beans. Beans are grown extensively throughout the Florida Peninsula, as well as in Mississippi, southern Louisiana, and Texas (Figure 8–5). In Florida, which produces the bulk of the nation's early crop, the upland area of the north and the southeast coast predominate.

Cabbage. Early cabbage comes largely from the Lower Rio Grande Valley and the Corpus Christi area of Texas, although southern Louisiana, Mississippi, and Alabama are also producers (Figure 8–6). While the crop is grown in many parts of Florida, it is of only minor importance.

Onions. Commercial production of early onions, particularly the Bermuda variety, is confined to the Lower Rio Grande Valley and the Corpus Christi area (Figure 8–7). The Laredo area of Texas which lies outside this region is a large producer also.

Tomatoes. Most of the commercial crop of early tomatoes is grown in Florida and the Lower Rio Grande Valley (Figure 8–8), which, together with southern California, produce the entire early crop.

Watermelons. Especially important in Florida, watermelons (Figure 8–9) are shipped from early in April until the middle of July. Although not a winter crop, they add largely to Florida's total truck production.

Strawberries. The centers of early strawberry production are the Plant City district of Florida and southeastern Louisiana (Figure 8–10). Louisiana, the leading producer, also has an important berry-canning industry.

Other early truck crops and their major producing areas are: (1) *celery* – the Plant City and Sanford districts of Florida, (2) *early white potatoes* – the Hastings area of Florida, and to a less extent the Lower Rio Grande Valley, (3) *beets and carrots* – the Lower Rio Grande Valley, (4) *peppers* – the New Iberia district of southern Louisiana, and (5) *cucumbers* – north Florida. *Lettuce, escarole, eggplant, romaine, squash, okra, Brussels sprouts, mustard, spinach, parsley, cauliflower, broccoli,* and *green corn,* are produced locally throughout the region.

The Subtropical Atlantic-Gulf Coast is also an important producer of figs, particularly in that section of Texas between Houston and Beaumont, which with California produces most of the nation's crop.

Transportation and Marketing. Marketing the winter truck crops in this region is a serious problem. Recent improvements in highways and railroads have made possible the shipment of much of the early crop to the northern markets in time to command a high price. Co-operative marketing associations have helped, but as yet the region is not so well organized in this respect as is California. Vegetable canning has aided in utilizing much of the crop that cannot be marketed fresh. The vegetable-freezing industry which began about 1929, has grown rapidly in recent years because freezing alters the fresh character of foodstuffs least of all preserving methods. The term "quick freezing" often used in connection with food freezing has no particular significance as most commercial vegetables are frozen at temperatures of about zero degrees Fahrenheit in an hour or less. The pack of frozen vegetables in the United States was about 400 million pounds in 1949, but most of it was processed in about 60 plants located in the North or on the West Coast.[9]

Citrus Fruits. Citrus fruit trees cannot endure below-freezing temperatures for even a few hours at a time without serious damage, and hence are grown only in those parts of the United States where killing freezes seldom occur. The major citrus-producing areas of the nation are in southern California, Arizona, the Rio Grande Valley of Texas, the Mississippi Delta of Louisiana, southern Alabama, and nearly all of peninsula Florida.

Oranges, most resistant to cold of the citrus family, are found in all the areas listed above (Figure 8–11). *Grapefruit,* next in resistance to cold, are grown commercially in this region only in Florida and the Lower Rio Grande Valley (Figure 8–12). *Lemons,* having still less resistance to freezing temperatures, are not produced commercially in this region. *Limes,* the most sensitive of the citrus fruits, cannot withstand frost and hence are grown commercially in the United States only on the frost-free offshore Florida Keys.

---

[9] James A. Berry and F. E. Lindquist, "Nine Principles for Freezing Vegetables," *Crops in Peace and War, The Yearbook of Agriculture, 1950–1951,* pp. 217–220. Washington, D. C.: Government Printing Office, 1951.

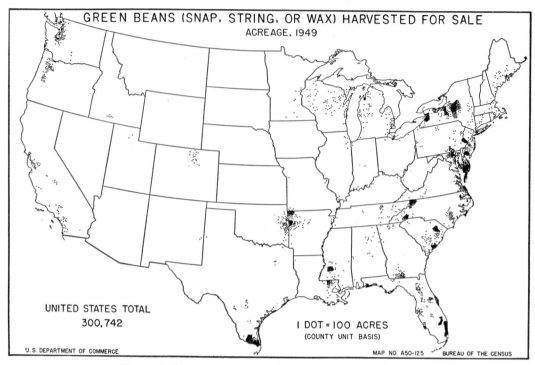

Figure 8–5. Acreage in green beans in the United States.

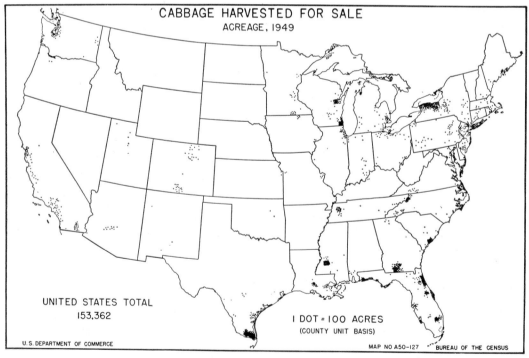

Figure 8–6. Acreage in cabbage in the United States.

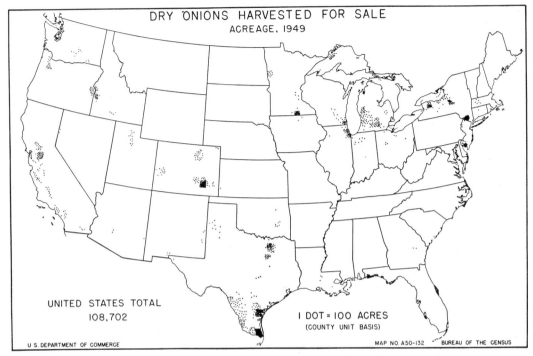

Figure 8–7. Acreage in dry onions in the United States.

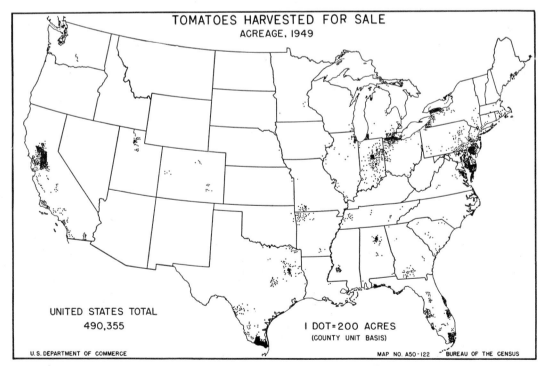

Figure 8–8. Acreage in tomatoes in the United States.

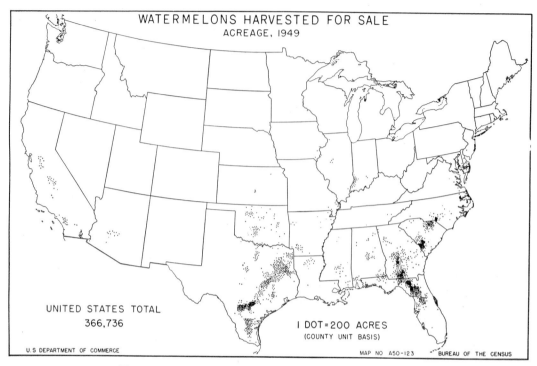

Figure 8–9. Acreage in watermelons in the United States.

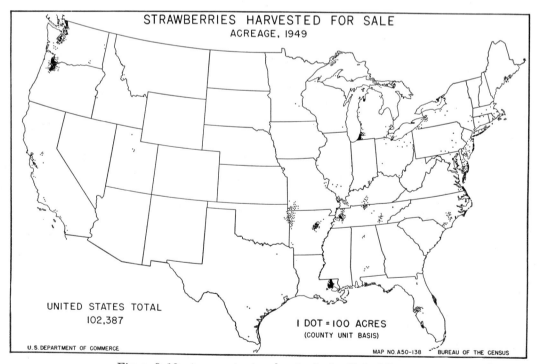

Figure 8–10. Acreage in strawberries in the United States

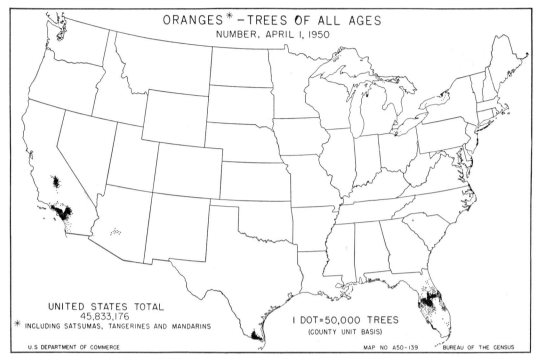

Figure 8–11. Acreage in orange trees in the United States.

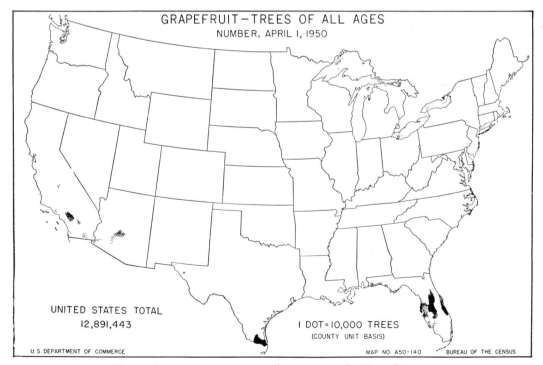

Figure 8–12. Acreage in grapefruit trees in the United States.

Great expense and labor are at times required to protect citrus groves from frosts. Even the southern parts of Texas and Florida have destructive freezes. The citrus fruit industry of the Lower Rio Grande Valley suffered a severe setback in early 1951 when cold weather killed a large percentage of the trees. As this followed closely upon the destructive freeze of 1949, the rehabilitation of the orchards will require several years before production can be brought back to normal.[10]

Florida's citrus groves lie on both the Atlantic and Gulf Coasts of the peninsula, but are most important in the central lakes district. Southern Florida would be a safer locality since frosts there are less common, but there is relatively little suitable land. The slightly rolling terrain of the lakes district provides some protection from the occasional frosts because (1) orchards planted on slopes benefit from air drainage, and (2) the many lakes ameliorate low winter temperatures. The high humidity stimulates growth of juicy fruits which have little objectionable pulp.

The Texas citrus area is located on the terraces of the Lower Rio Grande Delta in about the same latitude as southern Florida. In contrast, however, practically all production is based upon irrigation, the waters being diverted from the Rio Grande. This area specializes in grapefruit.

On the rest of the Gulf Coast, between the Lower Rio Grande and Florida, citrus culture is of minor significance, except in southern Alabama and Mississippi and the Louisiana Delta. This last district, relatively free from frost hazards, produces high-quality oranges, but limited area prohibits large-scale production.

The canning of citrus products. During recent years the canning of grapefruit and grapefruit juice has become important in both Florida and the Lower Rio Grande Valley. Numerous small canneries have sprung up in many of the towns in the citrus-producing areas, and the industry continues

to grow. Hence the surplus citrus crop can now be preserved to a great extent and be marketed at off seasons and in more distant places. The juice of the grapefruit seems to meet wide market demands, as is shown by the fact that several well-known brands from the Lower Rio Grande Valley may be found on grocers' shelves in most parts of the United States. Canned orange juice, produced largely in Florida, soon surpassed grapefruit juice in volume of production, but pasteurization which was necessary in the canning process affected adversely the flavor so that the market demand did not come up to expectations. Soon after the close of World War II, frozen citrus concentrates (largely orange juice) suddenly appeared on the market. During the 1950 season nearly 22 million gallons of the concentrate were produced in Florida [11] and by 1952 the retail volume of this new industry (largely a Florida business) amounted to more than $175 million.[12] In spite of apparent success, however, this new frozen juice industry has suffered financial difficulties because of the initial costs, increasing prices for raw materials, and a more or less ceiling on the retail price which the consumer will pay. Canning and quick-freezing of citrus juices are here to stay, but the industries may remain speculative for a long time before they will become stabilized.

Tung Production. The tung tree produces one of the best quick-drying oils for use in the manufacture of paints and varnishes. The oil is extracted from the kernels of the fruit of the tree, which is a prolific producer. Tung trees were introduced into the United States from the Far East in 1905, but the first commercial orchard was not started until 1924. The first oil-extracting mill was placed in operation near Gainesville, Florida in 1928. From this slow start the production of tung fruit increased rapidly, from a little more than 1,000 tons in 1939 to

---

[10] *The Texas Almanac 1952–1953*, p. 200. Dallas: A. H. Belo Corporation, 1952.

[11] M. K. Veldhuis, "Chemistry and Technology of Citrus," *Crops in Peace and War, The Yearbook of Agriculture, 1950–1951*, p. 264. Washington, D. C.: Government Printing Office, 1951.

[12] "Troubles in Frozen Orange Juice," *Fortune,* March 1952, p. 102.

87,900 tons in 1949, yielding about 26 million pounds of oil.[13]

Because of its exacting climatic requirements, the producing area for the tung tree is limited to a belt about 100 miles wide that extends from eastern Texas along the Gulf of Mexico to the Atlantic Coast. The tree requires at least 45 inches of rainfall, evenly distributed through the year. Dormant, well-nourished trees have withstood temperatures as low as 8 degrees Fahrenheit but protracted periods of subfreezing temperatures prove disastrous.

The fruit, which is about the size of a small apple, matures and drops to the ground late in September or October. As a rule about 86 per cent of the oil can be extracted from the fruit, so that a ton of whole fruit will produce an average of about 300 pounds of marketable oil.

The Livestock Industry

The Gulf Coast Region has been an important producer of beef cattle since French and Spanish colonial times. After the Great Plains were opened to grazing in the 1870's, the poorer pastures of the Gulf Coast found difficulty in competing. For several decades cattle raising was all but abandoned except in the Acadian French country of southwestern Louisiana and the coastal grasslands of southwestern Texas. In recent years, through the introduction of new breeds, particularly the Brahman (Figure 8–13), the cattle industry has expanded to other parts of the coastal region.

Today, large herds of beef cattle graze throughout most of Florida and on the coastal pairies of Louisiana and Texas. In the thornbush pastures of the southwest Texas coast is located the King Ranch, one of the largest on the continent, which contains more than a million acres of grazing land.

The Gulf Coast Region, with large areas of grassland, plentiful rainfall, and mild, open winters, should be able to expand its cattle industry in the future, especially since crossbreeding has produced animals more nearly immune to tick fever.

One of the most interesting developments in the Humid Subtropical Coast Region has been the rapid rise of the beef cattle industry of peninsular Florida. Today the ranching area extends from the lakes district in the northern part of the peninsula to lands south of Lake Okeechobee. In this area more than 1,250,000 head of beef cattle, valued at $150,000,000 are roaming the range. Because of this rapid expansion, Florida now ranks

Figure 8–13. A herd of Brahman cattle on the Texas Gulf Coastal Plain. (Courtesy Beaumont Chamber of Commerce.)

thirteenth among the cattle-raising states of the nation, ahead of Wyoming, New Mexico, Arizona, and Nevada. Livestock markets and packing houses are developing in the state, and sections of Florida are definitely taking on a "western" appearance.

Florida's spectacular growth as a beef producer can be attributed to (1) improvements in pastures, through the introduction of Bermuda, St. Augustine, and other nutritious grasses, (2) improvements in breeds of cattle and (3) the discovery that citrus pulp and citrus molasses, formerly waste products, make excellent cattle feeds.[14]

While Florida is still far behind Texas,

---

[13] George F. Potter and Harley L. Crane, *Tung Production,* pp. 1-6, U. S. Department of Agriculture, Farmers' Bulletin No. 2031. Washington, D. C.: Government Printing Office, 1951.

[14] *The Wall Street Journal,* June 30, 1952.

Nebraska, and Iowa in beef cattle population, the industry is showing a healthy growth and will continue to increase in importance.

Lumbering and Forest-Products Industries

Except for the prairie sections of East Texas and Louisiana, and the Florida Everglades, most of this region was originally forest-covered. Accordingly, forest-products industries — lumbering, naval stores, pulp and paper — have been important. Being common also to the Cotton Belt, however, they have been discussed in the preceding chapter.

An additional word seems desirable, however, in connection with the pulp and paper industry, since some of the larger mills are located on tidewater within the boundary of this region. One of the most complete paper mills in the entire South is that of the Champion Paper and Fibre Company located on the Houston Ship Channel. Representing an initial investment of 10 million dollars, the plant has recently been enlarged to make the glazed paper for *Life* and *Time* magazines. The Houston mill gets its pulpwood from East Texas pine and its power from natural gas. The pulp is run wet into an adjacent paper mill, or is dried and sent by barge through the Intracoastal Canal and up the Mississippi and Ohio rivers to Cincinnati, and thence overland to the company's mill at Hamilton, Ohio. The daily production is 450 tons of pulp and 230 tons of paper.[15] Since the close of World War II, Champion has spent more than 12 million dollars on expansion of its Houston plant.

Mineral Industries

Phosphate Rock. Florida is the continent's most important producer of phosphate rock, accounting for approximately 80 per cent of the total. Most of the remainder comes from Tennessee, Idaho, Wyoming, and

----

[15] "Champion Paper," *Fortune*, January, 1949, p. 85.

Montana. Two types of deposits are worked in Florida: (1) the hard rock phosphate of the north-south belt about 100 miles wide and parallel to the west coast of the peninsula, and (2) the land-pebble phosphate from the smaller area east of Tampa Bay. The former, consisting of boulders and lumps mixed with sand and clay, contains 10 to 25 per cent phosphate, while the latter, a pebbled conglomerate, has a much higher phosphate content. Open pit mining is followed in both areas, after which the materials are crushed, washed, dried, and screened for shipping. Most phosphate used in the United States is converted into acid phosphate or superphosphate by treatment with sulphuric acid. Uranium has been detected in the land-pebble phosphate rocks of Florida and since 1947 the United States Geological Survey and the Atomic Energy Commission have been studying the deposits. The economic importance of the uranium deposits has not yet been disclosed.[16]

Sulphur. Coastal Louisiana and Texas produce more than 99 per cent of the continent's native sulphur. The deposits are found in the cap rock overlying certain salt domes; most of the domes however, do not contain sulphur in paying quantities. Although sulphur (brimstone) is found at depths from 500 to 1,500 feet below ground, commercial exploitation by shaft mining proved unsuccessful, because of danger from caving-in of the overlying sands and gravels. When the Frasch process was perfected in 1903, commercial success was assured, and the Gulf Coast soon took first rank among the world's sulphur-producing regions.

The Frasch process is made possible by the fact that crystalline sulphur melts at 240°F., only slightly above the boiling point of water. Wells are drilled into the deposits on top of the salt plugs. Then by pumping superheated water into the deposit, the sulphur is converted into a liquid. Compressed air is used to force the molten material to the

----

[16] Bertrand L. Johnson and E. M. Tucker, "Phosphate Rock," *Minerals Yearbook, 1949*, p. 1000. Washington, D. C.: Government Printing Office, 1951.

surface. The pipes are heated to prevent the sulphur from solidifying until it reaches the vats on the ground. The vats, constructed either of wood or of steel sheeting, are 1,200 feet long, 50 feet high, and 160 to 200 feet wide. The molten sulphur solidifies immediately upon being poured into the vat and in a short time the gigantic bin is filled. The sides of the vat are then stripped off, exposing a huge block of sulphur which can be blasted. After being shattered into fragments the sulphur, almost chemically pure, is loaded into open freight cars by power shovels (Figure 8–14) and hauled to the shipping port to be loaded on coastwise or ocean vessels for the large industrial consuming markets. Most Texas sulphur moves out through Galveston, while the Louisiana mine has its loading docks at Port Sulphur on the lower Mississippi River.

At one time or another more than a dozen domes have been worked, but in 1949 only five domes in Texas and one in Louisiana were in operation. One new dome came into production in 1951 and others are expected to yield elemental sulphur by 1952 or 1953. At the same time, however, some of the older domes are becoming exhausted.[17] These were being worked by two large and two medium-sized companies that have a monopoly on production. Some sulphur is used in elemental form in the manufacture of rubber and insecticides, and a large tonnage is converted into other sulphur compounds for making such products as paper pulp. Most of the total supply, however, is converted into sulphuric acid which is then used to manufacture fertilizers, industrial chemicals, paints and pigments, and for petroleum refining.[18]

The sulphur industry of the Louisiana-Texas Gulf Coast is one of Anglo-America's major mineral industries. Increased consump-

Figure 8–14. Loading sulphur into gondola railroad cars with large clamshell power shovel, after edge of huge blocks have been broken down by blasting with explosives. (Courtesy Texas Gulf Sulphur Company.)

tion of sulphur, however, is causing a shortage to develop and the United States is no longer self-sufficient in this basic strategic mineral.

Salt. Rock salt is mined in several places along the Louisiana coast, making that state one of the leading national producers. The salt, practically pure sodium chloride, is found in numerous domes throughout the west Gulf Coast. The reserves are enormous. Though only a few domes are being mined in the region at present, they are producing great quantities of salt and none is approaching exhaustion.

The mine usually lies in the top of the salt plug, 600 feet or more below the surface. A shaft is driven down and huge chambers are dug out. By leaving in the supporting columns an amount of salt equal to that removed, no mine props are necessary. The huge chambers are frequently 65 feet or more in width and height. Rock salt is mined by electrically operated shovels. While the Gulf Coast has no monopoly in salt production, it has sufficient reserves to make it an important producer for a very long time. There are many known salt domes (some of

[17] "Report of the Sulphur Committee," *The International Materials Conference,* pp. 46–47. Washington, D. C.: Government Printing Office, 1952.

[18] G. W. Josephson and M. G. Downey, "Sulphur and Pyrites," *Minerals Yearbook, 1949,* p. 1169. Washington, D. C.: Government Printing Office, 1951.

them now producing petroleum) where salt can be obtained when needed.

Oyster Shells. Although oyster shells have been used for many years as a road-building material, the big development in this 25 million dollar industry did not begin until the heavy chemical industry started its phenomenal growth in the 1940's. Today, one sees large mounds of gray, gravelly material piled up at many industrial establishments, representing oyster shells which have been dredged from the shallow bays along the Gulf Coast. With the nearest source of limestone in Texas more than 200 miles from the coast, oyster shells from dead reefs provide industry with a cheap and abundant supply of lime. Lone Star Cement opened its Houston plant in 1916 using oyster shells in place of limestone, and in 1934 Southern Alkali Corporation of Corpus Christi began using shells as a source of lime for their process. Today oyster shells provide one of the principal raw materials needed by such widely diversified plants as Mathieson Chemical Company at Lake Charles, Champion Paper and Fibre Company at Houston, and Dow Chemical Company at Freeport.

The chief dead oyster reefs being dredged today are in Atchafalaya Bay in Louisiana, and in Galveston, Matagorda and Nueces bays in Texas. A modern oyster shell dredge, a complete unit in itself, is capable of processing approximately 900 cubic yards of shells per hour.[19]

Petroleum and Natural Gas

The Subtropical Gulf Coast includes the entire area known as the Gulf Coast Petroleum Province, one of the continent's major oil producers. Although in 1949 it accounted for only 355 million barrels out of a total of 1,840 million barrels produced in the United States,[20] recent well completions have increased yields so that in 1951 oil was being produced at the rate of 2 million barrels per day from the many Gulf Coast fields. This was more than one third of the United States total and almost 20 per cent of the world's production.[21] The oil fields, almost exclusively of salt-dome origin, are scattered along the west Gulf Coastal Plain from the mouth of the Mississippi to the mouth of the Rio Grande. More than 200 salt domes have been discovered in this area most of which have produced oil. Numerous new discoveries are being made and some fields have been developed in the shallow coastal margin of the Gulf of Mexico. This province not only holds the record for the first large gusher but it also has the largest number of producing deep wells in the United States. The Gulf Coast Province has many fields producing at depths of more than 12,000 feet and some which reach depths below 15,000 feet. One company recently completed a well in south Louisiana which bottomed at 18,660 feet, establishing a new depth record for the Gulf Coast Province. This well was extensively tested before being abandoned.[22]

Some unique features of this petroleum province are: (1) the technique and type of equipment developed in geophysical prospecting, (2) the concentration of large refineries along the Gulf Coast, and (3) offshore fields on the continental shelf.

Following the discovery of oil at Spindletop in 1901, many other fields in the Gulf Coast were opened. Geologists, however, found it difficult to locate possible oil structures, since no rock outcropped on the flat expanses of prairie, marsh, and forest lands. Some salt domes gave slight surface indications of their presence by forming small hills on the flat terrain and they were drilled first. Further scientific prospecting was impossible until some means could be devised for discovering deeply buried plugs. Between 1901

[19] Will H. Shearon, Jr., "Oyster-Shell Chemistry." *Chemical and Engineering News,* Vol. 29, 1951, pp. 3078-3080.

[20] *Minerals Yearbook, 1949,* p. 878. Washington, D. C.: Government Printing Office, 1951.

[21] Walter Rose, "The Gulf Coast Today: It Produces More Than Two Million Barrels of Oil Per Day," *The Oil and Gas Journal,* Vol. 51, 1952, p. 199.

[22] W. Van London and L. D. Owen, "The Gulf Coast Today: Development Drilling Continues Apace Despite Tubular-Goods Shortage," *The Oil and Gas Journal,* Vol. 51, 1952, p. 204.

and 1922, this region became a "wildcatter's paradise" for despite the crude methods of exploration employed, 39 of the 46 domes discovered during that period were producers.[23]

In the early 1920's several types of geophysical instruments were developed, (1) the magnetometer, (2) the torsion balance, and (3) the seismograph. The last, which measures the rate of movement of sound through different media below the earth's surface is the most popular of the geophysical instruments today. By its use many deeply buried salt domes have been discovered and large production secured.

Geologists and geophysicists experienced great difficulty in traversing the wet coastal terrain and in transporting their heavy scientific equipment over swamps, marshes, and open lagoons. Boats were used in many places but these could not cross marshy areas. Several types of amphibious crafts, known as "marsh buggies" (Figure 8–15) were developed to transport geophysical crews and their equipment over this almost

[23] Virginia Bradley, "The Petroleum Industry of the Gulf Coast Salt Dome Area," *Economic Geography,* Vol. 15, 1939, pp. 399-400.

impassible terrain. Recently, the helicopter has been used with considerable success in this exploratory work and in some cases they are operated in conjunction with the marsh buggies.

Since much crude oil is transported today by pipelines, the Gulf Coast port cities have become the termini of most pipelines from the Gulf Coast and Mid-continent Oil Provinces. These pipelines have permitted the rapid development of the refining industry along the West Gulf Coast between Baton Rouge and Corpus Christi. Enormous quantities of both crude and refined petroleum are shipped also by tankers to the North Atlantic Seaboard or to foreign countries.

The Continental Shelf Problem. Much controversy has arisen over State versus federal ownership of the continental shelf (tidelands) since the president's executive order of 1945 placed such areas under the Department of the Interior. Between 1945 and 1952, Congress twice passed legislation to restore title of the tidelands to the states and each time it was vetoed by President Truman. In June 1952, the bill was considered again with the possibility of its being passed over the President's veto.

Figure 8–15. "Marsh buggies" used by exploration crews for seismograph operations in the swampy lowlands of the Gulf Coast. (Courtesy of *The Oil and Gas Journal.*)

Following the national election of November 1952, which swept the Republican party into power, and the inauguration of President Eisenhower in January 1953, new legislation was started. On April 1, 1953, the House of Representatives passed a new tidelands bill by a vote of 285 to 108, and a month later (May 5) the Senate passed a slightly different version of the bill by a vote of 56 to 23. Since the Senate bill was slightly different from the one passed by the House it was returned to the House which accepted the Senate's version on May 13, by a vote of 218 to 116. On May 22, the tidelands bill was signed by President Eisenhower and became a law. Since then the states of Arkansas and Alabama have threatened suit against the federal government to prevent the tidelands from being returned to the individual states.

The legislation recognizes the states' rights

Figure 8–16. Aerial view of an offshore drilling rig and platform. This well, located on the continental shelf off the coast of Louisiana, was drilled to a depth of 13,636 feet. (Courtesy Magnolia Petroleum Company.)

to all land between the low-water mark and the three-mile limit, except for Texas and the Gulf Coast of Florida where the limit is set at ten and one-half miles. Beyond these outer limits the law holds that the submerged resources are the sole property of the federal government, and legislation is being prepared to establish the procedure under which the Secretary of the Interior will issue leases for the exploration and development of the continental shelf.[24]

During the period of nearly eight years while the tidelands bill was being considered, oil and gas development on the continental shelf was suspended. Before 1945 about twenty wells which were showing good production and the possibilities of a profit to the companies developing them, had been completed in the shallow waters of the Gulf, despite the high cost of drilling in offshore waters (Fig. 8–16). Through geophysical prospecting the oil companies had discovered the presence of vast supplies of oil and gas in the tidelands, and with the cooperation of friendly state legislatures they were progressing rapidly in the development of these resources when the executive order of 1945 caused all drilling activities to cease. The federal government's assertion of a doctrine of "paramount right and domain" made the oil companies fear for the security of their offshore leases. With the return of the tidelands to the states, it is presumed that exploration and drilling will be started again although there may be some hesitation on the part of the oil companies to invest large sums of money in areas which might again be transferred to the federal government with a change in the administration. At this time one wonders if the tidelands dispute can be finally settled.

Natural Gas in the Gulf Coast Region. The Gulf Coast Region contains one of the greatest producing areas and also one of the largest reserves of natural gas in the United

[24] *The Oil and Gas Journal*, Vol. 51, No. 48, April 6, 1953, p. 71; Vol. 52, No. 1, May 11, 1953, p. 88; Vol. 52, No. 2, May 18, 1953, p. 224; and Vol. 52, No. 4, June 1, 1953, p. 58.

States.[25] Estimates in 1951 place the reserves in this region at about 85 trillion cubic feet — a sufficient quantity to supply the Gulf Coast with gas for the next twenty years if no future reserves are discovered. Estimated gas reserves in the offshore area may add another 50 trillion cubic feet when they can be utilized.

Conservation problems, however, are important. Although gas flares are still common, they have been reduced to a considerable extent through the activities of the Texas Railroad Commission and the Louisiana Conservation Commission. Further reduction will be made when new laws are enacted which require a report on the disposal of gas from each well. Great quantities of gas are being piped to industrial and metropolitan areas in the North and East. As yet this represents surplus gas which is not needed locally. However, as industry continues to expand along the Gulf Coast and continues to use gas as a fuel and as a raw material for petrochemicals, greater demands will be made to keep the gas in the coastal area.

Manufacturing

Since the beginning of World War II, the Subtropical Gulf Coast Region has advanced rapidly in industrial development. A few large industries moved in the 1930's to Mobile, New Orleans, Houston, and Corpus Christi, but the large scale development came in the 1940's. Some advantages this region offered were (1) large supplies of basic minerals such as sulphur, salt, lime (oyster shells), magnesium (from sea water), and natural gas; (2) an abundant supply of natural gas for fuel; and (3) tidewater location to provide cheap ocean rates for bulky manufactured products. Other factors such as labor supply and availability of capital were also important but they were of less significance in attracting industry.

The manufacturing industries of the Gulf Coast Region represent a variety of types, but the major ones may be classified as:

1. *Food products industries,* such as rice cleaners and processors, sugar refineries, and the Corn Products Corporation at Corpus Christi, manufacturing starch, corn syrup, and corn sugar from milo maize grown in the immediate vicinity.

2. *Wood products industries,* including sawmills, and pulp and paper mills.

3. *Extractive industries,* such as withdrawing oil and gas, mining sulphur and salt, and dredging oyster shells.

4. *Refineries,* producing gasoline, lubricating oils and similar products from petroleum and natural gas.

5. *Chemical industries,* utilizing petroleum, natural gas, sulphur, salt, or oyster shells as raw materials to produce such items as acetate salts, formaldehyde, and other chemicals from natural gas; soda ash, caustic soda, and chlorine from salt and oyster shells; sulphuric acid from the large supplies of sulphur; synthetic rubber from petroleum; and nylon salts from natural gas.

6. *Metallurgical industries,* extracting magnesium salt from sea water and refining it into metallic magnesium, or producing zinc, tin, and iron and steel from ores or concentrates imported largely from overseas[26]

All these types of industries represent an outlay of more than a billion dollars — some of it private capital invested before World War II, much of it government money spent on war plants now operating under private control, and an increasing amount of it postwar investment by private capital from other parts of the United States.

The first four classes of industries have been considered with agricultural production, forest products, or minerals, and hence only the last two types will be discussed here. Space limitations prohibit any detailed analysis of the many large industries under each class, so for brevity only one type illustration will be given for each.

[25] Walter Rose, "The Gulf Coast Today: It Has Third of Nation's Gas-Expanding Transmission Facilities," *The Oil and Gas Journal,* Vol. 51, No. 6, 1952, pp. 196-198.

[26] Foscue, "Industrialization of the Texas Gulf Coast Region," pp. 7–8.

Figure 8–17. Aerial view of a part of the Humble Oil & Refining Company's plant at Baytown, Texas. The installation in the foreground produces the Buna-S type of synthetic rubber from petroleum, while the plant in the background produces another type of synthetic rubber known as Butyl. (Courtesy Roy M. Huffington and the Humble Oil & Refining Company.)

The Petrochemical Industries. The demand for aviation gasoline has revolutionized petroleum refining and indirectly created many new-products industries. Along the west Gulf Coast in the early 1940's leading oil companies built subsidiary plants to process the by-products of aviation gasoline. Included were butadiene plants for the manufacture of synthetic rubber (Figure 8–17), toluene plants for the manufacture of a basic ingredient for tri-nitrotoluene (TNT), and many others. Recycling plants that "strip" natural gas of gasoline, butane, and other minerals, also were established. Another important industrial product made from natural gas is carbon black, about 80 per cent of which is produced by Texas although not all of this comes from the coastal region.

As a result of these by-product industries,

an entirely new group of industries, known as petrochemicals has developed which produce an amazing number of synthetic products from oil and natural gas — chiefly the latter. During 1951 and the first half of 1952, nearly 500 million dollars was earmarked for the petrochemical industry along the Gulf Coast.[27]

Although the industry is concentrated in five areas along the coast: (1) Baton Rouge, (2) Lake Charles, (3) Port Arthur – Port Neches – Beaumont, (4) Texas City – Freeport, and (5) Houston (Figure 8–1), many petrochemical plants are scattered through the region from Baton Rouge on the east to Brownsville on the southwest. One of the

[27] F. Lawrence Resen, "The Gulf Coast Today: Its Billion-Dollar Petrochemical Industry Geared for War or Peace," *The Oil and Gas Journal,* Vol. 51. No. 6, 1952, pp. 190-192.

largest and most interesting of the petro-chemical plants is the industrial establishment of the Celanese Corporation of America at Bishop, some 45 miles southwest of Corpus Christi.

As early as 1932 the Celanese Corporation of America, one of the three largest producers of rayon yarns in the United States, began a research program to develop a process of securing acetic acid from natural gas. The company felt this was essential in order to have an unlimited supply of this basic raw material for its process. By 1941 the process was well enough developed that a small plant was established at Cumberland, Maryland. Then came World War II and with it a demand by the War Production Board for rapid expansion of the process so as to supply additional products — particularly butadiene for the synthetic rubber and chemical programs. Accordingly, Celanese built its plant at Bishop, near large supplies of natural gas. Construction was started in 1944 and completed the next year, initial operation began in April, 1945. The war ended before the Bishop plant got into the production of butadiene but with slight alterations the entire establishment was converted to manufacture acetic acid and acetone, the two chief chemicals required in the production of cellulose acetate.

Some 200,000 gallons of propane and butane (from natural gas) are required daily to supply the plant with its basic raw materials. These are piped largely from the La Gloria Field about 25 miles to the southwest. In addition this field furnishes 40 million cubic feet of dry gas (methane) per day for fuel to drive the compressors. Water needed in the process is piped from the Nueces River about 26 miles away. The 550 acre industrial site provides ample open space for long range expansion.

Acetic acid and acetone, the two major chemicals produced at Bishop, are consumed entirely by company plants in the manufacture of textiles and plastics which are marketed as Celanese products. In addition a number of other chemical products including formaldehyde, methyl alcohol, and propyl alcohol are sold to outside organizations for the production of textiles, plastics, solvents and anti-freeze mixtures. All products are shipped from the Bishop plant in specially designed railroad tank cars, and move either directly by rail to the ultimate consumer or by rail and water.

The Celanese Corporation regards its present operation at Bishop as just a beginning in the field of petroleum and natural gas chemicals. To stimulate investigation it has established a complete research laboratory at Clarkwood, a few miles west of Corpus Christi, for further study of petroleum and natural gas.

As one views this gigantic, sprawling industrial plant with its glistening fractionating towers and silvery tanks, the thought occurs that the industry is self-operating because of the apparent absence of workers. A relatively few men can run the push-button controls of the plant. However, in its various operations, the Bishop plant employs nearly 900 workers including about 75 technical men.

The Inorganic Chemical Industries. Although newcomers to the Gulf Coast, these industries are growing in importance. The abundance of sulphur, salt, and lime, the cheapness of fuel, and the advantage of cheap ocean freight rates, all conspire to attract industries which use large amounts of fuel and pay heavy freight costs on their fabricated products.

Southern Alkali Corporation (now called Columbia Southern Chemical Corporation) located its plant in the Corpus Christi area in 1933 because of the nearness to (1) raw materials — salt and oyster shells, (2) an abundant supply of natural gas for fuel, and (3) deep water to provide low freight rates for the transportation of its bulky, heavy chemicals. The original plant which is owned jointly by the Pittsburgh Plate Glass Company and the American Cyanamid Company, two large consumers of soda ash, began operation in September, 1934. At first it produced only soda ash and caustic soda, but in 1937 a chlorine producing unit was added to utilize the great amount of free chlorine released in the chemical operation. In 1940 the nation's defense program increased the demand for alkali and chlorine. Plans were drawn for expanding the facilities to meet these demands and the new additions were completed in 1941 which increased by 50 per cent the output of all three manufactured products.

A number of other alkali plants have been located in the Gulf Coast area since 1940.

Metallic Industries. For a long time the lack of a suitable coking coal prohibited the development of an iron and steel industry along the Gulf Coast, although low-grade brown iron ores from East Texas were available and there were ample supplies of scrap in the Gulf Southwest. Lime from limestone or from oyster shells was also available. The first plant was not constructed, however, until 1942 when Sheffield Steel, a subsidiary of Armco Steel Corporation, opened a large mill on the Houston Ship Channel. This plant has been enlarged several times and today uses scrap, east Texas ores, and some high-grade ores from Brazil. In the summer of 1950 a plant for the production of large-scale welded steel pipe for the oil and gas industry, was built adjacent to the Sheffield plant, and this has necessitated further expansion of the initial steel mill.

The Gulf Coast area has had a locational advantage for alumina-reduction plants, since most of our supply of bauxite comes from northern South America or from some of the islands of the West Indies. The first plant of this type was constructed by Alcoa at Mobile. Just prior to World War II, a similar plant was built at Baton Rouge by the government, but was sold to the Kaiser interests after the war. Increasing demands for metallic aluminum caused a revolution in the industry. During the war period a

Figure 8–18. The San Patricio Aluminum Reduction Plant of the Reynolds Metal Company. This plant is designed for the sole purpose of reducing aluminum oxide to aluminum pigs or ingots. (Photo by Bell, courtesy Reynolds Metal Company.)

number of aluminum plants were located on the West Coast. With the cessation of hostilities, however, Reynolds Metal Company, and Kaiser Aluminum Company began an expansion program, locating some of their new plants on the Gulf Coast to utilize natural gas as a fuel for generating electricity needed in the reduction of the ore. Alcoa also expanded its production in the Gulf Coast area by constructing a plant at Point Comfort near Port Lavaca, Texas. In a short time, Reynolds built two large units on Corpus Christi Bay (Figure 8–18), utilizing

than 100 miles apart. In the immediately adjacent Cotton Belt, Alcoa has recently completed the first alumina-reduction plant to use lignite as a fuel to generate electricity.

Numerous other metal industries are located along the coast primarily because of cheap fuel and cheap water transportation. In practically every case the ore is imported from overseas or from a distance by land. The only exception is the magnesium plant of Dow Chemical Company where metallic magnesium is extracted from salts dissolved in the waters of the Gulf of Mexico.

Figure 8–19. Aerial view of the Longhorn Tin Smelter at Texas City. This plant, the only tin smelter in the United States, secures its ores and concentrates from overseas. It is owned by the federal government and operated by the Tin Processing Corporation. (Photo by Elwood M. Payne, courtesy of Tin Processing Corporation.)

natural gas as a fuel. The alumina reduction plant is securing its bauxite from new deposits in Jamaica, and the adjacent refinery is converting the alumina to metallic aluminum. This is America's first integrated plant which carries on the entire aluminum manufacturing process at one site.[28] After purchasing the reduction plant at Baton Rouge, the Kaiser interests built a large aluminum metal refinery in New Orleans, thereby establishing another completely integrated industry on the Gulf Coast in two cities less

---

[28] Stanley A. Arbingast, "Metals Industries of Texas," *Texas Business Review*, Vol. 25, No. 10, November 1951, pp. 16-17.

In 1942 the American Smelting and Refining Company built an electrolytic plant at Corpus Christi for refining zinc ore, imported largely from Mexico. The site was selected primarily because of cheap natural gas for fuel and because of its tidewater location.

In 1940, the Dow Chemical Company built a multi-million dollar plant at Freeport, Texas, for the purpose of extracting metallic magnesium from the salts in the waters of the Gulf of Mexico. This plant has been expanded and today produces a number of synthetics as well as magnesium.

One of the most uniquely located metal industries of the entire Gulf Coast Region is

the plant of the Tin Processing Corporation at Texas City on Galveston Bay (Figure 8–19). This plant, known as the Longhorn Tin Smelter, is the only tin smelter in the United States. It was built at the outbreak of World War II, to process the large stockpile of tin ore which the United States had accumulated on the Gulf Coast. With the capture of Malaya and the Dutch East Indies by the Japanese in 1942, the chief supply of tin was cut off, and this smelter had to begin using a lower grade tin concentrate from Bolivia. This concentrate contained oxides of silver, antimony, arsenic, bismuth, tungsten, and copper, but in nuisance quantities only. In the tin smelting process, large quantities of hydrochloric acid were used, and the waste from the process was originally dumped into Galveston Bay on the assumption that the tide would take it out to sea. When this waste material began to kill the fish and oysters, the company was forced to impound it in large earthern tanks. A new unit was then added to the plant to recover hydrochloric acid from this waste material, and in so doing, small quantities of silver and other metals are recovered. The Longhorn Tin Smelter has had difficulties in securing ore because of the widely fluctuating prices, but despite all difficulties it has continued to operate as the only tin smelter in the United States.

Shipbuilding

During the first World War several Southern shipyards were established to build wooden vessels, but with the cessation of hostilities, they were abandoned. World War II revived shipbuilding along the Gulf Coast. Nearness to steel mills at Birmingham and Houston along with cheap water transportation by rivers and by the Intracoastal Canal, make possible the construction of ships on the Gulf Coast at a price comparable to that of other areas.

Shipyards were in active operation in 1941 at Tampa, Mobile, Pascagoula, and Beaumont, and others were being built at Chickasaw (Alabama), New Orleans, Orange, and Houston. An interesting feature of Southern shipyards is that practically all steel parts are welded instead of riveted.

With the close of the war, many of these shipyards were closed, others remained in production on a much reduced scale. In some cases great difficulties were caused by the abandonment of such plants as that of the Gulf Shipbuilding Corporation at Mobile.[29] Except in an emergency, the Gulf Coast Region is not likely to be a major shipbuilding area.

The Fishing Industry

The Gulf Coast is less important for commercial fishing than either the Atlantic or the Pacific Coasts. Its accessibility to the interior of the continent, however, plus the fact that several delectable varieties of fish found in Gulf waters are scarce elsewhere, make this region one of growing importance. The most highly prized fish include sheepshead, pompano, grouper, and red snapper. The last two are caught in great numbers on offshore banks and on the large Campeche Bank off the coast of Yucatan (Figure 4–8). The center of the red snapper industry is now Pensacola. From that port large schooners operate to the Campeche Banks between October and April, while small boats being more dependent on good weather operate largely during the spring and summer.

Oyster and Shrimp Fishing. Almost every small bay or lagoon along the Gulf Coast has an oyster-fishing industry, characterized by its fleet of fishing vessels, large piles of shells, and packing plants. The Mississippi and Louisiana coastal areas now lead in the production of oysters.

Shrimp are caught along the South Atlantic and Gulf Coasts, but Texas coastal waters now outrank all others in the volume of the catch. Most of the small white shrimp are caught in lagoons, but in recent years the industry has invaded offshore banks where the larger Brazilian, or red shrimp are caught.[30]

---

[29] "Mobile, Alabama, After the Storm," *Fortune,* Vol. 33, No. 3, March 1946, pp. 106–115.

[30] Robert H. Ryan, "Texas Shrimp and Oysters," *Texas Business Review,* Vol. 26, No. 2, 1952, pp. 16-17.

The shrimp are iced, if to be sold fresh, or boiled if to be canned. Sun-dried shrimp are marketed abroad. The by-products of this industry are used to make meal for feed-stuffs or for fertilizers.

Sponges. Key West formerly dominated the sponge industry of the continent, but in recent years Tarpon Springs has replaced it. In normal times about 90 per cent of the sponge catch of the United States is landed at that port.[31] Two methods are used to gather the sponges from the ocean floor: (1) hooking, where the sponge is brought to the surface by a long hook operated by the fisherman from the boat's deck, and (2) diving, where the sponge fisherman goes to the bottom in a diver's suit and by means of instruments tears the sponges from the bottom. Practically all diving is done by Greek fishermen. After the sponge is brought to the surface, it is pounded with clubs or trodden with bare feet to rid it of the animal matter. It is then washed, strung up, and dried. This process is repeated until only the skeleton (the commercial sponge) is left. Nassau in the Bahamas and Batabanó, Cuba, are Tarpon Springs' chief competitors. In recent years there has been a steady depletion of the sponge beds.

Sport Fishing. Sport fishing has assumed great significance all along the Gulf Coast, and is particularly important in Florida waters where it has taken on the proportions of a multimillion dollar industry. The chief game fish include the tarpon, shark, and sailfish, most of which have no food value. After the average fisherman makes his catch and has his picture taken beside it, he has no further use for the fish, unless he plans to have it mounted.

Trapping

Several Gulf Coast areas produce furs including mink, otter, skunk, muskrat and nutria. The swamps of southern Louisiana provide the best home for muskrats, and nearly three fourths of Anglo-America's sup-ply is trapped here even though the area has relatively mild winters. Louisiana law allows each trapper to operate 250 steel traps, and requires him to inspect them daily.

The trapper at the end of the day returns to his cabin in the marshes with his load of muskrats. He skins them and hangs their pelts on a rack by the side of the house to dry. Fur buyers visit these trappers, select and grade the furs they wish to buy, and pay cash for the pelts.

The muskrat is extremely prolific, and there seems to be little danger of extermination, despite the average catch of more than six million a year. Mink and otter are trapped to some extent in Louisiana but the total value of their peltries does not equal that of the muskrat.

Nutria, recently imported from South America are larger than muskrats and hence their pelts bring a higher price. They are multiplying rapidly and may some day replace the muskrat in the Gulf Coast fur industry.[32]

Spanish Moss Gathering

Travelers along the Gulf Coast from Florida to southeast Texas, are impressed with the quantities of moss that festoon the trees. Being an epiphyte, which propagates by fragments of the plant and not by seeds, it derives nourishment entirely from the air and will grow wherever sufficient warmth and moisture can be secured. In colonial times this moss was used in making bridles, saddle blankets, horse collars, and as stuffing for pillows and mattresses.

When the furniture and automobile industries discovered its value for upholstery stuffing, a profitable business of moss gathering developed, mainly in the swamp country of the Mississippi Delta. Since the supply seems limitless, it can easily be expanded when the market demand increases.

Resorts

The Subtropical Gulf Coast is one of the major resort regions of Anglo-America. In

[31] A. H. Stuart, *World Trade in Sponges*, U. S. Department of Commerce, Industrial Series No. 82, p. 45. Washington, D. C.: Government Printing Office, 1948.

[32] "Muskrat Trapping," *Fortune*, Vol. 40, 1949, p. 117-122.

Figure 8–20. Miami Beach, Florida, an all-year vacation resort, stretches for nine miles along the Atlantic Ocean. Its 375 hotels, mostly less than 15 years old, include some of the most luxurious hostelries in the world. (Miami Beach News Bureau Photo.)

addition to Florida, the coast of Mississippi, and to a lesser extent the Texas coast, have a resort business which is increasing in im- portance. The entire coast of Mississippi from Pascagoula to Bay St. Louis is almost a con- tinuous resort town. The resort industry of the Louisiana and Texas coasts has not been developed to the extent of that of Florida or Mississippi.

Florida Resorts. The resort industry is of great importance on both coasts of the Florida peninsula (Figure 8–20) and is confined largely to the winter season. In recent years, however, the summer tourist business has increased so rapidly that it now compares favorably with that of winter.

Winter tourists begin coming in large numbers about the middle of January, increase steadily until the last of February, and begin to leave soon after the first of March.

Visitors come from practically every state and from many foreign countries but the majority are from east of the Mississippi and north of the Ohio and Potomac rivers. They come in all kinds of conveyances — steam yachts, airplanes, streamlined trains, busses, and automobiles. Some even "thumb it" on the highway.

Toward the close of the nineteenth century Henry M. Flagler built a large modern hotel (The Ponce de Leon) at St. Augustine and made plans for others along the east coast. He also built the Florida East Coast Railroad to Palm Beach, Miami, and ultimately to Key West — more than 100 miles beyond the end of the peninsula. This overseas section which cost $100,000 a mile never was profitable. In the 1930's a hurricane destroyed some of the bridges causing abandonment of rail service to Key West. However, Florida repaired the bridges and built a motor highway that extends to the island city. On the west coast, Henry Plant completed another railroad line to Tampa and points south. Although considerable resort business has developed around Tampa Bay, the west coast gets a minor part of the tourist trade.

Transportation

The Humid Subtropical Coast has a number of important ports including Charleston, Savannah, Jacksonville, Miami, Tampa, Mobile, New Orleans, Lake Charles, Beaumont, Orange, Port Arthur, Galveston, Houston, Corpus Christi, and Brownsville. These, in varying degrees, carry on an important coastal and overseas trade for this region and also for the Cotton Belt.

Rivers, particularly the Mississippi and Tombigbee, have played an important role in transporting freight from the interior to Gulf Coast ports, and coastal waterways have grown in importance in recent years.

The Intracoastal Canal was originally planned to extend from New York to Brownsville as a continuous waterway, utilizing lagoons behind barrier beaches where possible, and cutting through the coastal plain where necessary. The link across northern Florida was never completed. One part of the canal now runs down the east coast as far as Key West and another begins in western Florida, and extends to Brownsville. Between Mobile Bay and New Orleans, and between New Orleans and Galveston Bay, considerable heavy barge traffic traverses the canal, which is linked with the Mississippi River system. Southwest of Galveston some traffic moves to Corpus Christi but little goes beyond that point. The portion of the canal along the east coast of Florida carries many small pleasure craft, particularly during the tourist season, but little freight moves south of Jacksonville.

Railroads, highways, and airways have been developed into a complete transportation network so that today no part of the region is more than a few miles from rapid transportation.

Most large petroleum refineries are located on tidewater. Mid-Continent and Gulf Coastal oil fields are connected with Gulf ports by a maze of pipelines, through which flows a major part of the petroleum from southwestern fields, as well as considerable quantities of refined gasoline. Practically all crude oil that is not refined at Gulf ports is shipped by tanker either to eastern seaboard cities or overseas.

The Outlook

The Humid Subtropical Coast Region remained one of the most backward parts of Anglo-America until almost the beginning of the present century. Prior to 1900 its chief activities were forest exploitation, agriculture, and ranching. The few badly run-down ports were in need of modernization.

With the discovery of oil at Spindletop, Texas, in 1901, and the development of phosphate, sulphur, salt, and lime (oyster shells), the coastal region began to attract industry, although no major development took place until the 1940's. In this region industry has found a favorable habitat.

In addition to deep water, the Gulf Coast offers many advantages to certain classes of industry. As an industrial region during times of peace it is superior in some respects to either the Atlantic Coast or the Pacific Coast of the United States, but in times of war it has the additional advantage of being the most remote and hence the least vulnerable of our three coastal areas from an aerial attack by a possible transpolar enemy.

Few regions of Anglo-America present a brighter outlook for manufacturing than this Humid Subtropical Coast, described as "The Golden Coast" where one finds the world's most extensive industrialization of a subtropical region. The end of World War II had little effect here because "people are still busy exploring, digging, drilling, draining, dredging, planting, building, rebuilding, buying, selling, competing, merging, speculating, boosting — all as though a world had to be made." [33]

[33] "The Golden Coast," *Fortune*, Vol. 40, October 1949, pp. 83 ff.

Table 7

SELECTED CITIES AND TOWNS OF THE HUMID SUBTROPICAL COAST

City or Town	Urbanized area	Political center	City or Town	Urbanized area	Political center
Baton Rouge	128,864	125,629	Lake Charles		41,272
Beaumont	94,169	94,014	McAllen		20,067
Biloxi		37,425	Miami	458,647	249,276
Brownsville		36,066	Miami Beach		46,282
Brunswick		17,954	Mobile	182,963	129,009
Charleston	120,289	70,174	New Orleans	659,768	570,445
Corpus Christi	122,956	108,287	Orange		21,174
Daytona Beach		30,187	Orlando	73,163	52,367
Fort Lauderdale		36,328	Panama City		25,814
Gainesville		26,861	Pensacola		43,479
Galveston	71,527	66,568	Port Arthur	82,150	57,530
Gulfport		22,659	St. Petersburg	114,596	96,738
Harlingen		23,229	Savannah	128,196	119,638
Houston	700,508	596,163	Tallahassee		27,237
Jacksonville	242,909	204,517	Tampa	179,335	124,681
Key West		26,433	West Palm Beach		43,162
Lafayette		33,541			

Selected Bibliography

C. C. Aldrich and M. W. de Blieux, and F. B. Kniffen, "The Spanish Moss Industry and Louisiana," *Economic Geography*, Vol. 19, 1943, pp. 347-357.

Robe B. Carson, "The Florida Tropics," *Economic Geography*, Vol. 27, 1951, pp. 321-339.

G. S. Corfield, "Spanish Moss: Forest By-Product of the South," *Journal of Geography*, Vol. 42, 1943, pp. 308-317.

Sigismond de R. Diettrich, "Florida's Climatic Extremes: Cold Spells and Freezes," *Economic Geography*, Vol. 25, 1949, pp. 68-74.

_____, "Florida's Human Resources," *Geographical Review*, Vol. 38, 1948, pp. 278-288.

Edwin J. Foscue, "Industrialization of the Texas Gulf Coast Region," *Southwestern Social Science Quarterly*, Vol. 31, 1950, pp. 1-18.

Charles B. Henderson, "The Longhorn Tin Smelter," *Mining and Metallurgy*, Vol. 24, 1943, pp. 196-200.

Bertrand L. Johnson, "Economic Factors in the U. S. Phosphate Industry," *Mining and Metallurgy*, Vol. 25, 1944, pp. 455-464.

Peveril Meigs, III, "An Ethno-Telephonic Survey of French Louisiana," *Annals of Association of American Geographers,* Vol. 31, 1941, pp. 243-250.

James J. Parsons, "Recent Industrial Development in the Gulf South," *Geographical Review,* Vol. 40, 1950, pp. 67-83.

Richard Joel Russell, "Flotant," *Geographical Review,* Vol. 32, 1942, pp. 74-98.

L. LeMar Stephen, "Geographic Role of the Everglades in the Early History of Florida," *Scientific Monthly,* Vol. 55, 1942, pp. 515-526.

Warren Strain, "Florida Phosphate Industry," *Journal of Geography,* Vol. 44, 1945, pp. 257-264.

S. J. Swainson, "Washing and Concentrating Florida Pebble Phosphate," *Mining and Metallurgy,* Vol. 25, 1944, pp. 469-474.

9.

The Agricultural Interior

THE world's greatest storehouse of farming wealth, a region ideally fashioned by nature to become the home of a thriving population is the Agricultural Interior (Figure 9–1). It produces more corn and oats and meat than any other area of equal size. It also produces much hay, winter wheat, barley, soybeans, tobacco, fruits, vegetables and dairy products. During World War II, it served as the bread basket of the United Nations. The Agricultural Interior falls almost wholly within the United States. Canada has no agricultural Middle West; instead it has the inhospitable Canadian Shield, which does not give way to arable lands until it meets the Manitoba Basin.

The influence of the Agricultural Interior on the United States politically, economically, and socially cannot be overestimated. Of all the regions in Anglo-America, this one is indisputably the most self-contained and independent. It is basically agricultural; most of the cities are little more than "farm-rimmed factory towns."

Boundaries

The Agricultural Interior occupies only part of the vast interior plain of North America; it is set off from adjoining regions to the west and north by rather indefinite

boundaries that have been shifting because of improved strains of corn (hybrid), earlier maturing and drought-tolerant varieties of grains, new methods of tillage, and moisture conservation.

On the west the region merges with the Great Plains; scanty rainfall separates the prairie margin from the short grass country of the Great Plains at about the 98th meridian. Here precipitation is inadequate for the profitable production of corn, except in eastern Colorado, and the crop tends to be replaced by those that are more drought-resistant. On the east lies the rugged Allegheny Plateau with its prevalence of relatively infertile sandstone and shale soils which produce little corn for sale (Figure 9–2); here livestock, particularly sheep, dominate the agriculture. On the north lies the Northern Continental Forest, characterized by the relatively infertile soils of the Canadian Shield and a less important agriculture, and by the Spring Wheat Subregion, which is now in a stage of transition from wheat growing to dairying. On the southwest, it is bordered by the Cotton Belt, the Ozark-Ouachita Uplands, and the Hard Winter Wheat Subregion. This last boundary is drawn where the rainfall and hot summer winds tend to replace corn by wheat and the grain sorghums.

Figure 9–1. The Agricultural Interior. A region of corn, small grains, hay, tobacco, fruit, livestock, and dairying. It includes the Corn Belt and parts of the Hay and Dairy Belt and of the Corn and Winter Wheat Belt.

The Subregions

The Agricultural Interior, despite its homogeneity falls into several subregions — the Corn Belt, The Corn and Winter Wheat Belt, the Hay and Dairy Region and the Tobacco and General Farming Subregion.

The presence of these subregions within a universally recognized region, such as the Agricultural Interior, indicates that even the most closely-knit region is but relatively homogeneous.

Appearance of the Region

There is a certain similarity in the landscape from boundary to boundary; but similarity here is not synonymous with absolute uniformity. The best way to get the "feel" of this region is to fly over it — particularly in late spring. The landscape then unrolls like a map and it is a beautiful sight. The flat to undulating terrain is laid out in squares and looks like a checkerboard (Figure 9-3). The roads are laid out at right angles and mostly cross at one-mile intervals. Here are deep green fields of winter wheat, pale green pastures, and still paler green blocks of oats just coming through the earth; and there lie squares — black, brown, and tan (depending on the type of soil) — plowed and ready to be planted to the ubiquitous corn. Most of the land is under cultivation with very little in forest or wood lot.

The farms, as a result of the system of

homesteading, contain about 160 acres or one quarter of a square mile, but many are larger and some are smaller. For the most part the larger ones are to be found on former prairies, the smaller ones on former wooded areas. Everywhere, however, the tendency is for greater size. Many small part-time farms are near the cities. In the cattle-producing portions the buildings consist of large barns, often painted red, and

these farm houses were built when the price of lumber and foundation material was high on a basis of agricultural products.

The Physical Setting

Few if any agricultural regions in the world have a more favorable combination of climate, terrain, and soils, or had a superior cover of natural vegetation.

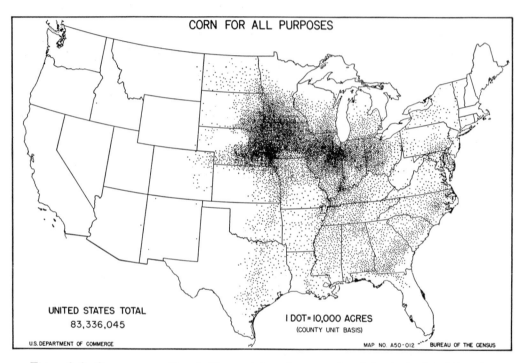

Figure 9–2. Corn acreage. Corn is the great American cereal and the Agricultural Interior grows the bulk of it. The Corn Belt Subregion alone produces nearly one half.

small houses. The farmhouses suffer in comparison to the architectural gems of New England, New York, eastern Pennsylvania, and Maryland. Many of the farmhouses in New England were built on stony hillsides, but they were well constructed and are almost as good now as a century ago. If such was the case at a time when hand labor and poor livestock characterized agriculture, one wonders why in this Midwestern land of generally rich soil and more recent settlement the people did not build more attractive houses. The answer seems to be that

Climate. As a result of interior location, the area has a humid continental climate (mostly long summer phase), which is characterized by a wide range of temperature. Winter temperatures have fallen as low as −30°F., whereas those of summer have soared as high as 108°. Summers are nearly always hot. Even the nights are warm; July night temperatures seldom fall below 65°F., except in the northern portions. Winters, especially in the western and northern parts, are severe though changeable. Because winter temperatures are mostly below freezing

Figure 9–3. Characteristic checkerboard arrangement of fields over the interminable acres in the Corn Belt. The farms here are more closely spaced than those in the wheat regions to the west and northwest. Note the village in the foreground and the straight roads. (Courtesy of the *Daily Pantagraph,* Bloomington, Illinois.)

in the northern part of the region, there is a minimum of soil leaching; in the southern part, where freezing and thawing occur daily, the reverse is true. In pioneer days, winter storms (blizzards) were things of terror, but with coal, petroleum and natural gas for fuel, closed automobiles, cleared roads, and better houses, this is no longer true.

The growing season is long — about 140 days along the northern border and 200 along the southern.

Precipitation varies from about 18 inches near the western boundary to 40 at the eastern border. Rain falls during every month in the year with the maximum in spring and early summer; about three fourths of the rain falls in the frostless season — a significant factor in a great agricultural region. Summer precipitation is predominantly of the thundershower type.

Thunderstorms, which travel in an easterly direction, are both harmful and beneficial

but the good they do far outweighs the bad. The value of such a storm depends on when it arrives: coming when crops are suffering from a prolonged dry, hot spell, a single thundershower may increase the average yield of corn several bushels per acre and hence be worth millions of dollars to the farmers of a given area.

Occasionally severe summer droughts reduce crop yields and turn pastures brown.

In the northern part of this region, snow characterizes the winter precipitation. Although single snowfalls seldom remain long, subsequent ones keep the ground covered practically all winter. Southward the precipitation falls either as rain or snow; the snow generally melts quickly.

Floods are so common in this region as to have become an accepted part of the natural environment for farmers living on the flood plains of the Mississippi, Missouri, Illinois, Ohio, Wabash and others. Sometimes they result from heavy spring rains falling on frozen ground but often they happen because of prolonged rain with rapid runoff.

Terrain. Most of the Agricultural Interior is a plain characterized by level to gently rolling land. Exceptions are the lands south of the Wisconsin glaciation which are often quite hilly, the comparatively rugged Driftless Area, and the rims around the Blue Grass area and the Nashville Basin. The part known as the Corn Belt is topographically one of the best agricultural areas in the world.

The physiographic uniformity is due in part to the nearly flat-lying rocks and to the fact that most of the region was invaded several times by ice during the glacial period. The glacier left lasting traces; it sometimes planed off the hilltops 100 feet or more and filled up old gorges and deep valleys, covering both with glacial drift often to a depth of 100 feet. The greater part of the Agricultural Interior is thus indebted in no small part to the ice age for its rich heritage and agricultural importance.

In southwestern Wisconsin and adjacent Minnesota, Iowa, and Illinois lies the Driftless Area — an unglaciated island in a sea of glacial drift. Missed by the continental ice sheet, it differs from the surrounding territory both topographically and economically. In fact, its landscape is like that which existed before the glacier came.

The Kentucky Blue Grass area and the Nashville Basin have long been outstanding in the geography of the nation. The Bluegrass proper and the Nashville Basin are areas of relatively smooth to undulating surface separated from each other by the hill country of Eastern Kentucky.

Soils. No more fertile and productive soils combined with a humid climate exist than those found here. Especially is this true of the region's kernel — the Corn Belt. The Blue Grass area and the Nashville Basin also are highly productive. Some of the soils, however, as in central Michigan and central Wisconsin, in the Driftless Area and in the Highland Rim of Kentucky and Tennessee, are far from rich.

Most of the region is characterized by gray-brown podzolic soils and prairie soils.

While the former, which develop under deciduous forest in the milder of the humid continental climates, are among the best of the pedalfers, the fact that they are forest soils means that they are in general less productive than the dark-brown to black prairie soils. Nevertheless some of the forest soils, such as those in western Ohio and north-central Indiana, yield about as well per acre as the prairie soils. It may be said that forest soils which develop on calcareous till or on limestone, granite, gneiss, and schist are superior to those which evolve from shale and sandstone. All forest soils, however, are permanently leached, acid in reaction, and poor in humus.

The true prairie soils are the best of all pedalfers. They develop in cool, moderately humid climates under the influence of grass vegetation, are characterized by a dark-brown to black topsoil underlain by well-oxidized subsoils. Being relatively well supplied with moisture, they are moderately leached and acid in reaction, and they lack a zone of lime accumulation. They are mostly silt loams and clay loams in texture and are derived largely from glacial till.

In summarizing it may be said that: (1) most of the soils of east-central Minnesota, central Wisconsin, and the northwestern part of lower Michigan are too sandy for the profitable production of crops; these areas also have numerous deposits of peat and muck,[1] which without drainage are unsuited to growing crops; (2) the soils of the Corn Belt, of the Kentucky Blue Grass, of the Nashville Basin, and of western, southern, and eastern Wisconsin, southern Michigan, and southern Ontario, all in considerable part derived from limestone, are very fertile; (3) the soils of the Driftless Area and of the Highland Rim are of medium fertility.

It should be emphasized that there is a high degree of correlation between soils and types of farming in the Agricultural Interior.

---

[1] *Peat* is unconsolidated soil material consisting largely of undecomposed or slightly decomposed organic matter accumulated under conditions of excessive moisture. *Muck*, on the other hand, is fairly well decomposed organic soil material, relatively high in mineral content, dark in color, and accumulated under conditions of imperfect drainage.

The kind of soil determines the kind and quality of the crops that can be grown. Thus the Corn Belt coincides closely with the prairie soils, especially the dark-brown silt loams, and the principal dairy areas are found on the stony loam podzolic soils of the Hay and Dairy Subregion.

Natural Vegetation. The Agricultural Interior's original vegetation consisted of forest and of grass. The eastern part was forested; western Ohio, southern Michigan and Wisconsin, and southern and west-central Illinois all were a part of the oak-hickory southern hardwood forest, while the Kentucky Blue Grass and the Nashville Basin were a part of the chestnut, chestnut-oak, yellow-poplar southern hardwood forest.[2]

The forest near the northern boundary of the region was characterized by conifers on the sandy soils and by magnificent stands of hardwoods on the clay lands; elsewhere the forest consisted wholly of hardwoods.

Southern Minnesota, all of Iowa, northern Missouri, eastern Nebraska and Kansas, and northeastern Oklahoma composed the prairie[3] — a vast billowy sea of virgin grass without timber except along the streams. It was *tall* grass with long blades and stiff stems, growing to a height of one to three feet and frequently six to eight feet. Men and horses could be lost in it. The trees growing along the streams were chiefly cottonwoods, oaks, and elms in the western portion with occasional sycamores and walnuts farther east.

The true prairie extended from Illinois (small patches existed in western Ohio and northern Indiana) to about the 98th meridian, where it was gradually replaced by the short grass of the steppe. The boundaries of the prairie were never sharply defined. They were not the meeting place of two contrasted vegetation belts; rather were they broad mobile zones that moved with pronounced changes in precipitation. Many interesting theories for the origin of the prairie have been advanced, but none as yet has been wholly acceptable to botanists, plant ecologists, and plant geographers.[4]

Minerals

In this outstanding agricultural region, mining is in many localities also a cardinal enterprise. Coal, petroleum, natural gas, salt, clay, sand, gypsum, and building stones provide a livelihood for large numbers and simultaneously supply the sinews for rail and motor transport and for manufacturing.

Coal. Coal deposits are widely distributed in three of the nation's leading fields — the Northern Interior, Eastern Interior, and Western Interior. While this coal, generally speaking, is not of such good quality as that mined in the Appalachian Province, its location near numerous manufacturing cities insures cheap fuel and hence supplies a large part of the industrial requirements of the Midlands. Much of it is strip-mined. The mines of Illinois employ about twice as many workers as the meat-packing plants.

Petroleum and Natural Gas. Important oil and gas reserves have been tapped in Michigan, Ohio, Indiana, and southern Illinois (the Centralia-Salem Field). This last field in recent years has been one of the most active in the entire country enabling Illinois to rank among the important oil-producing states. Petroleum played an important role in establishing Cleveland, Chicago, and Toledo as early refining centers. The surplus gas from these fields is piped to nearby cities for industrial and domestic uses. Oil experts believe that as a result of deeper drilling this region, especially Illinois and Michigan, will obtain increased production.

Limestone. In south-central Indiana in the Bedford-Bloomington area are the famous limestone quarries, which supply a superior limestone used in buildings throughout the East and Middle West. The building stone business is declining, however, for it

---

[2] Hardwoods may be defined as broad-leaved trees which usually lose their leaves in winter. The wood produced from hardwoods may be either hard or soft in texture.

[3] The French, who had never seen such large areas of grassland, called them *prairies*, which in French means "large meadows."

[4] James C. Malin, *The Grassland of North America*, Chapter 7, "The Grass Formations: The Ecologists' Views," pp. 62-81. Lawrence, Kansas: 1948.

encounters much difficulty competing with cheaper materials — concrete, brick, and lumber.

Settlement

Settlement in the Agricultural Interior flowed from three fountain heads: (1) New England, whose Puritans came by way of the Mohawk Valley; (2) the South,[5] whose frontiersmen broke through the mountains of Kentucky and Tennessee via Cumberland Gap,[6] and (3) Pennsylvania, whose Scotch-Irish and Germans came via Pittsburgh and the Ohio River country as well as by way of Cumberland Gap. Thus, whereas only a million Americans were living west of the Appalachians in 1800, their numbers had increased by 1820 to 2,500,000 and by 1830 to 3,500,000. Settlement was by single families, scattered groups, or small companies.

European immigration is commonly divided into two periods: (1) that from northwestern Europe, consisting of English, Germans, Scandinavians, Bohemians, and Dutch — land-hungry people whose goal was to acquire a piece of unoccupied land that through tillage would insure a living, and (2) later immigrants — Poles and southern Europeans who settled largely in urban centers in the eastern half of the region to become industrial workers.

The American pioneers, whose forebears had come from humid, forested Europe, had a heritage of forest rather than grassland. Hence when they met the prairie in their migration westward, they were surprised and puzzled by the fact that the land was clothed with grass rather than forest. They were even suspicious, reasoning that soils bearing no timber must be inferior. Hence for the most part they avoided the prairie. In 1836 Alby Smith, an Illinois pioneer, lost an election because the voters decided that anyone so stupid as to settle in the prairie should not be entrusted with the responsibilities of public confidence.[7]

If the early settlers took prairie land, they assured themselves it was contiguous to forest land, which they made the real base of the farm establishment. Several reasons have been advanced for the retarded settlement of the prairie, some of which apparently apply to different kinds of grassland: "wetness, difficulty in plowing grass sod, low degree of fertility, prevalence of disease, lack of water, of wood, of navigation, and of protection against the hazards of climate."[8] There was also the menace of prairie fires.

The taming of the prairie was not easy, for the iron plows then in use would not "scour" in the heavy soils and many of them broke. The soil stuck till the plow couldn't move in the furrow. The prairie was really not conquered until 1837 when John Deere, a blacksmith living in the tiny village of Grand Detour, Illinois, invented the steel plow.

In one respect the settlers were particularly fortunate; a British breed of beef cattle, the Hereford, found the grassland environment so well suited to it that it ultimately dominated the entire area from Canada to Mexico.

The Present Occupance. The average population density is higher in the eastern portion than farther west as a consequence of the many large cities and the smaller farms. The larger of these cities, however, owe their importance to the Great Lakes and to manufacturing rather than to agriculture.

Farming has become so highly mechanized that all the children can no longer remain on farms. Hence large numbers of youths annually migrate to the cities and bolster up the low urban birth rate. Without them American cities could not maintain themselves. It is estimated that one out of every three American urban workers comes from villages and farms. Some 500,000 persons left farm work for industry in the past several years — particularly in 1950 and 1951. Despite the drop in farm population, how-

---

[5] Virginia, Maryland, North and South Carolina.

[6] The absence of a strong tribe at or near the western end of this gap accelerated the westward movement.

[7] Harlan H. Barrows, "Geography of the Middle Illinois Valley," *Illinois Geological Survey, Bulletin 15*, p. 78. Urbana: 1910.

[8] James C. Malin, "Ecology and History," *Scientific Monthly*, Vol. 70, May 1950.

ever, production of crops and livestock steadily increases.

The population north of the Ohio River contains foreign as well as American stock, the principal nationality other than British in the rural communities probably being German. There are, however, large numbers of Bohemians, French, Poles, Scandinavians, and others. South of the Ohio the white stock is almost all native. The large Negro population with its low standard of living has discouraged European immigrants from settling there because they were loath to accept the subordinate social status implied in manual employment. Lower wage rates have been a contributory factor also.

The Agricultural Interior is not static. In fact a veritable revolution is noted from census to census. Changes occur continuously in both the natural and cultural landscapes: soil erosion increases; farm woodlots are cut and the land used for crops; the original prairie has almost disappeared before the plow; and annual floods take their toll.

Farms, too, are becoming fewer in number but increasing in size. Technological advances in farm machinery, plant and animal breeding and transport facilities all are altering the cultural landscape.

Automobiles and good roads, electricity, telephones, and other conveniences, have become commonplace on the farms over most of this region. More than 90 per cent of the farms are electrified, as compared with 85 per cent for the entire nation.[9]

Education, religion, and social life have shared in the inevitable change. The rural school and the village church, in fact the village itself, all are changing.

Yet the Agricultural Interior is a farming region and its fine farms still are the broad enduring base upon which much of the economy of the entire nation rests.

The Mixing Bowl of America. Strange as it may seem there still are some who believe that the United States is but the area that lies east of the Alleghenies and that all the territory beyond is wild and uncouth.

It has been said facetiously that some New Yorkers believe New York is synonymous with the United States. Those who have traveled widely and have studied Anglo-America, however, know that the great ethnic mixing bowl, the part ranking high in "American" quality, past and present — the most completely assimilated part of the continent — is the Agricultural Interior. Here, through migration and westward movement, the first immigrants became in reality Americans rather than transplanted Europeans. The melting pot has melted most here — more in the western than in the eastern part and more in rural than in industrial areas. It was here that the challenge of opening up and settling a continent was first met.

The Region's Political Power In National Affairs. Probably no single region wields so much power in Washington as this one. During years of prosperity, when prices for agricultural commodities are high, life moves smoothly, and for this condition "the President residing in the White House . . . claims credit, even though the good times be due to rainfall in the Middle West."[10] During years of depression, however, or when lack of rain and burning sun bring small crops, or when a lavish nature gives too plentiful harvests with resultant low prices, this region rumbles ominously. In times of low prices, political instability develops and people vote for him who promises the most. In recent years farms generally have yielded well; corn cribs have been filled to overflowing, elevators strained under burdens of wheat, and large herds of beef cattle and swine have dotted the landscape. Few economic or political panaceas contrived by man have not been tried out at some time.

Agriculture

The leading business is farming, for which the natural environment is highly favorable. The land is not too hilly or stony, the precipitation is generally adequate for all crops, the growing season is sufficiently long to mature

---

[9] *The New York Times,* March 11, 1952.

[10] William F. Ogburn, *Machines and Tomorrow's World*, p. 3. New York: Public Affairs Committee, Inc., 1938.

all products save those needing more than six months free from killing frost, and the soil is generally fertile. But even though agriculture dominates, no simple system of farming such as characterized the Cotton Belt exists.

Throughout the greater part of this region the country appears to be under complete cultivation, with four or five farmsteads to each square mile in the eastern portion, and two or three in the western portion (Figure 9–3). The farms comprise fields based on the subdivision of sections — half-sections, quarter-sections, and 40-acre plots. Nearly all farms are family-operated.[11] Corn, winter wheat, spring oats and hay are almost universal crops, with soybeans gaining annually in acreage. Tobacco and fruits are important locally, and much land is in pasture. The region not only grows tilled crops but supports the densest population of cattle, horses, and swine in Anglo-America.

Systems of Farming. Mixed farming char-

[11] Earl O. Heady, "Why Farms Are Larger," *Farm Policy Forum*, Vol. 1, January 1948, p. 59.

Figure 9–5. Combining wheat. Harvesting has developed from the sickle, scythe, and cradle through the reaper and the self-binder to the "combine" which cuts 30 or more acres of wheat a day, threshes and cleans the grain, and delivers it to a truck. (Courtesy of International Harvester Company.)

acterizes much of the region, with the major emphasis on corn in nearly all parts. Since the climatic range of corn on a commercial basis is more restricted than that of other crops grown, it nearly always gets first choice of the land. Corn is a very productive crop, yielding two, three, or more times as much per acre as wheat and oats. Corn yields the largest money return of any of the cereals. Other crops are grown (1) to equalize the seasonal distribution of labor, (2) to provide balanced feed for livestock, and (3) to improve the soil — the rotation preferably including a legume.

The most widely used rotation consists of (1) a tilled crop, (2) a small grain, and (3) a legume or grass crop, grown in this order. On the choicest soils a five-year rotation is followed — (1) corn, (2) corn, (3) oats or soybeans, (4) winter wheat, and (5) clover.

The flat to undulating land which favors the use of labor-saving machines has contributed much to the formation of larger farms. By utilizing a great number of different kinds of machines (Figure 9–4), the larger acreage can be handled without additional labor. One farmer in 1930 did as much crop work as three in 1830. That American agriculture, centered primarily in this region, has been revolutionized is indicated by the fact that more farm implements and techniques have been invented, discovered, or perfected in the past hundred years (Figures 9–5; 9–6)

Figure 9–4. The modern Corn Belt farm is almost a farm factory — machinery being used for almost every operation. Modern farm implements in the barnyard of a Corn Belt farm guarantee a higher crop yield and more leisure time for the farmer and his family. (Courtesy of *Steelways*.)

Figure 9–6. The cradle, introduced into America about 1776, was the best means of cutting grain prior to the invention of the reaper in 1831. This crew could cut and bind about six acres per day. (Courtesy of International Harvester Company.)

than during all the preceding centuries of human history.

Winter wheat dominates the subhumid western margin; spring wheat, the northwest border; hay and oats for dairy cattle, the cool moist northern border; tobacco, parts of Kentucky, Indiana, Wisconsin, Tennessee, Ohio, and Ontario. Fruits and vegetables are important on the "light soil and lake-locked peninsulas of Michigan and Ontario."

In the southern part of the region, as a result of significant physiographic differences, no one or two crops predominate, though corn, wheat, and hay are most important. In several counties in the Nashville Basin and the Blue Grass area, tobacco is the crop of greatest value.

Seven types of farming characterize the region:

DAIRY
SUBREGION

1. *Dairy farms,* which contribute fresh milk for urban centers but also specialize in the production of butter, cheese, and canned milk.

CORN
BELT

2. *Livestock farms.* More than one third of all the farms (in the Corn Belt Subregion) are livestock farms which specialize in swine and beef cattle for meat.

3. *Cash grain farms.* Almost one fifth of all the farms are cash crop farms, which specialize in the growing of corn and feed grains for cash sale.

4. *General farms.* About one fourth of all farms are regarded as general farms, which derive less than half their gross cash income from any one type of farming.

CORN AND
WINTER
WHEAT BELT

5. *Subsistence Farms.* Two fifths of the farms are of this type, where more than half of what the farm produces is consumed by the family.

6. *Cash crop farms.* Here, for example, in the Kentucky Bluegrass area and in the Nashville Basin tobacco is a major crop.

7. *General farms and livestock farms.* These two types,

though much less important than the others (Nos. 5 and 6), nonetheless are worthy of mention.

A Corn Belt Farm. Within the smaller subdivisions of regions, farmsteads are similar, but within a large and diversified region, they are dissimilar. Thus farmsteads in the Dairy Belt, the Corn Belt, and the Corn and Winter Wheat Belt differ considerably.

Within the Corn Belt are innumerable exceptional farms — marvels to behold. In this area farms are scattered along the rural roads at an average of about two per mile. The average square mile of farm land includes four farms of 160 acres each. This does not mean, of course, that there are not variations. In fact a study made by Ohio State University agricultural economists indicates that the average size of farms in this subregion has been 266 acres.

Size depends upon many things: whether the farm lies in the part originally in forest or originally in prairie; the type of farming practiced, the total investment, the amount of mechanization, and the government programs of paying farmers to grow less corn, oats, and wheat.[12] Competition is today so keen that it forces farmers to adopt a farm size that is reasonably efficient.

The average farm is square or rectangular in shape; it is thus highly compact. It contains the operator's house, his barn and sheds for livestock, storage of feeds, and protection of tools and machinery, truck and automobile. Adjacent to the barn, invariably the largest building, are the feed pens and yards. Nearly always there is a farm garden and occasionally a farm orchard. If the farm consists of approximately 160 acres, it might have during a given year 50 to 80 acres in corn, and the same acreage divided among winter wheat, oats, and hay. More and more farms include soybeans in the rotation. There is invariably a block of land in pasture — usually the least desirable piece from the stand-

point of crop production. It may be too rough for crops, too poorly drained, too infertile, or too stony.

In many instances a farm has been in the same family for many years. Often there is no debt on the property. In other instances, the farms are heavily burdened by mortgage. While most of the farms are operated by their owners, increasing numbers are being rented to tenants; this is particularly true in the richer areas. Such farms represent a large investment of capital; the income is substantial and the standard of living is high. This family type of farm is deeply rooted in American life.

The Importance of the Motor Vehicle to Farming

The internal combustion engine has contributed greatly to improved farm efficiency. Since 1941 the number of trucks on farms has risen to 2.5 million and farm passenger cars to 5.5 million. Tractors now number 3.4 million,[13] though some sources give 5 million. While these figures apply to the entire nation, they are even more germane to the Agricultural Interior.

About 70 per cent of all farms have one or more passenger cars and they are among the farmer's most essential tools, for they are used for essential trips to town, for hauling farm products in trailers, and for other tasks. One survey indicates that 67 out of every 100 miles traveled by the average farm car are connected with making a living. Trucks are now so essential that 90 per cent of all farm products are moved by them to initial markets.

The great majority of farmers in the Agricultural Interior live on hard surface or gravel roads — all-weather highways. Many, however, are served only by roads in poor condition, some even being impassable in bad weather. This situation should not be permitted in a region where the farmer is so dependent on the truck and automobile.

---

[12] When payments were made to plant less of a given crop, the idea was to avoid creation of unmanageable surpluses in that product. Farmers then put more acres in grass, pasture, or other crops for which there was a forseeable market.

[13] "Motorized Farmers Have Increased Yields with Reduced Manpower," *Automobile Facts*, Vol. 10, December 1950, January 1951, p. 8.

The Influence of Machinery on the Region's Agriculture

As recently as three generations ago, with hand tools and a team of oxen or horses, the farmer was fortunate indeed if he was able to grow enough food for himself and three other persons. Hence, it is small wonder that so many sons of the soil were lured to the cities, for they afforded about the only escape from the drudgery of this so-called man-and-horse type of farming. Even 25 years ago a 25-foot combine, pulled by 28 horses and manned by a crew of 3 could harvest only about 35 acres of wheat in a 10-hour day; today that same field could be harvested in the same time by one man operating a 12-foot self-propelled combine, and modern trucks would haul the grain directly to the elevator.

The farmer of the Agricultural Interior today is essentially a machine tender and a power user. Many of the machines now so indispensable to the farmers have been contributed in large part by the very young men who left the farms for the cities. They understood the problems involved and were interested in reducing the drudgery of farm work. Today the farmer grows enough for himself and 13 other people and he does it with less effort and in less time than ever before.

Whereas in America there is only one farm worker in every eight persons so that the other seven are available for non-agricultural pursuits, in Asia three or four out of every five workers sweat long hours on the land to produce only a meager per capita supply of food and fiber.

One of the best ways to fully appreciate the magnitude of the mechanical revolution is to note the importance of tractors. In 1950 the 5,400,000 farms had about 3,500,000 tractors or roughly two tractors for every three farms, and early in 1952 it was estimated there were four million tractors in use on American farms. Tractors have permitted farmers to sell most of their horses, thereby releasing extra feed for producing marketable livestock.

It is not only tractors, however, that have revolutionized farming in the Agricultural Interior and in the nation; there are all kinds of machines — combines, corn-pickers, seeders, high-wheeled platforms for detasseling corn, huge sprayers, tractor-operated hay balers, hydraulic loaders, manure spreaders, flame weed killers, potato harvesters that dig, gather, grade, sack and weigh, and others.[14] They all lower the cost of production and reduce the demand for millions of hours of man labor.

Mechanization, by making it profitable to farm on a larger scale, is a major cause of the increasing size of farms. It takes larger acreages to cover the first high cost of machinery and at the same time keep production costs low. In turn machinery encourages new farming methods.

Science and Farming in the Agricultural Interior

Production per acre and per man is greater now than it has ever been. Year after year the farmers in this region meet the peak production goals set for them by the government. Production is about one third greater than in the 1930's and has increased 40 per cent in the past decade. Science is the answer to the question *"How do they do it?"* The significance of machinery, usually considered the biggest single contributing factor, has already been discussed. Additional factors are better farming practices, modern methods of soil management, improved seed and greater use of commercial fertilizers and insecticides, pesticides and similar substances.

The Use of Fertilizer. The Agricultural Interior, originally extremely fertile, has been having its plant food reserves depleted as a result of 50 to 100 years of cropping. Hence the farmers are using fertilizers in ever-growing quantities. This results primarily from the widespread adoption of new high-yield strains of hybrid corn, oats, and soybeans and the present high prices for farm crops. More fertilizer is used in growing corn than

[14] R. B. Gray, "Some New Farm Machines," *Yearbook of Agriculture, 1943-1947*, pp. 815-824. Washington, D. C.: Government Printing Office, 1947.

in growing any other crop in the nation and since the Agricultural Interior is the leading corn-growing region, its importance as a market for fertilizer is readily apparent.

It is estimated that fully 25 per cent of America's crop production comes directly from the use of commercial fertilizers. The use of fertilizers enables farmers to plant more high yielding, high nutrient-demanding seed per acre, and hence reap a greatly multiplied yield per acre.

A survey by the National Fertilizer Association indicates that an acreage return of $6.81 is procured from each $1.00 invested in fertilizers.

Use of Insecticides and Pesticides and Fungicides. Man is engaged in a constant battle against insects and in this struggle our enemy has the advantage, because he can multiply with incredible speed and adapt himself to almost any condition and an endless variety of foods.

Pest control in the United States used to be relatively simple, involving only the use of lead, arsenic, sulphur, nicotine, and later of rotenone. The picture is different now. This results largely from the fact that pests develop a tolerance to a given insecticide and that modern highly specialized farming methods with their large scale production aggravate the problem; apples in orchards covering a square mile obviously present a more serious pest problem than does a single apple tree in the farm yard.

Taking the United States as a whole, the annual crop losses due to insect pests are estimated at between three and five billion dollars (1951). Corn borers alone destroy more than 100 million dollars worth of corn annually. Also the labor of one million men each year is lost through insect damage to crops.

This would appear to make a black and discouraging picture. However, the manufacturers of insecticides are contributing products annually that are reducing greatly the plunder and depredations of insects. Among these the best known are DDT, pyrethrum, rotenone, nicotine, derris, and cube.

Plant Breeding. Because many farmers have seen the prospect of an abundant and profitable crop ruined before the onslaught of an insect pest before which they were powerless, scientists have worked on the problem of developing crops or varieties that could be planted with reasonable assurance of freedom from destruction by one or another insect. Several examples are the breeding of winter wheats resistant to the hessian fly and rust and of lines of corn that are resistant to the earworm, European corn borer, chinch bug, and stored-grain insects. The victory is not yet complete but such strains suffer only one-tenth to one-fourth as much injury as the most susceptible lines.

Scientists also discovered a fundamental law of nature when they learned in their experiments with tobacco that many plants can flower and produce seed only when the duration of light — when the length of day, is right for a particular plant.

Hybrid corn, possibly the most discussed contribution of the plant breeders, not only is resistant to certain insects but is a huge yielder of grain.

Hybrid corn involves inbreeding — fertilizing the silk from the tassel of the same plant rather than from many plants. By using this method, the farmer can get from his corn those qualities he desires, since each plant has a personality of its own. In growing ordinary corn, the farmer gets long ears and short ears, tall or stubby stalks, high or low starch content — in short a mongrel mixture. To get hybrid seed, a bag is tied about the tassel (the male) to collect the pollen and then the bag is emptied by hand over the silk (the female).

Hybrid corn has now replaced open-pollinated varieties on a major portion (almost 100 per cent) of the corn acreage in the Corn Belt Subregion and on about 25 per cent of the national acreage. This popularity is deserved, for hybrid corn has greater vigor, greater resistance to lodging, plant diseases, and insects and increases the yield per acre by 10 to 20 per cent in the Corn Belt and on thousands of farms by as much as 50 per cent. Because of their resistance to lodging, the hybrids are particularly well adapted to the use of the mechanical picker (Figure 9–7).

In this region, the growing of hybrid corn for seed is a special business carried on by large concerns. In Urbana and De Kalb, Illinois, are two of the largest concerns. Their growing corn is detassled and pollinated by hand. The market for their seed is good, for farmers must purchase their seed corn every year; the old farm scene of seed corn hanging on the windmill to dry or hanging on racks on the porch is no longer a part of the Agricultural Interior.

Soil Conservation

Only a small proportion of the Agricultural Interior is flat — the bulk of it being undulating or rolling and much possessing a considerable gradient. With heavy summer rains, and with the wide adoption of clean-tilled crops, soil erosion (except in winter — northern portion only) is bound to be serious.

A moderate amount, however, such as occurs with a rotation including corn, wheat, oats, and clover is actually beneficial, for it keeps the soil *young*, utilizing the enormous reserves of plant nutrients in the subsoil. It is only when topsoil is removed faster than it can be formed under good farm management that erosion is dangerous.[15]

Floods. In the Agricultural Interior floods annually cause much damage to land, crops, livestock, buildings and equipment, and roads. Even human lives are lost. Such floods result from many factors among which are type and occurrence of precipitation, the soil-vegetation complex which influences the amount of runoff and the topography of the drainage basins.

The Missouri. The Missouri or "Big Muddy" rises in the Rockies, is fed by many tributaries, and debauches into the Mississippi above St. Louis.

The river has two regular flood periods annually, usually in March–April and again in May–June during which time parts of the flood plain suffer.

In 1951 during the exceptionally heavy rains of the May–June period, occurred a dramatic flood of the Kansas River. Towns, cities, and farmlands were innundated, property destroyed, transportation disrupted, in-

[15] Richard Bradfield, "Surpluses Today: But Will There Be Enough Food in 50 Years," *Farm Policy Forum*, Vol. 3, January 1950, p. 28.

Figure 9–7. Mechanical corn picker harvests two and one-half acres per hour enabling the farmer to do his own harvesting as soon as the crop is ready and the weather right. The machine gathers the stalks, snaps and husks the ears, and delivers them to the wagon in a matter of seconds. (Courtesy of International Harvester Company.)

dustry brought to a complete standstill. Damage exceeded one billion dollars. Writing of the damage at Armourdale, where the Kansas River flows into the Missouri, Arthur Krock wrote that it was as though 100 B-29's had dropped 100 explosives on the spot in a perfect pattern.[16] In 1952 occurred a flood on the Missouri with the crest higher than at any time since the arrival of white men.

An MVA? The Missouri Valley does not have to become a man-made desert. It can be a prosperous region with rich farms and industrial cities. The ten great needs of the valley, not independent but interdependent, are:

1. Adequate flood control.
2. Soil conservation.
3. Dependable navigation.
4. Abundance of cheap water — both for domestic and industrial purposes.
5. Reforestation.
6. Irrigation at reasonable costs to farmers.
7. Low cost electric power.
8. Industrialization.
9. Recreational facilities.
10. Wildlife conservation and management.

Such a program involves the entire Valley and that accordingly means several geographical regions. Basic conflicts are accordingly inevitable. No stroke of administrative genius can eliminate these conflicts.

Today there is rivalry between the Corps of Engineers and the Bureau of Reclamation. They have, however, come up with a plan — the Pick-Sloan Plan. But it has been called a "shotgun marriage" of the proposals of the two organizations; the Hoover Commission observed that it was planned very nearly backward and without adequate data.

What has been needed is an overall plan, one working in the national interest — integrated, watershed planning on the order of the TVA. Such a plan involving the work of an impartial board to review the entire water control picture, would control the entire river system so that dangers would everywhere be minimized and the best possible use made of the entire basin. Such a board

[16] *The New York Times,* November 20, 1951.

now exists and on it is a member from every state in the basin.

Dikes and levees alone cannot suffice: for example, Kansas City, one of the nation's most important industrial and railway centers, is built on bottom land, which is vulnerable every time an excess of water moves down the Kansas and Missouri rivers. Protection requires control in the headwaters for diverting water *before* it reaches the densely settled areas. The Missouri is at present an underdeveloped river badly in need of attention.

Crops

Corn. Corn (maize) thrives under the favorable conditions of hot, humid summer weather, fertile, well-drained loamy soils, and level to rolling terrain. No other country has this favorable combination of growing conditions over so wide a territory. Thus the United States produces one half to two thirds of the world's corn, most of which is grown in this region (Figure 9–2). Corn to be grown commercially has rigid temperature requirements; it should have an average night temperature above 55°F., an average summer temperature of 70° to 80°F. up to the time of ripening, and a growing season of at least 130 days. Corn benefiting from frequent showers and warm nights in June, July and August has been known to grow as much as two to five inches in one night. In fact there is an old saying in the Corn Belt that "it's so hot you can almost hear the corn growing." It is a fact that corn makes 80 per cent of its growth at night.

Soils for corn should be deep, well-drained, fertile, and rich in humus. The terrain should be level or undulating to permit the utilization of labor-saving farm implements and to retard soil erosion — always destructive on slopes where clean-tilled crops are grown. With this favorable combination of environmental conditions, yields are of 50 to 150 bushels per acre on the richest soils. The high yields obtained in the Corn Belt Subregion are mostly attributable to the almost universal adoption — about 100 per cent in Iowa — of hybrid corn, to the rotation which always includes a legume, and to rather generous use of manure and commercial fertilizers. The heaviest concentration is (1) in central Illinois and Iowa, where considerable corn is sold for cash, the growers being grain farmers and not feeders, and (2) along the Missouri River between southern Minnesota and northern Kansas. Most of the Corn Belt grows corn for feed. Corn is the only important feed grain produced in the southern and southeastern part of the region, oats dropping out because of high summer temperatures. In order to maintain soil fertility a rotation of corn for one or two years, followed by a year in oats or wheat, and finally by one or two years in hay — usually clover but sometimes timothy or alfalfa — is followed. Corn production per man and per farm increases from east to west well into the state of Iowa.

The seed is planted mechanically by a corn planter and is "checkrowed," that is dropped so as to be equally spaced in two directions. This permits both lengthwise and crosswise cultivation by cultivator (Figure 9–8). The two-row lister is also widely used in corn planting. The crop is cultivated three to five times and then the field is "laid by" in July.

Because corn is bulky in proportion to value, it cannot be shipped long distances as many other crops. Since more than three fourths of it is fed to hogs, cattle, horses and poultry, it is patent that a very close correlation exists between the distribution of hogs and cattle on the one hand and of corn on the other.

Only in restricted areas and then mostly outside the Corn Belt portion of the region is corn put up in picturesque shocks, because this operation requires much hand labor. Instead the crop is hand picked, reaped by machines, hogged-down or grazed-off. Hand picking still leads all other methods, but mechanical picking grows in importance each year.

Only about four per cent of the total American corn acreage is devoted to ensilage. Such corn is grown largely in the Dairy Belt, for this area is too cool for growing corn for grain.

Figure 9–8. Cultivating corn. This machine, designed for fast, close work, is used advantageously on the large farms of the level-to-undulating Corn Belt, where rows are straight and rocks and boulders scarce. (Courtesy of International Harvester Company.)

Winter Wheat. An important cash crop is winter wheat. Most of the acreage is in the southern half of the region — in the southern Corn Belt and the Corn and Winter Wheat Subregions. In the latter it is one of several crops grown on general farms. Wheat is secondary to corn over the greater part of the region because it is less restricted in its range of adaption. It is produced to equalize the seasonal distribution of labor, being seeded in autumn after corn cultivation is over and threshed before corn is harvested. Thus since wheat harvesting interferes but slightly with corn cultivation, the competition is not serious. Winter wheat also helps to control erosion during the winter months. Moreover, it is planted to provide a "nurse crop"; when sown with hay, its quick growth shields the young hay plants from the blistering summer sun. The grain is cut sufficiently early to allow the root systems of grass to withstand the succeeding winter.

On the better soils corn is slightly more profitable than wheat, but even where corn finds optimum conditions, wheat remains a strong potential competitor. Important also in this competition is the fact that usually wheat yields are higher here than elsewhere in Anglo-America.

Wheat *can* be grown over much of the

region. Exceptions are those parts where the winters are too severe or where there is too much rain in June and July. Winter wheat is not adapted to the frequent showers that so greatly favor the successful production of corn. In the Agricultural Interior winter wheat must compete with both corn and oats, both of which yield far better. In the heart of the Corn Belt wheat is less preferred than oats—a spring-sown grain.

Though the entire Canadian production of winter wheat is grown in southern Ontario, it constitutes only five per cent of the total Canadian crop.

Scientists are gradually improving wheat varieties against injury from disease—particularly rust; they are also maintaining yields in spite of declining soil fertility by widespread use of nitrogen fertilizers and permitting extension into areas of high risks and low average yields.

Oats. The Agricultural Interior, especially the northwestern part of the Corn Belt, is the most important oats-growing area in Anglo-America. Unlike other small grains, oats during seeding, harvesting, and threshing do not compete with corn but fit into the characteristic crop rotation. Oats are seeded in the spring before work on the corn crop begins and are cut in summer when corn cultivation is about over. Thus the farmer is kept busy throughout most of the summer. Oats, often used as a "nurse crop" for clover, alfalfa and timothy, are grown almost exclusively as feed for livestock being fed directly to horses, ground with corn for young animals, and fed to beef cattle in a ration. Oats are fed mostly on the farms where produced. This results from the crop's low value per unit of bulk and its limited industrial uses, which discriminate against its entering trade channels. Only about 3 per cent of the crop is utilized for human consumption.

Oats are ordinarily a crop of cool, moist areas. Yet the northern Corn Belt which is not cool in summer, ranks as possibly the world's leading oats-grower. It must be admitted that the Corn Belt is not ideal climatically: early summer is too warm, frequent and severe thunder showers cause "lodging," and the rich soils facilitate rank

growth of straw, and occasional droughts result in low yields. Hot, dry weather even for a few days, at the critical period of development, may greatly reduce the yield.

The huge acreage in oats in this region results from the crop's high feed value and the fact that no other small grain fits so well into the labor-use pattern.

Oats generally follow corn in the rotation, except in the southern part of the region, since corn is customarily harvested too late in the season for the sowing of winter wheat. When oats follow corn, plowing is not necessary in preparing the seedbed in the spring, discing sufficing. The crop is threshed in July and early August.

Alfalfa. The legume, alfalfa, is well adapted to the region—especially to the prairie portion, where winter rainfall is less abundant and the soils less leached and hence higher in calcium. It thrives only on soils rich in lime. The crop has greatly increased in importance in the Corn Belt and the Dairy Belt since 1920—even in the eastern part of the Agricultural Interior. When grown in such areas, however, due consideration must be given to soil conditions—especially to the availability of phosphates and to drainage.

Since alfalfa is harvested several times each season and recovers quickly after cutting, the per-acre yield exceeds that of any other hay crop.

Clover. Another crop of major importance is clover, which is well suited to the hot humid summers, limy soils, and level to rolling terrain. Especially is it important in the northern and eastern sections where precipitation is heavy and where droughts and hot sun do little damage. Ninety eight per cent of the nation's clover is grown east of the Dakotas, Nebraska, and Kansas. Clover produces hay of excellent quality—rich in protein and mineral content.

Timothy. This is the most widely cultivated hay grass in Anglo-America. Since it has the same general soil and climatic adaptation as red clover (much moisture and good soil drainage), the two are often seeded together. Especially is this crop important in the Dairy Belt and the northern Corn Belt.

Since timothy cannot tolerate the combination of high summer temperature and high atmospheric humidity, the crop is relatively unimportant in the Corn and Winter Wheat Belt and declines considerably even in the southern Corn Belt. Nearly all the crop in the Agricultural Interior is produced north of the Ohio River.

Soybeans. Soybeans were introduced into the United States as early as 1804 but be-

It is, however, a *soil depleter!* In fact this crop has upset the theory that legumes are soil builders. Soybeans extract relatively large quantities of minerals from the soil, each bushel removing one pound of phosphoric acid and one and one-third pounds of potash from the soil.

The soybean belt is approximately co-extensive with the Corn Belt (Figure 9–9). The crop's climatic and soil requirements are

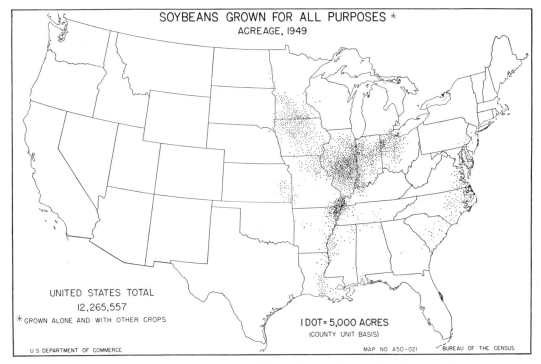

Figure 9–9. The United States is the world's leading producer of soybeans and the Agricultural Interior is its outstanding growing region. The great expansion in soybean acreage was a significant wartime change in American crop production.

came a major crop only during the 1920's and reached really high acreage levels during and since the 1930's. Probably the greatest stimulus came when it was recognized that soybeans could be processed for oil.

The soybean, a shallow-rooted legume, is a heavy feeder on the elements of plant food in the surface soils. It is popular because it yields a heavy crop of beans, is valuable for meal and oil, makes good hay, silage and pasturage, has few diseases, and is not attacked by pests. Every part of the plant is useful.

about the same as for corn. Of the region's crops, only corn brings in more money.

In this area the soybean has served as a mortgage lifter: long-standing farm debts have been paid off and countless tenants have become farm-owners. "There is no doubt that it has muscled itself into a prominent place in Corn Belt agriculture.[17]

Tobacco. In northern Kentucky, south-

[17] A. L. Lang, "The Soybean – A Mortgage Lifter and Soil Depleter," *Fertilizer Review,* Vol. 22, May-June 1947, p. 10.

western Ohio, and northwestern Tennessee lies one of the most important tobacco-growing areas in Anglo-America. Southern Wisconsin and southwestern Ontario also are impressive producers. Little tobacco is grown west of the Mississippi River. In this part of Anglo-America tobacco competes neither with corn nor winter wheat for the best land, except in the Bluegrass and the Nashville Basins.

The Blue Grass Basin of Kentucky is the most important tobacco-growing area in the Agricultural Interior. The limy soils, high in phosphorus, are among the best in Anglo-America. In the Inner Blue Grass, though more than 90 per cent of the land is improved and has been producing for generations, little soil depletion has occurred. Of the three essential minerals supplied to most crops, tobacco requires potassium in greatest quantities, followed by nitrogen. Its phosphorous needs are modest. Maximum yields of white burley tobacco are obtained on the silt loams and level to undulating terrain. The same type of tobacco — burley — is grown under almost identical conditions in the Nashville Basin. This light aromatic "air cured" leaf was grown originally for use in plug chewing tobacco but now is blended with other tobaccos in the manufacture of cigarettes and pipe-smoking mixtures.

Since labor requirements for tobacco are large and the work back-breaking, a given family cultivates only a limited acreage — less than five per cent of the farmland in the subregion. Whereas most tobacco farms are operated by owners, much of the production is in the hands of share-croppers who rent 5 to 20 acres of land — the size of the tract depending mostly upon the number in the cropper's family. Under this system the landlords furnish land and advance money for the crop. However, many owners of small farms grow their own tobacco; often it serves as their only cash crop.

Dark-fired tobacco, where the leaves are cured by the use of open fires and smoke, is grown on the rather fertile rolling lands north of the Highland Rim, whose climate is relatively free from extremes and whose location is favorable with respect to markets.

In this area tobacco is the pivot crop, and around it revolves the whole system of farming. A four-year rotation is employed by the more progressive farmers, in which tobacco is followed by wheat, hay (frequently the legume, lespedeza), and corn. In the area as a whole, corn leads in acreage.

Lying between the burley and dark-fired growing areas is that specializing in dark air-cured leaf, which is used for making chewing tobaccos and snuff. Total production is small, however, less than two per cent of the national tobacco output, and is declining because of the lessened demand for these two products.

While tobacco is not generally considered an important Canadian crop, it is the leading one in several counties bordering on Lake Erie, particularly in Norfolk County. The nation's first commercial tobacco production (heavy varieties) was on the clay and loam soils in the western counties of Ontario. Now production is centered considerably eastward. Three fourths of the soils of Norfolk County are sandy — poorly adapted to most crops but well suited to growing flue-cured tobacco. The climate, too, is favorable; killing frosts are conspicuously rare after the first week in May and prior to the last week in September. The production is small compared with that of the United States, but it is very important to Canada.

Vegetables. The farm vegetable garden is so universal that one may assume that vegetable production is to be found wherever there are farms. But the products from these farms are consumed mostly on the home farm. The areas of densest vegetable production in the region are those engaged in commercial production. Almost invariably these areas are close to large cities — Cleveland, Toledo, Cincinnati, Indianapolis, Detroit, Chicago, Milwaukee, Louisville, St. Louis. The importance of the Agricultural Interior in the production of its leading vegetables is disclosed on the maps of tomatoes (Figure 8–8), peas (Figure 9–10), sweet corn, cabbage (Figure 8–6), snap beans, lima beans, and asparagus.

The Dairy Belt and the Corn Belt do not grow the same vegetables. The former's cool

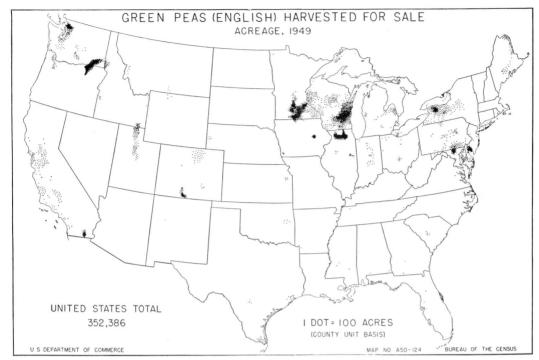

GREEN PEAS (ENGLISH) HARVESTED FOR SALE
ACREAGE, 1949

UNITED STATES TOTAL
352,386

1 DOT = 100 ACRES
(COUNTY UNIT BASIS)

U S DEPARTMENT OF COMMERCE   MAP NO A50-124   BUREAU OF THE CENSUS

Figure 9–10. Green peas are grown for consumption as fresh peas or for canning or freezing. Note particularly the importance of Wisconsin, Minnesota, and New York in the East and of Washington, Oregon, Idaho, and Utah in the West.

summers and light soils make it outstanding for growing peas, beans, cabbage, asparagus and sweet corn. The short frostless season is excellent for growing sweet corn for canning in as much as the cool days and nights keep the kernels in the milk stage. Sweet corn is grown in the Corn Belt but the hot weather makes the ears dry and tough. The Corn Belt's hot, humid summers and heavy soils, however, enable it to be a major tomato-growing area.

Canning. The Agricultural Interior is one of Anglo-America's outstanding vegetable-canning regions. The leading vegetable for canning in Indiana, Illinois and Ohio is the tomato, in Minnesota sweet corn, and in Wisconsin peas, green beans and cabbage for sauerkraut.

The canning factories are located in the vegetable-growing areas where climate, soil, and terrain approach the optimum as closely as possible. Of the ten leading American canning states (based on the number of estab-lishments), five lie wholly or in part in the Agricultural Interior — New York, Indiana, Wisconsin, Illinois, and Ohio.

Fruit. The commercial growing of fruit is not a widely distributed enterprise but is concentrated in definite localities — mostly those originally forested, for the fruits do not need extremely fertile soil. Tree fruits, more exacting in climate than in soil re-quirements, frequently suffer from extremes of temperature. Hence the areas best suited are those with a minimum of danger from late spring and early fall frosts — notably peninsulas, hillsides, and the leeward sides of lakes. This tempering effect of a large body of water has given rise to a fruit belt on the eastern shore of Lake Michigan, where peaches and cherries are of great importance and on the southern shore of Lake Erie where grapes, peaches and apples are dominant crops (Figure 9–11). The Niagara Peninsula in Canada, benefiting from the same climatic principle, is famous for fruits — particularly grapes and apples. Fruits grown on hillsides benefit from air drainage.

Pasture. In a region where most of the crops are grown for feeding livestock and where dairying is important, pastures of necessity play a prominent role in the systems of farming.

Pastures fall into two main classifications: (1) *permanent pastures* — areas covered with perennial or self-seeding annual plants that

pasture. The combined acreages of tame hay and pasturage approximate those in corn and small grains in Illinois, Iowa, and Minnesota and exceed them in Indiana, Michigan, Missouri, Ohio, and Wisconsin.

Too many farmers in the Agricultural Interior have given insufficient attention to their pastures; they have treated them as "stepchildren," allowing them to have a thin turf and to become weedy and run-down.

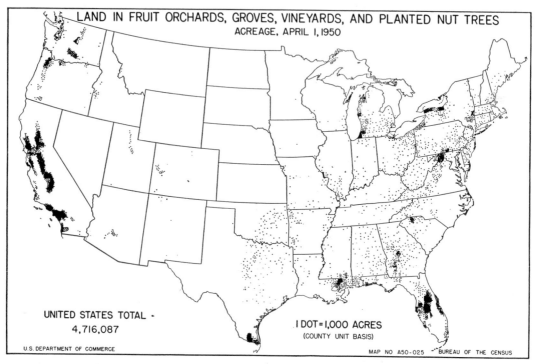

Figure 9–11. Fruit is widely grown throughout the United States. Distribution is an adjustment to climate — particularly length of the frostless season and of moisture — to air drainage, transportation, labor supply, and markets.

are pastured by livestock, and (2) *improved pastures* — areas planted with domesticated plants. Permanent pastures, which are seldom plowed or cultivated, comprise a large percentage of the pasture area in the Dairy Belt and the Corn and Winter Wheat Belt and a considerable percentage even in the Corn Belt. Since nearly every farm has some livestock, it must reserve some land for pasture. Moreover, a portion of nearly every farm is unsuitable for cultivation and can be utilized most advantageously for permanent

They do not fertilize them. Hence their animal-carrying capacity is lower than it should be.

As fertility of pasture soil declines, and as overgrazing reduces grass to impotency, certain weeds appear which animals refuse to eat. Animals raised on such pastures reflect the soil poverty in their physiology. Only pastures on soils receiving the necessary lime and phosphates can provide healthy livestock. Deficiencies in animal growth and reproduction stem from neglect of soil fertility.[18]

The Livestock Industry

The Agricultural Interior concentrates on growing feed for livestock rather than on food for man. In few areas elsewhere in the world is the system of farming based to so large an extent upon livestock. From two thirds to three fourths of the income from Corn Belt farms comes from livestock – a situation in sharp contrast with that in most other outstanding agricultural areas.

The farmers here have several possible choices for the utilization of their corn. Accordingly certain well-defined areas of corn-use have arisen. The "cash-grain" areas (east-central Illinois, and northwestern Iowa) sell

corn as grain to industry; this is possible because of low freight rates to nearby cities. Here, obviously, swine and beef cattle are relatively less important than elsewhere in the Corn Belt. In the eastern Corn Belt swine and dairy cattle predominate, though some beef cattle, too, are raised (Figure 9–12). Fresh milk finds a ready market in the large cities. In the western Corn Belt (western Iowa and eastern Nebraska), both beef cattle and swine are important. It is significant that the less weathered soils in the Agricultural Interior grow crops high in protein and hence lead in beef cattle, whereas the more weathered soils in the humid half of the region grow carbohydrate crops (fats) and lead in swine.

Beef Cattle. Beef cattle are most numerous in the central and western parts of the region, the old prairie portion, for, unlike swine, they are essentially grass eaters. Only 15 per cent of our total beef production tonnage is made from grain, though grain finish-

------

[18] W. A. Albrecht, "Better Pastures Depend on Soil Fertility," *Fertilizer Review*, Vol. 19, January-February-March 1944, pp. 2 ff.

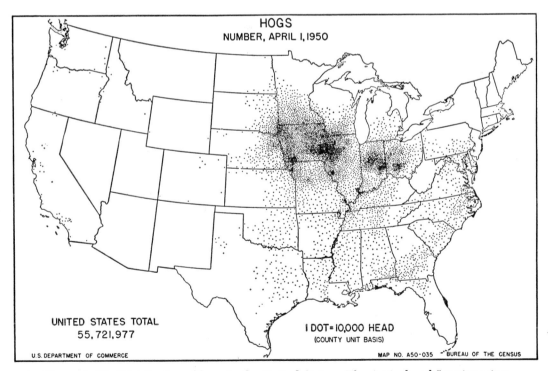

Figure 9–12. Distribution of hogs in the United States. The Agricultural Interior raises about three fourths of Anglo-America's hogs and pigs, the Corn Belt alone accounting for two fifths of them. Note the close relation of the maps of corn and swine.

234   *The Agricultural Interior*

ing contributes much to improving the grades of beef.

Since cattle lose more weight in transportation than do hogs, the tendency is to fatten them on farms within a single night's journey of the great markets. Few live cattle are now sent from the western part of this region as far east as Buffalo, Cleveland, and Pitts-

run with the cattle and act as scavengers. These animals root out of the ground and manure the corn which has spilled from the feeding bunks and which the cattle will not touch (Figure 9–13).

Swine. Of all domesticated animals, swine convert corn into meat most efficiently and rapidly. Spring shotes, for example, are

Figure 9–13.   Swine and cattle on a feeder lot in the Corn Belt. When cattle are fed in this region, they are invariably followed by hogs which pick up the corn wasted by the cattle.   (Courtesy of the Bureau of Agricultural Economics.)

burgh. The development of good highways and the universal adoption of the truck has altered the method of getting livestock to market.

Contrary to the common notion that the range states provide only the grazing and breeding lands and the Corn Belt the fattening areas, the fact is that about two thirds of the animals slaughtered within the Corn Belt are bred in it.

Feeding is a major agricultural enterprise in the western part of the region, the animals being carried through the winter on hay and other home-grown feeds and fattened on corn. Most cattle feeders keep swine, which

ready for market in approximately eight months. During the feeding period, they gain in weight from one to one and one-fourth pounds per day. Three fourths of the swine in the United States are raised in this region, where the density is about four times the average for the rest of the country (Figure 9–12). Where swine are most numerous is where corn is cheapest and can, therefore, move to market advantageously in the concentrated form of live or slaughtered animals. It is much more economical to ship one pound of hog than five pounds of grain (roughly the quantity required to produce one pound of live weight).

Formerly the Corn Belt specialized on the lard type of hog. Now, because of the competition of vegetable oils and shortenings with lard, emphasis is placed on dual-purpose swine — animals that produce plenty of lard but at the same time are noted for their high-quality meat.

Swine are kept in several kinds of movable houses placed near the barn and corn crib. Adjacent to each group of houses are self-feeders into which the feed drops from above. This method is much safer for the small pigs than the old swill trough with its excessive crowding and pushing of animals.

Dairy Cattle. In the heart of the Agricultural Interior, mixed farming based on corn and meat animals is the most profitable enterprise, though nearly every farmer keeps milk cows for home use, for the sale of fresh milk to nearby urban markets, and for utilizing pasturage advantageously. Moreover, dairy cows provide the farmer with profitable winter work which would be impossible if crops only were grown. Except for the fertile level plain on either side of the Illinois-Wisconsin line, which specializes in fresh milk rather than in corn and meat, the portion of this area west of Lake Michigan generally goes in for manufactured dairy products — butter, cheese, evaporated milk and casein. The farther a farm lies from a city, the higher the transport cost on fluid milk, which, being 87 per cent water, is the most expensive of all dairy products to ship.

It is in the Dairy Belt, however, that dairy cattle are most numerous and where the dominant system of farming is built around them. Here the short growing season and cool summers limit the growth of many crops; much land is in marsh, swamp, and lake; large areas are too wet for tillage but are satisfactory for pasture or marsh hay; and much soil (where there are podzols) is of low fertility or strewn with glacial boulders and stones. This combination of geographical conditions tempted the immigrant Germans, Swiss, and Scandinavians toward dairying rather than toward crop production. Most of the land here had been logged, then worn out by several successive crops of wheat and

before the arrival of the immigrants, virtually abandoned. Using grass and small grains, they revived the land, and ultimately developed a prosperous dairy industry.

Horses. The number of horses in the Agricultural Interior has declined sharply and their place has been taken by the tractor. In fact, in the "cash-grain" parts of the Corn Belt, in east-central Illinois and northwestern Iowa, some farmers keep no horses whatever. With no stock to care for in winter, they sojourn at that season in Florida or California.

The reduction in the number of horses has released tens of thousands of acres of land from growing feed for them and has permitted such land to be employed for growing feed crops for beef cattle and for pasturing beef cattle. However, on many farms, particularly on the smaller ones, some horses are still used.

Some Problems of the Farmers

Inflation of Land Values and Its Consequences. The pioneers procured choice land in the Agricultural Interior for nothing or for as little as $1.25 per acre. Even as late as 1877 good land in central Iowa could be purchased for $7 per acre. It increased in value, reaching the top in that state in 1918 at $100 to $500 per acre. The goad was the first World War and the terrific demand it brought for bread and meat. By 1921, however, Europe was no longer a heavy buyer of these commodities and prices in the great heart of American agriculture slumped. Thousands of farmers had mortgaged their farms and were heavily in debt. Depressed agricultural prices prevented many of them from paying interest on mortgages and the sheriff "sold them out." Thus did the nation learn a bitter lesson in mortgage foreclosure.

During and following World War II prices of farms in this region soared again. This time, however, prices of agricultural commodities have been artificially maintained by the federal government and land values have held up. Should there be another depression, or even recession, however, this region would no doubt suffer again, for land values are too high.

Homesteading is definitely over in this region. No longer is there any cheap land that is at the same time good land. No longer can the country boy start for himself as a farmer with only:

> . . . a plentiful supply of grit, a wagon, a team, a plow, and a wife. Land prices are high and modern farming requires stock and tools in considerable amounts. To be successful the modern farm boy also needs more than the "3 R's" which constituted almost the entire education of his [grand] father.[19]

So far as his own efforts are concerned, he must in most instances, be a renter or must find a new vocation.

Parity. When President Franklin D. Roosevelt in 1942 asked for emergency powers to control farm prices at parity, he started something that is still being argued. Parity involves three steps (1948 Farm Bill):

1. Getting the average farm price of the products in the United States for the past decade.
2. Adjusting the ten-year average price to the 1910-1914 price level of all United States products.
3. Adjusting the answer to (2) to the present level of prices of things farmers purchase compared with the 1910-1914 average.

In short then parity is intended to maintain a fair relationship between the prices the farmer receives and those he pays — the law assuming that the fairest relationship is the one prevailing from 1910 to 1914.

In maintaining parity, the government maintains prices in competition with the consumer. This has enabled the farmer for more than a decade to benefit beyond what many people consider to be a "fair return."

Transportation

No region, subregion or district can advance far in *commercial* agriculture without

[19] Warren S. Thompson, *A Handbook of Social Psychology,* p. 68. Worcester, Mass.: Clark University Press, 1935.

an abundance of efficient and relatively economical transportation. Lacking it, the area, unless it be fortunate enough to produce an exotic product, must be doomed to *subsistence* agriculture.

In the Agricultural Interior, which constitutes the crossroads of the nation, transportation is now of the best. Until a railroad web was developed over the region, interior location was a distinct handicap and hardship.

Before 1850 the principal avenues for the disposal of farm products were (1) the Mississippi and its navigable tributaries and (2) the Great Lakes with their eastern connections.

The first railroads in the Middle West were not built as competitors to navigable waterways but as links connecting them. The rapid extension and improvement of railway facilities after 1850, however, profoundly changed agriculture and revolutionized the whole course of internal trade. Railroads by spanning the great interior with a network of steel rails also stimulated the growth of cities and the development of manufacturing.

Roads. The truck and the automobile have revolutionized transportation in the twentieth century almost as much as the railway did in the nineteenth. Approximately one third of the nation's total mileage of highest-type surface roads is in the Middle Western states. This region is laced by a network of all-weather highways. One of the main problems connected with agriculture in this region is the provision of adequately coordinated distribution. Good roads are a prime factor in bringing the farm nearer the major centers of consumption. Nearly every farmer has a car or a truck or both; some even have several of each.

Over much of the region, roads run in east-west or north-south lines 100 miles at a stretch. Most roads follow section lines and are a mile apart.

The lone disadvantage of such a road system is that distance is increased to towns and villages in those cases where the farms are not in one of the cardinal directions from them.

Figure 9–14. A small village (Graymont, Illinois) in the Corn Belt. Hundreds of such villages with their buildings and trees rise prominently out of the checkerboard fields of crops and pasture. (Courtesy of the *Daily Pantagraph*, Bloomington, Illinois.)

Hamlets and Villages

There are relatively few large cities in the Agricultural Interior. There are, however, an amazing number of hamlets and villages scattered throughout the region at about five-mile intervals. A *hamlet* is a small agglomeration of people (20 to 150) at a crossroads, with its houses and work units sufficiently prominent to indicate a node in the rural landscape. The typical *village* (both incorporated and unincorporated) of which there are thousands, consists of a combination of brick and frame buildings irregularly spaced along a street or streets bordered by trees

and concrete or brick sidewalks. It usually contains a railroad station, a post office, one or more churches, a bank, a garage or two, a cream station, a feed store, grocery, hardware, drugstore, and bakery. The most imposing building, invariably built of brick, is the school. Along the railroad tracks are a grain elevator and livestock loading pens (Figure 9–14). There are usually no factories or mills. At least a third of such villages cover less than one square mile and possibly a quarter exceed one square mile (based upon an actual survey of a large area in the Corn Belt). The average village supports what it considers to be the essential minimum in amenities of life. If the village prospers, it adds a library, a historical society, and more adequate health facilities. Around it extend open-country areas occupied by farms. The majority of the inhabitants are apt to be retired farmers, who have rented or sold their holdings. Most everyone has a vegetable garden.

The frequent roads in the area focus on the scattered villages. During the great depression, many of these villages declined — the result of (1) the attraction of large cities for the younger people and (2) the widespread ownership of the automobile, which enables a person to go 20 miles as easily as he formerly did 5 with a horse. Some students of planning in this region believe there is an excess of such villages. Their role in the region must not be under-rated, however. They are the base of supplies for the surrounding farming area, the market place for a large portion of the output, and the hub of a considerable territory whose inhabitants depend upon them for a number of services. Incorporated villages contain one-twelfth of the nation's population; in Illinois alone nearly half a million people live in villages having less than 1,000 inhabitants.[20] Farm villages have no urban ambitions. Most of them are destined to remain small communities.

The Outlook

The future of the Agricultural Interior as a whole must depend upon agriculture more than upon any other activity. The big problem is not one of production but rather one

[20] Clarence B. Odell, *The Functional Pattern of Villages in a Selected Area of the Corn Belt*, p. 5. Chicago: University of Chicago Libraries, 1939.

of marketing the output at a profit. In the past several years farmers have benefited from government control of farm prices (parity).

It is believed that the United States (in large measure the Agricultural Interior) can feed at least 50 per cent more people at home than are now being supported.

Tenancy decreased between 1945 and 1950. Nevertheless there is still 27 per cent tenancy for the nation and a higher percentage for the Agricultural Interior. With high land values, widespread mechanization, increasing use of chemicals, reduced labor requirements and good prices for agricultural products, the farm can support reasonably well both the landlord and the renter. This does not mean sharecropping: it means that the farmer now at or past 50, who has worked hard all his life, can let down. Many of these retired farmers keep an observant eye on the farm operation. Some, however, spend their winters in California or Florida.

There will, of course, be years when the farmer will suffer, for even the most efficient operator, making the best possible use of agricultural research and practicing the most scientific methods, is subject to the whims of nature — drought, flood, tornado, hail, freezes and insect pests — all beyond his control.

The exodus of young people from the farms to the cities will no doubt continue as indicated by the 1950 census and this despite the fact that farming is now profitable. However, agriculture never will be able to pay wages comparable with those paid in manufacturing and commerce. In addition to the higher wages received in cities, is the fact that young people in large numbers are no longer needed on farms.

Table 8

SELECTED CITIES AND TOWNS OF THE AGRICULTURAL INTERIOR

City or Town	Urbanized area	Political center	City or Town	Urbanized area	Political center
*Ann Arbor		48,251	Brantford		36,727
Aurora		50,576	*Buffalo	798,043	580,132
Battle Creek		48,666	Cedar Rapids	78,212	72,296
*Bay City		52,523	*Chicago	4,920,816	3,620,962
Berwyn		51,280	Cicero		67,544

* Also in the American Manufacturing Belt.

City or Town	Urbanized area	Political center	City or Town	Urbanized area	Political center
*Cincinnati	813,292	503,998	*Lorain		51,202
*Cleveland	1,383,599	914,808	Louisville	472,736	369,129
Cleveland Heights		59,141	Madison	110,111	96,056
*Columbus	437,707	375,901	*Milwaukee	829,495	637,392
*Covington		64,452	Minneapolis		521,718
Davenport		74,549	Minneapolis–St. Paul	985,101	
Davenport–Rock Island–Moline	194,925		Moline		37,397
*Dayton	346,864	243,872	*Muncie		58,479
*Dearborn		94,994	Muskegon	85,245	48,429
Decatur	73,713	66,269	Nashville	258,887	174,307
Des Moines	199,934	177,965	*Niagara Falls (N.Y.)	97,620	90,872
*Detroit	2,659,398	1,849,568	*Niagara Falls (Ont.)		22,874
Dubuque		49,671	Oak Park		63,529
*East Chicago		54,263	Omaha	310,291	251,117
*East Cleveland		40,047	Oshawa		41,545
*East St. Louis		82,295	*Oshkosh		41,084
*Erie	151,710	130,803	*Ottawa	281,908	202,045
Evanston		73,641	*Peoria	154,539	111,856
Evansville	137,573	128,636	Peterborough		38,272
*Flint	197,631	163,143	*Pontiac	92,573	73,681
*Fort Wayne	140,314	133,607	*Racine	76,537	71,193
*Gary		133,911	*Rochester (N.Y.)	409,149	332,488
*Grand Rapids	226,817	176,515	Rochester (Minn.)		29,885
**Green Bay		52,735	*Rockford	122,226	92,927
**Guelph		27,386	Rock Island		48,710
*Hamilton (Ohio)	63,270	57,951	*Saginaw	105,939	92,918
*Hamilton (Ont.)	259,685	208,321	St. Catherines		37,984
*Hammond		87,594	St. Joseph	82,290	78,588
*Hull		43,483	*St. Louis	1,400,058	856,796
*Indianapolis	502,375	427,173	St. Paul		311,349
*Jackson		51,088	Sarnia		34,697
*Joliet		51,601	Sioux City	90,101	83,991
*Kalamazoo	83,332	57,704	Sioux Falls		52,696
Kansas City	698,350	586,175	*South Bend	168,165	115,911
*Kenosha		54,368	*Springfield (Ohio)	82,284	78,508
Kingston		33,459	Springfield (Ill.)	97,371	81,628
Kitchener		44,867	Terre Haute	78,028	64,214
La Crosse		47,535	*Toledo	364,344	303,616
Lakewood		68,071	***Topeka	89,104	78,791
*Lansing	134,052	92,129	*Toronto	1,117,470	675,754
Lexington		55,534	***Tulsa	206,311	182,740
Lima		50,246	Valleyfield		22,414
Lincoln	99,509	98,884	*Warren		49,856
*London		95,343	Waterloo	84,386	65,198
			*Windsor	157,672	120,049

* Also in the American Manufacturing Belt.
** Near the Northern Continental Forest.
*** Near the Great Plains.

Selected Bibliography

William A. Albrecht, "Better Soils Make Better Hogs," *Hampshire Herdsman*, June 1947.

———, "Soil and Livestock Work Together," *Meat* (American Meat Institute, Chicago), September 1947.

———, "Sound Horses Are Bred on Fertile Soils,' *Percheron News*, July 1942.

Joseph E. Baker, "The Midwestern Origins of America," *American Scholar*, Vol. 17, 1948, pp. 58–68.

P. W. Bryan, "Natural Environment in Relation to Human Activity in the Corn Belt of North America," *Geography*, Vol. 15, March 1929.

Everett E. Edwards, "American Agriculture — The First 300 Years," *Yearbook of Agriculture, 1940*, pp. 171–276. Washington, D. C.: Government Printing Office, 1940.

Harold U. Faulkner, "Farm Machinery and the Industrial Revolution," *Current History*, Vol. 33, 1931.

Charles M. Hardin, "A Proposal for Organizing the Missouri Valley," *Farm Policy Forum*, Vol. 2, April 1949.

F. L. Lewton, "Notes on the Old Plows in the United States National Museum," *Agricultural History*, Vol. 17, 1943, pp. 62–64.

James C. Malin, "The Adaptation of the Agricultural System to Sub-Humid Environment," *Agricultural History*, Vol. 10, 1936, pp. 118–141.

———, *The Grasslands of North America, Prolegomena to Its History*. Lawrence, Kansas: Privately printed, 1948.

———, "Mobility and History: Reflections on Agricultural Policies of the United States in Relation to a Mechanized World," *Agricultural History*, Vol. 17, 1943, pp. 177–191.

Earl B. Shaw, "Fertilization: Route to a New Continent," *Journal of Geography*, Vol. 47, October 1948, pp. 284–290.

Helen L. Smith, "Agricultural Land Use in Iowa," *Economic Geography*, Vol. 25, July 1949, pp. 190–200.

10.

The Northern Continental

Forest

ANGLO-AMERICA's largest and possibly least-known region (Figure 10–1) is largely an interminable coniferous forest, with a sprinkling of broad-leaved trees, covering an area of flat to rough terrain. A map showing distribution of population superimposed on a map indicating regional boundaries will show the area's relative emptiness (Figure 10–2). Maps of terrain, soils, and climate show *why* there is a paucity of human beings. Much of this region consists of the Canadian Shield, a land of Pre-Cambrian crystalline rock, rounded hills almost devoid of soil, fast-flowing rivers, and innumerable lakes, swamps, and muskegs. Long cold winters characterize most of the region; its amazingly short growing season makes agriculture relatively unimportant. On the mainland proper, true agricultural settlements persist only in the Pioneer Fringes. From boundary to boundary, most of the inhabitants whether they be French Canadians, Anglo-Canadians, Labradorians, Newfoundlanders, Indians, or "Americans," are engaged overwhelmingly in *extractive* pursuits. The natural environment discourages most other types of enterprises. A considerable part of the population is semi-nomadic. Much of this region remains as it was originally – a land of the Indian. The central part, however, in the Clay Belt and in the mining region, is a part of settled Canada.

The Northern Continental Forest Region of Anglo-America falls naturally into four geographic subregions: A) Newfoundland and Coastal Labrador; B) the Canadian Shield; C) the Upper Lakes; and D) the Northern Great Plains.

Newfoundland and Coastal Labrador

This subregion occupies a strategic position across the mouth of the Gulf of St. Lawrence and along the trade route connecting America and northwest Europe. It is advantageously situated with respect to important fishing grounds. Newfoundland, the most important part of this subregion, has long been the western terminus for transatlantic cables, wireless stations, steamer lanes, and airplane crossings. More recently the island has become one of the most important places for naval and air bases in eastern Anglo-

241

America. During the second World War these new bases, along with developments in Bermuda, largely protected the industrial part of the continent.

The Natural Environment

Terrain. Newfoundland, a part of the Acadian (Appalachian) Region, has rolling

Climate. The climate is largely the result of a clash between continental and oceanic influences. Its winters are much colder than those in British Columbia or Britain in the same latitude. As a result of the deeply serrated shoreline, no point in Newfoundland is more than 70 miles from the ocean. Altitude plays its role, as evidenced by the replacement of forest by tundra at

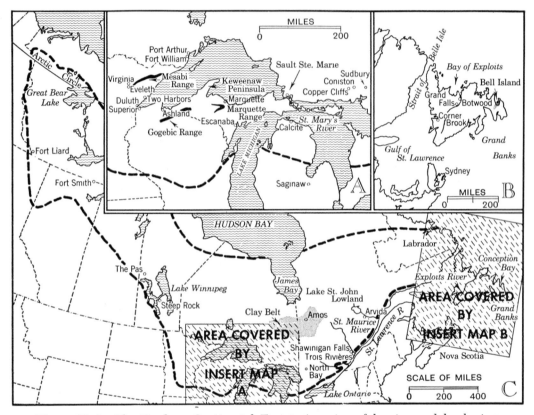

Figure 10–1. The Northern Continental Forest. A region of logging and lumbering, trapping, mining, manufacturing, and resorts.

plateaus of 500 to 1,000 feet with elevations of 2,600 feet in the Long Ranges. The Labrador coast is the rugged, elevated, fjorded edge of the Shield. Glaciation left much of the area studded with lakes, almost soil-bare, and swampy. Southeast of Newfoundland, the ocean bottom consists of a submarine plateau or tableland — one of the major fishing banks of the entire world. Geologists affirm that Newfoundland had a small independent ice cap of its own.

elevations exceeding 1,000 or 1,200 feet.

Because the ocean waters are above the freezing point of salt water, winter temperatures are higher than would be expected for the latitude. In the Gulf of St. Lawrence all harbors freeze over, the Strait of Belle Isle being completely blocked by ice. The bays on the Labrador coast and large areas of the adjacent sea freeze solid by October or November. Summers everywhere are cool, because the Labrador Current, laden with floe-ice and icebergs, moves southward along the east and south coasts.

Considerable snow falls: except for the south coast of Newfoundland the entire sub-region gets more than 100 inches of snow in winter. Ice storms, more common here than elsewhere in Anglo-America, occur when a south wind sets in. Rain freezes as it contacts the ground, which is below freezing. Fog is prevalent on the coasts of Newfoundland and on the Grand Banks, but no more

— black spruce and reindeer moss. The coast of Labrador is almost completely lacking in forest, though the sheltered stream basins support some tree growth, particularly in the Hamilton River Valley.

Minerals. Newfoundland contains considerable mineral wealth. At Bell Island is one of the notable iron-ore reserves of the world. The ore, high-grade hematite containing 54 per cent metallic iron, extends a great distance under the sea. Only there in all

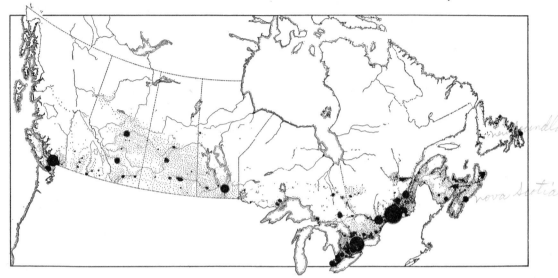

Figure 10–2. Distribution of population in Canada in 1951. The most significant aspect of population distribution is its concentration without much depth along the 4,000-mile ribbon of the international border. Here the natural environment is most suitable for settlement. (Courtesy of C. C. Lingard and Dominion Bureau of Statistics.)

so than on the southern coasts of Nova Scotia.

Winds from all points on the compass change direction suddenly, and are sometimes so strong that houses must have double walls, double doors, and double windows to keep the wind and fine snow out. Even trees on the shores of Labrador and Newfoundland are affected by these winds and are stunted as a consequence.

Natural Vegetation. The natural vegetation consists largely of coniferous forest — white spruce and balsam fir in the main body of the island. In the southwest is a small area of mixed forest — red maple and yellow birch. On the Long Peninsula is forest tundra

Anglo-America can iron ore be mined close to the ocean. Valuable lead and zinc ores are found at Buchans near Red Indian Lake in Newfoundland's interior. In addition, the Burin Peninsula has one of the world's most extensive deposits of fluorspar, which is valuable in the aluminum industry.

Settlement

The Newfoundland-Labrador Subregion was the first part of Anglo-America to be discovered and used by white men. Though Newfoundland was England's oldest colony, for many generations it was considered unfit for human habitation. Moreover, settlement was discouraged because the mother country wished to use it exclusively for the fisheries, which in turn served as "a school of seamanship" for the British Navy. Speaking of a group of naval recruits who arrived in England in the summer of 1941, Wallace Reyburn said:

> There could be few men better fitted to take on the duties of the Navy than these hardy Newfoundland lads. Having spent all their lives in this island colony off the east coast of Canada, they have the sea in their very bones. At an age when the average English youngster is attending preparatory school, their boys are out in their tiny fishing boats off the coasts of Newfoundland and Labrador, living up to the Newfoundlanders' claim of being the best fishermen in the world.[1]

When settlement finally did get under way in the eighteenth century, practically all the population became concentrated along the coast near the fishing grounds. Today more than 90 per cent of the inhabitants live there (Figure 10–2).

Most Newfoundlanders are small in stature but wiry, and are of English, Scottish, and Irish extraction. Their standard of living is low; families are large and incomes small. The interior is unsuitable for farming and is plagued by myriads of mosquitoes during the two or three warm months. Among Britain's North American possessions, Newfoundland alone failed to become primarily a colony of settlement.

Economic Geography

This subregion has three principal sources of income all of which are based upon the exploitation of natural resources — the fisheries, the forest, and the mines. The soil contributes little, since agriculture is little-developed.

Fishing. Some authorities declare that French and Portuguese fishermen came to the banks before Columbus reached the New World. Whether this be true or not, it is known that fishermen from Europe were on

the banks in the sixteenth century. Permanent settlement by fishermen, however, did not begin until the close of the eighteenth century. Certainly commercial fishing goes back to the days when small sailing vessels carried to Europe commodities having immediate sale and bringing large returns. For 400 years fishing was Newfoundland's only industry: codfish could always (it was solely a summer enterprise) be caught off the Grand Banks and at the mouth of the St. Lawrence.

Fishing employs more people than any other occupation — about 33 per cent of the gainfully employed males, although the numbers have been declining during the past century. In 1945 there were about 32,000 men working in the three types of fisheries: (1) inshore, (2) Labrador, and (3) bank. *Inshore* fishing, most important of the three, is carried on particularly along the east and south coasts and accounts for about three fourths of the catch. The fisherman operates as an individual unit using a dory or motorboat and returning home each night with his catch. Most of the fish are caught in June and July. *Labrador* fishing is carried on along the shore of Labrador by Newfoundlanders who travel north each summer, and by a very small number of resident fishermen or *liveyeres*. There is also some fishing by schooners on the off-shore banks. *Banks fishing* is conducted by schooners of up to 150 tons which make about three trips to the Grand Banks each season. A schooner carries about 20 to 25 men who, once on the fishing grounds, leave the vessel to fish from dories. This is one of man's most dangerous occupations, for the fishermen frequently get caught in storms or heavy fog, become separated from the parent vessel and are lost.

Some of the cod are salted when the ships are at sea and dried when the men are fishing close to shore. However, trawlers and draggers are becoming common since they can make more rapid trips from the banks. The fresh fish trade is becoming important. In 1949 there were 13 quick-freezing plants in operation along the coast, including two at St. John's.

Lumbering. Newfoundland's forests are one of her most valuable resources and pro-

---

[1] The British Library of Information, *Bulletin from Britain*, No. 40, June 4, 1941, p. 4.

vide her people with much employment and revenue. In fact, since 1930 forest products have been more important than fish. About 47 per cent of the land area, some 17,150 square miles, is forested, of which about 83 per cent is exploitable.

The best timber, consisting of mixed stands of conifers and broad-leaved deciduous trees — predominantly balsam fir, white spruce, and birch — lies in the interior, particularly on the better-drained valley slopes. The trees are inferior to those grown along the Pacific Coast, in Eastern Canada, the Lake States, or New England. Trees cannot attain large proportions when temperatures are low and winds strong. Though some lumbering is carried on, the bulk of the forest is better suited for pulp and paper.

In Labrador exploitable or commercial forest occurs only in sheltered valleys on well-drained slopes in the interior south of latitude 55° N.

Pulp and paper. The forest, dominated by spruce and fir, supplies the raw material for pulp and paper the exports of which, based on value, now surpass those of fish. The industry benefits not only from accessible timber, but from cheap hydro-power, transport of logs by stream, and from a plentiful supply of labor.

Newfoundland's first paper mill was built at Grand Falls in 1909. There were both forest and power. The mill is still in operation as is one situated at Bishop's Falls just downstream from Grand Falls. Both are connected by rail with Botwood, the summer shipping point at the head of the Bay of Exploits.

A huge mill, one of the largest in the world, built in 1924 at Corner Brook almost at tidewater on the estuary of the Humber, is well located with respect to its raw material and export markets. Its wood is obtained from some 7,000 square miles of holdings. Ice, however, locks the bay during the months from January to the end of April at which time the mill's products move by rail southward to ice-free Port aux Basques. Logs are stream-driven to the mill. Hydroelectric power is generated nearby.

Mining. Mining is one of Newfound-land's three principal economic enterprises. Despite rich endowment, however, mining is retarded by the high cost of development. Hence there are only two major producing areas.

Bell Island in Conception Bay is the location of one of the most valuable iron ore deposits and mines in the world. The ore was discovered by accident; some sailors having picked up heavy stones for ballast, left them in their dories while at anchor in St. John's. A canny Englishman who suspected these stones were iron ore, had them assayed, and found that they ran about 55 per cent metallic iron.

Since 1899 the mines have been operated by the same interests as the iron and steel industry in Sydney, Nova Scotia. This plant has reduced in its furnaces more than half of the 60 million tons so far mined. Annual production averages about 2 million to 2½ million tons. Nova Scotia and the United Kingdom are the principal markets. Newfoundland itself smelts no ore.

The workable beds are mined on the northwest side of the island and mining extends out for a distance of 2½ miles under Conception Bay. The underwater mines with reserves of about 2½ billion tons, contain ore in three beds separated from one another by thick layers of rock. The room and pillar method of mining is employed.

The Buchans Mines, located five miles north of Red Indian Lake in the center of the island, yield zinc-lead-copper sulphide ores. Production is more than twice as valuable as that of the iron of Wabana (1950). New reserves have been found recently.

Agriculture. There is no agriculture whatsoever in Coastal Labrador and even in Newfoundland it plays but a minor role. The people here have always looked *to the sea* and *away from the land*. The natural environment — short growing season, acid podzol soils, rugged terrain — is hostile to farming. Moreover, the planting and fishing seasons conflict. What farming there is is largely of the subsistence type, being carried on mainly by the families of fishermen and loggers on small holdings. Seldom does a farm exceed 50 acres and most farms comprise but a few acres. However, some commercial farming is carried on in the Avalon Peninsula and in the valleys of the west coast, near the larger urban centers. Limited transport facilities also restrict commercial farming. Owing to the small humus content of the soils, considerable fish and compost must be used to make the soils productive.

What agriculture there is falls into the hay, dairy, root-crop system. More than half the arable land is in hay and pasture. Actually less than one half of one per cent of Newfoundland's surface is devoted to crops. Hay and potatoes, along with hardy vegetables (cabbages, beets, carrots, and parsnips) and fruits (currants, gooseberries, raspberries, and strawberries) are the leading crops.

The fishing population should give more attention to gardening. Vegetables, especially, are badly needed to combat nutritional diseases.

Trade. Newfoundland is dependent upon trade for its existence. The fish, pulp and paper, the iron ore, the copper, lead and zinc concentrates, and fluorspar are exported, but unfortunately the prices of all, especially of fish, upon which so large a proportion of the people depend, fluctuate widely, and poor prices enforce a standard of living dangerously low. About two thirds of the food and consumers goods are imported, mostly from other parts of Canada.

Transportation

So long as Newfoundlanders engaged solely in fishing and lived in settlements along the coast, the sea was the highway. As exploitation of the island's other resources took place, however, man had to go into the interior. The railway (now a part of the Canadian National) was begun in 1881 and completed in 1896. The main line and its branches consist of 705 miles of narrow-gauge track.

There are 5,800 miles of all types of road on the island. Most of this mileage consists of gravel highway; the only stretch of hard surface road is that connecting St. John's with Carbonear. There is not a mile of hard surface road in coastal Labrador.

The Outlook

Grim climate, poor soils, and immature drainage, all conspire to discourage any bright future for this subregion. The coasts of Labrador and of northern Newfoundland are frozen solid from December till late in June, though the Atlantic coast of the island has ice floes and is frozen part of the time. Agriculture and manufacturing, the two economic enterprises over the earth that sustain the largest populations have in this subregion little future. And the enterprises that do have a future — fishing, logging, pulp-and paper-making, and mining — do not give opportunities and jobs to many persons. Despite the importance of the mines they give employment to and affect but a relatively small number of persons. For the total capital invested and the value of the output, mining the world over gives employment to but a small part of a nation's or a region's total population.

Though only a few thousand people are affected, it should be mentioned that Newfoundland's global position gives it a place of prominence in the present air age. Gander Airport, established by the governments of Newfoundland and the United Kingdom prior to World War II, is an important base for transatlantic flights. It was useful also during the war.

The Canadian Shield

For a long time this huge area of some two million square miles (Figure 10–1) was, except for the furs it supplied, considered to be worthless wilderness. It was practically unknown except to trappers and fur traders, to lumbermen, prospectors, and sportsmen — people whose numbers always are small. So inhospitable was much of the Shield that, despite determined efforts to put roads across the rocky, shallow soil and the filigree of lakes and rivers, Canadian expansion was deflected around the southern rim. Thus the

Shield stood as a wall between eastern and western Canada, denying the nation the "strength, vigor, and development which comes from geographical and political unity." This situation has changed in the past half century, however, with the tapping of the area's wealth of forest, minerals and water power. What had been a liability to the country has now become an asset. Even its soils are being utilized locally, especially in the Clay Belt (Figure 10–1), though for agriculture the area is precariously marginal.

The Upland, though enormous in size, is isolated. Its location has been and ever will be a handicap to development. The thin humus-less soils, poor drainage, hostile climate, and pestiferous insects magnify the unattractiveness to the average immigrant. The Shield is a magnet only to people of the pioneer type or to those interested in quick wealth.

The Natural Environment

Terrain. The Canadian Shield, a vast U-shaped peneplain of ancient crystalline rocks (granites, gneisses, and metamorphosed sedimentaries), covers one half of Canada, its rim towering above the St. Lawrence and Ottawa Valleys and the coast of Labrador and reaching southeast of Georgian Bay and west of Lake Superior. It was so thoroughly glaciated that its rivers were dammed, forming numerous lakes and rock basins. Drainage is poor; swamps or muskegs are extensive. Lakes are so numerous that "the country might almost be described as water with land between it." The rocks have been reduced to a peneplain of uniform height over a considerable area, although the subregion is far from uniform. Though there are local hills and valleys, there is little difference in elevation, the average being approximately 1,000 feet. The landscape should be considered hilly (Figure 10–3).

In addition, the icecap, which carried enormous quantities of debris, deposited this material as the ice melted after the last invasion — an event estimated at 15 or 20 thousand years ago. A veneer of glacial till is a prominent feature over the Shield and

Figure 10–3. Hilly terrain of the Shield as seen from the air. (Courtesy of Dr. J. Wreford Watson and of the Royal Canadian Air Force.)

is the basis of the soils.[2] In some parts the land was scraped bare even over extensive areas (Figure 10–4). Within the Shield, however, are areas of reasonably level terrain and fair soils that owe their origin to old glacial lakes. Lake Ojibway (Clay Belt) and the Lake St. John Lowland are examples and are favorable for settlement.

Climate. In so enormous an area, important differences of climate from north to south or east to west might be expected, but actually the differences are relatively slight. Everywhere the climate is continental — the result largely of interior location, great distance from oceans, and of the barrier influence of the Cordilleras, which keep out the moderating effects of the Pacific Ocean. This continentality is the dominating feature of the Shield's natural environment. Winters are cold and long; summers short and warm, with occasional hot spells. The total precipitation is light.

Soils. Since no complete survey has been made of the soils of the Shield, the area pedologically speaking is *terra incognita*. Owing to the fact that the soils have been

---

[2] Griffith Taylor, *Canada*. London: Methuen and Co., Ltd., 1950.

subjected to rain and cold for thousands of years, a large part of them belongs to the soils known as podzols, whose reputation for agriculture is not enviable. However, there is no reason to believe that these soils are any worse than in similar marginal country of Finland and the Soviet Union. In the Timiskaming area the zonal soils are <u>brown podzolic</u>.

Natural Vegetation. The distinctive nat-

A scientific inventory of the *taiga*, or great northern forest, has been progressing since the development of aerial photography, which is making every locality accessible regardless of distance from settled areas or difficulty in land transportation. From aerial photographs, even the heights of the trees can be determined by measuring the shadows, and from the density of the forest the volume of the standing timber can be

Figure 10–4. Ice-scoured rock on the Clearwater River, Richmond Gulf, Quebec. The stand of trees here is thin, for the area is near the northern limit for trees and close to the Tundra. (Courtesy of the Royal Canadian Air Force.)

ural vegetation of the Shield is coniferous forest with a deciduous admixture (Figure 10–5). From south to north the trees become smaller, those in the extreme north being "worthless little trees." The forest has been known in detail only since the advent of aerial photography. The northern limit is determined mostly by climate and partly by drainage. The poor drainage which characterizes the flat land south of James Bay and the west coast of Hudson Bay makes this area so waterlogged that tree growth occurs only along the rivers.[3]

estimated. Not only is this method faster but it is more economical than that made on land — the cost being about one tenth as much.

This forest is characterized by relatively few species, those of the greatest commercial value being spruce, with much pine, fir, and aspen on the southern side; in the subarctic belt before it merges with the *tundra,* is to be

[3] A. R. M. Lower, "Settlement and the Forest Frontier in Eastern Canada," in *Canadian Frontiers of Settlement*, Vol. 9, p. 21. Toronto: The Macmillan Company of Canada, Ltd., 1936.

Figure 10–5. Fine stand of black spruce of pulpwood size with scattered white spruce, poplar, and white birch along the river and on the higher elevations near Abitibi, Quebec. (Courtesy of Royal Canadian Air Force.)

found considerable scattered and slow-growing spruce of little commercial value. Over much of the "Granite Shield" (in the east and center), where lakes and marshes are widespread, muskeg, consisting of small pine, spruce, and tamarack prevails.

There is a stand of hardwoods in the southeastern part of the Shield, but this forest until recently was little utilized. The increased demand for hardwood lumber and mechanical improvements in logging equipment have at last, however, enabled these forests to be tapped economically. The leading hardwood tree is the yellow birch.

Native Animal Life. Native animal life was originally abundant. Among the numerically more important animals today are the beaver, fisher, lynx, marten, mink, muskrat, porcupine, skunk, otter, caribou, moose, deer, wolf, fox, bear, and snowshoe rabbit. Many

species of fish inhabit the lakes. Many species of birds breed on the Shield. Insects, especially flies and mosquitoes, are so numerous as to make life for man and beast almost unbearable. Insects constitute an outstanding handicap to settlement and exploitation.

Water Power. Few areas in the world have better water-power sites than the Canadian Shield. Large rivers and small rivers seldom run more than a few miles without tumbling over a fall or rapid. Moreover, most of them have their sources in lakes which serve as excellent storage reservoirs. Many too have storage lakes along their courses. About 80 to 85 per cent of the developed and roughly 60 per cent of the Dominion's potential water power is in the so-called acute fuel area — the provinces of Ontario and Quebec — where native coal is economically unavailable. Much of the un-developed water power lies far from centers of population (Figure 10–2), but the devel-oped power lies largely within the *ecumene*.[4]

The almost ideal combination of condi-tions for water-power development on the Shield is expressed by an engineer-economist connected with the Shawinigan Water and Power Company:

The strategic location of water power in Quebec, the dependable flow of its rivers, the availability of huge storage reservoirs, con-structed in large part by the province, the gen-erally low cost of development of the various power plants, and, above all, the bold spirit of initiative shown by private enterprise, are the factors which have contributed most to the prog-ress of the hydroelectric industry in Quebec.[5]

The abundance of hydro-power is reflected in low rates and in the types of industry util-izing the power. The extremely low rate in Quebec results from huge sales to the pulp and paper industry, to aluminum plants, to other electro-chemical and electro-metallur-gical industries. Wholesale rates are made to Ontario and the United States.

It is this power that has become the main-spring of Canadian industry and has con-tributed so much to Canada's recent meta-morphosis from an almost pure agricultural and extractive economy to one of industrial prominence.

The Occupance

The Indian. Before white men came, the Shield was occupied by nomadic Indians who subsisted by hunting and fishing. It is not known whether they ever tried agricul-ture, but if they did it was unsuccessful, since the climate is too severe for maize.

Their numbers were small — possibly 500,000 for all Anglo-America north of the Great Lakes.[6] The density of population has been estimated for that time at approxi-mately two to five persons for each 100 square miles. It is significant that these in-land Indians were by area even less numer-ous than the Eskimos along the shore of the Arctic.[7] This relative emptiness of inhabi-tants was due to a "war-like social tradition" and to the fact that hunting and trapping always preclude a dense population, since they entail the great disadvantage of uncer-tainty: today game may be plentiful, tomor-row it may be lacking. Hence life was pre-carious, poverty extreme, and starvation not uncommon.

These Indians, backward Algonquins in the east and south, Athabascans in the north-west and Crees in the Clay Belt[8] were highly mobile both within and between their tribal areas. Marking off their hunting grounds by blazing trees, they never encroached on one another's territory until after the arrival of white men.

Culture here was lower than in the Amer-ican Southwest. The paucity of formidable barriers east of the Rockies meant in general terms a similarity of environment and of culture.

With the coming of white men, trapping for furs became important. So keen was the competition for peltries between the French and English traders that Indian tribes warred upon one another.

Many Indians intermarried with whites, especially in the earlier years of contact, and it is believed that there are today few full-blooded Indians among the hunting tribes of the Shield.

The submarginal portions of the Cana-dian Shield still are the land of the Indian, whose way of life demands a thorough knowledge of the habits of wild animals and ability to move over wide areas in pursuit of food and peltries. Some tracts are now specifically reserved where only Indians may hunt and trap.

White Settlement. The wide scope of this book does not permit a detailed treat-ment of white settlement on the Shield. One

---

[4] The land within ten miles of a railway.

[5] Cyril Bassett, "Canadian Hydro Keeps Pace with Industrial Development," *Public Utilities Fort-nightly*, Vol. 48, August 2, 1951, p. 138.

[6] A. L. Kroeber, *Cultural and Natural Areas of Native North America*, p. 164. Berkeley: University of California Press, 1939.

[7] Kroeber, *Cultural and Natural Areas of Native North America*, p. 145.

[8] Kroeber, *Cultural and Natural Areas of Native North America*, p. 194.

of two motives actuated those who dared enter the wilderness: (1) to utilize the natural resources or (2) to make homes there and build new societies.[9] The fur trader, miner, and forester exemplified the first, the farmer the second.

Though the land never can accommodate many settlers, nevertheless, much money and time have been spent in a fruitless effort to push the frontier beyond its natural limits. By 1855 the better lands of eastern Canada had been acquired and settlement was "washing the shores" of the Shield. At this time and for decades afterwards the Shield was known only superficially.

As in the Intermontane Basins and Plateaus (Chapter 13) two interests were working against each other: one, trying to administer the natural resources in the wisest way, was desperately attempting to keep settlers from those areas where they would do more harm than good, whereas the other used all its power to encourage settlement. That the Shield is a restrictive environment seems proved by the fact that after a century following pioneer penetration, the Crown still has title to all but a miniscule percentage of the land.[10] Many who did settle have moved away from the pines and rocks. It is now generally believed that pioneers should be discouraged from engaging in "hot-house colonizing." Public acceptance of such an idea is difficult to obtain, for one of the deepest-seated human instincts is that "the land is for the people." Despite difficulties, however, portions of the Shield are being settled.

Present Population. The first whites were French explorers and fur trappers who did not settle permanently on the land. Later French immigrants whose descendents comprise the present French Canadians occupied the St. Lawrence Valley between Montreal and Quebec as well as several tributary valleys. As a result of the limited arable land and the high birth rate, some of these spilled over into adjacent areas and now comprise

a considerable part of the Shield's population. Later came English fur trappers and traders, rivals of the French. The transfer of Canada by France to England increased the number of Anglo-Saxons in Canada, though most of these went into southern Ontario or later into the Prairie Provinces. Some, however, were drawn onto the Shield by its timber, minerals, and, to a lesser degree, its agriculture. More recent immigrants are the Germans, Finns, Hungarians, Italians, Russians, Poles, Slovaks, and Swedes. On the Shield these nationalities tend to segregate into blocks, as they do in the large metropolitan centers of eastern United States.

The introduction of mining started an influx of peoples from all types of climates, some well fitted and some poorly fitted to cope with the harsh environment. Those who remained had to develop initiative and resourcefulness.

The Shield, which is largely marginal and submarginal, supports about 8 per cent of the total population of Canada or about 1.2 million persons (Figure 10–2). The population has doubled in the past quarter century and although this is significant it can hardly be expected that the area ever can support any appreciable proportion of the total Canadian population.

Economic Development

Much of the Shield remains undeveloped but that portion lying immediately north of the St. Lawrence River and the Great Lakes is now partially conquered. Regardless of whether man has engaged in fur trading, lumbering, mining, farming, or pulp and paper making, his activities have been dominated by the forest. The explorer and fur trader, unable to go cross-country on foot or horseback, had to take to the canoe and river because of the forest. To lumbermen and pulp manufacturers the forest was a great natural resource from which they desired to keep out all but themselves. The prospector and the farmer, however, did not look kindly upon the forest; to them it was an enemy that had to be destroyed (Figure 10–5). The prospector sees in the forest

---

[9] Lower, "Settlement and the Forest Frontier in Eastern Canada," p. 28.

[10] Lower, "Settlement and the Forest Frontier in Eastern Canada," p. 28.

simply a covering that prevents his knowing what kind of rock underlies his feet. Extractive industries have held and probably always will hold sway on the Shield. Agriculture will expand briefly but will be relegated to a secondary place unless science makes contributions now unknown.

Trapping. Fur trading began along the coast of Canada, but it never attained great proportions there because the short rivers were poorly suited to transportation and because the population was concentrated along the coast. The enterprise really became important and migrated onto the Shield in the latter part of the sixteenth century when beaver hats became fashionable in Europe. Beavers were most numerous in the more northerly forested parts of the Shield, where agriculture and manufacturing had little chance of success and where the environment provided a favorable habitat for fur-bearing animals. The beaver was not a migrant, and its destruction in any locality forced the hunters to enter new areas. Prime furs were taken only in winter and in the more northerly parts of the forest (Figure 10–6).

Fur hunting still is important here; Canada ranks as one of the world's two chief suppliers of furs, though this subregion does not furnish the entire output. About two thirds

Figure 10–7. A canoe brigade. These Indians take supplies to interior posts and return with the season's catch of furs. The canoe is a contribution of the hunting Indians of the Shield. (Courtesy of Hudson's Bay Company.)

of Canada's peltries based on value are from animals trapped in this area and one third from those raised on farms throughout the Dominion.

When possible the animals are caught in snares or traps to avoid damaging the pelts. Because fur is longer and thicker in winter, Indians and half-breeds at that time scatter out along the streams, sometimes going hundreds of miles to get their peltries. The more desirable animals — the beaver, otter, and muskrat — live along the streams. Moreover, waterways are highways (Figure 10–7), even in winter, when they form ready-made hard roads.

When ice melts in the spring, hunters take their catch to trading posts. Birchbark canoes and larger boats are used. Many of the fur-trading posts belong to the historic Hudson's Bay Company, oldest company in Anglo-America (established in 1670), which accounts for nearly half of Canada's furs. It has more than 200 trading posts strategically located with respect to navigable water. Some of its posts are found more than 600 miles north of the Arctic Circle. As a market, New York City has become the "fur capital of the world," having displaced Brussels, Leipzig, London, and Paris.[11]

[11] E. T. Ransom, "World Fur Production and Trade," *Foreign Agriculture*, Vol. 14, December 1950, pp. 270-273.

Figure 10–6. Hurricanaw River Indian trappers removing trapped beaver from basin hole on northern Canada's Shield. The spruce boughs are used for removing the snow and ice that cling to the beaver's fur. (Courtesy of National Film Board of Canada.)

The railway, motorcar, boat, and airplane have made some changes in the fur business during recent years. The advance of lumbering, mining, and agricultural settlement, along with more efficient methods of trapping, has driven the frontier of furbearing animals farther afield and has greatly reduced their numbers.

Wild life destruction and conservation. The federal and provincial governments have set aside national parks, game sanctuaries, beaver and mink farms, and have put into effect closed seasons where natural conditions provide suitable habitats. They have organized preventive patrols and are issuing hunting and trapping licenses with special care in order to retard excessive exploitation.

The provinces and territories now have trapping regulations. Individual trappers are licensed. Some provinces register traplines, others trapping areas. Indian and Metis populations are increasing beyond the "carrying capacity" of this economy.

Lumbering. Logging and lumbering superseded trapping in the more accessible territory when the beaver was destroyed. The industry has been based largely upon the pines which grow as far north as the Hudson Bay drainage. Trees grow slowly in cold, windy climates and on thin, rocky soils and poorly-drained land. Thus about 100 years are required for a tree in such a habitat to reach sufficient size to be used for saw timber.

Lumbering on the Shield has declined in importance in recent years because of (1) the competition of British Columbia and of northern Europe, whose forests are more accessible, (2) the exhaustion of the best pine near the St. Lawrence, and (3) the high tariffs in the United States. If the forests of British Columbia should be removed as have those of the St. Lawrence Lowland, the Shield would become a more important source of lumber, though in the northern part species dwindle in number and size.

Logging depends upon snow in this region of long cold winters. The cutters begin their work in autumn. Where small trees, destined for pulp mills, are cut, the work must be done before the snow buries the forests. The logs must be got out while the ground is frozen. Ice-roads are built up by continual sprinkling with water over terrain absolutely impassable in summer. Tractors pull the sleds laden with logs to rivers, where the cut is piled awaiting the spring thaw and the freshets, which transport the logs by the hundreds of thousands to strategically located mills (Figure 10–8). River-driving is an economical method of transporting logs, though this applies almost entirely to softwoods. Logging employs the workers (mostly Slavs, Swedes, Finns, and French Canadians) for only about 100 days per year. Some of the lumberjacks are farmers who must supplement the living they eke from the land by other means.

Pulp and paper is Canada's leading industry and Canada is now the world's largest manufacturer and exporter of newsprint. In 1949 almost 80 per cent of the nation's output of pulp and paper was marketed as newsprint, constituting 56 per cent of the total world supply. Beginning in 1866, the industry grew steadily until the termination of the first World War, then boomed between 1920 and 1930, when new towns sprang up over night, huge hydro projects were installed,

Figure 10–8. Logs by the hundreds of thousands are driven down streams in this region. Loggers are breaking up a "jam" with pike poles and peaveys on the Desert River, a tributary of the Gatineau. (Courtesy of National Film Board of Canada.)

and thousands of persons became employed. Much of the industry is controlled by American capital. The United States, the world's largest consumer of newsprint, is interested in Canada (the Shield in particular) because it is nearby and because newsprint since 1911 has been admitted free of duty. A great deal of pulp and some pulpwood also are exported.

At first the paper companies, which engaged only in manufacturing, purchased their pulpwood. So great, however, became the demands that they were unable to meet the requirements by purchase and hence were obliged to get either freehold or Crown grants. Fortunately for Canada, 90 per cent of the forested area is retained by the Crown, whereas in the United States 80 per cent is in private ownership. Canadian pulp and paper manufacturing, however, is not restricted to the Shield, though it leads all other parts of the country by a wide margin.

A close correlation exists between the location of the pulp and paper industry, the spruce-balsam forests, and the distribution of water power. Spruce, though existing as far north as trees can grow, really reaches its optimum along the Hudson Bay Divide. So extensive is this forest that it would appear to be able to supply present needs in perpetuity, provided reasonable conservation is carried on. The method of transporting pulp logs is similar to that used by the lumber industry.

Relation between water power and pulp and paper mills. Cheap power is an important factor in the location of pulp plants, as is shown by their distribution (Figure 3–21). A string of mills (all water-driven) lines the southern edge of the forest from the mouth of the St. Lawrence to Lake Winnipeg. If, in addition to power and to proximity to resources of wood of superior quality for the manufacture of newsprint, the mill has abundant and dependable supplies of clean, fresh water, can receive river-driven logs, and lies on navigable water so that imported raw materials can be secured cheaply and finished products be shipped economically, its location may be considered strategic. A paper mill is a huge and costly

plant which cannot afford to migrate even if its tributary area is denuded of forest cover. The practice now is to follow reforestation as a means of insuring a continuous and permanent supply of pulp wood. A company having a large area with trees at all stages of growth has little to worry about if fires can be avoided. Moreover, the large-scale processes and the enormous cost of the plants have a good psychological effect upon the people who live in the region, for they look upon this industry as a permanent one — one not out to exploit or mine the forest, as has been the case with too many sawmills.

Mining. The Canadian Shield is world famous for its mineral wealth — metals, not coal or petroleum. Prospecting over much of the area is facilitated by (1) bareness of the rock, (2) accessibility by canoe routes or lakes for airplane landings, and (3) the existence of an accurate geological map for areas along stream courses. Had the region not been glaciated, prospecting would have been far more difficult. Several of the outstanding mineral deposits were discovered by chance — mining having begun as a by-product of railroad building, the fundamental purpose of which was the development of agriculture in the Clay Belt of northern Ontario.[12] Much prospecting today is done by airplane and helicopter, the greatest single aids to the extension of mining. This is a far cry from those early days when the prospector roamed over the Shield. Now discovery and actual mining depend upon geological science, precision instruments, and the diamond drill.

When a mineral is discovered in a wilderness such as the Shield, the men at first live in camps. Life is grim and hard (Figure 10–9). Bread and water are expensive. But if conditions essential for successful and profitable mining be present in sufficient force, the camp grows in size to a village, town, or perhaps even a city. In this way began such thriving centers as Sudbury, Rouyn-Noranda,

[12] Harold A. Innis, "Settlement and the Mining Frontier," *Canadian Frontiers of Settlement,* Vol. 9, p. 372. Toronto: The Macmillan Company of Canada, Ltd., 1936.

Figure 10–9. Eldorado Mine, Port Radium, near the Arctic Circle on Great Bear Lake, lies in a grim, cold, rocky, barren milieu. Pitchblende, a source of uranium, is taken from the mine. (Courtesy of National Film Board of Canada.)

Kirkland Lake, Timmins, Cobalt, Val d'Or, and many others.

Power, essential for operating the mines and mills, was at first supplied by wood, but as nearby forested areas were cut off, the cost of using wood became too great. Water power accordingly replaced it, being first used for this purpose in Ontario in 1906. Today the mines are among the chief users of hydroelectric power. Among the Shield's more important minerals are nickel, copper, platinum, gold, silver, iron, uranium, lead, and zinc.

Nickel. As one of the more important ferro-alloys, nickel gives steel specific physical properties such as hardness, toughness, and strength. Certain combinations of nickel and copper are exceedingly resistant to corrosion.

Canada, whose ores were discovered in 1883, is the largest producer of nickel, accounting for about 75 per cent of the world's supply. Almost all of the output comes from the Sudbury district in Ontario, an area about 550 square miles in extent lying some 35 miles north of Georgian Bay. The area is well located with respect to the United States market. The deposits are sufficiently extensive to meet world requirements for at least a century at the normal rate of consumption. For many years open-pit mining was followed. The tremendous demands for nickel, however, during World War II, and since then for defense, necessitated the installation and expansion of underground operations to compensate for the reduced quantities of ore available from open-pit surface mines. Production in 1951 was 7,780,143 short tons of underground ore and 4,019,177 short tons of open-pit ore. Proven reserves at the beginning of 1952 (International Nickel Company) stood at 253,704,771 short tons. Though no metal-mining center can be considered as permanent, Sudbury approaches closely the goal of permanency. Its future seems assured for at least another century.

Copper. A high grade of copper occurs with nickel in the Sudbury District; for every pound of nickel procured, there is a simultaneous yield of about two pounds of copper. Additional important copper mines are Noranda-Rouyn, Lynn Lake, Horne, and Flin Flon.

Uranium. The atom bomb is made largely from uranium which is removed from its ore, pitchblende — a grayish-black, opaque mineral. There are many sources of uranium of which the Belgian Congo, Canada,

Czechoslovakia, and the United States (the Colorado Plateau) predominate but the first two of these supply the bulk.

Pitchblende ore was discovered in Canada in 1930 at the east end of Great Bear Lake, 28 miles south of the Arctic Circle. It is the source of radium, so useful in peace, and of uranium, so essential in war. Since the coming of the atom bomb, an intense search for uranium has been made over the entire surface of the globe. It is highly possible that deposits of this ore will be found in many countries and in many parts of the Canadian Shield. A new and richer deposit than that at Port Radium was recently discovered at Uranium City near the earlier settlement of Goldfields.

Pitchblende at the Port Radium mine on Great Bear Lake is secured at a depth of 1,300 feet. After concentration, the ore is sent by steamer and barge to Waterways, Alberta — 1450 miles distant — and thence by rail to Port Hope on Lake Ontario, east of Toronto, for refining.

The United States which uses most of the world output of uranium dares not depend too heavily on a source as far away as the Belgian Congo. The ship lanes are too vulnerable.

Platinum. A by-product of nickel is platinum, and today Sudbury accounts for about one half of the world's output. The Soviet Union, South Africa, the United States, and Colombia are the other platinum-producing countries.

Gold. Canada is now the world's second largest producer of gold. Most of the workings (90 per cent of Canadian production) are being developed in the Shield. Mining has been so successful as to have stimulated prospecting from the eastern to the western ends of Ontario and Quebec, and important discoveries have been made some hundreds of miles from railways. Many authorities believe that so far as gold is concerned, the surface has barely been scratched. Among the most famous districts are the Porcupine, Kirkland Lake, and Yellowknife, whose mines contribute more than half of Canada's gold. Chief production comes from the "Gold Belt," which extends from Kirkland Lake

through Larder Lake (Canada's largest gold producing mine) and Rouyn to Val d'Or.

Silver. Cobalt became the great silver center of the Shield in 1903. High-grade ore (some of it native silver) was found close to the surface in small exposed veins ranging in width from 1 to 20 inches. In the early stages of development this pure silver could be picked out and shipped to smelters, little capital being required. Later on substantial returns received from working high-grade ores were reinvested to furnish capital for more expensive undertakings. The Cobalt silver deposits were about exhausted by 1925.

Considerable silver is recovered in refining copper, lead, zinc, and gold. In fact, the total amount from this source exceeds that from so-called silver mines.

Iron Ore. Few places have jumped so suddenly from obscurity to possible renown as has Labrador through the recent discovery and development of extensive and rich iron ore deposits in the hitherto lonely Ungava[13] Trough on the Quebec-Labrador border (Figure 10–10). This deposit is regarded as one of the great iron ore discoveries of all time.

The discovery was especially timely because the bottom of the cup of the Mesabi's high-grade ores is in sight as a result of two exhaustive world wars in a period of about a quarter century. While American companies have access to rich ore deposits in Chile, Brazil, Venezuela, and Liberia, the American iron and steel industry, which accounts for almost half the world's steel production, dares not be wholly or even largely dependent upon such distant sources. Packs of submarines operating in a future war as they did in World War II could cripple our iron and steel industry if it were dependent upon distant foreign sources of iron ore.

The Labrador reserves of proven ore are placed at more than 500 million tons with exploration still going on. The quality of the ore varies with the different deposits; one averages 68 per cent iron, another 65 per cent, and still another 60 per cent.

Transportation was the big problem until

----

[13] Eskimo word for "far away."

the completion of the railway. So difficult is the terrain that during construction bulldozers and other heavy equipment, food, supplies of all kinds as well as men, had to be flown into the area. The railway, 360 miles long, follows the winding Moisie River for part of the way from the mines at Burnt Creek to Seven Islands on the shore of the of the St. Lawrence at Havre St. Pierre. A railway connects the mine to a dock at this port. Smelting takes place at Sorel.

Agriculture. It has been reliably estimated that 94.64 per cent of Canada is unsuited to farming and that only 5.36 per cent is arable. Nevertheless, following the common belief that all forest lands could be used

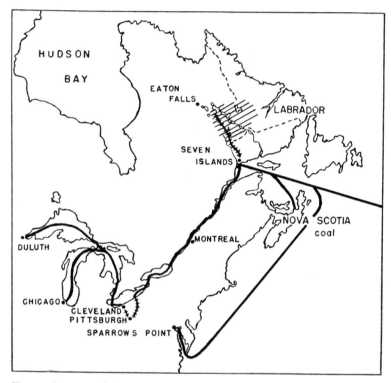

Figure 10–10. The new iron-ore deposits of Labrador are shown with respect to the Great Lakes area — the chief market for the ore. The 360-mile railway built from the mines through the wilderness to ore docks at Seven Islands on the St. Lawrence is shown.

Gulf of St. Lawrence. The cost of the railway averaged in excess of $100,000 per mile.

The distance between the ore docks at Seven Islands and the Lower Lake steel districts, particularly the 120 miles of rapids between Montreal and Ogdensburg, New York, is especially difficult to bridge and will remain so unless the St. Lawrence Seaway becomes a reality.

Titanium. A large deposit of ilmenite, an iron-titanium ore, has been discovered at Allard Lake, 25 miles from the north shore for farming, Canadians during the nineteenth century pushed into the northern wilderness of the Upland, which someone has called "an agricultural no man's land." Most settlers believed that the plow would immediately follow the woodman's axe. Later impetus to farming was given by the construction of railways, by the rise of mining, and by paternalistic provincial governments. Accordingly, enormous tracts of forest were cleared that have since proved to be ill-suited even for subsistence farming.

The agricultural pioneer has actually penetrated the Shield in only a few favored places, such as the Lake St. John Lowland and the Clay Belt (Figure 10–1). In the future, farming in the latter area promises to be subordinated to trapping, mining, lumbering, and pulp- and paper-making, because of poor soils, severe climate, isolation, limited transportation, and restricted market. Only the French Canadians have been willing to fight nature on *her* terms, to clear the forest, and to withstand the possibilities of repeated crop failures. Farming was their preferred way of life and the safest from the Anglo-Saxon influences that go with industrial life. But life has changed much in the past several years for the French Canadians.

The climate is not conducive to farming. Winters are long and extremely severe, and the growing season, always short, varies in length from year to year. The rainfall (24 to 34 inches) is ample, but crops often are ruined as they stand in the field by the drizzle and dampness. There are cases, though they are extreme ones, of farmers who have harvested only four crops out of nineteen.[14] If livestock are kept, the long, cold winters necessitate costly feeding.

Most of the farming (except where local markets exist) is of the subsistence type. The mining and the pulp and paper industries have brought in their wake an increased population which has stimulated agricultural development in nearby areas. The principal crops, hay, barley, oats, potatoes, and vegetables are of the hardy type. Since it is extremely difficult to live solely from the land, some farmers work during the winter (their off-season) in a lumber camp, a mine, or a pulp mill.

Agriculture in the Clay Belt. The Clay Belt (Figure 10–1) remained almost empty for two centuries following its discovery. This area, like an island in the ocean, is separated by the wedge of the Shield from Toronto (450 miles), Montreal (600 miles), and Winnipeg (1,000 miles). Its isolation may always be a distinct handicap.

The Clay Belt is more than a mere pocket

in the Shield but it does have notable limitations. The official estimate of potential farm land in the Clay Belt of Ontario is placed at five million acres out of a total of 14 million. Only one million of these are reasonably well drained and these occur for the most part in narrow strips along stream courses, on ridges, swells or flats underlain by sand and gravel. This acreage, along with another four million acres, which are more difficult to drain give the greatest promise of successful development. These five million acres, however, are scattered throughout the entire Clay Belt and hence their development is tied up with that of their poorly drained associates.

Settlers first came into the Clay Belt about 1910 when the better lands near the Great Lakes became occupied. Expanding northwards, they noted the overwhelming poverty of the soils of the Shield. They also observed that about 150 miles north of the southern edge of the Shield, the character of the soils changed considerably — the sterile granite soils giving way to white clay interspersed with much peaty material. Settlement is difficult, farming is fraught with physical dangers, and market problems are well-nigh insurmountable. Transport costs usually tend to swallow up all the profits. One of the best informed men on the area believes the future lies in combining forestry with farming "for much of the area can produce better 'harvests' of spruce than of any other crop.[15]

Many middle-latitude crops cannot be produced because of the short growing season. The principal agricultural products are oats, barley, hay and hardy vegetables. Some dairy and beef cattle are raised to meet local requirements and for some of the mining districts which border on the area to the south. It is believed that the Clay Belt will not become a "rural slum" as have some other sections of the Shield. At the same time it is as certain that the area will not become of primary agricultural importance to the Dominion.

Lake St. John Lowland. This small isolated agricultural area lies in the midst of 41,000

---

[14] Lower, "Settlement and the Forest Frontier in Eastern Canada," p. 135.

[15] G. A. Hills, "Pedology — The Dirt Science and Agricultural Settlement in Ontario," *Canadian Geographical Journal*, Vol. 29, 1944, pp. 106-127.

square miles of rugged, forested plateau country. There are in the area about 6,500 farms averaging 145 acres, each with about 70 acres of improved land. The population is about 200,000. Since the lowland opens to the St. Lawrence by the fjord-like Saguenay, which has an important aluminum industry, the farms are quite well located with respect to markets. More than half the people in the area are urban dwellers.

Manufacturing. With 8 per cent of the population of Canada, the Shield produces 7.5 per cent of the nation's manufactures based on value. Containing some of the largest hydroelectric power developments and many raw materials, the Shield's importance is not surprising. Most of the manufactures are closely tied to the power and to the raw materials of the subregion, particularly wood and metals. The area would be even more impressive industrially if aluminum manufacture and pulp and paper making, both very important, were included here rather than in Chapter 3 (the American Manufacturing Belt). The Sudbury area's great smelters and refineries handle most of Ontario's base metals. Here the International Nickel Company of Canada operates a smelter at Coniston and a smelter and refinery at Copper Cliffs. The latter handles copper, nickel, gold, silver, selenium, and tellurium. The copper electrolytic refinery at Copper Cliffs is the most important in the British Commonwealth.

Trade. The products of the Shield are those badly needed by great industrial nations. Either they are necessities, such as minerals, lumber, pulp, and paper, or luxuries such as furs.

Transportation. The first transportation in this area was by canoe in summer and by dog team and sledge in winter. The maze of waterways with only short portages enabled the canoe to go unbelievable distances, and the accumulation of snow due to the absence of thaws in winter made sledging relatively easy. The Hudson's Bay Company, because of its policy of relying largely on Indians, has been little interested in the transport business.

Railway construction was begun as a means of encouraging agricultural settlement and, in the case of the Hudson Bay Railway, to enable the wheat growers of the Prairie Provinces to compete more favorably in world markets with Argentina and Australia. Other lines were built into areas known to have minerals as a means of stimulating mining. The lines to Flin Flon, Noranda and elsewhere are notable examples of this type. Yet the mining industry creates a demand for high-grade produce, supports an important traffic, and tends to encourage mixed farming in its tributary area insofar as nature permits. The Hudson Bay Railway (part of the Canadian National Railway) was built by the Dominion Government, is owned by it and did not have as its primary purpose the opening up of mineral lands. Yet the line serves as the key to the mining possibilities over a vast stretch of the Shield. This is because the owner builds branches to mining developments as the need arises.

The Grand Trunk Railway (included in the Canadian National Railway System), which the government constructed, went through empty land all the way to Winnipeg. Later, however, the line was found to have tributary to it valuable mineral country and the fairly good soils of the Clay Belt.

For a long time after mining was developed in the Upland, the traffic was heavy only one way, inbound, and it was not until 1918, with the boom of the pulp and paper industry, that outbound or southbound traffic became more important than inbound or northbound traffic.[16]

Not a single mile of railway existed in Labrador and southeastern Quebec until the line was constructed from the iron mines in Ungava to Seven Islands in the early 1950's. Railway building here faces terrific odds.[17]

If maps of Canadian population and railways be superimposed upon a map showing landforms, it will be noted that between the settled areas of the several natural regions are large wastelands. From the standpoint of

---

[16] Innis, "Settlement and the Mining Frontier," p. 372.

[17] "Rugged Road to Iron: Ungava, Labrador," *Life*, November 9, 1951, pp. 122-127.

rail transportation, this means that much of this subregion is unproductive. Particularly is the "Superior Bridge" (that barren part of the Shield north of Lake Superior) an excellent example of this. However, these "gaps" must be crossed to link the productive areas, even though the costs will be high.

The airplane and helicopter are revolutionizing transportation on the Shield. A plane can cover more distance in one hour than a canoe in five days.

In winter, by using skis and "nose warmers," airplanes can penetrate the most remote parts of the Shield, placing prospectors on the ground before the spring breakup. In summer, pontoons are used on the planes.

Much prospecting is done from airplanes and helicopters, because the lack of overburden on the Shield permits the geologist to detect rock structures. This is particularly true north of the tree line.

Tractors and trucks are used almost exclusively today both in the mining and the forest industries. In fact many mining camps are supplied by tractor trains during winter.

Recreation

The Laurentian Upland is excellently adapted to recreation. Because of the relative nearness of portions of it to population centers in southern Canada and northeastern United States, this subregion is building each year an increasing number of summer hotels and cottages to accommodate tourists who want the solitude of the great "North Woods." As motor roads are built, the summer population of the Shield increases. Fishing, hunting, and canoeing all are excellent. This subregion also is world-famous for its winter sports and winter resorts have sprung up in many places on the southern border

of the Shield — particularly in the Laurentians north of Montreal.

The Outlook

For many years the Canadian Shield was regarded as a useless waste of muskeg, rock, and water. In addition, it comprised a tremendous barrier to transportation and divided the nation economically and politically into two parts. Since 1920, however, the area has been regarded in a new light: in addition to its peltries, its minerals and newsprint are now world-famous.

The railway, highway, and airplane have made the Shield accessible. The real occupance in the future will be nucleated urban communities based upon water power, wood and minerals rather than upon the pioneer agriculture which characterized the past. The Shield is today one of the empty portions of Canada: seventy per cent of Canada's 14,500,000 people dwell in the south within 100 miles of the international boundary.

It is not known what science may permit in the way of agriculture in the future, but some progress may be expected in the conquest of the Shield within the next hundred years. There have been many failures to date, but the pioneer stock attempts to hold on.

Undoubtedly many new mineral discoveries will be made, and these will tend to stimulate local areas to boom. They will increase the population of the Shield to some extent by giving rise to smelting and refining centers.

The real future of this area would appear to depend upon the forest, which provides water storage, a permanent refuge for fur-bearing animals and the Indian population, a great source of lumber and pulpwood, and a primeval wilderness for the vacationist.

The Upper Lakes Subregion

The Upper Lakes Subregion includes northeastern Minnesota, northern Wisconsin and Michigan, and a part of Ontario lying north of lakes Huron and Superior (Figure 10–1).

Like the Northern Continental Forest Region as a whole, the Upper Lakes Subregion is a land where the population is primarily engaged in extractive industries — fishing, trapping, logging, and mining.

The Natural Environment

Terrain. The American part of this sub-region, often called the "cutover area" was treated roughly by the continental glaciers. The ice gouged out the softer rocks, the depressions later forming thousands of small lakes; it also deranged the drainage and threaded the area with a filigree of rivers. It mellowed the terrain over which it moved. Thus low hills characterize much of the land, though high steep hills locally called "mountains" lie along the shores of Lake Superior.

The rocks are much like those noted in the Canadian Shield of which this area is geologically a part; they are ancient, tightly compressed, and severely metamorphosed.

Climate. The climate, being continental, is subject to the severe variations that characterize the interiors of large land areas in middle latitudes. Winters are long and cold, summers short and cool. Extreme temperatures may range from −50° to 105° F. The growing season varies from 90 to 100 days, though at Marquette and other places on the south shore of Lake Superior it is 158 days long. There are large sections where the first autumn frost arrives early in September. Precipitation varies from 25 to 35 inches, falling mostly as rain. Though only 10 to 20 per cent is snow, the whole area is snow-covered for 90 to 120 days — a longer period than in any other area of comparable size in the United States.[18]

Soils. The soils, like those elsewhere in the region, are poorly suited for growing standard crops. They are also distributed in intricate patterns with pockets of fertility scattered here and there in the huge wilderness of non-productive land. All mature soils, gray *podzols*, are light in texture and acid in reaction, since they are derived from crystalline rocks and lie in a humid climate. Some areas are strewn with glacial granitic boulders, while others are characterized by deep, sterile sand or peat and muck.

When the frontier was moving over the Upper Lakes Subregion, no soil surveys had been made and nothing was known regarding the suitability of the soil for crops. Accordingly, settlers took anything that was cheap, believing that crops would grow wherever trees did. The result was an irregular, inefficient, and illogical pattern of land use. Public agencies are now trying to do the best they can for the people who settled in this area of meager resources.

Natural Vegetation. When the explorers and fur traders broke into this subregion, they found a virgin forest consisting of conifers in the northern and northwestern part and mixed forest in the southern part. White pine was the principal commercial tree, but jack and Norway pine and even spruce and fir were associated with it. In the southern portion were beech, birch, and maple, interspersed with the conifers. The hardwoods grew on the better soils; the conifers, in the more sandy sections.[19] The best of the forests was in northern Michigan, northeastern Wisconsin, and central and northern Minnesota.

Native Animal Life. The forests and streams abounded with wild life. Such fur-bearers as the beaver, marten, fisher, and otter throve. Deer, moose, and bear were numerous, as were the ubiquitous wolf and fox. Migratory waterfowl and fresh-water fish were abundant.

The Occupance

During the first half of the nineteenth century, settlement spread rapidly over the trans-Appalachian region so far as rainfall would permit crop production. The Upper Lakes Area was less fortunate, remaining an unbroken forest for two centuries after its discovery — the only development of any sort being the trapping and trading of furs.

Lumbermen rather than farmers finally opened it up. They bought the land, built transport facilities, cut off the timber, and

---

[18] National Resources Committee, *Regional Planning Part VIII, Northern Lakes States*, p. 9. Washington, D. C.: Government Printing Office, May 1939.

[19] National Resources Board, *Regional Planning Part VI, Maladjustments in Land Use in the United States*, p. 27. Washington, D. C.: Government Printing Office, 1935.

got out. Their business was timber, not land.[20]

Trapping

The virgin wilderness abounded in wild life, with winters long and cold enough to put the furs in prime condition. The early *voyageurs* who came by way of the Great Lakes found ideal conditions for their vocation.[21] The interior location and the great distance from Europe meant that only products that were valuable, easily conveyed, and in great demand could bear the costly transportation. This enterprise was the principal business for two centuries after the discovery of the subregion.

Fishing

Fishing was a flourishing enterprise in Lakes Huron, Michigan, and Superior, antedating lumbering and mining. White fish and lake trout in 1880 made up 70 per cent of the catch. During the past 60 years, however, they have declined steadily as a result of over-fishing, depredation by the destructive sea lampreys, destruction of immature fish, and the fouling of waters by city sewage and industrial waste. Even so, these three lakes still account for 60 per cent of the fresh-water fish caught commercially in the United States, though they are of minor importance in Canada's inland fisheries. Nearly all of the fish are caught during the summer months.

Lumbering

This subregion had Anglo-America's largest and densest stand of white pine. When forests of this highly prized tree had been "mined out" of New England and the Middle Atlantic States, lumbermen led the onslaught into the Northern Lakes Area. Contributing factors were the rapid urbanization of the Middle West and improvements in transportation—the Erie Canal and the building of railroads. Yet the real mass attack on the forest did not begin until the termination of the Civil War. By 1870, Michigan ranked first in the production of lumber and reached its peak in the decade 1880–1890. In 1896 a traveler covering 40 counties and going 2,000 miles wrote that:

> The heart of the white pine country, from Manistee on the west to Saginaw on the east (is) an almost continuous succession of abandoned lumber fields, miles upon miles of stumps as far as the eye can see. . . .[22]

The horde then moved into Wisconsin and finally into Minnesota, which took leadership, attaining its peak in 1900. This army of lumbermen had one-track minds: they sought but one resource—*pine*. They cut any tree so long as it was big and they were not concerned when young growths were ruined by the fall of the tree they were cutting. Stripping the forest, leaving only slashings and stumps in their wake, they moved on.

Whereas in 1890 these three Lake States produced 35 per cent of the nation's total, by 1910 they could not supply their own needs, and today they produce only four per cent, the bulk consisting of hardwoods. By 1920 even the best hardwoods had been cut off.

Reforestation was hardly considered. Everyone thought that with so vast an area of dense growing timber and with much yet to be cut, the forest was inexhaustible. Accordingly the land was repeatedly burned over (Figure 10–11). These fires destroyed the seedlings and the forest litter and so ruined the topsoil that in many localities white pine can no longer grow. Carl Sauer, one of the pioneers in land-utilization surveying in Michigan, estimates that these sand-pine lands will require 500 years undisturbed by man to produce a pine forest like the original one. The growing and selling of Christmas trees has become an im-

[20] Charles Davis, "Unprofitable Pioneering," *The Quarterly Review of the Michigan Alumnus*, December 4, 1937, Vol. 44, No. 10, p. 45.

[21] National Resources Committee, *Regional Planning Part VIII, Northern Lakes States*, p. 9.

[22] W. N. Sparhawk and W. D. Brush, "The Economic Aspects of Forest Destructon in Northern Michigan," *Technical Bulletin*, No. 92, United States Department of Agriculture. Washington, D. C.: Government Printing Office, January 1929.

Figure 10–11. A burned-over area in Minnesota. These charred stumps and trunks are the remains of once-wonderful forests. (Courtesy of U. S. Forest Service.)

portant and for some people a highly profitable business in this area.

Mining

The Upper Lakes Subregion is one of Anglo-America's richest in minerals — not in variety, but in quantity, and of the type most in demand by industry. Southwest and northwest of Lake Superior lie the continent's best, largest, and most favorably located iron ores. On the Keweenaw Peninsula are the richest and longest used, though not the most profitably mined, copper accumulations. For some years copper mining in this area languished but in the early 1950's a revival set in. On the west shore of Lake Huron are most valuable deposits of metallurgical limestone.

Mining is the outstanding economic enterprise in this subregion today. The removal of copper, but more particularly of iron ore, caused the redrawing of much of the industrial map of the United States, for the center of the iron and steel industry migrated from the Ohio River to the shores of the lower Great Lakes.

Billions of tons of red hematite ore have been found in the Lake Superior district. These deposits do not lie in mountains, as the word "ranges" suggests, but in elongated east-west extending beds. They were formed during an ancient mountain-building period, but erosion has long since worn down the mountains and the terrain is now almost flat.

In the Mesabi Range, the ore deposits, shallow and extensive, are covered by glacial till to a depth of 10 to 150 feet. Mesabi ore is an example of deposition and concentration of ores in small valleys between hills.

In the Gogebic Range, the iron deposits lie hundreds of feet below the surface. Its ores exemplify the deposition and concentration of ore by circulating waters in underground channels. Eleven counties (three in Minnesota, five in Michigan, and three in

Wisconsin) comprise the famous "Lake Superior iron-ore region," which accounts for 85 per cent of American production. Minnesota alone contributes 61 per cent of the total. Without Lake Superior iron ore, the major portion of the American iron and steel industry might possibly have drifted to the Atlantic Seaboard and to Alabama. Upon the Mesabi Range, the greatest body of iron ore in the world, has been built the extensive American iron-ore and lake-shipping business, and indirectly most of the steel manufacturing of the Lower Great Lakes area. Billions of tons already have been removed, but at the present rate of mining about 100 million tons per year, the high-grade ore is not expected to last more than ten years. Data on reserves are not dependable, however, for the steel companies give out no more information than necessary, since they report no more taxable property than the public authorities choose to recognize.[23]

Production on a large scale began about the time the lumber industry was declining. Shipments from the Marquette Range (the only producer until 1877) started in 1854, and those from the Mesabi in 1892, when the first railroad reached it.

At first, mining in the Lake Superior area was done underground. In time large deposits of high-grade Mesabi ore in loose form were discovered near the surface. These ores could be mined with power shovels after the glacial overburden had been removed. Thus open-pit mining, the fastest and most economical method known, came into use (Figure 10–12). This mode of mining can be followed only in summer. Underground mining elsewhere in the area, is carried on the year round, the ore being stockpiled during winter.

As mining went forward, the richer and better ore was removed. Today, in order to send high-grade hematite down the lakes, the ore must first be sent to beneficiation plants or direct shipping stations for removal of much earthy material. There are 50 beneficiating plants (screening, crushing, washing, and concentrating) on the Mesabi Range alone.

The Mesabi Range contributes about three fifths of the total production of the Lake Superior area. Since 1892, it has sent down the lakes more than a billion tons of ore. The greatness of the Mesabi Range is due to (1) large size, (2) nearness of ore to the surface, (3) quality of the ore, (4) proximity to Lake Superior, and (5) ease of mining. The ore was first recovered with hand shovels; later came steam and finally electric shovels, which remove 16 tons at a single bite.

In getting the ore out of the huge man-made caverns, railways were used at first — the tracks being built into the pits. Later came crawler trucks on giant rubber tires. Now much of the ore moves out in a continuous stream on conveyor belts directly to concentration plants (Figure 10–12). The world's greatest single mine, the Hull Rust at Hibbing, Minnesota, is 350 feet deep, from one-half to one mile across, and two and one-half miles long, with an area of 1,100 acres.

Taconite. The quantity of ore removed from the Lake Superior region, particularly from the Mesabi, in the past two world war periods, and more recently during the rearmament program, took a terrific toll of American high-grade iron ore reserves. No one knows exactly how long the remaining top-grade ore will last, but the estimates run from 10 to 20 years. Whatever the forecast, however, "the curtain is falling" upon the open-pit mining of high-grade Lake Superior area ore capable of being shipped to Lower Lake districts. The end will come in different years for different companies —in less than five years for some, perhaps as long as 24 for others.

Estimates for all ore (high grade and poor) range from 18 to 40 years. These wide differences in estimates are accounted for by the uncertainty of the future rate of consumption and by the lack of accurate data on the extent of reserves. In adjusting to the use of lower-grade ores, and as a means of heading off the decline in output of regular iron ore, which is expected in 1956, the fed-

23 Marion Worthing, "Iron Ore Reserves and Their Relation to the Steel Industry," *Pittsburgh Business Review*, Vol. 6, No. 10, October 28, 1936, p. 21.

eral government is co-operating through the Defense Production Administration by issuing certificates of necessity (accelerated tax amortization privileges). It is estimated by many mining geologists that by 1970, taconites will be produced at an annual rate of 60 million tons.[24]

Taconite is a dense, hard rock containing only 25 to 35 per cent iron, and a considerable amount of such impurities as silica, quartz, and oxides. The iron oxide is finely dispersed (like specks of pepper) in the silica and firmly held by it. Since there are billions of tons of taconite in the Lake Superior area (five to ten billion tons of concentrates), the

[24] The *New York Times*, February 9, 1952.

Figure 10–12. Open-pit mining in the Mesabi Range, Minnesota, where huge electric shovels seize 14 or more tons of iron ore at a bite. This is both fast and economical mining. Getting the ore out was once a big problem — the ore being hauled out of the mine bottom by railways or trucks. When the pits got too deep for railways and trucks, conveyor belts were introduced. (Courtesy of B. F. Goodrich Company.)

perfection of an economic method of extracting this iron oxide from it would solve much
of the iron ore problem. Research is now
proceeding toward the economical processing of taconite to bring it up to the standards
required by blast furnaces. The expense is,
however, very great, the capital investment
being estimated at $15 to $20 per ton of annual capacity for producing concentrates. In
most instances companies treating taconite
ores are formed by two or more of the big
steel companies. It is estimated that the cost
of solving the taconite problem will run between 600 million and one billion dollars.[25]
Already more than 500 million dollars has
been invested.

Even the mining of taconite is costly. The
ore is so hard that the bits used on steel
churns wear down and have to be removed
and sharpened after drilling through a depth
of only five feet. An improved method is the
flame jet machine which drills holes seven
and one-half inches in diameter as deep as
47 feet. This machine also helps ease the
man-power shortage: six jet-piercing machines, operating three shifts, turn out 50,000
tons of taconite daily. To produce the same
tonnage with churn drills requires 300 men.

After processing, the taconite emerges as
pellets with about 64 per cent iron content.
The iron-ore particles are too fine for use in
blast furnaces, for the blast of air being
used in reducing iron would blow the particles out of the top of the furnace.

Some of the taconite is magnetic while
some is non-magnetic. Each type calls for
different concentrating processes. But in both
cases the taconite must first be crushed and
ground to a powder about the fineness of
cement.

Description of the "processes" of separating the iron from the low-grade taconite does
not belong in the field of geography. Suffice
it to say that the end product is a "tailor-
made" ore of much more uniform consistency
than natural ore and richer in iron units than
any ore that has come out of the Lake Superior region.

The huge investments in taconite plants
bring up an interesting question. Previously
we've been told this country could get its
iron ore from Brazil, Chile, Venezuela, Canada (Steep Rock, Quebec, Newfoundland,
and especially Labrador), and Liberia. Now,
apparently, the bulk will be gotten from taconite. This seems to result from three conditions: (1) vulnerability of the sea lanes in
time of war, (2) no assurance that the St.
Lawrence Seaway can be salvaged from
politics,[26] and (3) the determination not to
allow the steel industry of the United States
to become wholly dependent on imported
iron ore, especially from distant overseas
sources.

America's future iron-ore needs then, appear to lie mostly in processing the enormous
reserve of taconite ores, even though recovery be expensive (it involves both quarrying
and manufacturing operations). To get one
ton of "blast furnace feed" requires three
tons of iron-bearing taconite rock.

Taxation of Iron Ore. Most of the inhabitants in this subregion live in mining
communities, and the mines are largely
owned by steel interests in the East. Minnesota counties, especially, have been taxing
these absentee owners heavily. As a result,
tourists are amazed at the fine roads and
well-equipped schools in an otherwise exceedingly poor region. The State of Minnesota has a commission of experts in mining
accounting, mineralogy, geology, and mining
engineering who permit no discovered ores
to escape assessment. The iron and steel

---

[25] "There Is Plenty of Ore," *Steelways*, January
1948, p. 3.

[26] An interesting aspect of this problem appeared
in *The New York Times*, April 6, 1952:

"To help in the fight, Wisconsin leaders are trying to consolidate the bargaining power of the states
in the Great Lakes region in a joint effort. Organized
labor has joined the battle. . . . The Committee
(appointed by the governor of Wisconsin) has
warned anti-Seaway Senators and Representatives
that their flood control, hydraulic, reclamation and
navigational projects might have strong opposition
from the Great Lakes area in the future unless they
concur in legislation to make the United States a
partner with Canada in construction of the Seaway
and power project.

"Wisconsin's officials feel that opposition to the
Seaway is not based on the merits of the project,
but on selfish sectional interests."

manufacturers complain bitterly, pointing out that Minnesota's mining tax is ten times as great proportionately as that for the nation as a whole.

On the other hand, public sentiment in Minnesota, whence comes 60 per cent of the ore, is averse to sending millions of tons of the red metal down the lakes each year, leaving in place of the rich heritage vast holes in the ground. Ore shipped down the lakes means only a few dollars or so to the state — a mere fraction of its value when converted into iron and steel at Gary, Cleveland, or Pittsburgh. Minnesota used this as a major argument in getting the United States Steel Corporation to construct the plant at Duluth.[27] It seems certain that the iron and steel industry will remain largely where it is so long as the chief source of ore is the Lake Superior district. The influence of the ore-producing area never will be strong enough to draw the iron and steel industry to it. Moreover, the large steel markets lie hundreds of miles to the southeast, and the restraining influence of freight rates from the coal fields of Pennsylvania, West Virginia, and eastern Kentucky will keep most of the steel plants where they are.[28]

Whereas Minnesota taxes all known high-grade ores, Michigan levies only against the exploited ones, those adjacent to them, and those most evident. It would appear that the different mode of taxing in the two states is (1) a political expression of Minnesota's predominant agrarianism — indicated by the fact that the taxation of a dollar invested in a mine is twice the rate on a dollar invested in a farm, and (2) a desire on the part of Michigan ore owners to compete with Minnesota ore, which has certain natural advantages.

Steep Rock. About 140 miles northwest of the head of Lake Superior and relatively near the international boundary, lies Canada's Steep Rock Mine — a recent iron ore development. Before mining could begin here, Steep Rock Lake had to be drained for the ore lay beneath its waters. The lake was 130 feet deep. Pumping caused the level to fall six inches a day; 20,000 gallons of water a minute were removed. In a year the lake had been drained and 120 billion gallons of water had been removed. Big power shovels then began scooping out enormous bites of rich hematite ore averaging 60 per cent metallic iron. Open-pit mining, however, has been confined to a depth of 400 feet from the surface. Below 400 feet, mining must be done underground for reasons of safety.

In 1951 more than one and three-fourths million tons of ore were removed and Steep Rock now is reputed to be the second largest iron mine in Anglo-America. The ore is sent by rail to modern high-level docks in Port Arthur.

The discovery and development of this rich and well-located deposit have been especially timely because one of Canada's industrial deficiencies has been the lack of a domestic iron-ore supply. Up to now the Canadian steel industry, except for that at Sydney, has depended largely upon Mesabi ore and local scrap. It is a timely discovery, also, because the Mesabi is running out of high-grade ore. The importance of iron and steel mills in the Lower Lakes area having available a supply of ore that does not have to run the gantlet of submarine packs during a war cannot be overestimated. For example, in a single morning during World War II one U-boat commander sent three of four Wabana ore carriers to the bottom.[29]

Limestone. In Alpena County, Michigan, lies Anglo-America's leading source of metallurgical limestone. The quarries lie so close to the lake shore that, despite the fact that they are geographically 300 miles from the blast furnaces, they are economically only 30 miles away, since water rates are only one tenth as much as rail rates. Accordingly, this area has become the largest and the cheapest source of stone for the great iron

[27] C. Langdon White and George Primmer, "The Iron and Steel Industry of Duluth: A Study in Locational Maladjustment," *Geographical Review*, Vol. 27, January 1937, pp. 82-91.

[28] Worthing, "Iron Ore Reserves and Their Relation to the Steel Industry," p. 19.

[29] Alex Skelton, "Canadian Mining Industry Today," *Annals of the American Academy of Political and Social Sciences*, Vol. 253, September 1947, p. 70.

and steel plants of the Great Lakes area. About 14 million tons move down the lakes each year. Limestone is used in blast furnaces to remove from the ore such impurities as silica and alumina, which have a stronger affinity for lime than for iron.

The quarry of the Michigan Limestone & Chemical Company at Calcite has nine and one half miles of vertical quarry side from which electric power shovels of 23 tons capacity remove the stone. This company has its own harbor and loading slip. As the stone is brought from the quarry, it is crushed into pieces less than nine inches in their maximum dimensions. Conveyor belts then carry it to storage, separate piles receiving that to be used for open-hearth furnaces, blast furnaces, cement plants and chemical companies. Even in the same pile the stone is graded both as to size and chemical composition. The boats used to transport this particular limestone are "self-unloaders"; they all carry "pickaback" a great steel boom, an unloader. One of these ships, the Bradley, is 639 feet long and has carried cargoes exceeding 16,000 gross tons. It makes 80 or more trips during the season of navigation handling more than a million gross tons of limestone (Figure 3–11).

Moving Iron Ore Down the Lakes. Ore from the Minnesota mines is loaded into cars, which are made into trains and taken to weighing and classification yards before continuing on their way to Duluth, Superior, or Two Harbors. The distance from the mines to Duluth is only 60 to 80 miles and the trains coast much of the way. The railroad charge for delivering ore from mines to ships, a distance of approximately 79 miles, is more than that by freighters which carry it ten times as far. Hence all three states ship nearly all their ore to Lower Lake ports by water; there is no other choice.[30]

The ease of mining Mesabi ore plus the efficient and low-cost water transportation have contributed to keep the price of Lake Erie iron ore extremely stable. The price of ore includes the delivery price to Lower Lake ports. Iron ore sold for $4.25 per ton from 1925 to 1929; for $5.05 in 1946 and for $7.70 in 1950.[31]

The docks jut out into the lake like huge peninsulas. The trains, after being moved onto the docks, dump their ore into "pockets," from which it drops by gravity through hatches into the holds of the lake vessels (Figure 10-13). Ordinarily three to four hours are required to load a vessel, but the job has been done in much less time. In 1952 the Great Northern Docks loaded 22 boats in 24 hours. When a boat reaches a Lower Lake port, the ore is discharged in four or five hours by means of huge clam-shaped unloaders (Figure 3–22).

The Great Lakes can be utilized for only seven or eight months, because the connecting links such as the "Soo" Canals are locked by ice (Figure 10–14). No time is lost by a vessel during the season of navigation. Every effort is made to complete as many round trips as possible — the number usually being 23 to 30. It is a race against time to accumulate enough ore at the Lower Lake ports to keep the mills operating throughout the year. Numerous collisions occurred prior to 1911 in hot summer months when fog was bad. Vessels on the down trip are now required to follow a slightly different course from those on the upbound voyage. Thus steamers passing on the open lake are at least five miles from each other, and are also separated so far as possible in rivers and channels.

The traffic tonnage moving through the "Soo" Canals is almost unbelievable. In a normal year it exceeds that of the Panama, Suez, Welland, and New York State Barge Canals combined. Nowhere else in the world is so much bulk traffic handled.

In an effort to procure a return cargo,

---

[30] When the defense program got into high gear, shipment of frozen Lake Superior iron ore by rail to Chicago, Pittsburgh, Youngstown, and Birmingham (for blending with local ores) was undertaken on a small scale. Ore so transported costs about $1.50 more per ton than that brought in by lake vessel in summer. This extra cost results partly from the thawing process. Some *high-grade* (open hearth) iron ore is even being shipped by rail from Utah to the Chicago-Indiana Harbor-Gary District. This is the longest rail haul in United States steel-making history.

[31] L. Gregory Hines, "Price Determination in the Lake Erie Iron Ore Market," *American Economic Review*, Vol. 41, September 1951, p. 652.

Figure 10–13. Iron-ore docks at Duluth. (Courtesy of Robert Yarnall Richie and *Fortune.*)

principally coal, a much lower rate is offered by northbound carriers. Most coal moving northbound from Toledo and other Lake Erie ports, however, is destined for such industrial areas as Detroit, Chicago, and Milwaukee, or for Canada rather than for the Upper Lake ports. Only a small percentage of the lake carriers haul coal up the lakes.

The "Soo" Canals, from the standpoint of tonnage, are the most important artificial waterways in the world. The St. Mary's River, connecting Lakes Superior and Huron, is about 63 miles long and at Sault Ste. Marie has a stretch of rapids three fourths of a mile long and a fall of 17 to 21 feet, depending on the stage of water in the two lakes. In order to afford passage for deep-draft vessels, canals and locks having a water depth up to 25 feet had to be built through this barrier. So important are they that when the canals freeze in winter, Great Lakes ore traffic comes to a halt.

The first "Soo" Canal was built on the Canadian side for the passage of small boats by the Northwest Fur Company in 1797-1798. The first canal on the American side was built by the State of Michigan in 1853-1855, following the discovery of iron ore in the Lake Superior area. This canal was transferred to the United States Government in 1881 when the Weitzel Lock was built. So great has Lake traffic become that four locks have been built on the American side. One constructed in the 1940's is 800 feet long, 80 wide, and 30 feet deep has been built on the site of one of the old locks — the Weitzel. It eliminates congestion and loss of time awaiting lockage, permits deeper loading of vessels, and assures adequate locking capacity for reasonably prospective commerce. The Canadian government constructed a lock and canal in 1895, but nearly all the lake carriers use those on the American side. During the season of navigation a vessel is

About 90 per cent of the nation's steel ingot capacity is located in the states tributary to the Great Lakes and these plants now rely almost wholly upon Lake Superior iron ore. Moreover, a tremendous proportion of our secondary steel fabrication capacity and of our steel consumption is centered in the

Figure 10–14. Ore boats locked in ice. Sub-zero temperatures trapped these down-bound cargo ships in six-inch channel ice. The boats are waiting for a Coast Guard icebreaker to free them. The lake's shipping season normally begins in April and ends around December first, when insurance rates become prohibitive due to the hazards of winter navigation. (Courtesy of Don Walker and the *Detroit News*.)

locked through the Soo Canals about every 15 minutes day and night.

Will the New Situation in Iron Ore Cause the American Iron and Steel Industry to Move? It has been pointed out that the end of direct-shipping ores is in sight. Since the Lake Superior area has supplied about 80 to 85 per cent of the iron ore utilized in the United States new sources of ore must be found and got ready before the existing top-quality open-pit deposits give out.

Lower Lakes area, close to the open hearths, Bessemers, and electric furnaces. Because of these facts, along with the abolition of the basing-point system, the extreme possibility that the American iron and steel industry might move to tidewater would have a momentous effect on American industry. Most steel men, however, expect the industry will remain largely where it is, though they recognize that some new capacity must be added to the Atlantic, Gulf and Pacific seaboards. One of the best informed men in the industry expresses it as follows:

> . . . the customer eventually will come to the maker of steel rather than the other way round. You can't shove a huge business like steel around like a pawn in a chess game.

Transportation

The Great Lakes provide the finest system of inland waterways in the world. Their traffic consists almost entirely of bulky products — iron ore, coal, wheat, and limestone. The vessels that move them are built solely for service on the Great Lakes and their connecting waterways. They would be useless for ocean service, as severe storms would break them in two. A single ship of the largest class can carry 18,000 to 20,000 tons. Some are self-unloaders. These carriers average 11 to 13 or more miles per hour, making a round trip in approximately a week if they are engaged exclusively in the iron-ore trade and if they carry no coal upbound. If coal is carried, the time is increased by one day. Since large carriers are more economical than small ones, those being constructed now are of the more efficient 600-foot type.[32] These are also speedier and can be loaded and unloaded in faster time. Such a vessel involves an investment of several million dollars.

Rail and highway transportation are available, though the former is relatively unimportant, since there are few main lines. An exception is the main lines of Canadian roads into Port Arthur and Fort William.

The net of branch lines built during the lumbering era is now largely abandoned, and in many instances the rails have been removed and sold for scrap. The significance of iron-ore shipments is well indicated by the fact that 99.75 per cent of the cars return empty to the mine area. This traffic situation probably will not change, since much of the mining country appears incapable of important agricultural or other development.

Hard-surface roads have had a remarkable development in the past 45 years, though

much remains to be done if the subregion is to capitalize on its recreation possibilities. Especially must attention be given the scenic roads along the shore of Lakes Superior, Michigan, and Huron.

For many years there was no through road across the Shield north of Lake Superior, in Canada. A gravel road was finally completed in 1942, making the first transcontinental link across Canada by road. It is now being paved as part of the Trans-Canada Highway.

Agriculture

Not more than ten per cent of the Northern Lakes Subregion is in crop land now, and possibly not more than 20 per cent ever can be utilized for agriculture. The crop acreage per family is too low and the tax burden too high to permit successful farming. Paucity of markets is a severe handicap in this essentially forest environment.

Unfortunately, poor lands as well as good lands were sold through high-pressure salesmanship to all kinds of people — miners, factory workers, former city white-collar employees, and Corn Belt farmers. Some accidentally obtained good land but most did not, since they "found themselves in possession of (1) outcrops of crystalline rock, of undrainable peat bogs and marshes, or of stump land covered with granite boulders [or] of (2) soil so light and sandy that, when cleared, it was blown about by the wind." [33]

Many of the farmers who first entered the area worked part-time in mines, mills, or logging camps. The amount of improved land on most farms (25 to 30 acres) has been so small that a complete living could not be made solely by growing crops.

It is unfortunate that no soil maps or agricultural experiment farms *preceded* immigration. Knowledge came only through trial and error and the crushing of human beings by a relentless nature (Figure 10–15). A large proportion of the farmers remaining are foreign-born or of foreign parentage, being mostly Scandinavian, Slavic, or Fin-

---

[32] The "Arthur M. Anderson," which was launched at Lorain in the summer of 1952, is 647 feet long.

[33] National Resources Board, *Maladjustments in Land Use in the United States*, Part VI, p. 27. Washington, D. C.: Government Printing Office, 1935.

nish. The Finns assert that they came into this area because they were shipped up to supply labor. They took to agriculture during periods of industrial inactivity. As "part-time" farmers they have made a fair living from the soil despite the short growing season, and they usually do better than most other nationalities as indicated by their re-

plots in barley, oats, potatoes, and other vegetables. Cows and pigs are kept, the latter being fattened on skim milk or whey. Dairying is not prosperous, because the cows require expensive winter housing and feeding. Moreover, all farm production suffers from the dearth of nearby markets. Much of the farming is submarginal. Away from the lakes,

Figure 10–15. An abandoned farm in the cut-over area. This extreme example of rural poverty shows well the futility of trying to farm lands not fit for cultivation. (Courtesy of Farm Security Administration.)

juvenation of farm lands abandoned by settlers of other ethnic stocks.

The Finns grow primarily hay, potatoes, and root crops and leave much land in pasture. Wheat, formerly of considerable importance, is no longer grown because the area cannot compete with better lands to the west and south. Most of the feed grains used on the farms are raised locally but practically none is produced for market. A typical clearing carved out of the forest consists of 20 to 30 acres planted largely in hay, with smaller

the short growing season is more of a handicap than the soils, for even on the better lands frost precludes the growing of most crops. A small new development but one that may indicate possibilities is the successful production of celery in 1952 on some 10,000 acres of abandoned, tax-delinquent muck land near Meadowlands, Minnesota.

In many instances it is as necessary to supplement the farm income now as it was in the beginning; hence much farming is "part-time." Many farmers cut pulpwood, ties, and poles from their land. The income on the average farm is too low to maintain the American standard of living. There is a scarcity of doctors, nurses, and hospitals: hence there is much neglect of medical and dental care, and what service there is must be largely at public expense. Few homes have electric lights or running water.

Farming is somewhat more prosperous on the Canadian side where pockets of good soil are being utilized, and the poor areas have not been settled. For example, in the Rainy River district, north of Minnesota, farms average 50 to 100 acres cleared, and produce good crops of oats, hay, and flax. The chief source of agricultural income is from the sale of livestock and livestock products.

Manufacturing

Manufacturing is not well developed in the Upper Lakes Subregion because of the small population and the great distance from the continent's principal markets for fabricated products. The chief industries are those making chemicals, lumber, pulp and paper, iron and steel. Throughout the entire subregion, the general trend of industrial employment is downward, except in the Port Arthur–Fort William area of Canada, where industry has been expanding.

Iron and Steel. Duluth, Minnesota, and Sault Ste. Marie, Ontario, are iron and steel centers. Although neither district is a major development in the continental picture, Sault Ste. Marie is outstanding to Canada. Whereas most Anglo-American iron and steel districts are located close to coal and have iron ore brought to them, these do just the reverse. Their low assembly cost is a result of the desire on the part of ship-owners to have a return cargo;[34] accordingly, the cost of shipping coal up the Lakes is appreciably less per ton than for bringing ore down. It is a truism that the location of iron manufacturing is primarily a matter of freight charges, not on raw materials alone but also

[34] In busy seasons, Lake vessels frequently return to Upper Lake ports with water ballast rather than coal, for they can then make more trips carrying ore.

on the finished products to points of consumption.

The Duluth District. In 1915, when the plant was completed in Duluth, many journalists enthusiastically wrote, "Pittsburgh is moving west." Yet Pittsburgh continues as the undisputed capital of America's and of the world's iron and steel industry, whereas Duluth carries on as a minor producer. Yet its output of steel ingots rose from 336,000 tons in 1940 to 918,000 tons in 1950. The United States Steel Corporation, which built the plant, did not wish to do so, realizing that Duluth was not a scientific location. Before construction, it stated that the total demand for steel in Duluth's tributary area would not keep the plant busy three months in the year. Public sentiment in Minnesota, however, threatening higher taxes, forced the issue. The district's past unimpressive record resulted from remoteness from great markets. The industry here may well gain in importance as a result of need for steel in the oil fields of the Williston Basin and Alberta and the need for pipe to transport crudes and gas. Certainly the industry in Duluth looks more promising than it did in the late twenties and early thirties.

The Sault Ste. Marie District, Canada. A steel industry was established here about 1898. The main plant, occupying an area of 185 acres on the shores of the St. Mary's River, is strategically located for assembling raw materials and shipping finished products by water. Iron ore was originally obtained from Michipicoten, to the northward on Lake Superior, but now comes chiefly from Mesabi and Steep Rock. Expansion in pig iron, coke, steel ingot, and rolling capacity amounting to about 100 million dollars has taken place in the past several years. The rated ingot capacity is now 1,250,000 tons per year.

Pulp and Paper. The principles involved in the location of pulp and paper manufacture for Canada have already been presented. The Upper Great Lakes states – Michigan, Wisconsin, and Minnesota — and northern Ontario are outstanding in this industry. Mills became established in both peninsulas of Michigan, in northern Minnesota, and in the valleys of the Fox, Black,

Wisconsin, and Chippewa rivers in Wisconsin. The area has about 130 paper and pasteboard mills and some 14 per cent of the national output of pulp and paper. Because spruce is scarce, almost no newsprint is made, emphasis being placed upon the manufacturing of fine grades of paper. The industry here uses about 40 per cent waste paper, rags, and straw and about 60 per cent new wood pulp, part domestic, part imported. So thoroughly cut and burned over was this area that it produces only a fraction of the nation's wood output.

The pulp mills on the south shore of Lake Superior, as at Munising, get much of their pulpwood from Canada in huge rafts pulled by tugs, which move at the rate of about two miles per hour provided there is no storm. As effort is made to deliver these rafts during that part of the summer when winds are weakest.

The northern Ontario portion of this subregion ranks high in the pulp and paper industry with 17 of the province's 45 mills (1950), all of which are relatively large. Some of the mills produce pulp only but others yield newsprint and still others various types of paper. Approximately 50,000 square miles of forest land have been set aside for supplying these plants under special agreement with the respective companies.

Bulk Cargo Movement

Unbelievably huge tonnages of cargo move out of and into Duluth, Superior, Two Harbors, Fort William and Port Arthur. Duluth and Superior are points of *transfer*. J. Russell Smith calls them "funnel towns," since their job is to pour bulky raw materials from gondola car to lake vessel and from lake vessel to gondola car. In addition to shipping iron ore and wheat out they bring coal and other products in. Superior is the terminus of the Interprovincial Pipeline from the Prairie Province oil fields whence the oil is shipped by tanker to Sarnia and other points. The twin cities and great ports, Fort William and Port Arthur, store and ship wheat. Some 40 giant elevators, divided

about equally between the two cities, line the lake shore for storage of wheat and other grains. Since only about 20 to 25 per cent of the wheat can reach Montreal before the season of navigation closes, the rest must be stored until the following spring and summer. Together the two ports handle more than six million tons of shipping.

Recreation

Recreation is important now and undoubtedly will be the leading business in the future. In the 1920's it was first realized that too much time, effort, and money had been wasted in farming worthless lands and that agriculture had no future. About the same time the once-rich timber and copper began to play out. On the other hand, the area has all the necessary features for a great playground — woods, lakes and streams, fish, game, cool summer climate, many good roads, and resort facilities. Eighty per cent is forest land, nearly half being publicly owned. The "cut-over area" is within easy driving distance from the densely populated centers of the Middle West, whose summer climate is so unbelievably trying as to drive people to the "North Woods." But the tourist season is short, lasting only from early July to Labor Day. Hay fever sufferers often remain somewhat longer.

The recreation industry gives employment to a considerable number of people: to farmers who furnish milk, eggs, and vegetables, and to others who sell petroleum products, rent cottages, boats, and fishing tackle, or act as guides. It is, however, a highly seasonal industry and cannot alone sustain the population. Winter sports are of some importance but less so than in New England, the Adirondacks of New York, and parts of the West.

The Outlook

The Northern Lake Subregion is a problem area to the United States. Both from a state and national viewpoint, these poor lands possibly will be with us always. Many people migrated after removing the timber and finding the land ill-suited for farming. Others, mostly unemployed miners, stayed on in the cut-over areas and now comprise stranded populations. The cost of local government in this land of few people and large open spaces is too high to justify isolated rural living. Recently science has made considerable progress in its ability to grow crops that mature earlier than those grown for so long a period. A tract of some 10,000 acres of abandoned, tax delinquent muck land was put into celery near Duluth in 1952 with considerable success. This land had been untouched for a quarter century. The yield was used in Duluth by the world's largest packer of ready-to-serve chop suey and chow mein. Perhaps onions, potatoes, cauliflower, carrots, and other truck crops could be grown and marketed successfully.

The major problem, that of unemployment, has been brought about by shrinkage of the principal enterprises — particularly lumbering and farming. Some persons believe that forest-development work offers the only large-scale employment possibility for thousands of families in the cut-over area; this is possible with reforestation and protection from fires.

The large scale development of taconite should contribute to stability of employment, to increasing payrolls, to stimulating all business activity in Minnesota, and to extending the life of iron mining for several generations. The revival of copper mining is also encouraging.[35] Huge tax write-offs are being granted also. The iron mines at Steep Rock and Michipicoten will help in Ontario.

The proximity of the area with its numerous lakes, streams and forests to the Middle West with its terribly hot summers guarantees a growing importance for the subregion as a vacation land. Much of the area is traversed by an excellent system of hard-surface highways.

―――――

[35] R. H. Ramsey, "White Pine Copper," *Engineering and Mining Journal*, Vol. 154, January 1953, pp. 72-73.

The Forested Northern Great Plains

The fourth and last subregion of the Northern Continental Forest lies between the ancient Canadian Shield on the east, the young Rocky Mountains on the west, the Spring Wheat Subregion on the south and the Tundra on the north (Figure 10–1).

Historically most of this region, of course, was occupied, often very thinly, by Indians. The first Europeans to enter, representatives of the Hudson's Bay Company, were on exploratory missions as were the independent fur traders (the "Pedlars"), who were based on Montreal. The Hudson's Bay Company representatives tried to get the Indians in increasing number to bring furs to the company's forts at salt water. Since the "Pedlars" could not hope to get the Indians to carry furs all the way to Montreal, they themselves penetrated the forests for on-the-spot trade. At that time the water routes comprised the only highways. The fur business was fabulously profitable for the traders.[36] While trapping for beaver, muskrat, weasel, mink, and fox still is important, a decline did set in with the introduction of the gun and the steel trap by the white man, the rise of the timber industry, the movement of agriculture northward, and the destruction to the forest by ravaging forest fires.

About 1900, logging became important in an area extending from Prince Albert on the south to the Churchill River on the north (Figure 10–1). Soon overcutting characterized much of the area. Recently, however, conservation measures have been inaugurated and though logging is being somewhat curtailed, its life is being prolonged.

The Natural Environment

This area consists of a wide lowland, representing a depression or downfold, which developed during the period of mountain building.[37] It has been built up by deposition

―――――

[36] Jim Wright, "Saskatchewan's North," *Canadian Geographical Journal*, Vol. 45, July 1952, p. 18.

[37] Griffith Taylor, "The Geography of Canada," *Annals, American Academy of Political and Social Scence*, Vol. 253, September 1947, p. 2.

from sands and silts washed off the Rockies and the Shield. It is here that two of Canada's largest rivers, the Mackenzie and Saskatchewan, are to be found.

Climatically this subregion is similar to that of the Shield in the same latitude. The one word that characterizes the climate is *continentality*, and it is this that is the dominant feature of the environment. Lying far from any of the great oceans with their ameliorating influence, the area's range of temperature exceeds 50°F. between the hottest and coldest months.

Most of this area too, lies quite far into high latitudes; even as far south as the latitude of Peace River there are in midsummer 18 hours of daylight. This is an important factor so far as agriculture is concerned, though nights are invariably cool. The many lakes and streams also counteract the effect of summer frosts locally over much of the area.

Of particular geographical significance are some of the summer isotherms — particularly that for 57 degrees in July which extends far north of latitude 60° N. into the Mackenzie River Valley of the Northwest Territories. It is believed that it will become an important factor in future settlement. Passing from western Newfoundland it crosses to the west corner of Labrador to the north of Lake Winnipeg, then northwest to the mouth of the Mackenzie River in latitude 67° N. and thence southward along the east front of the Rockies to the international border. Griffith Taylor calls this subregion the "Mackenzie Triangle" (between Edmonton and Aklavik in the far north and The Pas near Lake Winnipeg).

Anywhere in the Mackenzie Triangle early frosts may occur. The rainfall is low — but everywhere exceeds the 11-inch isohyet. However, the air is dry both in summer and in winter.

The soils of the Peace River and Central Saskatchewan are fairly well known. Most of them are classified as grey wooded soils and are considered as a separate group from the podzols. They have a leached A_2 horizon, like the podzols, but they have a distinct horizon of lime accumulation at the base of the profile. In this respect they resemble the grassland soils. Furthermore these soils are not very acid. Degraded black soils are to be found in parts of this subregion.[38]

Minerals

This subregion obviously has nothing in the way of metallic minerals though the adjacent Shield outcrops giving rise to numerous outstanding mining towns. Nearby, and probably the best known, is Flin Flon with one of the best copper-zinc mines in Canada.

The mineral wealth is in the organic fuels — coal, petroleum, and natural gas — but these are more logically discussed in Chapter 11, *The Great Plains*. An enormous potential resource of the future may be the tar sands along the Athabaska River in northeastern Alberta. In an area of 30,000 square miles is an estimated 250 billion barrels of oil. The cost of separating the oil from the sand is at present so great as to preclude competition with liquid crude oil drawn from wells.

Agriculture

Agriculture is pushing north from the Spring Wheat Subregion of Saskatchewan and Alberta and at present is at the northern extension of the Pioneer Fringe on the Great Plains of Canada. North of Prince Albert and into the Peace River area of Alberta and British Columbia is the dividing line between the farming community of relatively continuous cultivated land and the commercial forest region.

This area for farming is not comparable with that to the south, the Spring Wheat Subregion, where the black and dark brown grassland soils are so productive. Hence the rate of settlement slowed down as the more difficult environmental conditions to the north were met. Clearing in the mixed deciduous-coniferous forest became more difficult and costly and the grey-wooded soils

[38] Donald F. Putnam, "Pedogeography of Canada," *Geographcal Bulletin* (Ottawa), Vol. I, No. 1, 1951, pp. 68-71.

were less fertile. Rates of clearing during the 1930's averaged from five to seven acres per farm per year — an insufficient acreage for economical farming.[39] The farmers who are settling the Pioneer Fringe were largely former prairie farmers who were forced out of the southern prairies by drought and consequent crop failures. First they went into the "Parkland," where climate was reasonably reliable but where clearing was hard.

Since 1945 the Pioneer Fringe of agriculture is again moving northward but at a faster rate than during the 1930's — the result of mechanical brush-clearing equipment.

However, only the strong-willed and stalwart can live here for in addition to having to accept a lower standard of living, are such discouragements as high transport costs to distant southern markets, early killing frosts, poor soils, inadequate water facilities, and countless pestiferous insects during summer.

Any agriculture north of this area is at present in isolated pockets near small towns and beyond the Agricultural Fringe.[40]

Transportation

A major reason for the recent progress of this subregion has been the development of transportation. Studies of agriculture and settlement of the Prairie Provinces published in the 1930's are now obsolete. The farmers who moved out of the dry areas of the southern prairies after several years of crop failure, settled in the "Parkland" in strips along the northern railway branches which had been built prior to 1930.

Since 1945 settlement has been pushing northward at an accelerated rate aided by highway construction, the automobile and the truck on the one hand and by improved mechanized brush-clearing equipment on the

other.[41] Among the transport aids are the railways to the Athabaska River and river transport to Lake Athabaska, the Alaska Highway, and the Mackenzie Highway. This last, which has been called "The key to the development of the North," is a 384-mile all-weather road which penetrates some of the wildest and most unsettled parts of Canada to the shores of Great Slave Lake.

Prospects and Outlook

While most of this subregion forms today one of the great empty spaces on the population map of Canada (Figure 10–2), over which logging and trapping operations prevail,[42] agriculture is, nonetheless, pushing slowly but unmistakably northward. It seems certain that this area has some future agriculturally since the climate is sufficiently warm to grow such hardy crops as potatoes, hay, and special varieties of oats and barley. Barley forms grain as far north as Aklavik (in the Tundra Region) though the grain does not ripen in most years. Dairying is of considerable importance in the Pioneer Fringe. Hence it appears that human expansion will move into higher latitudes here than in any other part of Canada.

While the market for agricultural products is small, the rapid development of mining settlements on the Shield, where neither soil nor climate will permit the development of agriculture offers a growing market for fresh milk, eggs, butter, and vegetables. Dairy and other products are sent from The Pas–Carrot River area to Flin Flon. As marketing and transportation difficulties are solved, more agricultural products will be sold.[43]

Griffith Taylor who probably has no peer in knowledge of world restrictive environments believes that the farms of the near future will be sited along the northern fringe of farms in Saskatchewan and Alberta; that

[39] J. Lewis Robinson, "The Northern Extension of the Pioneer Fringe on the Great Plains of Canada," *Abstracts of Papers, Publication No. 6,* 17th International Geographical Congress, p. 75, Washington, D. C.: 1952.

[40] Robinson, "The Northern Extension of the Pioneer Fringe on the Great Plains of Canada."

[41] Robinson, "The Northern Extension of the Pioneer Fringe on the Great Plains of Canada."

[42] Commercial fishing is carried on in Lake Athabaska and Great Slave Lake, most of the catch being exported frozen to the Middle West of the United States.

[43] M. E. and A. C. Robinson, "The Pas–Crossroads of the New North," *Canadian Geographical Journal,* Vol. 45, August 1952, p. 59.

the first new district will probably be along the Liard River to the north of the Peace River; that an oats and hay economy may some day arise in the central Mackenzie River area, but only after man has more

___

[44] Taylor, "The Geography of Canada," p. 8.

fully occupied the Clay Belt, Prince Albert, and Peace River areas.[44]

The northern portion of this subregion, however, must ever be submarginal agriculturally and will be economically important only for limited logging, trapping, and transportation.

Table 9

SELECTED CITIES AND TOWNS OF THE NORTHERN CONTINENTAL FOREST

City or Town	Urbanized area	Political center	City or Town	Urbanized area	Political center
Arvida		11,078	North Bay		17,944
Ashland		10,640	Pembroke		12,704
Bell Island		10,291	Port Arthur		31,161
Bemidji		10,001	St. John's		52,873
Chicoutimi		23,216	Sault Ste. Marie (Mich.)		17,912
Corner Brook		10,276	Sault Ste. Marie (Ont.)		32,452
Duluth		104,511	Shawinigan Falls		26,903
Duluth–Superior	143,028		Sudbury		42,410
Escanaba		15,170	Superior		35,325
Flin Flon		9,899	The Pas		3,376
Fort William		34,947	Traverse City		16,974
Grand Mere		11,089	Virginia		12,486
Hibbing		16,276	Wabana		6,460
Jonquieres		21,618	Wausau		30,414
Marquette		17,202			

Selected Bibliography

American Academy of Political and Social Science, *Features of Present-Day Canada*, Robert H. Coats, ed., Annals, Vol. 253. Philadelphia: The Academy, 1947.

"Analysis of Pulp and Paper Industry and the Raw Material Supply: Canadian Resources," *Paper Trade Journal*, February 16, 1950 and March 16, 1950.

C. Bassett, "Canadian Hydro Keeps Pace with Industrial Development," *Public Utilities Fortnightly*, Vol. 48, 1951, pp. 135–146.

Avila Bédard, "Forestry in Quebec—Past—Present—Future," *Canadian Geographical Journal*, Vol. 28, June 1944, pp. 258–280.

R. N. Drummond and others, "Investigations in the Boreal Forest of Labrador-Ungava, 1948–1951," *Abstracts of Papers*, p. 22, Publication No. 6. Washington, D. C.: XVII International Geographical Congress, 1952.

"A New Process Builds an Industry," editorial in *Mining Engineering*, July 1951.

"Geographical Aspects of the Newfoundland Referendum," *Annals of the Association of American Geographers*, Vol. 39, March 1949, p. 70.

R. Glover, "The Difficulties of the Hudson's Bay Company's Penetration of the West," *Canadian Historical Review*, Vol. 29, 1948, pp. 240–254.

B. V. Gutsell, *An Introduction ot the Geography of Newfoundland*, Department of Mines and Resources, Information Series No. 1. Ottawa: 1949.

L. Gregory Hines, "Price Determination in the Lake Erie Iron Ore Market," *American Economic Review*, Vol. 41, September 1951, pp. 651–661.

C. D. Howe, "Canada's Industrial Potential," *Mechanical Engineering*, Vol. 73, 1951, pp. 618–620.

W. G. Jewitt, "A Mining Boom Again Strikes Yellowknife," *Mining and Metallurgy*, Vol. 25, 1944, pp. 580–583.

Ralph S. Knowlton, "Taconite—A Substitute Iron Ore," *Military Engineer*, Vol. 44, September-October 1952.

A. R. M. Lower, "What This Country Needs Is Ten New Provinces," *Maclean's Magazine*, Vol. 61, Oct. 15, 1948.

R. A. Mackay, editor, *Newfoundland: Economic, Diplomatic and Strategic Studies*, Royal Institute of International Affairs. Toronto: Oxford University Press, 1946.

B. J. McGuire and H. E. Freeman, "Wealth from the Canadian Shield," *Canadian Geographical Journal,* Vol. 38, 1949, pp. 198–227.

Donald F. Putnam, "Pedogeography of Canada," *Geographical Bulletin,* No. 1, 1951, pp. 57–85.

L. G. Reeds, "Land Utilization in Central Ontario," *Economic Geography,* Vol. 22, 1946, pp. 289–306.

G. R. Rumney, "Settlements on the Canadian Shield," *Canadian Geographical Journal,* Vol. 43, 1951, pp. 116–127.

Griffith Taylor, *Newfoundland: a Study of Settlement,* Special Series. Toronto: Canadian Institute of International Affairs, 1946.

E. J. Zavitz, "Reforestation in Ontario," *Canadian Geographical Journal,* Vol. 34, 1947, pp. 156–180.

11.

The Great Plains

THE Great Plains Region as discussed in this volume corresponds roughly with the Great Plains physiographic province,[1] although in places it extends eastward into the Central Lowland and southward into the Coastal Plain to include areas of extensive crop production such as winter and spring wheat, or areas of ranching activities beyond the borders of the Great Plains, as along the southwest Gulf Coast of Texas (Figure 11–1).

The eastern boundary corresponds roughly with the line (or zone) of crop land where corn, cotton, or other intensively-grown crops become dominant over wheat. The western boundary is the foot of the *Front Range* of the Rocky Mountains, from southern Canada to central New Mexico, and the western margin of the Pecos River Valley from that point southward to the Mexican border. To the north the region extends into the Prairie Provinces of Canada to include the Spring Wheat Area, and southward it reaches the Rio Grande and the Gulf of Mexico.

From the point of view of land use or the economy of the region five major subdivisions or subregions may be recognized: (1) the Winter Wheat Belt, where fall-sown, spring or early-summer harvested wheat is

the dominant crop; (2) the Spring Wheat Belt, lying largely in the Dakotas and the prairie provinces of Canada, dominated by spring-sown wheat; (3) the cotton and grain sorghum area of the Southern High Plains, dominated by those two extensively-grown crops; (4) the many small irrigated areas, found largely along the stream courses throughout the region, which specialize in such intensively-grown crops as vegetables, sugar beets, and alfalfa; and (5) the vast expanses of grasslands grazed by cattle, sheep, or goats.

Although somewhat diversified in its economic activities, the region shows a degree of unity in its level terrain, its low rainfall, and the ever-present danger of dry years which produce problem areas of great concern to all of Anglo-America.

The Physical Setting

Terrain. The wheat-growing parts of this region are mostly level to rolling, the slight relief being attributable in large part to the almost horizontal strata and to peneplanation. The fact that 90 per cent of the area can be farmed by labor-saving machinery indicates that there is little rugged or rough land, though there is some in the "Breaks"—in the valleys of the North and South Cana-

---

[1] Nevin M. Fenneman, *Physiography of Western United States*, pp. 1-91. New York: McGraw-Hill Book Co., 1931.

280

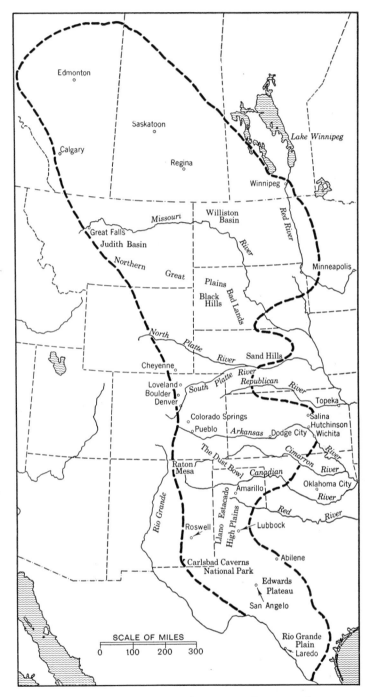

Figure 11–1. The Great Plains. A region of winter and spring wheat, grain sorghums, and cotton; irrigation agriculture; ranching; and mining.

dian rivers, along the eastern face of the Staked Plains in the Oklahoma and Texas panhandles, and in the Bad Lands of Nebraska, the Dakotas, and Montana.

A small part of this region was once the bottom of glacial Lake Agassiz, which came into existence when the continental ice sheet covered the country north of the present Lake Winnipeg, thereby forming a natural dam across the Red River of the North. When the ice retreated, the lake drained away, leaving an extensive plain. So level is much of it that a farmer can plow "league-long furrows in straight lines."

The western, semiarid part of the Great Plains was formed by the retreat of the great inland Cretaceous Sea. Subsequent erosion and deposition modified the original landscape. The heavier rainfall and more severe erosion in the mountains to the west has caused thick layers of sediment to be deposited on the plains in broad overlapping alluvial fans. Near the mountain front, some of these deposits have been removed by later erosion so that a trough appears between the mountains and the High Plains to the east. This trough is locally known as the Colorado Piedmont. The southern part of the Great Plains (the High Plains), with an average elevation of 4,000 feet, is dissected by several through-flowing rivers: (1) the North and South Platte, (2) the Republican, (3) the Arkansas, (4) the Cimarron, and (5) the Canadian. Almost all these streams have cut their valleys several hundred feet below the plain surface. South of the Canadian River, in western Texas and eastern New Mexico, is an area of more than 20,000 square miles (the Llano Estacado) which is practically untouched by erosion.

From south to north the physiographic subdivisions of the western Great Plains are (1) the Rio Grande Plain, (2) the Edwards Plateau, (3) the High Plains, (4) the Raton Mesa, (5) the Sand Hills, (6) the Black Hills, (7) the Bad Lands, and (8) the Northern Great Plains. Of these the Raton Mesa, the Sand Hills of Nebraska, the Black Hills of South Dakota, and the Bad Lands of the Dakotas have distinctly hilly to mountainous terrain. They are included in the Great Plains geo-graphic region because of their location in it.

Climate. The climate of the Great Plains is continental; the precipitation ranges from 15 inches in the northwest to 35 in the southeast, and varies greatly from year to year. There are periods of dry years when the westerly margins become almost desertic. The growing season varies from about 130 days in the north to about 200 days in the south. Summers are very hot; the maximum temperature for a typical station is more than 100°F. and it is the maximum rather than the average which harms crops. Thus, whereas temperature and growing season are adequate for most staple crops, the low rainfall, combined with hot dry winds, discourages the growth of most crops. In the western part of the region wheat gives way to pasture, and, along the southwestern boundary, to the grain sorghums and cotton.

Within the Spring Wheat Belt the climate varies from subhumid to semiarid. The precipitation ranges from about 13 inches in the west to 22 inches along the eastern border. Forty to 50 per cent of the precipitation falls in the three summer months, June, July, and August, and greatly favors the growth of wheat.

Winters are bitterly cold and dry, and therefore very hard on such perennials as tame hay and fruit trees. The differences in temperature between winter and summer are so great as to give this region the distinction of having the greatest range of any region in Anglo-America.

Precipitation is the most important climatic factor of the Great Plains. The rainfall is less than 20 inches annually throughout most of the area (hilly and mountain regions excepted), and it has wide annual variations. In a humid area an annual variation of approximately 15 inches would not be significant, but here where the average is less than 20, a decrease of only a few inches may create an extremely critical situation. Wet and dry years tend to run in periods of varying lengths and intensities, but data are not yet sufficient for climatologists to determine the exact nature of them nor to forecast future conditions with any degree of reliability. Evidence indicates that the period between

1825 and 1865 was relatively dry with few wet years. After settlers began keeping meteorological records in the late 1860's and early 1870's, an increase in rainfall was observed. Pioneers concluded that their settlements were responsible and offered many fantastic theories to prove their contention.[2] Then came the dry cycle during the 1880's and early 1890's, causing great distress among settlers, and wholesale land abandonment. Since that date wet and dry periods have alternated and the variations have always been serious. The last dry period (1933–1938), which probably caused the most widespread damage, created the Dust Bowl.

The high evaporation, ranging from 68 inches in southwest Texas to 37 inches in northern Montana, is due to high wind velocities and to a maximum of sunshine. These factors also reduce the precipitation effectiveness.

High winds, besides increasing evaporation and reducing rainfall efficiency, frequently assume destructive velocities, especially in the former Dust Bowl area.

Summer winds are so hot and dry and those of winter so biting and cold that nearly every farm needs a windbreak to reduce surface wind velocities.

Soils. The soils of the wheat belts, among the most fertile in Anglo-America, are mostly chernozems, though black prairie soils characterize the eastern margin and chestnut soils the western portion. They have a *lime zone*, a layer of calcium carbonate, at two to five feet beneath the surface within reach of plant roots. Because of the scanty rainfall, these soils have not had the lime leached from them. Their fertility combined with greater rainfall makes them the most productive zonal soils in the world, although there is less humus than in the types of grassland soils to the east.

Not all soils throughout the wheat belts are equally good, since considerable areas possess types ill-suited to wheat or any other cereal. In southern Saskatchewan, within a radius of 20 miles, occur the province's most productive lands as well as those that may have to be abandoned for crops.

A very close correlation exists between the distribution and density of population and soil types. Thus the population is densest on the excellent black soils which lie north and northeast of the brown soils. It is relatively sparse on the brown soils (many of which are submarginal) of the open semiarid treeless plains which extend from as far north as Edmonton, to southwestern Saskatchewan and southern Alberta and on across the border into adjacent parts of the United States.

Though the quality of wheat is little influenced by soil, the crop, for successful production, requires better soils than any other small grain.

The semiarid grazing section of the Great Plains lies entirely within the pedocalic soil group, but local soils vary widely in physical characteristics, particularly in their moisture-holding capacity. In general these soils have good texture and high fertility and need no lime or other commercial fertilizers. However, moisture deficiency prohibits their being used successfully for crops.

Natural Vegetation. Between the forests on the east and the mountains on the west lie the prairies and the steppe. The prairie, whose grasses attain a height usually of one to three feet, characterizes areas with 20 to 25 inches of precipitation in the north and 35 to 40 inches in the south.

They are practically identical with the area of the wheat belts except that there is a "park area" where bluffs of poplar and willow are interspersed with the heavy growth of grass in the northeastern portion in Canada. Merging with the prairie on the semiarid fringe to the west is the steppe, composed of grasses of low stature and characterizing areas with less than 20 inches of rainfall.

The native vegetation of the semiarid grazing portion of the Great Plains is dominantly short grass, with grama and buffalo grasses most conspicuous. Along stream courses and on higher elevations such as the Black Hills, trees are dominant. Before the introduction of beef cattle in the 1870's, luxuriant native

[2] Walter Kollmorgen, "Rainmakers on the Plains," *The Scientific Monthly*, Vol. 40, No. 2, February 1935, pp. 146-152.

grasses (mainly western wheat grass) covered extensive areas. Overgrazing, however, has reduced thousands of square miles to a semi-desert. Extensive wheat farming during the periods of the two World Wars has ruined large areas of grazing land which may not be able to graze livestock for some time. The white man seems to have done everything possible to make this subregion a desert.

Sequent Occupance of the Great Plains

When the region was first traversed by European explorers, they found millions of buffalo, antelope, and other animals grazing on the vast steppe. The Indian had not disturbed the balance of nature by destroying either the native animal life or the grassland vegetation. Had this simple type of land occupance continued, wind-erosion problems such as we know today would not have affected the region.

The land was originally "Indian country." Though the Indians were not at first mobile, they became so after acquiring horses introduced by the Spaniards. With the arrival of the white man, the Indians were dispossessed, their game was killed off and cattle were introduced. After the era of the cattle man on the open range, that part of the Great Plains included within the Hard Winter Wheat Belt was homesteaded.

Settlement of the Eastern Part of the Region. The first farmers believed that country unable to grow trees could not be good for agriculture. They shunned the prairie as they migrated westward, and they clung to the woodlands and river bottoms. The eastern part of the region was originally tall-grass country. Once crops were grown successfully on the prairie, newcomers arrived in large numbers; but settlement on a large scale had to await the arrival of the railroad.

No part of the world before had been conquered so rapidly for agriculture; clearing was unnecessary. True prairie soils, however, were not successfully turned over until the advent of the steel plow.

Adjustment was difficult. The settler encountered extremes of temperature and variable rainfall. Except at the edge of the forest, firewood and logs for homes were scarce or procurable only on a distant river bank. Where timber was scarce or lacking, a house made of sod had to meet the immediate need. But even this called for some wood. From the aesthetic point of view, the sod house was bad, but it was warm in winter, cool in summer, and it cost practically nothing. In some areas even water was unobtainable at ordinary depths.

The westward movement was in full swing and soon pioneer farmers had pushed beyond the tall-grass into the short-grass country. Their failure to understand the significance of short vs. tall grass proved to be an important factor, for they soon learned that rainfall on the steppe was inadequate for most crops and that tragedy would be widespread. The steppe was to prove itself less desirable for agriculture than the prairie.

The lands included in the Spring Wheat Subregion were originally inhabited by Indians who carried on some farming in the more favored spots but depended mostly upon the hunting of buffalo for a living. The Hudson's Bay Company later controlled the area.

The Dominion of Canada in 1870 took over the territories which the Hudson's Bay Company held by Royal Charter. The settlers had to learn by trial and error the agricultural possibilities of their country. It was known that the climate was dry, that the soil was fertile, that there were few obstacles to cultivation, since neither stumping nor stoning was required, and that crops might suffer from late spring and early summer frosts; but it was not known how variable the rainfall would be from year to year.

Settlement in the real sense did not begin until steel rails made their way across the continent. The Canadian prairie was settled long after its American counterpart — the lag being due to the dearth of wagon trails across the sterile Canadian Shield.

As a result of natural barriers, the older settled province of Canada appeared to have reached its limit of agricultural expansion even before Confederation. The so-called "Northwest" offered the only possible outlet to the area hemmed in by the Great Lakes on the west and the Canadian Shield on the north. As late as 1870 the Northwest area contained a scanty population. Settlement was limited largely to the shadows of the trading posts. The Canadian Pacific Railway which became the great colonizer, did not span Canada from the Atlantic to the Pacific until 1885. To speed up settlement, agents were sent out. They enticed settlers by promising them free land. The railway here did not follow population; instead population followed it. For half a century the Canadian Pacific worked feverishly to spread settlers over the prairie. It alone of all Anglo-America's land-grant railroads actually colonized; the others merely sold land.

Struggling against scanty and irregular precipitation and a short growing season, the settlers ultimately triumphed — winning with quick maturing varieties of wheat such as Marquis, Garnet, and Reward, and with the moisture-conserving practice of dry farming. At times rust played havoc with their crops, but again they triumphed by developing rust-resisting wheats.

The governments of Canada and the United States, along with their railroads, so encouraged immigration, although little was known of the area, that thousands of people poured into the Spring Wheat Belt and began to grow wheat. A mistake made by many was to locate too far from railroads. The market price of wheat determines how far the crop can be hauled. Moreover, during unusually favorable years when good crops could be grown, many immigrants settled on what later proved to be submarginal land. With the return of normal weather, crops failed and much land had to be abandoned.

Considering the numerous difficulties that have had to be overcome, the Spring Wheat Belt — American and Canadian — was transformed rapidly and on the whole successfully from the domain of the fur trader to that of the farmer.

Settlement of the Western Part of the Region. Following the Spanish explorers of the sixteenth century, few people attempted to cross this vast steppe, then considered a part of the Great American Desert. At first, the plains proved only a barrier to the westward movement that was seeking lands in Utah and Oregon. The first large party, the Astorians (1811-1813), followed the Missouri River to a point north of the Black Hills and then crossed westward into Wyoming. The following year a second group crossed the plains along the route of the North Platte River and established the Oregon Trail. A substantial migration to the Oregon Territory began about 1843. The next major trek was that of the Mormons (1846–1847), who followed the valley of the Platte from Omaha westward, but turned southwestward into the Salt Lake area after crossing the mountains. Soon after the Mormon trek came the California Gold Rush of 1849 and succeeding years. In addition to the well-established Oregon Trail, several others were used, but intermittent rivers with their water holes always marked the route. The rapidly growing population in California demanded closer contacts between the east and west coasts, resulting in several means of communication being developed — the stage coach, the pony express, and, most interesting of all, the camel caravans across the southern part of the Great Plains in Texas.

The completion of the Union Pacific Railroad in 1869, followed by several others in the 1870's and 1880's, ushered in the cattle era. A brief stage of buffalo hunting intervened, when for a few years white men with high-powered rifles all but exterminated the vast herds. By 1889 not more than a thousand head remained. The thousands of square miles of pasture lands left vacant immediately encouraged cattle drives from the Texas Gulf Coast. Although many cattle were driven northward to railheads at Abilene and Dodge City, during the 1880's large numbers also were driven into the northern Great Plains to establish the industry there.

The cattle era on the Great Plains was the most romantic stage in its utilization. Before the advent of barbed wire and its general use on the plains, the land was entirely open range. Individual cattle were branded and then allowed to run with the herds until the next season, when surplus animals were cut out and sent to market and calves were branded.

From the close of the Civil War period until about 1886, large herds grazed on the open range — a single open pasture thousands of square miles in extent. The increasing demand for meat both at home and abroad and improvements in transportation and refrigeration made the raising of livestock on the open range a highly profitable activity. Money poured into the region to establish large ranches and to increase and improve the herds. Much of this came from Europe, particularly from England and Scotland. Renewed interest in the range industry brought a demand for better strains of beef cattle, and several new varieties were introduced. Increasing numbers of cattle were being pastured and the open range was approaching its capacity. In some sections herders pastured large numbers of sheep on the open range. The closer grazing of sheep led to clashes between sheepmen and cattlemen over water holes and pasture rights.

The series of dry years which began in 1886 inaugurated a period of large fenced ranches. Before the development of barbed wire, fencing of the range would have been impossible even had it been desirable. A barbed-wire fence does not involve so much material as to make its cost prohibitive even on extremely large pastures.

The "cattle barons" attempted to secure from the Government all the land around a water hole; they had their cowhands do likewise. They would then fence in the entire area, sometimes more than they owned. Frequently they completely enclosed small ranchers or farmers within their fences who retaliated by "fence cutting." The large ranchers then ordered their cowhands to ride their fences and shoot anyone found cutting them. Conditions became so bad that laws were passed to prevent "fence cutting" and "fence riding," and the large rancher was required to provide gates at intervals.

There was only a slight increase in cattle on the plains after 1890. The encroachment of the wheat farmer curtailed the amount of land available for cattle ranches, and over-grazing on the drier western parts still further reduced the area.

After 1910, several new influences made themselves felt in the region. The development of the tractor, combine, and other power machinery made feasible the planting and harvesting of a much larger acreage of land than formerly had been possible. Numerous drought-resisting crops, especially wheat, and the grain sorghums, were planted on the plains. The high prices during both World Wars resulted in further expansion of the wheat area and many overstocked and overgrazed native pastures were plowed up and planted.

Errors Made in Settlement. It is always easy to see errors after they are made. Settlers coming into the region homesteaded quarter-sections, the amount permitted the head of a family in accordance with the Homestead Act of 1862. They ploughed up the grass on land never meant to be cultivated. They soon learned that they could not make a satisfactory living growing wheat on 160 acres, especially in the western margin. A family here needed more land than in humid regions where intensive methods were practicable. Accordingly thousands of families met disaster — losing their money, their labor, and finally even hope. They had gambled and had lost.

In 1904 the Kincaid Act increased to 640 acres the amount that could be homesteaded in western Nebraska, and in 1909 the Enlarged Homestead Act established the 320-acre homestead over a large area. But even these enlarged homesteads, including those made possible by the Stock-raising Homestead Act of 1916, proved to be little more than gestures in the right direction. The great weakness of all these acts was that they did not fit conditions west of the 100th meridian, and 20-inch rainfall line. The desire for small farms within semiarid Anglo-America was tenacious but untenable. In 1934 and 1935 all remaining unreserved and unappropriated public lands were withdrawn from homesteading by the federal government.

Unlike areas farther west, however, most of the Great Plains Region was already in private ownership. Some dry and rough lands in Montana and state-owned lands in west Texas, as well as several Indian reservations, are exceptions to the general rule of private ownership. Abandoned farmsteads are common both east of and west of the 100th meridian. In most cases the land has been incorporated into other farms. This reduction in the number of farms was accelerated by drought and depression.

The Mennonite settlers of Kansas were a notable exception to these failures, for they brought with them from Russia drought-resisting varieties of wheat. Up to this time only the varieties adapted to the humid East had been grown.

Possibly the biggest mistake of all was made during the first World War when the price of wheat skyrocketed and it was every farmer's patriotic duty to feed the Allies and win the war. This meant growing wheat and more wheat. Millions of acres that had never been anything but grazing land were attacked with tractor-drawn plows and seeded with wheat. Improved machinery enabled large amounts of power per man to be employed in crop production. The increase in wheat acreage took place mostly as a western extension outside the so-called Winter Wheat Belt. The yield was favorable at first, for the soil was fertile, rains were plentiful, and there was much moisture in the subsoil. Farmers grew wheat year after year. Before long, however, the soil-binding quality of the humus became depleted by continuous cropping. Livestock were turned in to graze the poorly developed crop, and their hoofs pulverized the ground. Then in the spring of 1934 winds, mostly from the south and north, began to blow the soil. Great clouds of dust swept eastward from this land largely devoid of anchoring vegetation. Thus must the nation pay a high price for having grown wheat on grazing land. Yet that is what might be expected from a people who had inherited the deeply rooted idea that in America land was practically unlimited and soil inexhaustible.

The Dust Bowl at its greatest extent covered 16 million acres. Here during the months December to May (the blow season),

fine fertile soil particles were whisked hundreds of miles away, forming "black blizzards." The heavier particles remained as drifts and hummocks. Sand dunes attained heights of 20 feet. The atmosphere was choked with dust; in some areas people had to put cloth over their faces when going out of doors. The vegetation in the fields was coated and rendered inedible for cattle, and whole groups of counties became almost unlivable.

But the Dust Bowl has been shrinking due to greater and better-distributed rainfall, to the regrassing of extensive areas, and to the soil-erosion preventive measures or new farming techniques of the Soil Conservation Service and other federal and state organizations. New techniques, including contour plowing and strip cropping, have been devised to utilize all the rain that falls.

From the national point of view, the Dust Bowl has been one of the most uneconomic farming areas in all Anglo-America. The drier and sandier portions should be returned to grass, as a means of controlling soil drifting, for grass more than anything else ties down the soil during the years of recurring droughts. A combination of factors caused dust storms to appear again in the northern Great Plains in 1945 and in the southern High Plains in the early 1950's.[3]

Wheat Farming

Wheat is grown widely throughout the United States and Canada, but the two most important areas are (1) the Hard Winter Wheat Belt in Kansas, Nebraska, Colorado, Oklahoma, and Texas, and (2) the Spring Wheat Belt in the Dakotas, Montana, and the Prairie Provinces of Canada.

The two wheat-growing areas are not contiguous (Figure 11–2). Between them is a belt (in southern South Dakota and northern Nebraska) where little wheat is grown, because the climate is not suited to the crop — winters are too cold and have too little

[3] Louis A. Wolfanger, "The Great Soil Groups and Their Utilization," *Conservation of Natural Resources*, p. 37. New York: John Wiley & Sons, 1950.

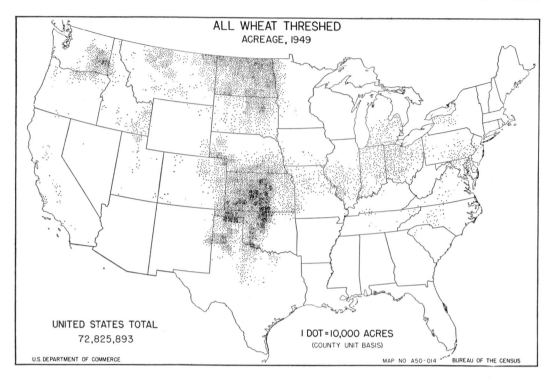

Figure 11–2. Wheat acreage. Note concentration in the Winter Wheat Belt of Kansas, Oklahoma, and Texas, and the Spring Wheat Belt of the Dakotas and Montana.

snow cover for winter wheat to survive, and summers are too hot for spring wheat.

The Winter Wheat Area. Farmers in the Hard Winter Wheat Belt who practice a high degree of specialization, face two big problems: (1) will they get a crop, and (2) if they do, will they be able to sell it? The first depends upon physical hazards — blistering heat, inadequate precipitation, hail, heavy rain, freezing and thawing without a snow covering, a grasshopper or Hessian fly invasion, rust, or smut. If one or more of these occur, the yield is usually reduced. The second depends upon world conditions, since the price farmers receive, at home or abroad, fluctuates with world wheat prices. In recent years, however, government aid has reduced greatly the hazards of one-crop farming.

The typical farm in the Winter Wheat Belt is large — it has to be. The size is greater in the western than in the eastern part. In central Kansas, the heart of the area, farms

vary from 300 to 400 acres. Many farmsteads have windbreaks on their windward sides, and these are conspicuous features of the landscape. Windbreaks offer, among other advantages, protection from the cold, dry northwest winds of winter and the hot southwest winds of summer.

Most of the land in crops is in wheat, though grain sorghums are probably more important on those farms in the southwestern part of the area. One may look in any direction and see little else growing in the fields than wheat. Actually only about a quarter of the land is in such crops as grain sorghums, alfalfa, and barley. Alfalfa and sorghums remove so much water from the subsoil that they cannot be grown continually on the same land.

Hard winter wheat is a variety having more "strength" than *soft wheat*. The same amount of hard wheat will produce a larger loaf and will stand more severe treatment in mechanical mixers. It is more desirable for bread, though less desirable for hot biscuits and pastries. Other advantages of hard wheat are that it usually brings a higher price and it is more productive.

The leading varieties of hard winter wheat are Pawnee, Comanche and Triumph, which together constitute a major part of the acreage. They are all high-quality wheats and are admirably suited to the subregion: they are not easily winter-killed, they are early-maturing (and so avoid hot winds, drought, and rust), they have stiff straw, and are resistant to plant diseases and insects.

The Spring Wheat Area. The entire Spring Wheat Area grows hard wheat, which contains more and better gluten than soft wheat. Great progress has been made in both plant exploring and plant breeding, scientists having been challenged to develop high-protein[4] types which mature early, yield well, and resist drought and rust. Efforts have been and still are being made to develop varieties that will grow farther north in the Spring Wheat Belt and will be more resistant to disease and drought.

Canadian spring wheat is mainly of the hard red type, though considerable durum is grown in the east where the hazard of rust is greatest. Canadian spring wheat is considered the world's best because it provides a higher flour yield, a bushel outweighing by several pounds one bushel of American spring wheat, and because it has also a higher protein content, which makes a stronger flour and a larger loaf of bread.

The leading varieties of hard wheat grown in this area are Marquis, Ceres, Garnet, Reward, and Thatcher. Considerable amounts of durum wheat also are grown.

Farms of the Spring Wheat Area are large but they are larger south of the international border than north of it. They also increase in size from east to west. The tendency is toward still larger holdings. In the drier part three, four or sometimes as many as seven

sections are required to support the family unit. This means, of course, a thinner population in the western than in the eastern portion.

The spring-wheat farmer, particularly the Canadian, reaps the advantages and disadvantages of specialization. His production costs (land and labor) are low; at the same time he is a great gambler, since he "carries all his eggs in one basket." Moreover, the Prairie Provinces suffer because of their dependence on foreign markets.

In the eastern part of the region, particularly the United States segment, the wheat acreage is being reduced in favor of diversified farming with emphasis on dairying. This is true also in the Winnipeg area where longer settlement, more moisture, and larger population are encouraging mixed farming and dairying. Diversification is also developing in the western part of the subregion as far north as Edmonton and especially in the foothills. Here crops are grown under irrigation; alfalfa forms the basis of important winter feeding of range cattle and sheep. Sugar beets, too, are grown, there being two sugar factories at Lethbridge. The growing and canning of vegetables, especially peas, is also being developed.

Specialization has encouraged soil deterioration, weeds, plant diseases, and reduced yields. Accordingly scientific farming is becoming increasingly urgent.

Systems of Farming. Commercially the Winter Wheat Belt is a one-crop area dominated by wheat. The heaviest concentration is in central southwestern Kansas and in northwestern Oklahoma, where the cereal is grown on a large scale.

Farmers build up their systems of farming around wheat. The best ones diversify, producing feed crops for livestock on part of the acreage. Diversification gives employment throughout the year, brings in constant returns, and maintains the fertility of the soil. Rotation in the eastern and central parts of the Hard Winter Wheat Belt includes alfalfa, sorghum, corn (on the better lands), oats or barley, and wheat, in this order, resulting in higher yields. Rotations are more difficult and less satisfactory in the western part of

---

[4] The percentage of protein is commonly employed for determining the milling and baking qualities of wheat. The protein content is said to be dependent upon climatic conditions — being high if dry weather prevails during the six weeks preceding harvest.

the subregion, for here wheat may be grown for a longer period on the same land without suffering losses in yield, and fewer other crops can be raised. The best rotation consists of one year each of a grain sorghum, preferably kafir or milo, and fallow, followed by two or three years of wheat. Where wheat is the only crop, probably the best system consists of one year of fallow and two or three years of wheat. About one third or one fourth of the acreage intended for wheat should be fallowed. When land is in fallow, it is cultivated but not sown. Weeds are thus controlled and moisture is conserved. Care must be taken not to pulverize the soil, for a surface of clods absorbs water more effectively than a surface of mulch and is less given to blowing. Fallowing is advantageous because it increases yields and, since the land is prepared before harvest, a slack period, it better equalizes the seasonal distribution of labor.

In the Spring Wheat Area, wheat gets first choice of the land though oats, barley, hay, flax, and corn (for silage) are grown as rotation crops. In the very dry areas the rotation followed (if it may be called a rotation) is summer-fallow and wheat. Strips from 6 to 20 rods wide are placed at right angles to the prevailing wind. In preparing summer-fallow, the mould-board plough has been replaced by some form of cultural implement that destroys vegetational growth, but leaves the stubble on the surface of the land to aid in the control of soil drifting. Only during about the last two decades has this "trash cover" method of cultivation in the drier areas been generally adopted. It is proving very effective in checking soil drift. In the more humid parts oats and barley may follow wheat. Because of the difficulty of growing row crops and controlling weeds, fallow is more popular north of the international boundary than south of it. In North Dakota where corn does not thrive, two thirds of the crop area is devoted to wheat.

Harvesting Problems. To equalize the seasonal distribution of labor is difficult anywhere but particularly in a one-crop region. In the early days of wheat growing labor was scarce, especially during harvest. Ac-

cordingly migratory workers — lumberjacks, hoboes, and college students — tempted by substantial wages and a relatively short working period, poured into the area. They started in Texas and Oklahoma, where the harvest begins in early June, and moved northward at the rate of about 100 miles a week. They arrived in Nebraska in early July and in the Dakotas in August. Some of them went on to the Prairie Provinces of Canada, where the harvest begins in September. Such labor was expensive, but when the kernels are ripe, wheat must be harvested, threshed, and put under cover before rain falls. The upward trend of wheat prices from 1896 to 1920 was terminated by the close of the first World War. Falling prices necessitated a saving in cost of production, and machinery, especially the combine, was the solution (Figure 11–3). Having reduced by

Figure 11–3. Wheat harvesting in the Prairie Provinces of Canada, near Edmonton, Alberta. (Courtesy Canadian National Railways.)

more than one half the per-acre cost with only one fourth the manpower, combines have been a potent factor in increasing the size of farms and in opening up to wheat growing those lands near the southwestern border of the area.

Transportation of Wheat. Since the population in this region is so small and wheat production is so great, the bulk of the crop is shipped elsewhere. Accordingly wheat regions must have good transport facilities. The crop is first carried by wagon or truck from the farm to one of the many small country elevators distributed throughout the wheat belt alongside the railroads. From there it goes by rail to some large primary market.

Getting the grain to elevators before rains set in has long been a major problem necessitating the bringing in of freight cars by the tens of thousands.

The Prairie Provinces ship most of their wheat from field to country elevator, nearly 6,000 of which dot the Canadian Prairie. Elevators occupy railway sidings, and many small towns consist of little else (Figure 11–4). A large part of the grain moves to Winnipeg for grading whence it is hauled to Port Arthur and Fort William for shipment by lake carrier to Montreal or Buffalo. From September 15 to December 15 wheat flows through Winnipeg, the world's largest primary market, en route to Fort William and Port Arthur at the rate of 1,000 to 2,500 cars daily, trains departing every 20 min-

utes. From Montreal, St. John, and Halifax, the grain is exported to Europe; from Buffalo it goes to New York City for transshipment. An appreciable quantity of wheat from the Prairie Provinces is exported from Vancouver as well as from Victoria and Prince Rupert via the Panama Canal to Europe. Some also travels over the Hudson Bay Railway to Churchill. Much of America's spring wheat goes to Minneapolis, which is the leading terminal storage center. Some also moves via lake carrier to Buffalo.

Because of the Spring Wheat Area's interior location and because water transportation is cheaper than rail, enormous grain elevators have been built at strategic points on navigable water; for example, Fort William and Port Arthur have some of the largest and finest elevator equipment in the world. Duluth and Superior also are well equipped as are Montreal, Vancouver, and Churchill.

Rail rates in Canada are lower, distance for distance, than are those in the United

Figure 11–4. Grain train passing some of the many country elevators that mark the skyline in Canada's Spring Wheat Belt. These elevators serve as emergency stations during the busy harvest season. (Courtesy Canadian National Railways.)

States. This is a matter of charter provisions; in return for a subsidy and a land grant the Canadian Pacific Railway agreed to reduce rates from western Canada to Lake Superior wheat ports by three cents per 100 pounds and maintain these rates in perpetuity.

Milling. Between 1855 and 1870, flour mills of three types evolved:

1. *Custom mills*, which ground the farmer's grain, making a definite charge per barrel.

2. *Exchange mills*, which exchanged flour already ground for wheat. The farmer usually got about 25 to 30 pounds of flour for a bushel of wheat. Most of the mills were of this type prior to 1870 and were largely a response to the extremely bad and often impassable roads of winter.

3. *Merchant mills*, which bought the grain and sold the flour and by-products outright. The roller process of milling sounded the death knell of the small mill. Today nearly all, if not all, are of the merchant type — either (a) *interior*, which mill flour for the local market, or (b) *terminal*, which mill flour for distant markets, including those in foreign countries. Until recently about 20 per cent of the flour of Kansas was exported.

Prior to 1892 the bulk of the Hard Winter Wheat Belt's grain was shipped to the ultimate market for milling, since "freight rates were so regulated that wheat could be shipped more cheaply than flour." Some milling took place within the area but it was mostly confined to the eastern part, to the larger cities, and, to the transportation terminals. To a certain extent this is still true. The dominant centers today in the Hard Winter Wheat Belt are Wichita, Salina, Topeka, Hutchinson, and Oklahoma City.

When Minneapolis became the world's leading milling center, the grist mill "struck a snag." Whereas soft winter wheat made a beautiful white flour, hard spring wheat and hard winter wheat made a dark, distasteful flour. This was attributable to flinty particles and to friction caused by the buhrstones, which completely crush wheat kernels.

The hard-wheat flour, therefore, was sold at a great disadvantage in the East, and even the wheat from which it was made sold for about 20 cents a bushel below soft winter wheat. Something had to be done, and the roller mill resulted. The steel-roller process, which revolutionized flour milling, was invented in Budapest (1820), then the world's leading milling center. It was a trade secret, but Hungarians were induced to come to Minneapolis. The essential feature of the roller process was the use of iron or porcelain rollers instead of buhrstones. Smooth rolls were unsuccessful, however, and porcelain was given to chipping. Accordingly, a corrugated roll was perfected which produced more flour from the wheat and performed 30 per cent more work on 47 per cent less power. Other contributions to milling were the dust collector for preventing explosions; the purifier for eliminating middlings (flinty particles); the "middlings purifier" for separating the dust and fluffy particles or bran from the middlings; and the bolting machine, which passes the flour through a very fine silk cloth.

Though this region is the world's leading producer of wheat, it is not outstanding in milling, because (1) the domestic demand (Canada) for flour is small, (2) ocean freight rates are lower on wheat than on flour, and (3) foreign countries want the by-product for animal feed.

Other Crops of the Great Plains Region

Grain Sorghums. With the exception of a small but concentrated area along the coastal plain of south Texas, most of the grain sorghums of the United States are grown along the western margin of the Winter Wheat Area on the High Plains of Kansas, Oklahoma, and Texas (Figure 11–5). These drought-resisting crops, introduced into the United States from the semiarid parts of Africa, have grown in importance in the southwestern part of the area, where they are being used for fodder and as a binder crop in strip and terrace cultivation. In dry years grain sorghums produce a partial crop for feed and cover even when wheat withers and dies. They have been known to grow on as little as ten inches of annual rainfall. Moreover, the stubble stands erect against

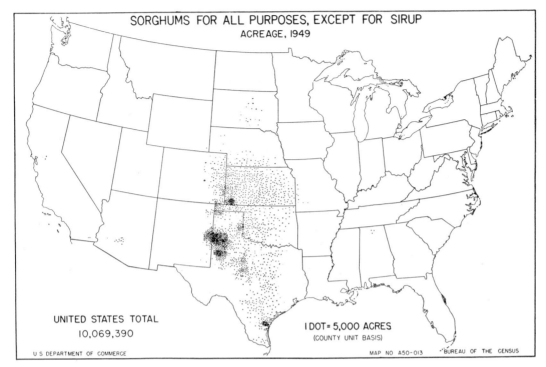

Figure 11–5. Grain sorghums grown in the United States. Note the concentration on the High Plains of the Texas Panhandle.

the wind, thereby reducing erosion. Since the sorghums require much heat they are less important north of the Arkansas Valley.

Sorghums must be fairly mature before they are harvested (Figure 11–6). The corn (row) binder is the most efficient machine for harvesting sorghum, since a farmer, assisted by two men to shock the bundles can harvest from six to seven acres per day. The feeding value of sorghum is 50 per cent higher when fed as silage instead of as fodder.[5]

Some of the more important varieties of grain sorghums grown on the Southern High Plains include the kafirs, milos, feterita, darso, and hegari.

Cotton. The southern part of the Great Plains which is an important cotton-producing area is included frequently with the lands of the Cotton Belt (Chapter 7), but in this

text the cotton grown here is treated as one of the crops of the Great Plains.

When the potentialities of the High Plains[6] area for cotton production became known, the acreage increased rapidly and by the close of World War I, a great cotton-growing area had developed there. At first practically all of the crop was grown by dry-farming methods, but in time much of the cotton area was irrigated by means of shallow wells. The total area in cotton under irrigation in 1948 in the Panhandle High Plains was 482,700 acres.[7] This has changed the appearance of this area from a land of ranches and extensively cultivated cotton and grain sorghums, to one of intensive cultivation of cotton through irrigation methods (Figure 11–7). Growing cotton under irrigation, however, has reached its maximum de-

[5] J. J. Martin and J. C. Stephens, "The Culture and Use of Sorghums for Forage," U. S. Department of Agriculture, *Farmers' Bulletin*, No. 1844. Washington, D. C.: Government Printing Office, 1940.

[6] This area goes by a number of names, including the *South Plains*, the *High Plains*, the *Staked Plains*, and the *Llano Estacado*.

[7] *The Texas Almanac*, 1952-1953, p. 188.

Figure 11–6. Extensive field of milo maize on the High Plains of West Texas. Note the well-developed grain heads. (Courtesy of *The Dallas News*.)

velopment in the Great Valley of California and hence will be considered in detail there (Chapter 14). Since most of the water for irrigation in the South Plains Area comes from wells drilled into water-bearing sands which have no large surface outcrop, and since this area lies within a region of low rainfall, many individuals feel that the underground water source is being depleted at too rapid a rate and that the number of wells drilled in the area should be regulated so that the supply of irrigation water will not be exhausted. Because of the development of irrigated land, the population of the area has increased at a very rapid rate as shown by the growth of Lubbock, the agriculture center of the area, from 31,853 in 1940 to 71,390 in 1950, an increase of nearly 125 per cent.[8]

Irrigation on the Great Plains

Irrigation was practiced in the Southwest long before the coming of white men but, except for that developed by the Spaniards in the middle Rio Grande Valley, the re-

claimed area was increased only slightly. The first irrigation project to be established on the Great Plains dates from 1870 when the Greeley Union Colony developed a large tract of land in northern Colorado by using

Figure 11–7. Mechanical harvester working in cotton field near Lubbock, Texas. (Courtesy Lubbock Chamber of Commerce.)

[8] *The Texas Almanac, 1952-1953*, p. 578.

water from the South Platte and Cache la Poudre rivers.

Irrigation projects are developed under four types of ownership and management: (1) mutual irrigation companies, such as the Greeley Union Colony, where every farmer is automatically a part of the organization, (2) commercial irrigation, where privately-owned companies construct all facilities and sell services to water users at a profit, (3) irrigation-district movements, involving public support but depending upon private capital for construction financing, and (4) federal irrigation districts, organized under the National Reclamation Act of 1902, where the government bears all construction costs, and the settlers pay for their land and water rights on comparatively easy terms. Of these, the first and fourth have been the most successful, although much land in the West is also irrigated under the third. In 1936 the President's Great Plains Committee found that counties with adequate irrigation systems had only five per cent tax delinquency while adjacent counties had as high as a 95 per cent tax delinquency, despite the fact that irrigated lands had tax valuations ten times as great as dry farming or grazing lands.

Great Plains Irrigation Districts. The irrigation districts of this region are too numerous to mention, since almost every stream flowing from the Rocky Mountains provides water for some project. The Federal Bureau of Reclamation has under construction or active operation on the Great Plains a number of large projects, but there are many more under other types of ownership. In Texas where the federal government does not own public lands, the Bureau of Reclamation has made no improvement. However, some land in Texas is supplied with water from the federal Rio Grande project. The irrigated area of Texas is scattered throughout the arid parts of the State and in the rice-growing areas of the coastal plain, but more than half of the developed area lies within the Great Plains grazing area. On the High Plains more than one million acres depend upon shallow wells. In south Texas, the Winter Garden area utilizes artesian water,

and the Laredo district draws upon the Rio Grande.

All irrigated areas have much in common, but there are many varied problems involved in their construction and maintenance. A brief description of the Colorado–Big Thompson project in northeastern Colorado follows.

The Colorado–Big Thompson project. The more than 600,000 acres in this project lie in northeastern Colorado and include the lands of the Greeley Union Colony that have been "under the ditch" since 1870. Water shortage in the area led the Bureau of Reclamation to undertake construction of this project at a cost originally estimated at 44 million dollars, one half to be assumed by the federal government for power development, and the other half to be repaid by farmers in the Northern Colorado Conservation District. Aside from comprising the largest single irrigated area on the Great Plains, this project has several unique features. The natural watershed of the Big Thompson River could not meet the needs of the irrigated lands, and since the waters of other streams on the east slope were already appropriated, sources on the west slope of the mountains had to be tapped. It was therefore necessary to drill one of the longest tunnels in Anglo-America. The tunnel is 13.1 miles long, has a diameter of 9.5 feet, and is capable of carrying 550 second-feet of water. Under the summit of the Continental Divide it is nearly 4,000 feet below ground. To prevent water users on the western slope from losing their water supply, reservoirs were constructed to supplement the volume of Grand Lake so that it can be maintained at a constant level. All reservoirs and tunnels lie outside the Great Plains, but the irrigated lands are within the region. In the area to benefit from this project live more than 200,000 people who derive their livelihood directly or indirectly from farming. Because of the severe water shortage during the 1930's, farmers in this area suffered an annual loss of nearly seven million dollars. This project is designed to meet all irrigation needs.

Because of changes in original plans, miscalculations, and the increased costs of labor and materials due to inflation, the original estimate of 44 million dollars may run above 170 million before the project is finally completed. Because of these costs, many people have expressed grave doubts over the economic practicability of the project, and considerable opposition has arisen within the State of Colorado concerning the entire project. Some have gone so far as to suggest its abandonment. Under the original estimates the farmers within the district could have paid their share, but with construction costs amounting to several times the original estimate, grave doubts have arisen as to the soundness of the undertaking. If the farmers have to increase their share of the cost it will place them under a financial burden far above their ability to pay. Since the Bureau of Reclamation cannot abandon the project without subjecting itself to severe criticism, the only solution seems to be for the federal government to assume all costs over and above the original estimate, and hope that the sale of electricity will ultimately pay for the project. Some electrical engineers, however, have expressed grave doubts concerning the possibility of the sale of electricity paying the balance.[9]

The Major Irrigated Crops. The length of the growing season within this region varies from more than 260 frost-free days in the Winter Garden and Laredo districts of south Texas to less than 120 in northern Montana and southern Canada. The most extensively grown crop is *alfalfa*, which is used for supplemental winter feeding of livestock. Alfalfa occupies the largest acreage of any irrigated crop from southern Colorado northward. The Winter Garden and Laredo areas in the extreme south produce early *Bermuda onions, spinach* and other winter truck crops.

On the several irrigated areas of the Pecos Valley in southern New Mexico, *cotton* has become dominant, although considerable acreage is devoted to alfalfa. On the High

[9] Harold A. Hoffmeister, "Middle Park and the Colorado-Big Thompson Diversion Project," *Economic Geography,* Vol. 23, 1947, pp. 228-230.

Plains of the Texas Panhandle, large acreages of cotton are irrigated by water from deep wells.

From Colorado northward, in addition to alfalfa, sugar beets occupy a large acreage. This crop is grown throughout the irrigated West, but northeastern Colorado and western Nebraska are outstanding.

Sugar beets belong fundamentally to a cool-summer region, where summer temperatures do not average above 70° F. Beets produce best on dark-colored silt and clay loams. The major requirement, however, is moisture, and since a uniform supply is needed at all times, the crop in this region must be irrigated. The average field of sugar beets requires from three to seven irrigations each season (Figure 11-8). Unlike sugar cane, the raising of sugar beets requires considerable farm equipment. The principal implements needed are beet-seed drills, beet cultivators, beet lifters, and special trucks for hauling the roots to the loading station or factory. Beet seeds are planted with drills in rows about twenty inches apart and covered to a uniform depth. As soon as the rows can be followed, they are cultivated and the beets thinned out so as to stand 10 to 12 inches apart. During the early growing period beets are cultivated to keep down weeds. When the plant becomes large enough for the leaves to cover the ground, the crop is "laid by," and no further work is done until it is fully grown. Warm days and cool nights are essential for satisfactory maturing of the beets.

The crop is harvested by lifting the roots from the soil and placing them in piles. They are then topped, loaded into trucks, and transported to the sugar factory or loading station. Beets should not be hauled more than four or five miles. If farms are more remote from the factory, loading stations are provided by the railroads.

Sugar beets, an intensively grown crop, require a large amount of labor, especially during thinning and harvesting. Formerly, most beet areas depended on migratory Mexican labor for their activities but the industry is rapidly becoming mechanized

Figure 11–8. Sugar beets: (A) Irrigating field with plastic tubes that siphon water from the lateral ditch. (B) Pick-up loader elevating sugar beet roots from windrow to truck for hauling to sugar factory. (Courtesy of U. S. Department of Agriculture.)

and "field hands" are no longer of major importance.[10]

In the sugar factories, which are large establishments, the beets are cleaned, sliced, and placed in cylinders for the extraction of the sugar. Ultimately the sugar is separated from other liquors or molasses. At most factories the beet pulp (wet or dry) is sold to stockmen for feed. The tops and crowns left in the field are also used as stock feed. The beet-sugar industry is an exacting one, but it has proved to be very remunerative in irrigated areas throughout the West.

The Range Livestock Industry

Cattle, sheep, and Angora goats dominate the range of the Great Plains Region. Although cattle are the most widely distributed, overgrazing has resulted in their elimination from some areas. Sheep, introduced later than cattle, were pastured on the poorer lands, but have become dominant in parts of Montana, Wyoming, and southwest Texas, where formerly only cattle were considered of value. Many cattlemen, especially in southwest Texas, found it more profitable to

[10] S. B. Nuckols, *Sugar Beet Culture in the Northern Great Plains Area*, U. S. Department of Agriculture, Farmers' Bulletin, No. 2029. Washington, D. C.: Government Printing Office, 1951.

run sheep than cattle on their ranches, although it hurt their pride to do so. Angora goats are raised almost exclusively on the Edwards Plateau of central Texas.

The Range-Cattle Industry. Despite the fact that the Great Plains Region has fewer range cattle today than formerly, ranching is still important. The demand for better quality meat and the practice of fattening stock on farms before slaughtering them has resulted in the Agricultural Interior having more cattle than the western ranges.

Throughout the Great Plains the carrying capacity of the range varies widely. Practically all the region has been overstocked — a temptation that becomes greater during years of high prices, particularly if the rainfall has been good and pastures are greener than normal. Conservative cattlemen, however, have learned the approximate carrying capacity of their land and do not run more cattle than can be fed in dry years.

The size of the cattle ranches varies from less than 2,000 acres to more than 800,000 acres. One of the largest cattle ranches in the Great Plains Region is the Matador Ranch, located along the breaks of the plains in the Texas Panhandle. The three ranches controlled by the Matador interests, containing more than 800,000 acres, constitute one of the largest top-quality beef-producing areas of the continent. Each year more than 9,000 beef cattle and 10,000 calves are shipped to market from this large-scale, well-managed "beef assembly line." The Matador was the last of the large high plains ranches owned by foreign capital, although at one time millions of acres of the Great Plains from Canada to Mexico were held by absentee owners in Great Britain. In the summer of 1951 the ranch was sold for $18,900,-000, thus terminating its Scottish ownership which had been operative since 1882. Whether it will be broken up into smaller holdings and thereby allow more people to occupy the area, or whether it will continue to be operated as a large-scale ranch, is unknown. The possibility of finding oil under these many acres will undoubtedly influence its future development. Several dry holes have been drilled on the property but as yet no production has resulted.[11]

The small ranches are usually located near the eastern margin of the region or adjacent to irrigated areas, and they grow much of their own feed. Some of these fatten their cattle and market them directly at the pack-

[11] *The Dallas News,* August 26, 1951.

ing houses. Most of the range cattle, however, are raised on large ranches (Figure 11-9).

The Great Plains subregion has year-long grazing. North of the Texas Panhandle, snows temporarily interrupt winter grazing, necessitating supplemental feeding to prevent or reduce losses. In dry years, however, feed must be supplied both summer and winter to prevent wholesale starvation. During those periods the cattle industry is unprofitable.

Throughout the region, stockmen utilize native pastures so far as possible in order to reduce the expense of supplying hay or cottonseed cake. If beef cattle can be shipped out to the Agricultural Interior with little or no expense for supplemental feed, the ranchman can, as a rule, make a fair profit.

A typical large cattle ranch. A prime requisite for successful ranching is a good supply of water. An insufficient water supply prevents the utilization of thousands of acres of grazing land. At first ranchmen supplied their reservoirs (tanks) from natural sources — springs, seeps, and surface streams. The development of cheaper drilling methods and the perfection of the windmill added

Figure 11–9. Ranching scene on the Great Plains. Cattle at a water hole on the High Plains of Texas. (Courtesy of *The Dallas News.*)

many square miles to the ranching area of the Great Plains. Water is piped to a dirt tank or watering trough some distance from the well or natural spring to prevent the cattle from contaminating the supply.

Winter care of stock is an important item. In the southern Great Plains timber and broken terrain (breaks) afford sufficient protection. In the northern Great Plains, however, protection is provided by sheds, usually constructed with an open side. These open sheds face away from the direction of the prevailing winds, and they suffice for even the most severe blizzards. Other desirable equipment includes (1) pens for branding, (2) chutes for cutting or separating cattle from the herd for shipment, and (3) dipping vats for treating animals affected by ticks, lice, or other pests.

In early days each cowhand furnished his own "outfit" — horse, saddle, bridle, blanket, and bedding. Today, however, most large ranches furnish horses and equipment. While well-trained horses and good equipment may add to the initial investment, they decrease expenses in the long run. At the time of the roundup, cowhands must use a number of horses, sometimes two to four a day.

Working on the range. In small pastures or on ranges bounded by natural barriers, cattle cannot become widely scattered; hence comparatively little labor is involved. On large ranches, however, the annual or semi-annual roundup is a big job. Often neighboring ranches combine their cowhands. In this way cattle on the unfenced range which belong to different ranches can be separated, and driven back to their owners' ranges or to some shipping point.

Roundup time varies with different sections of the Great Plains Region. If the ranch ships grass-fat cattle instead of feeders, the roundup is scheduled to hold cattle a minimum of time prior to shipment as a means of preventing loss of weight.

A considerable part of the cowhand's time on a big ranch is spent in "cutting-out" steers that are to be sent to market or to northern feed lots and in branding calves. On the better equipped ranches, branding is usually done in "corrals." The brand must be recorded according to the laws of the state in which the ranch is located. To be successful the brand must not burn the hide but must mark the animal permanently.

Shipping to market. When beef cattle destined for market have been cut from the herd, they are driven to loading chutes built along the railroad tracks. Formerly long drives over cattle trails were necessary. As the railroad net grew throughout the cattle country the drives were reduced and today they are seldom more than a few miles long. Upon reaching the loading chute the animals are driven up an incline into waiting cattle cars. Formerly cowhands rode the cattle trains to their destination in order to supply the animals with feed and water, prevent their being trampled, and assure their arrival in good condition. The railroads now take care of the animals.

The Sheep Industry. Sheep ranches on the Great Plains are similar to cattle ranches; in fact, many cattle ranches today also run large numbers of sheep. The sheep industry, most concentrated in southwest Texas and northern Colorado, is also important in Montana (Figure 11-10). Since sheep graze closer than cattle and require less water, they can be pastured where the latter would die. In some respects sheep are easier to handle. In the northern Great Plains, however, they must be driven in summer long distances to mountain pastures and returned in winter to the plains. The ranchman works hard throughout the winter to protect and feed his flocks. Constant vigilance is necessary during extreme cold and heavy snow to prevent sheep from drifting with the wind and perishing in the deep snows.

Shearing. The sheep of the Great Plains are raised chiefly for their wool. The period of greatest activity on a ranch, therefore, is shearing time, which usually takes place in late spring or early summer, after all danger of further freezes has passed. In the Southwest a second shearing is sometimes made in early autumn, but the wool is never so good as that cut at the close of the winter season. The wool is sorted, cleaned, and baled, before it is shipped to market. In some respects sheep ranching is less a gamble than cattle ranching, but sheep need more individual care and the price of wool fluctuates greatly on the world market.[12]

Angora Goats. The Edwards Plateau of southwest Texas yields more than 80 per cent of the nation's mohair. Goat ranching is similar to sheep ranching, except that goats, being browsing animals can subsist on pas-

leader.[13] Mohair is used mainly in upholstering furniture and automobiles.

The demand for mohair which existed during World War II was reduced suddenly after its termination. Declining prices during the next several years forced many growers to curtail the production of mohair and to liquidate large numbers of goats. Many felt

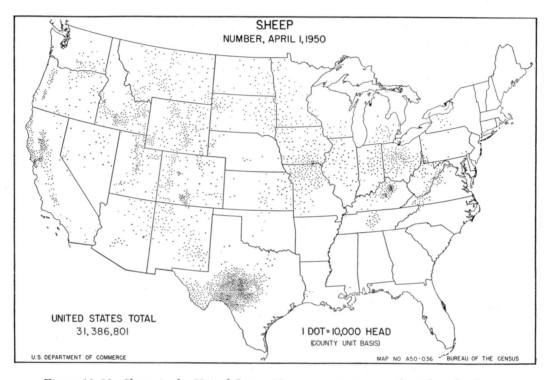

Figure 11–10. Sheep in the United States. Note concentration on the Edwards Plateau of southwest Texas in the Southern Great Plains.

tures not good enough for sheep. Most of the pasture land used by Angora goats is in the brush country where scrub oak and other small trees and shrubs supply browse (Figure 11-11). Goats are clipped during March and April and again in September and October. The mohair is shipped mainly to New England, though some is exported. Since 1927, Texas alone has produced more mohair than the Union of South Africa, the former

that the goat-raising industry was doomed. Increased prices, new uses for mohair, and an embargo on coarse Argentine wool, have caused many to believe that the mohair industry is at the beginning of an extended period of prosperity.[14]

---

[12] J. M. Cooper, *Range Sheep Production*, U. S. Department of Agriculture, Farmers' Bulletin No. 1710. Washington, D. C.: Government Printing Office, 1940.

[13] G. P. Williams, *The Angora Goat*, U. S. Department of Agriculture, Farmers' Bulletin No. 1203. Washington, D. C.: Government Printing Office, 1946.

[14] W. M. Pritchett, "The Mohair Industry in the Southwest," *Monthly Business Review of the Federal Reserve Bank of Dallas*, Vol. 35, 1950, pp. 193-201.

Figure 11–11. A herd of Angora goats on a ranch in southwestern Texas. (Courtesy *Sheep and Goat Raiser Magazine.*)

The Mineral Industries

The Great Plains Region consists of two types of terrain: (1) hilly to mountainous areas composed of intruded masses of igneous rock, as in the Black Hills, and (2) flat to gently rolling land, underlain by sedimentary rocks. The first type produces the metallic minerals such as gold, silver, copper, lead, and zinc, while the sedimentary areas produce the non-metallic and fuel minerals, such as petroleum, natural gas, helium, coal, and potash.

Metallic Minerals. The first gold discoveries in the Black Hills (1874) were placers. The news of the strike, widely publicized in Eastern newspapers, created a gold rush. Conflicts with the Indians in the Black Hills, at the time a part of the Sioux Reservation, caused the federal government to attempt to exclude white men. Prospectors entered the Reservation, however, and before they could be ejected they had succeeded in extracting considerable placer gold. A persistent demand to open the "hills" to prospecting led to a withdrawal of military regulations. In 1877, the entire area was thrown open to white occupation. The first settlements were made around the placer deposits near Custer, but when richer strikes were uncovered at Deadwood Gulch, Custer's population of 11,000 fell to about 100. Deadwood at the same time grew from nothing to a population of 25,000. This rich placer ultimately led to the discovery of lode gold.[15]

The Homestake Mine. The original Homestake claim, made in 1876, was purchased the following year for $70,000 by George Hearst, who organized the Homestake Mining Company. This mine, the largest gold producer in the United States, has operated continuously until it was closed down by the federal government during World War II. Its production up to that time exceeded 440 million dollars. Owing to isolation, mining

---

[15] Paul T. Allsman, "Reconnaissance of Gold Mining Districts in the Black Hills," *Bureau of Mines Bulletin 427*, pp. 6-7, 12-13. Washington, D. C.: Government Printing Office, 1940.

was greatly handicapped during the first decade, but in time railroads were built into the area. In the early part of the twentieth century when the cyanide process was introduced, the Homestake Mine improved in efficiency. Deep-shaft mining prevails, operations being carried on from the 3,200- to the 5,000-foot level. In hauling ore from the stopes to the mine shafts, 73 miles of narrow-gauge railroad track and 36 compressed-air locomotives are used. In addition to its mining property at Lead, the company holds extensive water rights, owns a coal mine in Wyoming, and has large timber holdings. It is easily the major industrial establishment of the Black Hills. After the end of the war Homestake Mine was reopened. By 1949 it had forged ahead to make South Dakota again the leading gold-producing state.[16]

Numerous other mining properties have been developed in the Black Hills but in most cases they have failed after a short period of prosperity or hope. The names of some of these describe the wild and adventurous life of the early mining community: Deadbroke, Two Bit, Gilt Edge, Holy Terror, and Legal Tender. Some of these still are worked from time to time but the majority are only memories of the wild and glorious days of the gold rush.

Petroleum and Natural Gas. The Great Plains Region, because of its extensive size, and because most of it is underlain with sedimentary rocks that are potentially oil-bearing, has many producing oil fields. It includes a considerable part of the mid-continent oil province, the Permian Basin area of west Texas, the Panhandle field of Texas and Oklahoma, the old fields in Colorado, Wyoming, and Montana, the newly developed fields of the Williston Basin of North Dakota and the extensive new development in the Prairie Provinces of Canada.

Since the oil industry has been discussed in considerable detail in Chapter 7, only some of the newer developments are considered here. Three oil fields areas are described either because of their recent devel-

[16] A. J. Martin, "Gold, Silver, Copper, Lead, and Zinc," *Minerals Yearbook, 1949.* Washington, D. C.: Government Printing Office, 1950.

opment or because they possess certain unique features. These are (1) the Williston Basin, (2) the Canadian fields of Alberta and Saskatchewan, and (3) the Panhandle Field of Texas, Oklahoma, and Kansas, which includes one of the world's largest natural gas fields.

The Williston Basin is one of the most promising and exciting oil provinces of Anglo-America. The original discovery of oil in the Beaver Lodge Pool (northwestern North Dakota) occurred in April, 1951, after more than thirty years of intermittent exploratory efforts in this area. This discovery was soon followed by others. By the summer of 1952, eight producing pools were opened, seven in the United States and one in Canada, and the general outline of the basin was established (Figure 11–12). By the end of 1952 the Williston Basin included about 118,500 square miles with estimated reserves at 2.5 billion barrels to be recovered. Forecasts

Figure 11–12. A drilling rig in the Williston Basin area of western North Dakota. Note the lower part of the rig is enclosed so as to protect drillers from the severe winter climate of the Northern Great Plains. (Courtesy of *The Oil and Gas Journal.*)

place the daily production at about 200,000 barrels at the end of ten years.[17] A big problem confronting this new oil field is that of moving and refining the oil. At present the oil is moving by railroad tank car to refineries in the Minneapolis–St. Paul area, an expensive means of transportation. Refineries in the basin itself are small, and large ones are not likely to be built. The relatively sparse population of the area makes it necessary to market any large amounts of petroleum produced outside the area. Pipelines may ultimately be built from the area to the large metropolitan centers such as St. Louis and Chicago, or perhaps to the head of water transportation on Lake Superior. Suggestions also have been made to pipe this oil to the West Coast but the cost would be almost prohibitive.[18] If the Williston Basin is as great a producer as some operators believe, its transportation problems will be solved in the near future.

The Canadian Prairie Provinces' oil fields are also among the newest in Anglo-America and, like the Williston Basin, represent a potentially gigantic reserve of petroleum. The discovery well in this field blew in on a cold day in February 1947. This well was located a few miles southwest of the city of Edmonton. The section in which this well was drilled is in the heart of the Spring Wheat Belt which was dependent almost entirely upon one-crop farming. The impact of this new potential wealth on the economy of the wheat-farming area will be interesting to watch.

This new field is strategically one of the most important oil discoveries in Anglo-America, as it is located in an area largely deficient in petroleum production. Most of the exploratory work and an overwhelmingly large part of the present development has been carried on by American companies and their affiliates. Edmonton, the largest city in the area has grown rapidly since oil was discovered. Refinery needs in the area caused one Canadian oil company to dismantle a wartime refinery at Whitehorse, 1350 miles to the north, and ship it by truck and rail to Edmonton to be set up. The cost was as great as if a new refinery had been built, but its construction required much less time. Pipelines are being built eastward to the head of Lake Superior at Duluth, and westward across the Rocky Mountains to Vancouver. An interesting feature of this new oil area is that the Canadian provincial governments control most of the mineral rights on the land.[19]

The Prairie Provinces of Canada also have a surplus of natural gas, particularly in the fields of the Province of Alberta. Some seven hundred miles to the west lie the industrial cities of the Puget Sound area which have a great need for additional power that could be supplied by natural gas. The building of pipelines across the Rocky Mountains and the Cascades, although a major undertaking, does not offer any unsurmountable difficulties — in fact oil will soon be flowing through a pipe from Alberta to Vancouver, some 700 miles away. Although Alberta, one of the most prolific gas-producing areas of Anglo-America, realizes that the gas belongs to the people of that province; at the same time it desires to co-operate in exporting a surplus commodity so as to maintain a favorable balance of trade. Gas pipelines have been proposed from the Pincher Creek Field to Spokane and Seattle, and from the Peace River Area Field to Vancouver, Seattle, and Portland.[20]

The Panhandle Field is one of the older oil and gas fields of the Great Plains Region. For a long time after the original discovery well was brought in on the Texas Panhandle in 1918, only gas was of significance, and relatively little oil was produced. It was not until 1926, however, that oil in large quantities was discovered in the Pampa and Borger areas. Following those discoveries additional gas production was developed, extending the field through Oklahoma into Kansas, and

[17] Philip C. Ingalls, "Williston Basin: Today's Most Exciting Oil Producing Province," *The Oil and Gas Journal*, Vol. 51, 1952, pp. 92 ff.

[18] John C. Casper, "Moving and Refining Williston Basin's Oil," *The Oil and Gas Journal*, Vol. 51, 1952, pp. 108-114.

[19] "Canada's Oil Frontier," *Fortune*, Vol. 44, 1950, pp. 71 ff.

[20] *The New York Times*, January 25, 1953.

making it the largest natural gas producing area of the world. At first there were very limited demands for natural gas in the area and hence it was allowed to escape and was burned. However, the great quantities of cheap natural gas attracted industries. By 1930, twenty four carbon-black plants, fifty three natural-gasoline plants, and one helium plant were using the gas from this area. With an increasing number of gas wells being completed, pipelines were built to the major urban centers of the East and Midwest, thus providing ready markets for the increasing amounts of gas being produced.[21]

An impressive number of discoveries or indicated discoveries in the Anadarko Basin of Kansas, Oklahoma, and Texas, occurred in 1952, causing many geologists to think that large oil reserves may yet be discovered in the Panhandle fields.[22]

Helium. The major helium-producing area in the world is located within the Panhandle gas fields. Because of its lightness this non-combustible gas is used chiefly for inflating lighter-than-air dirigibles, and as such is of vital significance to the United States Government. By act of Congress, approved March 3, 1925, the Bureau of Mines was authorized to control all production of helium. By 1937, however, Congress directed the Bureau to regulate the sale of helium for medical, scientific, and commercial purposes. Of the four plants in the United States producing helium, three are in the Great Plains Region. In 1949, only the Excell Plant (30 miles north of Amarillo) was operating — the others being kept on a standby basis.[23] At present, excess helium produced by the Excell plant is being re-injected into the Cliffside gas field through a connecting pipeline.

Potash. The Great Plains Region in west Texas and southeastern New Mexico contains the major supply of potash salts in Anglo-America and one of the largest deposits in the world. For nearly a century the Stassfurt Mines of Germany and the deposits in Alsace dominated the world market. At the outbreak of the first World War, the United States, lacking potash, began searching desperately for a domestic source. The price jumped from $40 to $500 a ton. Large investments were made in plants to extract the mineral from certain salt lakes in Utah and California and in the western Sand Hills of Nebraska. When the war ended, however, Germany, and France (which then controlled Alsace) again dominated the world market and most American production was discontinued. Congress, however, appropriated a small sum (2 million dollars) to continue the search for potash within the United States. The western Texas deposits of polyhalite (the best known potash-producing salt) had been known since 1912, but because of the German monopoly and because of the remoteness of this deposit from the large consuming area, little development took place. Even during the emergency of the first World War, the government felt that extraction of potash from salt lakes and even from kelp (seaweed), was more satisfactory than working the Texas deposits. Later, oil prospectors discovered sylvite deposits more than 250 feet thick in Eddy County, New Mexico, at depths of from 1,200 to 1,400 feet. Sylvite is a potash-bearing mineral containing more than 60 per cent potassium-oxide. Germany's famous Stassfurt deposits consist mainly of polyhalite carrying less than 20 per cent potash. Moreover, the Germany area extends over only about 24,000 square miles, whereas that in Texas – New Mexico covers more than 70,000. While this new area should have developed rapidly into one of the world's important potash producers, such has not been the case. Although some expansion took place during World War II, it seems doubtful that the district can compete with cheap European potash in normal times. In 1951, however, production exceeded that of any previous year in the history of the industry in the United States.[24]

Coal. The Great Plains Region contains

[21] John R. Stockton and Stanley A. Arbingast, *Water Requirements Survey: Texas High Plains,* Austin: Bureau of Business Research, 1952.

[22] P. C. Ingalls, "Anadarko Area Discoveries," *Oil and Gas Journal,* Vol. 51, June 2, 1952, p. 139 ff.

[23] Stockton and Arbingast, *Water Requirements Survey: Texas High Plains,* pp. 3.19-3.20.

[24] G. T. Harley, "Potash," *Engineering and Mining Journal,* Vol. 153, No. 2, 1952, pp. 106-107.

several large fields of sub-bituminous or semi-bituminous coal and an enormous deposit of lignite. The lignite is found in the Dakotas, eastern Montana, and Saskatchewan. Despite domestic demands for fuel in that area of severe winters little is mined.

The bituminous deposits, although of low grade, are worked in several places for local use. The most important bituminous-producing areas are the Assiniboine district of Saskatchewan, the Judith Basin of Montana, the Powder River district of Wyoming, the Denver area of Colorado, and the Raton Mesa area of southern Colorado and northern New Mexico. The coal in most of these areas lies in thick seams near the surface and is strip mined, particularly in Montana and Wyoming. In the Denver field coal seams lie some distance below the surface and are therefore shaft mined. In the Raton district, the coal has been exposed on the eroded sides of the mesa and a type of drift mining, similar to that of West Virginia, is practiced.

Industries of the Great Plains

While agricultural processing industries such as flour mills and meat-packing plants have been important for many years on the Great Plains, a relatively recent industrial development has taken place in those areas where large supplies of petroleum and natural gas have been available. This is particularly true in the Panhandle of Texas, and more recently in the Prairie Provinces of Canada. These industries include (1) petrochemical plants, using oil and natural gas as the base for the manufacture of organic acids, alcohol, glycerine, butadiene, carbon-black, and many other products, (2) zinc refineries, and (3) an iron and steel mill at Pueblo. In addition, there are numerous refineries and catalytic cracking plants located throughout the area producing high-octane gasoline and lubricating oils. As the petrochemical industry has been discussed in connection with the Texas Gulf Coast industrial district (Chapter 8), it will not be considered here, but the presence of two large zinc smelters in the Panhandle area at Amarillo and at Dumas needs further com-

ment. The location of these plants was due entirely to cheap natural gas for fuel, as all ores are supplied from the zinc-mining areas in the mountains to the west in Colorado, New Mexico, and Arizona. As a by-product of zinc smelting, large quantities of sulphuric acid are produced at each of these plants. Cadmium, gold, copper, lead, and silver are other by-products produced in small quantities at these smelters. Zinc smelting contributes substantially to the economic stability of the Texas High Plains Area.[25] At Pueblo, along the western edge of the Great Plains, is located one of the oldest and largest iron and steel industries in the West. Proximity to coking coal from the Raton Mesa area of southern Colorado, and iron ore from the mountains to the west and southwest and from southern Wyoming, led to the establishment of this sizable iron and steel industry. Although ranking far below eastern steel centers in total production, and being surpassed in recent years by new mills in Utah and California, Pueblo is an important steel center.

Transportation

The Great Plains Region has served primarily as a transit land. Most of the freight and passenger traffic passes through the region enroute to the Pacific Coast or vice versa. The transportation lines of the region show a predominance of east-west railways, highways, and airways. The only important north-south traffic flows along the western edge, at the foot of the Rocky Mountains where the major population is concentrated, or in the wheat belts where a well-developed network of railroads and highways appear. On the whole the regon is sparsely settled, but the major concentrations of population are found either in the eastern parts of the wheat belts, or along the extreme western edge near the foot of the Rocky Mountains. The cities of the western margin of the Great Plains such as Pueblo, Colorado Springs, Denver, Cheyenne, and Great Falls, serve both the Great Plains and the Rocky Moun-

---

[25] Stockton and Arbingast, *Water Requirements Survey: Texas High Plains*, pp. 3.27-3.30.

tains — their industries reflecting the major economic activities of each. Although they are frequently associated with the mountains they are cities of the plains.

Resorts

The Great Plains Region with its extensive area of level to gently rolling lands and with its continental climate of hot summers and very cold winters, offers few attractions for the tourist and hence is not important as a resort region despite the fact that it is crossed by thousands of tourists each summer, seeking a vacation in the mountains to the west. Three areas within the region, however, are of significance: (1) the Black Hills, (2) the Carlsbad Caverns, and (3) the Edwards Plateau of southwestern Texas — the last becoming an important dude ranch area, particularly for the winter season.

Of these areas, the most scenic and most important is the Black Hills. With its forest-clad mountains, its attractive Sylvan Lake area, its Wind Cave National Park, and its man-made Rushmore Memorial, the Black Hills area annually attracts thousands of tourists. A recent development within the upland is pheasant hunting which is calling the sportsmen from great distances to engage in that sport.

In southeastern New Mexico, in an area where the surface of the land is unattractive, lies the world famous Carlsbad Caverns National Park, with its extensive subterranean caves. As one of the most popular tourist attractions of Anglo-America, it is visited by great numbers of people each year. The area, however, does not encourage the tourist to tarry long and in most cases it is visited for a short time by persons on their way to more attractive resort centers.

The Outlook

In the Hard Winter Wheat Belt crops frequently are burned up by hot winds, eaten by grasshoppers, or destroyed by rust. In the early 1930's many farmers watched their livelihoods blow away into the sky, went bankrupt, and had mortgages foreclosed in large numbers. Wholesale migrations occurred, and discontent was almost universal among those who remained on the land.

Perhaps this wheat area will shrink in size, the shrinkage taking place along the western and southwestern margin — the part that possibly should have been left in grass. Perhaps the area, despite its rather sparse population, is actually overpopulated, considering the character of the land. On the other hand, science and technology may triumph, ultimately turning this area of uncertain and undependable wheat production into one of dependability.

The Canadian segment of the Spring Wheat Belt has suffered from protracted drought, rust, hail, and grasshopper infestation, causing some students of the area to believe that the only solution lies in removing the farmers and allowing the country to revert to range. However, as soil, climate, and economic conditions conspire to make cereal growing the chief enterprise of this area, a mass exodus is hardly probable. A way of life will be found that will fit *with* nature rather than suffer *from* nature. In all probability farms will become larger and population thinner in the drier parts. What is needed is a new farm technique that will enable the area to absorb the effects of variable and hazardous physical conditions.

In the American segment the eastern portion of the Spring Wheat Belt (the more humid part) is being absorbed by the Agricultural Interior and dairying is displacing wheat growing as the major enterprise. Dairying appears to be more profitable and helps the farmer employ his labor to better advantage. Moreover, the United States is consuming less wheat but considerably more dairy products than formerly. The western part seems to be best suited for ranching with the major emphasis on beef cattle.

Along the southwestern margin of the Winter Wheat Belt in the Panhandle of Texas, extensive acreages have been planted in cotton and grain sorghums, using ground water from numerous shallow wells for irrigation. While this has caused rapid development of this section in recent years, it appears to be based upon a somewhat limited supply of water, and one wonders what will happen when the supply of ground water is exhausted.

When the Missouri Basin Commission is approved and placed in operation, additional land in the grazing area of the Great Plains will be irrigated. Also, the hydroelectric power that will be generated at the numerous dams proposed, will aid materially in the development of local industry. The diversified mineral wealth of the region, particularly the presence of large oil and gas fields, will further stimulate industrial growth, al-though a large part of the natural-gas supply will continue to be piped out to the older industrial districts. Over the greater part of the region, however, ranching will continue to dominate. In the former Dust Bowl and elsewhere along the eastern border, the area devoted to extensive grain farming will prob-ably shrink, much of the land reverting to pasture.

The region has been and will continue to be an important transit land, because it lies directly across the path of all transcontinental railways, highways, and airways.

Table 10

SELECTED CITIES AND TOWNS OF THE GREAT PLAINS

City or Town	Urbanized area	Political center	City or Town	Urbanized area	Political center
Aberdeen		21,051	**Lawrence		23,351
Abilene		45,570	Lawton		34,757
Amarillo	74,443	74,246	Lethbridge		22,947
Arkansas City		12,903	Lubbock		71,747
Big Spring		17,286	**Manhattan		19,056
Billings		31,834	Medicine Hat		16,364
Bismarck		18,640	Midland		21,713
Borger		18,059	Minot		22,032
*Boulder		19,999	Moorhead		14,870
Brandon		20,598	Moose Jaw		24,355
Brownwood		20,181	Norman		27,006
Calgary	139,105	129,060	North Platte		15,433
Carlsbad		17,975	Odessa		29,495
Casper		23,673	Oklahoma City	275,091	243,504
Cheyenne		31,935	Pampa		16,583
Clovis		17,318	Plainview		14,044
*Colorado Springs		45,472	Ponca City		20,180
*Denver	498,743	415,786	Portage la Prairie		8,511
Dodge City		11,262	Prince Albert		17,149
Edmonton	173,075	159,631	*Pueblo	73,247	63,685
Enid		36,017	Rapid City		25,310
Fargo		38,256	Regina		71,319
Garden City		10,905	Roswell		25,738
Grand Forks		26,836	St. Boniface		26,342
Grand Island		22,682	Salina		26,176
Great Bend		12,665	San Angelo		52,093
*Great Falls		39,214	Saskatoon		53,268
Greeley		20,354	Scottsbluff		12,858
Hastings		20,211	*Sheridan		11,500
Hobbs		13,875	Snyder		12,010
Hutchinson		33,575	Sweetwater		13,619
Kearney		12,115	*Trinidad		12,204
*Laramie		15,581	Wichita	194,047	168,279
Laredo		51,910	Winnipeg	354,069	235,710

* Near the Rocky Mountains.
** Near the Agricultural Interior.

Selected Bibliography

Alfred W. Booth, "Portales Region: A Pump Irrigation District in the Llano Estacado," *Economic Geography*, Vol. 18, 1942, pp. 97-105.

John R. Borchert, "The Climate of the Central North American Grassland," *Annals of the Association of American Geographers*, Vol. 40, 1950, pp. 1-39.

Wesley Calef, "Problems of Grazing Administration in the Basins of Southern Wyoming," *Economic Geography*, Vol. 28, 1952, pp. 122-127.

————, "The Winter of 1948-49 in the Great Plains," *Annals of the Association of American Geographers*, Vol. 40, 1950, pp. 267-292.

James L. Culbert, "Cattle Industry of New Mexico," *Economic Geography*, Vol. 17, 1941, pp. 155-168.

John O. Galloway, "Developments in Western Canada in 1950," *Bulletin of the American Association of Petroleum Geologists*, Vol. 35, 1950, pp. 1388-1403.

Herbert D. Hadley and G. Wendell Smith, "Developments in Montana, North Dakota and South Dakota in 1951," *Bulletin of the American Association of Petroleum Geologists*, Vol. 36, 1952, pp. 1014-1022.

Lynn Harrington, "Ranch Round-up," *Canadian Geographical Journal*, Vol. 41, 1950, pp. 234–239.

Leslie Hewes, "Northern Wet Prairie of the United States, Nature, Sources of Information and Extent," *Annals of the Association of American Geographers*, Vol. 41, 1951, pp. 307-323.

A. J. Hooks, "Alberta, Nature's Treasure House," *Canadian Geographical Journal*, Vol. 35, No. 4, 1947, pp. 154-177.

Charles W. Johnson, "Relative Decline of Wheat in the Prairie Provinces of Canada," *Economic Geography*, Vol. 24, 1948, pp. 209-216.

C. B. Manifold, "Geographical Record — The Great Plains Shelterbelts," *Geographical Review*, Vol. 37, 1947, pp. 319-320.

Eugene Mather, "The Production and Marketing of Wyoming Beef Cattle," *Economic Geography*, Vol. 26, 1950, pp. 81-93.

A. W. Platt, "Breeding Wheats for Sawfly Resistance," *Canadian Geographical Journal*, Vol. 33, 1946, pp. 138-141.

James E. Rowan, "Mechanization of the Sugar Beet Industry of Scottsbluff County, Nebraska," *Economic Geography*, Vol. 24, 1948, pp. 174-180.

Ralph E. Ward, "Northern Plains as a Producer of Wheat," *Economic Geography*, Vol. 22, 1946, pp. 231-244.

Jim Wright, "Co-operative Farming in Saskatchewan," *Canadian Geographical Journal*, Vol. 39, 1949, pp. 68-90.

12.

The Rocky Mountains

THE Rocky Mountain Region is an extensive upland lying between the Great Plains to the east and the Intermontane Region to the west (Figure 12–1). The general trend of the mountains, which consist of a series of linear ranges with intervening basins, is from south-southeast to north-northwest.

Origin of the Rocky Mountains

During the Cretaceous Period most of the area of the Rocky Mountain Region as well as that of the Great Plains was covered by a shallow sea that extended from the Gulf of Mexico to the Arctic Ocean.[1] At the close of that period the Rocky Mountain Area was uplifted and the waters drained off. Sediments with a thickness of perhaps 20,000 feet were involved in this first great uplift.

A long period of erosion followed this early uplift during which time much material was removed from the summits and deposited in the basins. Later (Tertiary Period), the Rocky Mountains were subjected to another period of growth, accompanied by considerable volcanic activity, and followed by still another period of leveling. The region's master streams, flowing over sediments that had buried the mountain ranges, established courses which they con-

tinued to hold after they had cut into older rocks forming the major gorges and canyons through the front ranges. Mountain glaciation followed, which further deepened the valleys and greatly eroded the peaks. Glaciation was more extensive in the Northern Rockies and still is active there. In the Southern Rockies it was not so extensive and only a few small remnants of glaciers exist today.

The Rocky Mountains may be subdivided into four sections: (1) the Southern Rockies, (2) the Middle Rockies, (3) the Northern Rockies, and (4) the Basins and Parks. The Southern and Middle Rocky Mountains appear quite different from the Northern Rockies, which begin north of Yellowstone National Park and continue into Canada. The ranges of the Southern and Middle Rockies are for the most part linear features with their granitic cores generally flanked by steeply dipping strata forming hogback foothills such as the Flatirons of the Boulder area in northern Colorado. In contrast, the Northern Rocky Mountains, composed mainly of sedimentary rocks, are not so linear, but appear more like lofty plateaus that have been severely carved into majestic alpine peaks and deep U-shaped valleys by valley glaciers (Figure 12–2).[2] The basins

[1] Wallace W. Atwood, *The Physiographic Provinces of North America,* pp. 294-328. Boston: Ginn & Co., 1940.

[2] Nevin M. Fenneman, *Physiography of Western United States,* pp. 92-93. New York: McGraw-Hill Book Co., 1931.

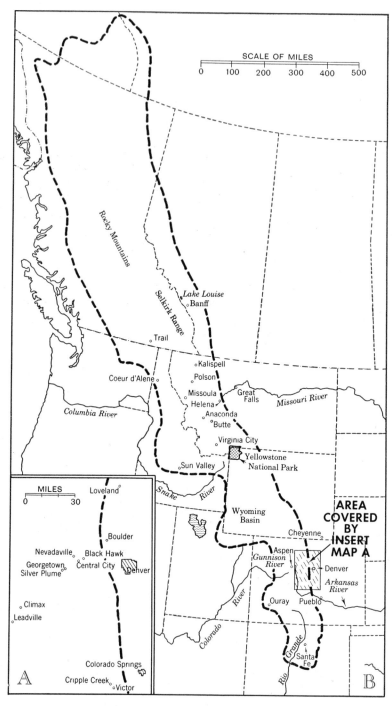

Figure 12–1. The Rocky Mountains: a region of mining, grazing, farming, logging, and resorts.

Figure 12–2. The glaciated Canadian Rockies — Maligne Lake in Jasper National Park.
(Courtesy of the Canadian Government Travel Bureau.)

vary in size from extensive areas such as the Wyoming Basin to small areas such as South Park.

Climate, Natural Vegetation, and Soils

Altitude modifies temperature and rainfall to a great extent in this region. The Southern and Middle Rocky Mountains have sufficient precipitation to support dense forests of pine and other conifers, whereas the adjacent plains have a short grass or desert vegetation. The basins of this region are usually covered with grass making them suitable for ranching. The timber line decreases in altitude from 12,000 feet in southern New Mexico to 11,000 feet in northern Wyoming. In the Northern Rocky Mountains the contrast in vegetation between the lowland and the upland is not so sharp. In these more northerly latitudes timber appears also on the plains and floors of intermontane basins. The timber line in the Northern Rocky Mountains decreases from 10,600 feet in Montana to the level of the adjacent plains in northern Canada.

Because of the great contrast in altitudes and its wide latitudinal extent, this region presents a range of plant associations varying from the Sonoran to the Tundra. The various plant zones that may be seen in any part of the mountains are well shown in the Rocky Mountain National Park in northern Colorado. The valleys or basins (Estes Park) are covered with short grass. As one ascends the lower slopes into the mountains, large western yellow (ponderosa) pines appear. At higher altitude are found the smaller Engelmann spruce, lodgepole pine, and limber pine. Still higher is a transitional area between the forest and alpine meadows — the timber line (Figure 12–3), which has been described as follows:

Figure 12–3. Gnarled and twisted trees near the timberline on the slopes of Mt. Evans in Colorado. (Photographed by D. L. Hopwood, courtesy of the State of Colorado.)

In the struggle for existence in the vegetable world, the tree line pushes as far up the mountain as conditions of climate and soil will permit. Then comes a season of fiercer storms, intenser cold and invading ice upon the peaks. Havoc is wrought, and the forest drops back across a zone of border warfare — for war belongs to borders — leaving behind it here and there a dwarfed pine or gnarled and twisted juniper which has survived the onslaught of the enemy. Now these are the stragglers in the retreat, but are destined later in milder years to serve as outposts in the advance of the forest to recover its lost ground. Here we have a border scene which is typical in nature — the belt of unbroken forests, growing thinner and more stunted toward its upper edge, succeeded by a zone of scattered trees, which may form a cluster perhaps in some sheltered gulch where soil has collected and north winds are excluded, and higher still the whitened skeleton of a tree to show how far the forest once invaded the domain of the waste.[3]

Above timber line lies the alpine meadow and tundra, surmounted by bare rocky peaks.

The forests not only retard the runoff on watersheds and provide raw material for lumbering in the more accessible sections, but they also help to sustain the resort industry.

Because of steep slopes and excessive erosion, only the basins and valley bottoms within the Rocky Mountain Region have mature soils. Despite the lack of true soils, however, the alluvium in most basins is comparatively fertile and becomes quite productive

[3] Ellen C. Semple, *The Influences of Geographic Environment*, p. 206. New York: Henry Holt & Co., 1911.

when water is available either through natural rainfall or through irrigation. The lower mountain slopes, although rocky and almost devoid of soil, usually support a fair stand of timber.

Boundaries

The eastern boundary is marked by the break between the Great Plains and the Rocky Mountains (Figure 12–1). From central New Mexico to northern Alberta the mountains rise abruptly from the plains, except in central Wyoming where the Wyoming Basin merges almost imperceptibly into the Great Plains. The western boundary, which marks the transition from the Rocky Mountain Region to the Intermontane Basins and Plateaus Region, is fairly definite in the southern and middle sections, but becomes somewhat vague in the Northern Rockies, where it merges with the Cascade Mountains in the complex Selkirk Range. The western boundary of this region in the Canadian section extends to the edge of the Coast Range and includes the Interior Plateau of British Columbia.

Early Exploration and Settlement

Except in the southern part of the region which was settled by the Spaniards in the sixteenth century, the first white men to see the Rocky Mountains were the French fur traders. They were followed in a short time by several military exploration parties sent out by the United States Government, such as the expeditions of Lewis and Clark in the Northern Rockies in 1803–1804, Lieutenant Zebulon M. Pike in 1806–1807, and Major Stephen H. Long in 1820 in the Southern Rockies. Meanwhile, fur trapping became important throughout the Southern and Middle Rockies, particularly in the area of the Tetons in western Wyoming. This colorful period, however, did not last long as the value of beaver fur declined in the 1840's, following changes in the style of men's hats. From that time until the discovery of gold in the late 1850's, the Rocky Mountains served only as a barrier to the westward movement — pioneers pushing through the lowest mountain passes as rapidly as possible on their way to the Oregon Territory or to California.

The discovery of gold at Sutters Fort in the newly acquired California Territory created a mad rush of gold seekers coming from all parts of the world. Although many prospectors went by ship from New York to San Francisco by way of Cape Horn, or by ship and caravan by way of Panama or Nicaragua, the majority braved the natural hardships and Indian dangers in the overland crossing of the continent. In crossing the Rocky Mountains some of them prospected for gold in the stream gravels and found traces of the precious metal. Although most gold seekers went on to California, many returned within a few years to prospect further in the numerous mountain gulches.

It was not until 1859, however, that gold in paying quantities was found in the Rocky Mountains. John Gregory's discovery of gold near Central City, Colorado, led to extensive explorations and many important gold discoveries throughout the region. Within the next two or three decades more people settled in the mountain country than in all its previous history. Practically every part of the Southern Rockies was prospected and many valuable mineral deposits were discovered. Boom towns sprang up in remote valleys and gulches of the high country and this in turn led to the development of a series of narrow-gauge railroads built at great expense per mile for the purpose of hauling out gold ore. As the higher-grade ores were exhausted production declined in these camps and in time most of them became ghost towns.[4]

Lumbering and logging, grazing activities, irrigation agriculture, and the tourist trade have brought additional population to the mountains, but none has been so significant in peopling the region, and bringing its advantages to the attention of the rest of the country, as gold mining.

---

[4] Muriel Sibell Wolle, *Stampede to Timberline: The Ghost Towns and Mining Camps of Colorado.* Boulder, Colorado: 1949.

The Mining Industry

The history of Central City, Colorado, il- lustrates the early mining activity character- istic of the mountain region. Central City sprang up in a rich mineralized zone that a "Forty-niner" discovered on his return to this region in 1859. Within a few months thousands of gold prospectors had come to the area. Almost overnight they also built the mining towns of Black Hawk and Neva- daville, but these did not reach the import- ance of Central City, which in the early 1870's was the largest urban center in the Rocky Mountain Region. Its growth and prosperity continued for a decade or two, but toward the close of the century the de- cline began. Little by little holdings were abandoned and the miners moved on to more productive areas. Nevadaville became a "ghost town," but Black Hawk and Central City retained a few inhabitants. Central City's famous Opera House, said to have been the West's finest show-house in the 1870's, has recently been reopened as a summer theater by the University of Denver. The attempt to revive the town is interesting, but the thriving metropolis of the gold-min- ing days can never return, even though the increase in the price of gold recently stimu- lated mining activities to a limited extent.

Wherever rich mineralized zones were found, mining camps developed. Colorado was especially important with its Central City, Ouray, Cripple Creek, Victor, Lead- ville, Aspen, Georgetown, and Silver Plume. Wyoming and New Mexico were relatively unimportant, but the southern part of the Northern Rocky Mountains produced im- portant minerals around Virginia City in southwestern Montana, in the vicinity of Butte and Anaconda, in the Coeur d'Alene area of northern Idaho, and at Trail in British Columbia. While gold was the min- eral chiefly sought, valuable deposits of sil- ver, lead, copper, tungsten, and molybdenum have been found.

Mining Today. In a region so complex as the Rocky Mountains, with its many min- eralized areas, a discussion of all districts is impossible in this volume. Therefore only five leading districts are selected: (1) Lead- ville, Colorado — a gold, silver, lead, zinc, and molybdenum district; (2) Cripple Creek, Colorado — a gold mining area; (3) Butte, Montana — copper, silver, lead, and zinc; (4) Coeur d'Alene, Idaho — gold, silver, lead, and zinc; and (5) Trail, British Columbia — lead and zinc.

The Leadville District. One of the oldest and most important mining areas of the en- tire Rocky Mountain Region, is located at Leadville in a high mountain valley near the headwaters of the Arkansas River at an ele- vation above 10,000 feet. Following the dis- covery of gold in the Central City area, pros- pectors searched the numerous mountain valleys of practically all highland Colorado. In the spring of 1860 placer gold was found in California Gulch near Leadville. News of the discovery immediately spread and by July of that year more than 10,000 people were in the camp. The first gold vein was dis- covered in 1868, and soon after that the first stamp mill was put into operation.[5]

In 1874 silver-lead mining began and gold soon ceased to be the dominant metal. With waning gold production most of the 10,000 miners departed and Oro City (Leadville), the original settlement, was practically de- serted. At that time the site of the present city of Leadville was an unbroken wilder- ness, the existence of the rich silver-lead and zinc ores there being unsuspected. The rich discovery at Fryer Hill led to the rapid de- velopment of the district. The first shipment of lead carbonate went out from the region in 1875, by wagon to Colorado Springs, and thence by rail to St. Louis. Within the next five years ten million ounces of silver and 66 million pounds of lead were produced with a total value of nearly 15 million dol- lars. Following this the real mining boom began. Railroads were completed into the city in 1880 and 1887. The decline in the price of silver in the early 1890's from $1.17 an ounce to 61 cents curtailed production,

[5] Charles W. Henderson, "Production, History, and Mine Development," *Geology and Ore Deposits of Leadville Mining District, Colorado, United States Geological Survey Professional Paper 148*, pp. 109- 137. Washington, D. C.: Government Printing Of- fice, 1927.

but silver-lead mining was revived somewhat after the Panic of 1893.

Copper production began in the 1880's but never became very important. Zinc, although discovered in 1885, was unimportant until after the close of the nineteenth century. In 1902 the zinc output exceeded that of lead and in 1903 that of silver.

In 1877 Leadville had a population of 200 persons, the business houses of the town consisting of a grocery store and two saloons. Within two years it had an estimated population of 15,000 and an assessed property valuation of 30 million dollars. In 1880 the city had 14 smelters and 30 producing mines. Since then its population has fluctuated, as shown by the following census figures:

1890	10,384
1900	12,455
1910	7,508
1920	4,959
1930	3,771
1940	4,774
1950	4,078

Leadville continues to be an important mining district, producing all of its former metals and adding molybdenum from the rich ores of the Fremont Pass area. In 1949, Lake County (Leadville) did not lead in a single mineral except molybdenum, although it ranked second among Colorado counties in the production of lead and third in the production of zinc. Most mines in the Leadville District were operated continuously in 1949, and the Arkansas Valley smelter of the American Smelting & Refining Company processed large quantities of lead, lead-copper-gold-silver, and gold-silver ores. In 1950 the Department of the Interior appropriated $500,000 for opening a tunnel to drain some of the older mines in the area.[6] The great development in recent years of the Climax Molybdenum Company at Fremont Pass, 13 miles north of Leadville, deserves special consideration.

Molybdenum became important in recent years only after it was discovered that the metal imparts the properties of toughness and fatigue strength when used with certain iron and steel alloys for machine-tools and for automobile and airplane motors. As a result there was a concentrated effort by various manufacturing companies to find workable deposits of molybdenum. The Climax Mine is at an altitude of more than 11,000 feet. Because of the difficulties of working at that level the mining company built a model town in the hope that more comfortable living conditions might induce the miners to stay longer on the job (Figure 12–4). Unlike most mining boom-towns, Climax was established by a single producing company that owned all the land and constructed all the buildings. Instead of typical miners' shacks, well-built residences house the miners. The company also has a large hotel, school, gymnasium, and recreation hall for its workers and their families.

The company is the world's largest producer, accounting for more than 70 per cent of the molybdenum shipped from mines in the United States between 1914 and 1948.[7] The rearmament program of the second World War has caused the United States to make huge demands on the mine.

The known reserves at Climax are estimated to be at least 95 per cent of all known deposits in the world, and are valued at close to one billion dollars.

Before 1948 the Climax deposit was exploited only for molybdenum, but since that date the recovery of tungsten, pyrite, and tin as by-products has been inaugurated.[8]

The Cripple Creek District. Gold in paying quantities was discovered in the Cripple Creek District of the Front Range of the Southern Rockies in 1892, and for several decades that area produced fabulous amounts of the precious metal. The mining area developed rapidly and numerous towns including Victor and Cripple Creek were established. In 1894 the mining district was

[6] A. J. Martin, "Colorado: Gold, Silver, Copper, Lead, and Zinc," *Minerals Yearbook, 1949*, p. 1436. Washington, D. C.: Government Printing Office.

[7] Hubert W. Davis, "Molybdenum," *Minerals Yearbook, 1948*, pp. 818-819, Washington, D. C.: Government Printing Office.

[8] Hubert W. Davis, "Molybdenum," *Minerals Yearbook, 1949*, p. 787, Washington, D. C.: Government Printing Office.

connected by railroad to Colorado Springs via Divide on the Colorado Midland Railroad. In 1901 the scenic Cripple Creek Short Line was completed which provided a second railroad for shipping gold ore from the mining district to Colorado Springs. In 1905 the Golden Cycle Mill was built in Colorado

Area with only the longer railroad outlet via the town of Divide (Figure 12–5). This, along with highways that had been built into the mining camps, continued to serve the area. All gold mining was suspended during World War II (gold being a nonessential metal for the prosecution of the War) but production

Figure 12–4. Climax, Colorado, a company-owned town, located at an elevation of more than 11,000 feet above sea level. In the mountains in the background is the world's largest known deposit of the ferro-alloy molybdenum. (Courtesy of the State of Colorado, Advertising & Publicity Department.)

Springs to treat Cripple Creek ore. The smelter was located on the plains some fifty miles from the ore-producing areas because large quantities of coal and other heavy materials were needed in the smelting process, and it was more economical to move gold ore down-grade to the smelter than to haul these heavy materials up to the mining areas. For a long time both railroads carried large quantities of ore, reaching peak production in 1914. Following the decline in gold mining during World War I, the Cripple Creek Short Line Railroad was abandoned and dismantled, leaving the Cripple Creek-Victor

was started in 1946 and heavy ore-trains again rumbled down the long grade to the smelter in Colorado Springs.

By that time, however, revolutionary changes in the process of treating gold ore eliminated the need for large quantities of coal and other heavy materials. The increased production of ore in tailings around the old mines of Victor and Cripple Creek, together with discoveries of new ore veins, led to the closing and dismantling of the Golden Cycle Mill at Colorado Springs and the building of the new Carlton Mill at a site halfway between Victor and Cripple

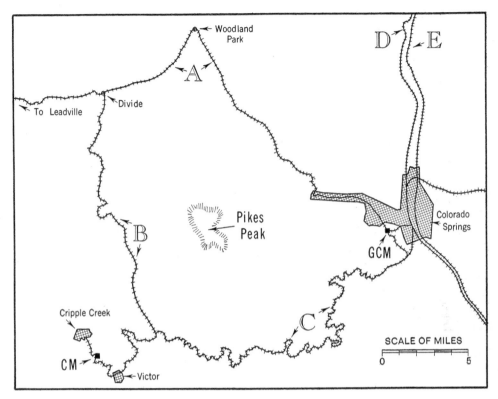

Figure 12–5. The Cripple Creek gold-mining district of Colorado. The railroads shown are: (A) the Colorado Midland, (B) the branch of the Colorado Midland built in 1894 to connect Cripple Creek with Divide, (C) the Cripple Creek Short Line, built in 1901 to haul ore directly to the Golden Cycle Mill (GCM on map); (D) the Denver and Rio Grande; and (E) the Santa Fe. When the new Carlton Mill (CM on map) was completed, the Golden Cycle Mill was destroyed, and all railroad connections between Cripple Creek and Colorado Springs were abandoned.

Creek.[9] Meanwhile, the Colorado Midland Railroad was abandoned and dismantled, leaving the Cripple Creek District without rail connections.

Today the district is an active mining area but without the colorful prospectors who frequented the mountain gulches of the early mining days. Gold mining is now a scientific and systematic industry. The new mill handles some 600 tons of ore each day in an economical manner and the waste materials are left in the mountain area with only the gold bullion being shipped out of the area. The Cripple Creek District should remain a

[9] A. J. Martin, "Colorado: Gold, Silver, Copper, Lead, and Zinc," *Minerals Yearbook, 1948,* p. 1468. Washington, D. C.: Government Printing Office.

profitable gold-mining area for many years.

The Butte-Anaconda District, Montana. In western Montana is located a copper-mining district that was surpassed in 1940 (national production) only by Bingham, Utah. The Anaconda Copper Company, which owns the mining properties at Butte and the large smelter at Anaconda, dominates the Montana copper production and also produces most of its silver, gold, lead, and zinc.

The large hill upon which Butte is built is honeycombed with mine tunnels that have produced more than two billion dollars worth of metal within the more than 80 years of operation, giving it the name "The Richest Hill on Earth." For a long time the smelter was located at Butte, but injurious fumes from its stacks destroyed so much vegetation in the city that it was removed to Anaconda, 23 miles to the west. The Anaconda smelter (Figure 12–6), famous for having the world's tallest smokestack (585 feet), throws the fumes high into the air. Since the smelter's removal from Butte, the city has had some success in growing trees and grass.

Mining at Anaconda Hill in Butte goes on 24 hours a day. Electricity is used in all operations including the hauling from stopes to mine shafts. The ore brought to the surface is transported to the Anaconda smelter where it is converted into blister copper. In 1949 the mines at Butte shipped two and one-half million tons of ore to the smelter, of which 47 per cent was copper ore, 46 per cent lead and zinc ores, and 6 per cent gold and silver ores. The 12,320-ton copper concentrator and the 2,000-ton zinc concentrator at Anaconda, as well as the copper smelter and two electrolytic-zinc plants at Anaconda and Great Falls, operated throughout 1949. During that year the lead smelter at East Helena treated lead-silver concentrates from Idaho, residues from the two electrolytic-zinc plants, and crude ores and old tailings from small mines in various districts in Montana.[10]

Figure 12–6. A battery of eight large rod mills at the Anaconda Reduction Works in Anaconda, Montana. These turbine-shaped mills grind low-grade copper ore mined by block-caving methods at the company's mine at Butte. (Courtesy of Anaconda Copper Mining Company.)

The Coeur d'Alene District. This mining area, one of the richest of the Northern Rocky Mountains, lies in northern Idaho. In 1940 it produced 89 per cent of the state's silver and more than 89 per cent of its zinc. It also is an important producer of lead, accounting for nearly one fourth of the nation's output. Since Coeur d'Alene became active in 1884, minerals to the value of almost 900 million dollars have been extracted.

The lead, silver, and zinc ores of the Coeur d'Alene District are so complex that effective recovery has been difficult. The gravity process used before 1922 was extremely wasteful because of the almost identical weights of lead and zinc. In 1922 the selective-flotation process was introduced, which made possible the extraction of the metals through their varying affinities to oils and chemicals after the ores had been ground to a fine powder. The concentrates are smelted either in the district or in the Pacific Northwest.

Because of its relative isolation, the Coeur d'Alene District has had difficulty in competing with the Ozark lead and zinc areas. Recent industrial expansion on the Pacific Coast, however, is providing an increasing outlet.

The Pine Creek area, lying to the east of the city of Coeur d'Alene, is one of the oldest mining areas of northern Idaho. Difficulties of access, however, and the complexity of the ores made development of the area practically impossible. In recent years, however, new techniques have been perfected to separate economically the complex ores, and a network of modern roads has been built to the various mines making them accessible to the large zinc-reduction plant and smelter at Kellogg only a few miles away. Today, Pine Creek is the largest zinc-producing area of the Coeur d'Alene District. It also produces large quantities of lead concentrates.[11]

[10] C. E. Needham and Paul Luff, "Montana: Gold, Silver, Copper, Lead, and Zinc," *Minerals Yearbook, 1949,* pp. 1505-1506. Washington, D. C.: Government Printing Office.

[11] J. C. Keiffer, "Pine Creek, Where Small Mines Are Becoming Major Producers," *Engineering and Mining Journal,* Vol. 152, June 1951, pp. 90-93.

The Trail District. North of the international boundary at Trail, British Columbia, lies an important lead- and zinc-mining district. The treatment of its ores was responsible for a critical international problem, because the sulphur fumes were formerly blown down the narrow Columbia Gorge into United States territory. Fumes from the Trail Smelter, drifting into the State of Washington damaged vegetation in the area. The sulphur content of the fumes also added to the acidity of the soils and restricted the range of crops that could be grown on portions of the Columbia Plateau. Furthermore, the dead foliage increased the fire hazard. The International Joint Commission rendered a verdict in favor of the state of Washington, allowed an indemnity of $350,000, and forced the smelter to reduce the sulphur content of the fumes.

The completion of the Canadian Pacific Railway in 1885, through the southern part of British Columbia created an interest in metallic mining other than gold. Numerous small smelters were built but most of them were abandoned. The one at Trail, however, was acquired by the Consolidated Mining and Smelting Company of Canada in 1906, and since then has been enlarged numerous times so that it is now one of the greatest non-ferrous metallurgical works in the world (Figure 12–7).[12]

Most of the lead and zinc mined in British Columbia comes from the great Sullivan Mine at Kimberly. That province accounts for 97 per cent of the lead and 58 per cent of the zinc production of Canada.

Although the mining industry has been declining throughout the Rocky Mountain Region for several decades, some people think that many valuable deposits are yet to be discovered. However, if new discoveries are made, it seems unlikely that new boom towns will evolve. Discoveries in the future can be made only on properties already privately owned, or on government lands without mineral rights to the individual. The

[12] John F. Walker, "Mining Developments in British Columbia," *Canadian Geographical Journal,* Vol. 45, 1952, p. 124.

Figure 12–7. The Consolidated Mining and Smelting Company's plant at Trail, British Columbia, is one of the greatest non-ferrous metallurgical works in the world. (Courtesy of Canadian Pacific Railway.)

cost of working minerals with modern mining methods also precludes the possibility that the individual prospector may acquire great wealth through methods used in the last decades of the 19th century. The ghost town (Figure 12–8), the abandoned mine shaft, and the dilapidated miner's hut located far in the mountain fastness provide mute romantic reminders of a picturesque phase in the occupance of the Rocky Mountain Region.

Forestry

The lumber industry never has been as important in this region as in the Upper Lakes Area, the South, or the Pacific Northwest, but logging has occupied the time of man in a number of places. Probably the best developed lumber camps are in the Northern Rockies where large trees occupy the lower slopes and are easily accessible. Owing to the steady demand for mine timbers and railroad ties from the great mining developments in the Butte and Coeur d'Alene Districts, northern Montana and Idaho have carried on a profitable lumber business for some years. Most of the large mills are located in the towns of Missoula, Polson, and Kalispell. Only about one fourth of the merchantable stand is privately owned, the bulk being in the national forests. This

Figure 12–8. A typical ghost town in the Colorado Rockies. Ashcroft, near Aspen, was a thriving settlement during the boom mining days. (Photograph by D. L. Hopwood, courtesy of the State of Colorado.)

section is traversed by three transcontinental railroads that provide a large market for cross-ties.

Throughout the Rocky Mountain Region most of the timber cut was used for mine props and for dwellings — frame houses in the mining camps and log cabins in the more remote areas. As a result of the limited market, large areas are still covered with virgin timber. Since most of the land never was occupied or claimed by individuals, it remained in the hands of the federal government, which made it comparatively easy to establish national forests (Figure 12–9). Today there are more square miles of national forests in the Rocky Mountain Region than in any area of equal size on the North American continent. Nearly one sixth of the total area of Colorado, or approximately 10 million acres, lies within the boundaries of the various national forests.[13]

The establishment of national forests has done much to preserve the natural beauty of the region as well as to protect the trees from reckless logging and destructive fires. Despite government vigilance, fires frequently burn over considerable areas before they can be checked. In many places throughout the region one can see the charred remains of a former great forest. While many fires are started by lightning and hence are unpreventable, far too many are due to sparks from trains and sawmills, incendiarists, careless campers, and cigarette smokers. If the summer visitor would observe the rules of the Forest Service in regard to fire protection both inside and outside the national forests, damage would be materially reduced.

Agriculture and Stock Raising

In any consideration of Rocky Mountain agriculture and ranching, it must be remembered that the region consists mostly of forested or bare rocky slopes. The occasional level areas are utilized for irrigation, dry farming, or ranching, and thus attain an

[13] Tom L. McKnight, "Recreational Use of the National Forests of Colorado," *The Southwestern Social Science Quarterly*, Vol. 32, 1951, pp. 264-270.

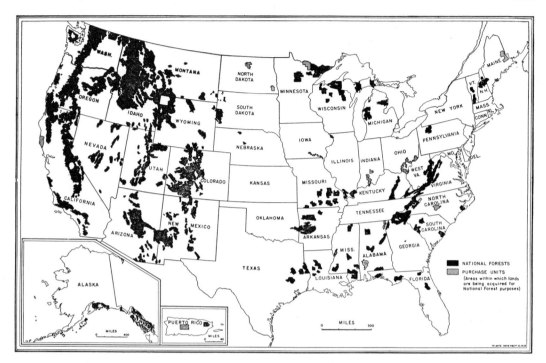

Figure 12–9. National forests of the United States. Note the large number of national forests in the West. (Courtesy of U. S. Forest Service.)

importance out of all proportion to their size.

When the Spaniards settled in the Santa Fe area of the Southern Rockies at the beginning of the seventeenth century, they were primarily prospecting for gold and silver. Finding little mineral wealth, they soon turned to ranching in the broad basins in the upper Rio Grande Valley. They received large land grants in the San Luis Valley from Spain and for the next two centuries the area was dominated by "cattle barons." After the close of the Mexican War and the annexation of this territory by the United States, the large land holdings were broken up. Because of semi-aridity, ranching has remained the dominant occupation of the San Luis Valley although considerable acreages are irrigated. Most crops, however, are supplemental to ranching, native grasses and alfalfa being dominant. Because of the high altitude (above 7,000 feet) and the resulting short growing season, corn cannot be grown successfully. This was a great disappointment to settlers

from the Corn Belt. In the absence of corn, wheat and potatoes became the chief crops. Though profitable at first, wheat yields have declined and potatoes now constitute the main cash crop. Sorting and bagging are done by migratory Mexicans who leave when the harvest has ended.

Ranching began much later in the valleys and basins to the north, as most of this land remained unexplored and unoccupied by white men until trappers and prospectors entered the mountains. In time each grassy plot in the Middle and Northern Rockies was homesteaded and turned into a ranch. Many areas, however, have been given over to dry farming or to irrigation agriculture. As is the case elsewhere, the best lands were the first to be cultivated and the poorest and most inaccessible remained in pasture. In the Northern Rockies and in the higher mountain valleys where frosts are common even during summer, ranching has remained the major activity because it is the best adaptation to the environment. On most ranches both cattle and sheep are raised. In many places sheep have become more important as they are better adapted to the short grasses and can graze the higher slopes in summer. The government through its permit system cooperates with ranchmen, allowing them to pasture sheep and cattle within the national forests, but it is careful to see that the land is neither overstocked nor overgrazed. This *transhumance* — the driving of grazing animals to high mountain pastures in summer and back to lower valleys in winter — is almost universal throughout the Rocky Mountain Region.

The ranching industry received a great stimulus through the development of the "dude ranch." Dude ranches, neither summer hotels nor farms, are usually located in scenic areas containing mountains, lakes, and streams. They appeal to a summer clientele from the East who enjoy riding, hiking, fishing, hunting, and "roughing it" in the great open spaces of the West (Figure 12–10). The visitors are respectfully called "dudes," the ranch owner a "dude wrangler," and his cowhands and business associates the "outfit." The Jackson Hole country of western Wyoming is especially noted for its many excellent dude ranches.

Some ranches which do not cater to tourists profit by renting saddle horses to summer visitors at nearby lodges or hotels.

Irrigation Agriculture. The establishment of mining towns throughout the Rocky

Figure 12–10. A "Dude Ranch" in the Colorado Rockies. (Courtesy of Union Pacific Railroad.)

Mountain Region which were isolated from the agricultural areas to the east, made it profitable to withdraw some of the more favored valleys and basins from pastures and plant them in wheat and other staple crops. High prices and a great demand also stimulated the production of vegetables by irrigation. Wherever water could be diverted for irrigation, additional land was placed under cultivation. At first all irrigation projects were either privately developed or under state supervision, but ultimately the United States Bureau of Reclamation established several projects within the region. One of the most interesting of these is the Uncompahgre Project in southwestern Colorado. Surplus waters from the Gunnison River along which there is little land suited to irrigation, were diverted through a mountain range via a six-mile tunnel to the broad flat semiarid valley of the Uncompahgre River, thus making it irrigable. A more recent development of this type is the Colorado-Big Thompson Project which diverts, by means of a 13-mile tunnel, the surplus waters of the Grand River on the west slopes of the continental divide to the Big Thompson River on the east slope. Most of this water will be used to irrigate additional lands on the Great Plains east of the Front Range (Chapter 11).

Great sums of money have been invested by the federal and state governments and by private concerns in the development of irrigation projects throughout the Rocky Mountain Region, but with the climatic handicap of a short growing season, it is doubtful whether some of the money has been wisely spent. In many cases these irrigated mountain farms are producing at greater cost the same crops as the Middle West with which their surplus must compete. In the Northern Rockies, little agriculture has been developed because of the short growing season; ranching and mining are the major activities of the occupied mountain valleys.

The Resort Industry

In new countries such as the United States and Canada people tend to become so materialistic that all other phases of life are neglected. Toward the close of the last century and during the first two decades of the present one, many great industries developed, large fortunes accumulated, and people worked at a feverish rate to acquire additional economic goods. Americans were accused by the older European civilizations of being "money mad"; their entire existence seemed to be aimed at making money and accumulating wealth. Then came the financial crash of 1929. Many large fortunes were swept away overnight; lesser fortunes and small family "nesteggs" were lost in the economic chaos that followed. People who had worked and saved all their lives, denying themselves minor luxuries including some leisure for play, saw their financial "air castles" crumble. As a result, out of the depression of the 1930's came a new people — a people determined to play as well as to work.

A recent survey has defined a tourist as "a vagabond with money to spend," and the type of industry which vacation travel supports is referred to as *tourism*.[14] Throughout the Rocky Mountain Region, many communities derive their chief income from the tourist's money. Where tourism is confined to the summer season, as in most mountain areas, the resort business is concentrated into a relatively brief period. During the long winter season most resort centers are practically deserted except for the relatively few permanent residents. An illustration of this may be found in the resort town of Estes Park at the eastern gateway to Rocky Mountain National Park in Colorado. The permanent population of the settlement in 1950 was only 1,594 but each summer this small town with its many hotels, cabins, trailer camps, and other types of accommodation in the immediate tributary area supports a population of more than fifty thousand. The annual number of tourists passing through the entrance of the National Park has exceeded one million for the past several years which represents a heavy summer concentration since Trail Ridge Road across the mountains is closed to traffic because of snows for eight months each year.[15]

Winter Sports. An ever-increasing number of winter-sports enthusiasts are being attracted to the Rocky Mountains during the period of heavy snows, but with the exception of a few famous resort centers most of the winter-sports areas serve only nearby urban communities. The relative remoteness of the Rocky Mountain Region prohibits it from becoming outstanding for winter sports in the sense of the Adirondack Mountains of New York or the Sierra Nevada of California. Sun Valley (Figure 12–11) in the Sawtooth Range of the Rockies in central Idaho, is perhaps the most famous and most glamorous "ski spot" in the western part of the United States. Its heavy snows and long, partly timber-free slopes attract both the expert and the novice. The Union Pacific Railroad, which developed the resort, provides excellent train services and hotel accommodations for the winter guests, and keeps the name "Sun Valley" before the public through its advertising literature. As a result, Sun Valley has become the "style center of the ski-fashion world, where celebrities are to be found along with spectacular scenery."[16]

The Rocky Mountain Region with its high rugged mountains, spectacular scenery, extensive forests, and cool summer temperatures, provides the natural setting for resorts. The location of the region between the Great Plains on the east and the Intermontane and Pacific Coastal areas on the west, places it directly across lines of travel. With the building of transcontinental railroads, most of the Rockies have been made reasonably accessible.

The development of specific resort centers depended upon accessibility; thus the first resorts were those sponsored by the railroads. Others were developed after highways were built through the region. Only where some unusual natural or scenic feature presented

[14] Clifford M. Zierer, "Tourism and Recreation in the West," *Geographical Review*, Vol. 42, 1952, pp. 462-481.

[15] Edwin J. Foscue and Louis O. Quam, *Estes Park: Resort in the Rockies.* Dallas: Southern Methodist University Press, 1949.

[16] Zierer, "Tourism and Recreation in the West," p. 469.

itself were resort hotels and lodges built in remote areas.

Space does not permit a description of even the major resorts of the Rocky Mountain Region. New Mexico in recent years has developed many interesting areas for summer travel and is rapidly improving its mountain highways. Colorado, for years a leading resort state, has an excellent highway system, and Wyoming, Idaho, and Montana are

turesque peaks, glacial valleys, and canyons of the region, as well as extensive forested tracts which provide protection for numerous native wild animals. This park, one of the most accessible in the country, may be reached by excellent highways from Denver, Boulder, or Loveland on the east, or from Grand Lake on the west. The Trail Ridge Road that traverses the park, connecting Estes Park with Grand Lake, crosses the

Figure 12–11. Sun Valley, Idaho, in winter. This is one of the most famous winter-sports resorts in Anglo-America. (Courtesy of Union Pacific Railroad.)

rapidly making their resort areas more accessible. The same holds true to some extent for the Canadian Rockies in Alberta and British Columbia, although much of this territory still is accessible only by railroad. The establishment of national parks in the region by the United States and Canadian governments has greatly stimulated the resort industry (Figure 12–12).

Rocky Mountain National Park. Following many years of agitation by the people of Colorado for the establishment of a national park in the northern part of the state to preserve the scenic beauty of that section of the continental divide, a rugged area of 400 square miles was set aside by Congress in 1915 as Rocky Mountain National Park. It includes some of the highest and most pic-

continental divide at an elevation of 12,185 feet above sea level.

Grand Teton National Park. In northwestern Wyoming, one of the first parts of the Rocky Mountain Region to be explored by fur trappers during the early nineteenth century, is, nevertheless, one of the youngest national parks, the Grand Teton, established in 1929. It contains only 150 square miles of territory, but within that area is found some of the most magnificent glacial scenery in North America. Grand Teton (13,766 feet above sea level), the dominant peak of the range, is 7,000 feet above the surface of Jenny Lake in the Jackson Hole area.

Yellowstone National Park. This is the oldest and largest of all the national parks. Established in 1872 and added to from time to time, it now includes nearly 3,500 square miles of wild natural scenery. While its mountains are neither so high nor so spectacular as those of other parks, Yellowstone has a magnificent forest which protects many species of wild life, a large lake (139 square miles of water surfaces at an elevation of 7,730 feet above sea level), spectacular canyons and waterfalls, and the only true geysers on the North American continent. If

southern Alberta, was made into an international park in 1932. Glacier National Park within the United States was established in 1910, after considerable land had been bought back from the Blackfoot Indians on the eastern slope of the continental divide. Until recently it could be reached only on the Great Northern Railroad whose line runs along the southern border of the park. The completion of the Going-to-the-Sun Highway

Figure 12–12. The national parks of the United States. (From *Conservation of Natural Resources,* courtesy of John Wiley & Sons, Inc.)

the park had nothing else to offer, the Norris Geyser Basin with its many fumaroles and the Upper Geyser Basin with Old Faithful, would be worth the tourist's trip across the continent. Yellowstone is very accessible. Branch lines of the Northern Pacific, the Burlington, the Union Pacific, and the Milwaukee railroads provide access to the north, east, and west entrances, where connections are made with motor stages. The park is easily reached by automobile through five entrance highways.

Waterton-Glacier International Peace Park. This park in northern Montana and

across the continental divide at Logan Pass and the building of connecting highways to the east and west made this park accessible to automobile traffic. The Waterton section is connected with the American section by motor highway and derives most of its trade from American tourists. This park contains magnificent scenery with sheer cliffs formed by intense glacial erosion rising abruptly 3,000 or more feet from glacial lakes.

The Canadian National Parks. The National Park system of Canada was started in 1885 when a small area in the vicinity of the mineral hot springs at Banff in the Rocky

Mountains of Alberta was reserved as public property. From this modest beginning the Canadian National Park system has expanded to include a great chain of national playgrounds extending across the continent. The spectacular scenery of the Rockies, however, led to the creation of seven Canadian national parks within this region —Waterton Lakes, Banff, Jasper, Yoho, Kootenay, Glacier, and Mt. Revelstoke (Figure 12–13). Access to

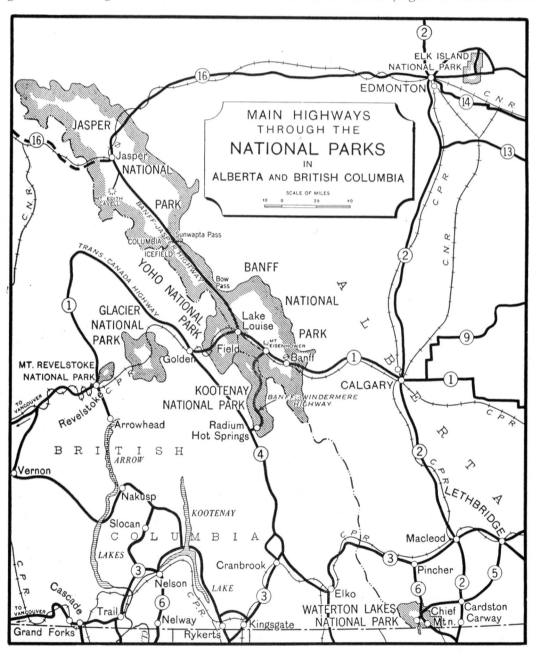

Figure 12–13. The national parks of the Canadian Rockies. (Courtesy of Canadian Government Travel Bureau.)

the parks was developed by the two transcontinental railways of Canada but today all but one of them may be reached also by modern automobile highways. Banff National Park contains also the famous Lake Louise area. It is crossed by the Canadian Pacific Railway which operates some of the largest and most elaborate resort hotels on the North American continent (Figure 12–14). Jasper National Park, with an area of 4,200 square miles in a region of magnificent mountains, canyons, and glaciers, is served by the Canadian National Railway (Figure 12–2).

Transportation

Like the Great Plains, the Rocky Mountains have been a major barrier to east-west travel. The early trails across the Rockies passed either around the southern end in New Mexico, or crossed through the Wyoming Basin between the Southern and Middle Rockies. The first "transcontinental" railroad (the Union Pacific) used the Wyoming Basin route. Railroad surveying parties explored all possible routes but in the end only nine lines succeeded completely in crossing the mountain barrier. Two of these, the Southern Pacific and the Santa Fe, were built through New Mexico, south of the mountains. Only the Denver and Rio Grande Western crossed through the highest part of the Rocky Mountains by way of Tennessee Pass (elevation 10,202 feet). Later, with the completion of the six-mile Moffat Tunnel, it succeeded in reaching the western slope by a shorter and lower route. Three "transcontinental lines," the Northern Pacific, the

Figure 12–14. Banff Springs Hotel in the Canadian Rockies is one of the most famous resort hotels in Anglo-America. (Courtesy of Canadian Pacific Railway.)

Great Northern and the Chicago, Milwaukee and St. Paul, crossed the mountains in Montana. In Canada only two lines were built: the Canadian Pacific to the south and the Canadian National farther north. Only these two are true transcontinental railways in that they link the Pacific ports of Vancouver and Prince Rupert with the Atlantic ports of Montreal, Halifax, St. John, and Sydney.

Highway development later followed similar routes, but the two southern routes and the one through the Wyoming Basin carry most of the traffic.

The Outlook

In a region as extensive and as undeveloped as the Rocky Mountains it is quite difficult to forecast the future. Mining will undoubtedly continue to fluctuate in importance as new discoveries are made and as old mines become exhausted. New discoveries are always possible and may add materially to the development of any individual area. The ranching, farming, and lumbering activities, although capable of some further extension, are developed almost to capacity and should experience no great progress in the future. The resort business, however, will continue to grow as more areas are made accessible through the building of new highways and the construction of more and better housing facilities. The resort industry, although confined largely to summer trade, is expanding into the field of winter sports in such famous centers as Sun Valley and Aspen.

Table 11

SELECTED CITIES AND TOWNS OF THE ROCKY MOUNTAINS

City or Town	Urbanized area	Political center	City or Town	Urbanized area	Political center
Alamosa		5,354	Leadville		4,081
Anaconda		11,254	Livingston		7,683
Bozeman		11,325	Los Alamos		9,934
Butte		33,251	Missoula		22,485
Canon City		6,345	Montrose		4,964
Coeur d'Alene		12,198	Rawlins		7,415
Golden		5,238	Rock Springs		10,857
Helena		17,581	Salida		4,553
Kalispell		9,737	Sandpoint		4,265
Kamloops		8,099	Santa Fe		27,998
Kellogg		4,913	Trail		11,430

Selected Bibliography

J. Wright Baylor, "Geography of the Glaciated North Idaho Panhandle," *Economic Geography,* Vol. 11, 1935, pp. 191-205.

Edwin J. Foscue and Louis O. Quam, *Estes Park: Resort in the Rockies,* Dallas: Southern Methodist University Press, 1949.

Harold A. Hoffmeister, "Alkali Problem of Western United States," *Economic Geography,* Vol. 23, 1947, pp. 1-9.

————, "Central City Mining District," *Economic Geography,* Vol. 16, 1940, pp. 96-104.

————, "Middle Park and the Colorado – Big Thompson Diversion Project," *Economic Geography,* Vol. 23, 1947, pp. 220-231.

Earl E. Lackey, "Mountain Passes in the Colorado Rockies," *Economic Geography,* Vol. 25, 1949, pp. 211-215.

Irene A. Moke, "Role of Pueblo Indian Economy in Santa Fe," *Economic Geography,* Vol. 22, 1946, pp. 148-152.

Robert J. C. Stead, 'The Yellowhead Pass – Canadian Rockies," *Canadian Geographical Journal,* Vol. 36, 1948, pp. 51-65.

Robert Wrigley, Jr., "Pocatello, Idaho as a Railroad Center," *Economic Geography,* Vol. 19, 1943, pp. 325-336.

Clifford M. Zierer, "Tourism and Recreation in the West," *Geographical Review,* Vol. 42, 1952, pp. 462-481.

13.

Intermontane Basins and Plateaus

THE relatively few occupants in this huge region (Figure 13–1) dwell mostly in valley oases and occasional mountain mining camps, which appear like islands in the desert wilderness. It is one of the most colorful regions in all Anglo-America.

By many regionalists it is considered several regions rather than one. Here, however, it is treated as one, since the whole is intermontane and every part arid or semiarid. Water is problem number one to every form of life be it plant, animal, or man. Moreover, the following types of human adjustment recur from north to south and from east to west:

1. Where water is available for irrigation and where the land is sufficiently level, intensive farming prevails.

2. On bench lands and plateaus where sufficient rain falls for a crop once in two years, wheat and a few other crops are dry-farmed.[1]

3. Where sources of irrigation water are wanting, where insufficient rain falls for dry farming but where there is adequate precipitation for grass and shrubs, grazing prevails

—cattle and sheep utilizing the semiarid areas and goats the strictly arid ones.

4. In mountains and on higher plateaus (Utah, Arizona, and New Mexico) too rugged for farming but receiving enough rain for trees, a limited amount of lumbering is carried on.

5. Where minerals occur in paying quantities and where they are accessible to railways or highways, mining is locally important.

6. Here and there throughout the whole region are scenic attractions, such as the Grand Canyon, which have no counterparts anywhere else in the world. Most of these are now national parks, national monuments, wilderness areas, or national forests which attract hundreds of thousands of tourists each year.

Climate

The greater part of this region, which constitutes almost one fourth of continental United States, is desert or semidesert. This, however, does not mean that it is everywhere a region of sand dunes and barren desolation. A desert is an area whose water supply is so small that agriculture is impracticable. "It is poor but not dead."

---

[1] Dry farming is discussed later in this chapter.

329

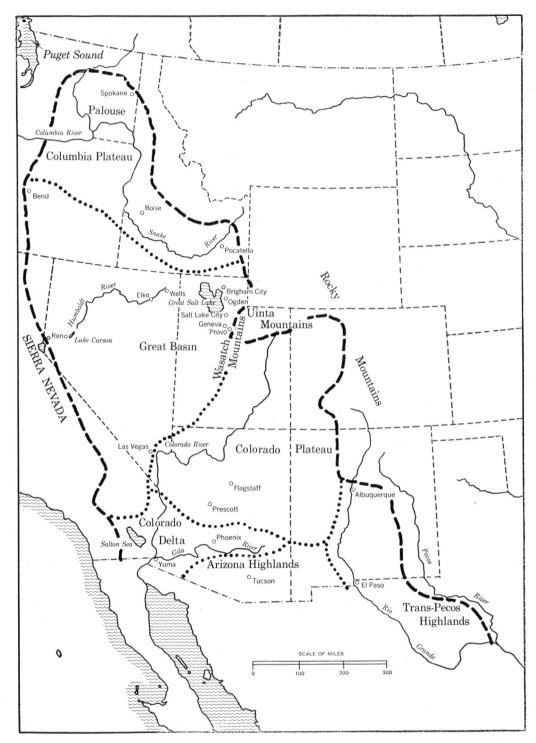

Figure 13–1. The Intermontane Basins and Plateaus. Limited water supply, the region's biggest problem, sets the ceiling on agricultural development, on industrial capacity, and on the population that can be supported. The dotted lines separate the six major subdivisions of this vast and empty region.

The climate is varied, but in each subregion evaporation exceeds precipitation over a period of time. Climatically the region falls into three realms: (1) the *semiarid*, (2) the *normally* or *moderately arid*, and (3) the *extremely arid*.

The *semiarid* is typified by the Columbia Plateau (except along its western and eastern borders which are arid and subhumid respectively); precipitation ranges from 10 to 20 inches per year and falls largely in the late autumn, winter, and spring. The growing season varies from less than 100 days at Bend to as many as 219 at Walla Walla.

The *normally arid*, characterized by most of the Great Basin, has a periodic rainfall — a season of fairly regular, though limited precipitation, during which vegetation bursts into life and the water table is replenished. The precipitation at Elko, Nevada, a typical station is 9.46 inches. The frostless season varies from 100 to 180 days.

In the *extremely arid*, the rainfall is episodic, coming largely in summer at irregular intervals and invariably as cloudbursts. The Mojave-Gila Desert exemplifies this type. Its annual precipitation is less than five inches — too little even for grazing. Almost the entire annual rainfall may come in a single downpour lasting but a few moments. So much water falls so quickly that little can penetrate the soil.

The diurnal range of temperature throughout the region is high. The days become generally very hot and the nights quite cool, even in summer, when cool morning temperatures of 50° or lower may rise to above 90° in the afternoon. This results from the small amount of cloud and water vapor in the air which permits the sun's rays to reach the earth promptly in the morning and hastens radiation after sunset. Elevation is a factor, too — the Colorado Plateau experiencing less-hot days and cooler nights than the Great Basin. The highest official shade temperature ever recorded in the United States was 134°F. at Greenland Ranch in Death Valley.

Surface Features

Physiographically this region consists of the Great Basin, Colorado Plateau, Colorado Delta, Arizona Highlands, Trans-Pecos Highlands, and Columbia Plateau.

The Great Basin. As large as France and lying between the Sierra Nevada–Cascade ranges on the west and the Wasatch Mountains and high plateaus of Utah on the east, the Great Basin includes most of Nevada and much of Utah. The most characteristic aspects of its physiography are the great number of isolated and broken north-south trending mountains and its interior drainage.

The Basin Ranges consist of numerous north and south trending ranges, most of which are tilted and block-faulted masses of previously folded and peneplained sedimentaries. The blocks have been turned up on edge giving the mountains a sharp crest with steep slopes on one side and gentle slopes on the other. They rise abruptly from the flat valley floors. The streams of the region are largely intermittent, losing themselves in shallow filled basins or alkaline flats.

Lying near the west foot of the Wasatch and the east base of the Sierra Nevada are low areas occupied by permanent bodies of salt water — Great Salt Lake and Lakes Carson and Pyramid. They are saline because they have no outlet and because the streams which feed them, like all streams, carry minute amounts of various salts. Great Salt Lake expands and contracts according to the amount of precipitation in the mountains, which supplies the streams feeding it. It is a shrunken remnant of prehistoric Lake Bonneville — a great body of fresh water that was as large as present Lake Huron. Probably there were several lakes that filled the basin area and then retreated, perhaps desiccating completely. Though Lake Bonneville and the other lakes disappeared thousands of years ago, the old beach lines still remain strikingly clear on the sides of the mountains. The highest shoreline, the Bonneville, lies about 1,000 feet above Great Salt Lake.

A unique part of the Great Basin is Death Valley, in the southeastern part of California near the Nevada border. More than 130 miles long and from 6 to 14 miles wide, it is a desert that came into existence when a slice of the earth's crust sank forming a rift valley. Its bottom lies 276 feet below sea level. Long ago the rainfall was much heavier and a lake in the valley had formed, into which rivers dumped great quantities of earthy materials and minerals.

The Colorado Plateau. This enormous area, consisting of several strongly differentiated parts but with sufficient unity to justify separation from adjacent subregions, stretches outward from the Colorado River and its branches in Arizona, New Mexico, and Utah. The greater part consists of a rather flat summit area, slightly warped or undulating as a result of earlier crustal movements, interrupted by erosion scarps in the eastern portions and fault scarps in the western parts. Physiographically, the area is distinguished by:

1. Great elevation; all but the bottoms of canyons and the highest peaks lie between 4,000 and 8,000 feet. The higher areas comprise the plateaus of Utah, the San Francisco Peaks, White Mountains, Chuska Mountains, and Zuñi Uplift.

2. Remarkable canyons, hundreds of which thread the Canyon Lands of southeastern Utah and Mesa Verde. These make the Colorado Plateau the most dissected, most difficult to traverse, and least known of all the regions of the United States.

3. An amazing amount of erosion extending through thousands of feet; nowhere in the world is there so impressive an example as the Grand Canyon.

4. Numerous arroyos which cut the region into a maze of steep-sided chasms, dry during most of the year but filled from wall to wall during the rare rains. (Not to be confused with badlands.)

5. Mesas, flat-topped islands of resistant rock found only on the borderline of arid and humid climates.

The Colorado Delta. This delta, which includes the Imperial Valley and the lower courses of the Colorado and Gila rivers, is a waste-filled area with many small mountain ranges rising above the alluvial plains.

The Imperial Valley, along with southwestern Arizona, the southern tip of Nevada, and southern California east of the mountains, is a part of the Colorado Delta, whose floor consists almost entirely of alluvium. The delta proper lies mostly in Mexico. Engineering operations, begun in 1901 for making the Imperial Valley available for agriculture, resulted in a huge inflow of water to the Salton Basin. As the result of floods in 1906 the river got out of control and remained so until February 1907, during which time the Salton Sea came into existence.

The Imperial Valley, which slopes from sea level at the United States-Mexican border to about 270 feet below on the deepest part of the depression, is separated from the actual basin of the Colorado by a deltaic ridge built by the river itself. The Salton Basin which occupies about a million acres lies more than 250 feet below sea level.

The Colorado River carries much silt — 0.6 per cent by volume. It is estimated that as much silt goes down the Colorado each year as was excavated during the entire construction of the Panama Canal.

The Arizona Highland, American portion of the Mexican Highland, lies south of the Colorado Plateau. Structure and erosion have made it a far different land from the plateau. Fenneman included it in the physiographic Basin and Range Province, for like that area it consists of mountain and plain and many of its mountains, though smaller, are typical basin ranges.[2] It is drained by the Gila River and its branches, especially the Salt River, which carries water great distances. This is the part of Arizona which possesses much of the commercial mineral wealth —especially copper ore.

The Trans-Pecos Highlands and Basins. These highlands and basins lie in east-central and southeastern New Mexico and adjacent southwestern Texas between the Mexican Highland and the High Plains. Just where this area belongs is not positive; some geographers include it in the Great Plains, others in the Intermontane Basins and Plateaus. Perhaps it is a boundary between them. Here they are considered a part of the latter region because of their human geography. The subregion consists of partly

---

[2] Nevin M. Fenneman, *Physiography of Western United States*, p. 380. New York: McGraw-Hill Book Co., 1931.

buried mountains and filled basin areas — many with only interior drainage.

The Columbia Plateau. The Columbia Plateau [3] lies between the Cascade Mountains on the west and the Rocky Mountains on the east and north, and grades almost imperceptibly into the Great Basin to the south. While called a plateau, which popularly suggests a rather uniform surface, the area has quite varied relief features of mountains, plateaus, tilted fault blocks, hills, plains, and ridges. In general, this intermontane area is covered with lava flows which originally were poured out over a nearly horizontal landscape and interbedded with a considerable quantity of silts that were deposited in extensive interior lakes. After the outpouring of the sheets of lava and the deposit of the lake beds, the surface of much of the region was strongly warped and faulted so that the present surface of the lava varies from a few hundred feet above sea level to nearly 6,000 feet in elevation. Numerous tilted fault blocks and upfolded ridges, called somewhat ineptly the Blue Mountains, extend from southeast Washington across Oregon to within 40 miles of the Cascade Mountains and divide the lava-covered area into nearly equal halves. The balance of the subregion consists predominantly of basins surrounded by plateaus, hills, and ridges. Thus in southeastern Washington is the Columbia Basin surrounded by a rim of higher uplifted lava-covered country. The eastern part of the Columbia Basin, called the Palouse, consisting of rolling hills covered with loess, receives sufficient rainfall to make it a very productive farming area. The Deschutes-Columbia Plateau is a triangular-shaped area in north-central Oregon that slopes in general from the Blue Mountains to the Columbia River. The Snake River Plain or Basin extends across southern Idaho in a broad arc. In central Oregon, the Harney Basin and the High Plains or Great Sandy Desert are shallow interior basins and flats between the Blue Mountains and the Great Basin. They may be considered a transition area between the so-called Columbia Plateau and the Great Basin.

Soils

Most of this region has not been carefully mapped and little can be said of its soils except that they are all pedocals.

Columbia Plateau soils vary from heavy silt loams to fine sand and sandy loams, the former predominating. They are well supplied with potash and phosphorus but are deficient in nitrogen and humus. In the driest parts there is considerable damage from blowing. Palouse soils, true *Chernozems,* and the most important in the Columbia Plateau, are exceptionally fertile, and, before their structure and organic content was destroyed by farming, absorbed moisture readily. They are presumably of loessial origin.

Palouse terrain is unique — wavelike in appearance. It is believed that it is largely the result of wind action and snow drift erosion or nivation which scoops out cirque-like forms on northeast-facing slopes. The hills are asymmetric, the northeast slopes being more concave and steeper than the southwest ones. Although this unconsolidated material is extremely deep, erosion has been comparatively slow due to the cohesive qualities of loessial material, the fine particles being bound together with grass roots. When this humus is destroyed by continuous cropping and fallowing, the soils erode readily.

Most true soils in the Great Basin lie on alluvial fans, piedmont alluvial plains, and playas.[4] With water, the first two become highly productive. The Basin Ranges have either a thin layer of soil or none whatsoever. The soils at the foot of the Wasatch (the Salt Lake Oasis) are dark-colored because the benches received enough precipitation to

---

[3] For maps and a detailed treatment of the Columbia Plateau see Otis W. Freeman, J. D. Forrester, and R. L. Lupher, "Physiographic Divisions of the Columbia Intermontane Province," *Annals, Association of American Geographers,* Vol. 35, No. 2, June 1945, pp. 53-75.

[4] Playas — both "wet" and "dry" — form in the lowest parts of desert basins. The former contain shallow bodies of water during rainy spells and are apt to be moist even during the nonrainy season. The latter occupy nonwatertight basins and their surfaces consist of hard sun-baked clay.

cause a vigorous growth of shallow-rooted vegetation. These soil constituents were carried originally by streams into ancient Lake Bonneville. Similar lacustrine materials occur around the eastern border of the Snake River Plains.

Much of the Colorado Plateau is devoid entirely of soils. When present, they are limy, light grayish-brown or gray in color, and contain little organic material. Where water is available for irrigation, those that are deep, well-drained, and free from an excess of salts, become highly productive.

The soils in the southern part of the Colorado Plateau are reddish in color and, like most desert soils, are rich in lime. When irrigated they are highly productive and capable of growing a wide variety of crops such as alfalfa, barley, corn, cotton, grain sorghums, and wheat.

Natural Vegetation

In so large an area and in one varying so greatly in land forms and hence in climate, marked differences in the natural vegetation occur. Some variations, however, as in the Great Salt Lake area of Utah, are due to physical and chemical properties of the soil.

Forests. Western yellow pine and Douglas fir forests are confined mostly to the higher elevations where the rainfall is relatively heavy. As precipitation declines, forest changes to woodland, then to types associated with inadequate moisture — piñon and juniper — and finally to chaparral. There is considerable juniper in the area north and south of Bend, Oregon.

More than half the Colorado Plateau is clothed with trees of some kind, though the forest area containing merchantable timber is limited.

Western yellow pine contributes most of the saw timber on lands lying at altitudes of 6,000 to 7,500 feet in Arizona and New Mexico. Piñon and juniper along with chaparral occupy the belt below yellow pine but are most common in southern Arizona and southern California. For the most part they are not found north of the forty-fourth parallel. The

forests in the higher western and southern margins of the Plateau are included in national forests.

Grasslands. Grasslands more numerous than might be supposed, characterize the highlands of southeastern Arizona, New Mexico, and the Columbia Basin. Mesquite grass grows where temperatures are high, evaporation excessive, and annual precipitation low. Short grass characterizes large areas in the high plateaus of New Mexico and Arizona as does bunch grass in the Columbia Plateau, and the noxious cheat grass is almost ubiquitous.

Desert Shrub. Xerophytic plants characterize deserts — those areas where irrigation is essential to permanent settlement. Vegetation grows in even the driest parts. Most desert plants, largely dwarfed in size, possess small leaves — nature's protective device against excessive transpiration.[5] *Sage brush,* which dominates as far south as southern Nevada, grows in pure stands where soils are relatively free from alkaline salts. Especially is it abundant on bench lands which skirt mountains and on alluvial fans at the mouths of canyons. *Shadscale,* a low, gray, spiny plant with a shallow root system, grows on the most alkaline soils but never in dense stands. Much bare ground lies between the plants. It is especially prominent in Utah and Nevada and is believed to cover even more land than sage brush. *Greasewood,* bright green in color and occupying the same general region as sage brush and shadscale, grows from one to five feet in height and is tolerant of alkali. *Creosote bush,* dominating the southern Great Basin as sage brush does the northern, merges in the *chaparral* zone where the creosote bush draws moisture from deep down under the surface. Creosote bush is a large plant attaining a height of 10 to 15 feet. *Mesquite grass* also occupies a large acreage in southern New Mexico and Arizona and is especially abundant on the fertile soils along drainage channels. *Cactus* and *yucca* grow over much of the Arizona Highlands

―――――
[5] A. E. Aldous and H. L. Shantz, "Types of Vegetation in the Semiarid Portion of the United States and Their Economic Significance," *Journal of Agricultural Research,* Vol. 28, April 12, 1924.

at slightly higher elevations [6] than creosote bush. They characterize the loose soils covering the rough rocky hills and low mountains that have been badly eroded. Their grazing value is slight.

Most desert plants stand in lonely isolation and have to fight to live: "In the warfare which is perpetual and of a ferocity elsewhere unequaled, water is the key, for water is life."

Much of the vegetation — some 50 different species of plants on 16 million acres — is useless. This is important in a region where water is so scarce, for the consumptive waste of water by these plants is equal to 20 to 25 million acre-feet of water annually or 75 per cent of the total storage capacity of Lake Mead — 31,142,000 acre feet. (An acre foot is a unit of volume of water equal to the volume of a prism one foot high with its base one acre in area.) Scientists estimate that this consumptive waste probably represents the largest source of reclaimable water in the region.

Sheep-killing Weed. Though not a native plant, a poisonous weed known as *Halogeton glomeratus* is causing great damage. Carried from Asiatic Russia in some imported crested wheat grass seed, it was first noticed in the important sheep-raising area near Wells, Nevada, in 1935. The seeds of the purple-stemmed bush, which thrives in semi-desert areas where other vegetation is sparse, are carried by wind, man, and animals. Most sheep which eat it die. It is believed that the poisonous halogeton weed could destroy one fourth of the nation's range sheep unless its spread is checked. Huge areas of rangeland are now infested in Idaho, Nevada, and Utah, and the weed has spread into parts of California, Montana, Oregon, and Wyoming. Fortunately rain and snow leach the poison from the weed during winter. It is believed that wheat grasses can be made to crowd it out.

Native Animals

Space permits mentioning only one phase under this topic. West of Brigham City, Utah

6 Below 3,500 feet.

is the 100-square mile Bear River Migratory Bird Refuge — largest resting place for water fowl in the United States. It consists of marshes and lakes and is today just as it was when Jim Bridger described it in 1824. It is on the "fly way" for mallards, pintails, Canada geese and whistling swans as these stream toward winter feeding grounds on the Gulf of Mexico and Gulf of California. It is estimated that a million water fowl stop here during the autumn migration season. The refuge was established in 1928 to prevent "market hunters" from destroying this valuable resource which is not at normal.

Land of the Indian

The Indian is discussed in greatest detail in this chapter because he is here in greatest number and has retained his heritage and way of life here better than elsewhere, except in the Northern Continental Forest and the Yukon-Kuskokwim Basins. But there he was a forest Indian who was a hunter; here, in the dry West where game was less abundant he was in some instances a hunter, in others a farmer. Now he is also a grazier.

The Indian is thus a part of the pioneer picture — the human element in the background against which the achievements of the pioneer whites are projected. Under these circumstances he must be studied.

In the arid Southwest the Indian reached his apex in culture and civilization. Here he made considerable progress prior to the white man's arrival and it is here that he is making his strongest stand today. So far as the United States is concerned, this is the only part that remains true Indian Country.

Land of the Navajo. The scope of this book precludes treatment of all the tribes in the Southwest; hence only the Navajos, who typify the nomadic Indians, and the Hopis and Zuñis, who typify the sedentary ones, are discussed.

The Navajo country is a reservation comprising some 16 million acres. For the most part it is a sun-scorched, water-sculptured land — one of high plateau, flat-topped mesa, sharp, deep canyon, and sandy and gravelly wash. It is larger than the state of West Virginia.

The rainfall, of about 3 to 15 inches, comes in the winter and summer seasons. Summer rains, mostly torrential, have stripped the top-soil from scores of square miles, which are now almost naked. Aside from the main arteries used by transcontinental tourists, motor roads are few and poor. Motorists from outside this region who have been caught on a dirt road in a summer afternoon downpour do not soon forget their nightmare. This then is more the land of the horse than of the motor car.

Water is scarce. Only five per cent of the Navajo country has permanent streams; man and beast depend upon pools, water pockets, or tanks.

Most of the land is classed as marginal by the land economist; little, however, is so desertic as to be positively worthless to sheep and goats.

When the Navajos first turned to the raising of livestock, the range was in good condition. But with increasing population, more animals were needed and with more livestock came overgrazing. This has diminished the carrying capacity of the range and erosion has attacked it, gnashing it with gullies and seaming it with arroyos. Springs have dried up and the Navajos have been threatened with starvation or with becoming public charges.

Distribution of the Navajos. The Navajo Reservation, which looks almost deserted to the traveler, has a population density of about three persons to the square mile. Yet, with hardly ten inches of rainfall and with a dearth of other natural resources, *it is overcrowded*, and the Navajos are frantically urging the federal government to give them more land. Much has been said about the Indians as the "vanishing Americans." This statement certainly is not applicable to the Navajos, the largest Indian tribe in the United States, which has increased from less than 10,000 in 1870 to more than 61,000 in 1950.

This growth is amazing considering that the life expectancy of the Navajos is 50 years in contrast to the national average of 68. Welfare officials reveal that the health conditions among this Indian group are the worst in the nation — with deaths from dysentery, pneumonia, and tuberculosis being triple the national average.

Grazing. North America was poor in domesticable animals: the bison, antelope, deer, and elk were not tractable and have never been domesticated. The Spaniards who settled in New Mexico attempted to domesticate the bison but failed.

Since grazing was a leading enterprise in their homeland, it was natural that the Spaniards should have brought their animals to the New World. Especially valuable to the Indian was the horse which for the first time assured mobility.

Today the Navajos are essentially pastoralists (Figure 13–2), their flocks of sheep and goats being driven into the higher timber areas in summer and back into the valleys in winter. In arid areas with small relief, they drive the flocks into the highlands in winter because at that season water is available only in the higher places.

There are too many head of livestock on the reservation. The Navajo sheep are hardy, subsisting throughout the year on the open range; their wool is easy to card, spin, and weave by hand, and it makes a high grade rug; however, the fleece is light, weighing but four pounds per head as compared with eight pounds for the entire country. Furthermore, these sheep are poor meat animals. As a means of enabling the Navajos to reduce the size of their flocks and thus improve the grazing lands, the government sought to improve the breed. Early in 1942 it announced progress: the Navajo ewe, which weighed about 60 pounds in 1934, with laboratory selection and good range management, now weighs about 100 pounds; her fleece which weighed two to four pounds now weighs five pounds; and her lambs, which weighed 40 pounds at weaning time now weigh 60 pounds.

Navajo dwellings. The Navajos have never been a pueblo people, have never lived in towns, and have never farmed very much. This is understandable, since formerly they were hunters and even now are mainly pastoralists. Their homes are well-adjusted to the surroundings; so widely scattered are their

Figure 13–2. A Navajo tending his sheep in Arizona. Since less than one per cent of the Navajo Reservation is suited to agriculture, the Navajos are essentially pastoralists. They did not graze sheep, however, until Coronado introduced this animal into the Southwest in 1540. (Courtesy of the Santa Fe Railway.)

hogans and so well do they melt into the landscape as to be seldom seen by unobservant passers-by. The *winter hogan* is constructed of logs, the cracks on the outside being chinked with earth; a hole is left in the roof for the escape of smoke. The door, formerly a blanket, is now made of wood. There are no windows. Hogans differ in size, the largest being about 15 feet across. They are dry, warm, and well-ventilated. Sheep skins cover the floor, serving as beds by night and seats by day. The *summer hogan,* made of brush closely piled against upright stakes, is shady and open to breezes but is unsatisfactory during rains.

Tribal crafts. The Indians of the Southwest are skilled craftsmen. They get a considerable part of their living from the sale of art wares to tourists. For example, when a Navajo mother needs provisions and clothing for her babies, she makes a rug of the size that can be exchanged for the bill of goods (Figure 13–3). Though machine-made articles have to some extent destroyed native arts, the federal government, through the Office of Indian Affairs, is trying desperately to prevent the extinction of Indian crafts by acquainting the public with the richness of the wares, by developing markets, and by encouraging the Indians.

The Hopis. Not all the Indians are nomadic graziers. One important sedentary group comprises the Hopis, who for thousands of years have occupied *pueblos.*[7]

The Hopis have been compared to the wild sheep which were compelled to move

---

[7] The Spanish word *pueblo* means *people*; apparently, then, a pueblo had to be large enough to accommodate a sufficient number of people to justify the use of the term.

to mountain peaks because of fierce animals. Surrounded by the more numerous Navajos, the Hopis perched their picturesque pueblos atop lofty steep-walled mesas accessible only by one or two tortuous trails, which they could defend against enemies. Here too, they kept food and water.

culture. In order to grow crops they learn the location of all moist soils for miles around their pueblos, and practice flood-water farming — placing their crops in valley bottoms near washes, or wherever moisture is available. The fields often lie far from their pueblos.

Figure 13–3. Navajo squaw making a blanket on the Navajo Reservation. The weavers clean, spin, card, and dye their raw wool. Ordinarily they dye at one time only enough yarn to make one blanket. (Courtesy of the Santa Fe Railway.)

The Hopi house, made of stone and adobe bricks, is easily constructed, easily repaired, and inexpensive. Thick walls make it warm in winter and cool in summer. Roofs are always flat.

Hopi agriculture. Among the best farmers of the Colorado Plateau are the Hopis, who occupy lands in the southwestern part of the Navajo Reservation. Long ago they realized that their rainfall was inadequate for agri-

They plant their corn in hills about six feet apart to conserve water and six to eight inches deep to keep it from sprouting until rain falls. They also put 15 to 20 kernels in a hill. Occasionally they erect small windbreaks about 30 feet apart in parallel rows and at right angles to the prevailing winds. Because of the short growing season (the result of altitude) they have developed quick-maturing strains.

The Hopis, reputed to be the most skillful of all dry-land farmers, cultivate intensively, each farmer handling only 2 to 10 acres. Seldom is their land in one continuous piece.

Religion. The Indian religion is a practical one designed to be of help on earth rather than in an uncertain future. Since life in the dry plateau is at the mercy of sun and rain, the Indians are extremely religious. Their religion was from the beginning woven about their intimate observations of nature.

In the Southwest among those Indians who were farmers, as for example, the Hopis and the Zuñis,[8] a deep reverence developed for those natural forces that control weather, especially rainfall. Following a custom inaugurated by their forebears at least 2,000 years ago, they pray for rain by dancing; the dances, little modified since first seen by whites 400 years ago, are held when crops are suffering from drought or when rain is needed to germinate newly planted corn. When, as often happens, rain begins to fall in the midst of the dance, the Indians whoop it up and prance with triumph.

Historical Settlement

The Arrival of the Spaniards. It is not definitely known when the first Spaniards came into the arid Southwest. About the middle of the sixteenth century, however, those in Mexico heard tales:

Far to the north are cities that make the palaces of Montezuma look like beggars' hovels. The golden cities of Cibola they are called. And gold they are — houses three and four stories high shining in the desert sun. Their inhabitants eat from golden vessels and their doorways are studded with the blue of turquoise stones.

Led by the black slave, Estevanico, those swashbuckling Spanish eventually found Zuñi and opened up an empire. Etched against the blue New Mexican sky, rose tier on tier of what looked to be a city of gold. But it was not gold. It was only puddled adobe guilded by the bright desert sun. Nor did the inhabitants eat from golden vessels, but from skillfully made yellow clay pots.

Disgusted, the Spaniards pushed on up the valley of the Rio Grande.[9]

Later on the Spaniards explored the entire Southwest and were responsible for the conquest of nearly one third of what is now the United States. Unable to find precious metals, some remained to convert the Indians.

The Spaniards left an indelible influence on the history of the Southwest as well as upon American civilization. Their livestock formed the basis of the later American cattle and sheep industry and their horses gave mobility to the Indian, the importance of which can hardly be overestimated. Small Spanish settlements and trading posts such as Santa Fe made up the population of the Southwest until the middle of the nineteenth century.

American Explorers and Trappers. American explorers began to filter into the region in the early nineteenth century. Lewis and Clark entered the Pacific Northwest in 1804–1805; the Astorians, in 1811–1812 and again in 1813; Smith explored the Great Basin in 1828; and Wyeth, the Pacific Northwest in 1832–1833. Bonneville in 1832 and 1836 traded in furs and casually explored the area drained by the Bear River, while Fremont in 1845–1846 entered the Salt Lake Basin by way of the Bear River, becoming the first to explore it systematically. These are but a few of the many who explored the region.

Trapping, a powerful incentive to exploration, was, as a matter of fact, the main object of many of the men who explored the West in the early nineteenth century. The trappers were a special breed — self-reliant, solitary individuals — largely freebooters constantly striving to outwit their rivals, to supplant them in the good will of the Indians, and to mislead them in regard to routes. They lasted until fashion suddenly switched from beaver to silk for men's hats. The mountain-men trappers were then through. Nonetheless, they left an indelible stamp upon our history.

It was the Canadians rather than the

---

[8] The Zuñi Reservation lies just outside the Navajo Reservation — south of Gallup, New Mexico.

[9] Dorothy L. Pillsbury, "Golden City of Peace," *The Christian Science Monitor,* March 15, 1947.

Americans who were in control of the old "Oregon Country" from 1811 until 1846. Although many American names are associated with it, no American fur company was dominant in the northern part of the Intermontane Region for any length of time. The "Snake Country" to the south was the great zone of conflict between the Americans and the Hudson's Bay Company.

The Farmer Invasion. The outstanding example of farmer invasion was the Mormon migration to Salt Lake Basin in 1847.[10] The Mormons had trekked from Ohio, Missouri, and Illinois to escape persecution and to find a sanctuary where they might maintain their religious integrity. To accomplish this, they felt impelled to establish themselves on the border of the real American Desert. The agricultural fame of the Utah colony was soon known far and wide. Utah is the only state in the Union that was systematically colonized. The leader, Brigham Young, sent scouts into every part of the "state" to seek lands suitable for farming. He personally selected the colonists, who were of sufficient number to build forts against Indian attacks and construct dams and canals for irrigation. He located all farm-villages near streams, for upon water the colonists depended for their very existence. Even before Utah was settled, he made several settlements outside to control territory and serve as a line of forts. Among his early outposts were Las Vegas, Nevada, Moab on Utah's Colorado Plateau, San Bernardino in California, Alamosa in Colorado, and Fort Lemhi in Idaho.

Before long all the arable land had been acquired; scouts were then sent outside Utah

to seek new irrigable lands. Thus Mormons made the first permanent settlement in Idaho, and were the first Anglo-Saxons to arrive in the Grand Canyon country.

The California Gold Rush. Following the explorers, trappers, and farmers came the gold-seekers of 1849. So large was the movement that it led to the establishment of trading posts and stations, where the migrants rested and refreshed themselves. The Salt Lake Oasis especially became a "Mecca" for the weary and exhausted. Farther west the wagon trains rested in Carson, Walker, and Mono basins. Important in the route through Nevada was the Humboldt River:

This is the paradox of the Humboldt, that it was almost the most necessary river of America, and the most hated. Americans came this way to stand on the mountain passes and look far upon the Pacific; Americans came back. Emigrant and immigrant came this way, Mormon and miner and soldier, Pony Express and Overland stage, Overland telegraph and Pacific Railroad, cattleman and sheepman, highway and airline. Indians fought for life in the river bottoms while the West went mad as the Comstock poured out its bonanzas on the heights . . . The Humboldt was a way, a means; few settled here until they had to, until greener lands were occupied.[11]

The Graziers. Most of this region was favorable for the grazier. For some years after the Spaniards came, cattle raising was almost the only range industry, though Navajo Indians and Mexican colonists herded some sheep. Northward in Utah and Idaho as well as in the Oregon Country cattle raising held sway in nonfarming areas. In fact the Columbia grasslands were major cattle-surplus areas for many years and shared the stocking of the Northern Great Plains ranges with Texas.

In the 1870's and early 1880's bands of Spanish and French Merino sheep were driven into the Southwest from California, furnishing a fine, short-staple wool in sharp contrast to the long coarse wool of the Navajo sheep. Transhumance was practiced: in Arizona the cool northern moun-

[10] On June 23, 1847, the Mormon advance party under Brigham Young met the famous Rocky Mountain trader and trapper, Jim Bridger, on the Big Sandy River. They were strongly advised by Bridger not to settle in the Valley of the Great Salt Lake because they would find it difficult to grow crops there. He said it would be unwise to bring a large colony into the Great Basin until it was proved that grain could be raised there and he offered to give a thousand dollars for the first ear of corn that matured in Salt Lake Valley. The Mormons received similar advice from all whom they met on the trail west of Fort Laramie. Bridger knew nothing of irrigation and hence based his thinking on the dryness of the Salt Lake Valley.

[11] Dale L. Morgan, *The Humboldt.* New York: Farrar & Rinehart, Inc., 1943.

tains were used from May until August; then the flocks were moved to the lower desert ranges. Late spring found them once more among the mountain pastures.[12]

In Utah the self-sufficing Mormons raised sheep for homespun and as early as the 1850's nearly every farmer possessed a few head.

Most parts of the range in this enormous region were overgrazed. The situation in Utah was typical: after only 35 years of use, the best pasture grounds showed scarcely a trace of the originally abundant grass and browse. By 1880 every locality west of the Wasatch Mountains showed the effects of overgrazing.

Errors Made in Settling Arid America

The Spaniards who settled in this region — one not fundamentally different from their Meseta — knew how to cope with its problems; according to the historian, the late H. E. Bolton, and, contrary to prevailing opinion, Spanish colonization was notably successful. The Anglo-Saxons, on the other hand, encountered a distinctly new type of habitat, for they came from lands of ample rainfall. Even the federal government blundered, its laws having been framed for humid and not for arid and semiarid land; accordingly the Homestead Act's gift of 160 acres, adequate for the humid East, was inadequate for the arid region. Says Paul Sears:

. . . a family might starve to death in the grazing country on a farm of one square mile, while a quarter or even an eighth of that would mean comparative comfort in the beautiful valley of Virginia.[13]

Only after the pioneer, through trial and error, had learned certain lessons, did the government act wisely and change the size of the Homestead unit from 160 to 320 acres. But this amount was inadequate for stock farming in the arid West. Investigators estimated that a family could support itself on 640 acres. Accordingly, after considerable agitation on the part of congressmen from the western states, the Stock-Raising Homestead Act was passed in 1916 allowing a family 640 acres.

Since nearly one quarter of the area of continental United States is arid or semiarid, it is obvious that greater knowledge of the region under consideration is needed. As a means of helping prospective settlers choose land more wisely, the Geological Survey and the Department of Agriculture are today classifying lands on the basis of their suitability for grazing, mineral production, crop production (with or without irrigation), or uselessness. That close settlement was pushed well beyond safe limits is proved by the hundreds of abandoned homesteaders' shacks (Figure 13–4). The history behind nearly every one is the same; land was offered for sale at low cost to people who never had lived in a dry region and hence knew nothing of its problems. Time and again people settled where they could not possibly make a living. In many instances they tried to grow crops totally unsuited to the climate. These people were not to blame so much as their government, which should have determined the true character of the land preceding settlement. It is significant that in 1878 Major John W. Powell, in reporting to Congress, pointed out the need of a special land policy for parts of the West that would allot 2,560 acres to each family.[14]

Nowhere in the world was land in such enormous tracts acquired so rapidly.

Almost over night, as history is reckoned, the white man moved into the territory that had been 'forever' reserved for the Indian, crossed the country that had been labeled 'impassable,' grazed, plowed, and settled the land that was 'uninhabitable' and on it built himself a thriving civilization. Within a few generations it was all over. The frontier was pronounced closed; the Wild West was domesticated.[15]

---

[12] Transhumance is carried on more extensively today in the Great Basin than elsewhere in the Intermontane Region.

[13] Paul B. Sears, *Deserts on the March*, p. 208. Norman, Oklahoma: University of Oklahoma Press, 1935.

[14] *1938 Yearbook of the Department of Agriculture*, p. 114. Washington, D. C.: Government Printing Office, 1938.

[15] Harold McCracken, *Portrait of the Old West*. New York: McGraw-Hill, 1952.

Figure 13–4. An abandoned homesteader's shack. Many factors contribute to land abandonment; alkaline soils, water-logged soils, inadequate or badly distributed rainfall, insufficient size of homestead grants, remoteness from railroads, sudden drops in prices, diseases, insect infestations, ruinous taxes, and inadequate knowledge about the region. (Courtesy of Farm Security Administration.)

Thus, within a century after the formation of the United States government the Director of the Census announced that there was no longer a frontier. Accordingly, in 1935 the Homestead Policy, which really had long been obsolete, was brought to an end.

Distribution and Growth of Population

What population there is in the Intermontane West congregates mostly in "islands" where (1) precipitation is adequate, (2) water is available for irrigation farming, (3) ore deposits permit commercial mining, or (4) transportation routes converge. In the entire region only four urban centers have 100,000 or more inhabitants: Salt Lake City, Spokane, El Paso, and Phoenix.

This is a region of considerable population movement — migration into, out of, within, and across. But the total change as yet is unimpressive and so far as the region as a whole is concerned, represents little more than natural increase.

The population situation in Utah is especially interesting and significant. Utah is one of the few areas in Anglo-America characterized by a high birth rate. With a large population, relatively high birth rate, and restricted arable and irrigable areas, outmigration is imperative. A study made in the 1940's showed that 85 per cent of Utah's farm boys leave agriculture. Many of these of necessity move out of the state. Professor Bowman Hawkes of the University of Utah says this trend is now being reversed — that many of the boys who left the state are now returning.

In Utah is a unique situation. More than three fourths of the total population dwells in the Salt Lake Oasis at the foot of the Wasatch, which comprises only about one per cent of the state's area. Moreover, most of the farmers here live in villages, not on isolated farms. This last apparently results from a combination of four factors: (1) sectarian ideology, particularly the plan of the "City of Zion"; (2) protection against the

Indians during the pioneer period; (3) marked solidarity; and (4) the advantages of such a plan in the natural environment encountered in the Great Basin.

Agriculture

Though agriculture is the dominant economic adjustment throughout the greater part of this region, only a fraction (three per cent in Utah) of the total land area is in farms and of this, little is actually in crops. Moreover, this picture will not change greatly in the future on account of (1) aridity, (2) alkaline, rocky or poorly drained soils, (3) rugged terrain, and (4) remoteness (great distance from efficient and cheap transportation and from large markets). Submarginal areas where the rainfall is most unreliable, the soil poorest, the surface roughest, and land most remote from railroads are better suited for grazing than for growing grain and other crops, since animals can be walked to market or to a railway.

Dry Farming. Dry farming is the growing of crops with water-conserving methods; it should be called "water-conservation farming." Usually only a single crop is grown in two years, the crop being alternated with summer fallow. In the Palouse many farmers fallow only one year in three. Fallowing is one of man's devices for conserving moisture by eliminating weeds and retarding evaporation.

This method of farming was carried on by aborigines before 1000 A. D. in the Mesa Verde, San Juan country, and west of the Little Colorado River.

The first Anglo-Saxons in Anglo-America to practice dry farming were the Mormons. In 1863 a company of Danish Mormons left Salt Lake City and founded Bear River City, some miles to the north, where they utilized the water of the Malade River to irrigate their fields. After repeated experiments, they became convinced that something was wrong with the water they were using (it contained too much salt), since their seed did not germinate. As the season was well advanced, they were desperate, and accordingly plowed up some sagebrush land on the bench above

the ditch, planted grain, and awaited results. They obtained fair yields which indicated that dry farming with an alternate fallow year could succeed.

The proportion of the region actually being dry-farmed is small indeed. That the area is so small is significant. Dry farming is highly uncertain, except in the Palouse, because the Intermontane Basins and Plateaus frequently have years of drought followed by periods when the precipitation is well above average. With more rainfall, dry-land crop production flourishes and is accordingly pushed farther into the more arid sections; conversely, periods of lower precipitation reduce soil moisture causing the farmers to blame their troubles on lack of current rainfall.

The Columbia Intermontane Area,[16] the White Wheat Belt, is one of the most noted dry farming areas on the continent and is a major world wheat region. Most of the crop is dry-farmed though along the eastern margin some is grown by customary farm methods. At any one time about half the cultivated land is in fallow and wheat constitutes about four fifths of the total harvested crops (Figure 13–5). This might be increased to seven-eighths if the hay acreage, which really is grain hay, were included. Thus the area is essentially a one-crop region, and the yield per acre and the price per bushel for a given year are vital regional indexes to prosperity.

Because of the extremely erodable topsoil and the hazards of the one-crop system of farming, wheat acreage is declining. Crop rotations were unimportant until a few decades ago. Moreover, burning of the stubble, which was formerly customary, removed the soil-binding humus and its protection against blowing and washing. Wheat stubble is now seldom burnt but is disked in to a depth of about seven inches, forming a low bristling hedge, which extends over the newly broken fields, retarding soil blowing. Trees too are being planted and alfalfa, sweet clover and barley are entering the rotation with wheat.

The large landholdings, 320 to 2,000 acres,

---

[16] This discussion of wheat deals with but a small part of the Columbia Intermontane Area — the Palouse and Big Bend of Washington and north-central Oregon.

are operated for the most part by their owners. In Washington's Big Bend country, west of the Palouse, however, tenancy runs high — up to 33 per cent.

Large ranches and small population encourage the employment of machinery — tractors, gang plows, disks, weeders, and combines. By utilizing large power units, one man does the work of three.

Both spring and winter wheat are grown

riod and are extremely important where labor is scarce.

Most wheat produced in the Columbia Intermontane Area is soft and starchy and under modern baking practices is not well-suited for bread making.

After about 70 years of growing wheat, the land here seems to be going the way of wheat farming in other parts of the country. After 30 to 70 years of cultivation, yields

Figure 13–5. The Palouse Hills — one of America's leading wheat-growing areas. Almost 100 per cent of these dune-like hills are in cultivation. (Courtesy of W. Rockie and the Soil Conservation Service.)

in this area — each in the part whose natural endowment is best suited to it. Some spring wheat, however, is grown in the winter wheat area when a dry autumn has prevented the germination of winter wheat or when snowfall is so light and winter temperatures so low as to have killed the planting of the winter variety.

The most popular wheats are the white wheats (both common and club). These have strong stiff straw, are resistant to lodging, have firm tough heads, and do not shell even in dry windy weather. These qualities enable harvesting to extend over a long pe-

fall so low as to make the crop unprofitable. This situation, however, is more the result of erosion than of soil exhaustion. Dairying or beef cattle (depending upon the economics of time and place) appears to afford a solution in the moister portion, but has not had much appeal as yet to the farmers.

A crop that has become extremely important since 1929, when seed was first planted in the foothills of the Blue Mountain area of eastern Oregon and Washington, is peas. In this former checkerboard area of wheat fields and summer fallow, peas now occupy considerable land on slopes of the Blue

Mountains between 1,400 and 3,400 feet in elevation. The 2,000-foot variation in altitude permits a long planting season and a long harvesting season. The rainfall varies from 17 to 20 inches. Frost is a threat but only locally — the effect being spotty; some valleys may escape, whereas others may have fields that suffer heavy damage.

This crop uses less moisture than wheat and, being a legume, puts nitrogen into the soil. The farmer replows and sows wheat for the alternate season as soon as the pea crop is harvested.

The pea grower must race against time: overexposure to heat and dust for example, results in reduced moisture in the peas and affects adversely color, flavor, and texture. Hence, during the pea pack, both field crews and packing plants operate around the clock. Since the area is but sparsely populated, labor is somewhat of a problem. Accordingly, mechanization has been adopted wherever possible. Peas are grown only for canning. There are six canneries in the area and in 1950 the total pack was 7,168,500 cases.

Unlike the Blue Mountain district which cans peas but raises almost no seed, the Palouse district raises peas solely for seed. Peas fit in as an alternative crop with wheat instead of leaving the land in fallow. The area has highly favorable physical conditions for the crop — cool temperatures and adequate rainfall. And the same equipment is used as for wheat. The crop is highly concentrated in its distribution, being largely grown in the eastern edge of the Palouse counties. This area, now the most important dry pea area in the United States, appears to be replacing the older dry pea-growing states of Wisconsin, Michigan, New York, and Colorado.

Irrigation Farming. The importance of irrigation farming to the Indians and Spaniards has been pointed out. The Mormons in Utah were the first Anglo-Saxons to practice it on a large scale on this continent and by this means transformed an inhospitable desert into a productive oasis. Since 1847, when the first pioneers entered Salt Lake Valley, irrigation has been followed wherever water was available. In the dry

lands it is the water of the stream rather than the land itself that has value; hence he who controls the water controls the land.

Since irrigation is restricted to the smoother, less sloping terraces and to alluvial belts along rivers, and since the total amount of water is definitely limited, it is obvious that most of the Intermontane Basins and Plateaus — probably more than 95 per cent — can never be irrigated.

The silting of reservoirs. Farming and grazing on slopes have resulted in soil erosion, which has skimmed off much topsoil from an extensive area. Much of this silt has been transported into reservoirs which were built to store water for irrigation. Without these reservoirs only a pastoral civilization could be supported. Yet today every principal irrigation reservoir below an altitude of 7,000 feet is in jeopardy of becoming silted up. Since mechanical removal of silt costs 5 to 50 times as much as the original reservoir, the cost is too great to justify taking the mud out and letting the reservoir fill up again. This is a significant argument for fighting soil erosion throughout the West.

Oases. Only representative irrigated areas and those of greatest interest are discussed. These are (1) the Salt Lake Oasis, (2) the Reno Oasis, (3) the Snake River Plain, (4) the Salt River Valley, (5) the Imperial Valley, (6) the Columbia Plateau Apple Valleys (Yakima and Wenatchee), (7) the Columbia Basin Reclamation Project (Grand Coulee), and (8) the Rio Grande Project (Figure 13–6).

Salt Lake Oasis.[17] Utah is of especial interest to the geographer for nowhere on the continent is there a closer adaptation of agriculture and its institutions to nature.

The Valley of the Great Salt Lake, one of the most favored spots in the entire West, was settled by the Mormon Church which claimed a vast territory extending from the Sierra Nevada to the Rockies and from Oregon to Southern California. Settlement of much of it began immediately after hundreds

---

[17] Charles Langdon White, "The Agricultural Geography of the Salt Lake Oasis," *Journal of the Scientific Laboratories of Denison University*, September 1925, Vol. 21, pp. 117-283.

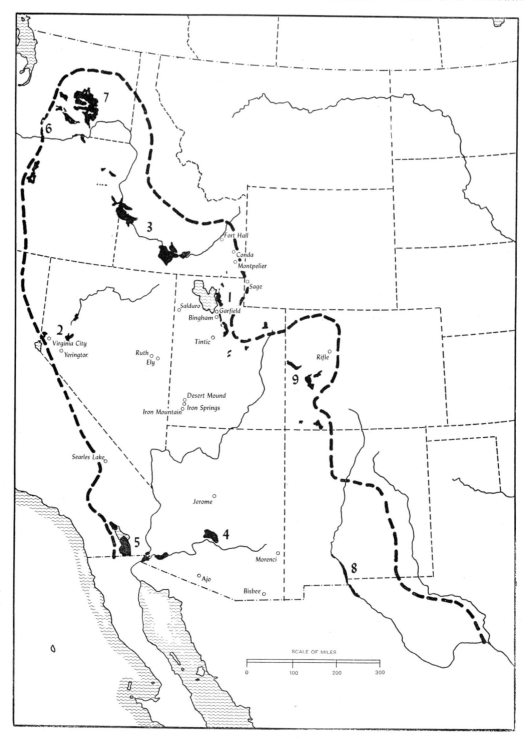

Fort Hall
Conda
Montpelier
Sage
Salduro
Garfield
Bingham
Tintic
Virginia City
Yeringtor
Ruth
Ely
Desert Mound
Iron Springs
Iron Mountain
Rifle
Searles Lake
Jerome
Morenci
Ajo
Bisbee

SCALE OF MILES

0   100   200   300

of land-hungry immigrants from the East and even from Europe arrived. Brigham Young, carefully picking leaders and families, sent them to definite locations and by means of these outpost colonies, based on irrigation farming, systematically colonized Utah.

The area occupied by the Oasis in 1953 coincides with that in 1857 (10 years after the arrival of the Mormon pioneers) which indicates that land suitable for habitation was rapidly acquired. Some irrigated areas have been added as a result of water sources brought from outside the watershed but for the most part these have not changed the map of irrigated land very much.

The lofty Wasatch Mountains tower above the Oasis on the east; from their snow-clad slopes comes the life-giving water for the valleys below. The greater part of Utah is rugged. Hence the levelness of the area at the foot of the Wasatch and the depth of its fertile soils are additional reasons for the virtual restriction of settlement in Utah to the Salt Lake Oasis. As Egypt is primarily the Nile Valley and Delta rather than the large political block portrayed on the map, so Utah is really but an insular strip of human habitation at the foot of the Wasatch. This, the heart of Utah, contains about three fourths of the state's inhabitants.

At the mouth of almost every stream canyon, as it emerges from the Wasatch, is located a city or village girdled by green fields and adorned by orchards and shade trees. Each town is separated from its neighbors by five to ten miles of field, orchard, or pasture. Both north and south of the Oasis, where there is less water, the towns and irrigated farms lie at greater intervals.

Small holdings, cultivated thoroughly, prevail — a result of scarcity of arable land, a limited supply of water for irrigation, the early Mormon land system, and dense population. Here the birth rate is high — a conse-

quence of high fertility and approval by the Mormon Church of early marriage and large families.

Possibly 90 per cent of the farmers dwell in towns — the Church, the desert, and the canyon stream conspiring to produce this village concentration. Farms lie one to five miles from towns, each of which has its church and school buildings, its public hall and stores; each is compact and amazingly self-sufficient.

Crops are so diversified that farms resemble gardens, yet three fourths of the cropped land is devoted to sugar beets, wheat, and hay (primarily alfalfa), the remaining one fourth being devoted to fruits and vegetables. Most farmers concentrate on those products which give a high return per acre and can be sold locally. If distant markets are sought, products that can travel in concentrated form are grown, for these can better stand high transport costs. Much farm land is in pasture and dairying is outstanding. About 30 per cent of Cache Valley, for example, is used for pasture. Milk is trucked from Salt Lake City to Colorado and even to California.[18]

The water-logged land near Utah Lake is pastured by dairy cattle and the alkaline soils near Great Salt Lake are grazed occasionally in winter by sheep if water for drinking is available. If it is not, snow suffices. On the higher portions of the old lake plain and on the coarse soils of the benches are grown the irrigated crops (Figure 13–7). Most orchards occupy benchlands, since trees do well on coarse soils and benefit from air drainage. On lands above the ditch, considerable winter wheat is dry-farmed. Such areas, however, are merely adjuncts of irrigated farms, and are largely devoid of dwellings and trees.

The Reno Oasis. On the west side of the

[18] Elbert E. Miller, University of Utah. Personal communication.

Figure 13–6. *Facing page:* Mining towns and major irrigation areas in the Intermontane Basins and Plateaus Region. The irrigated areas are: (1) the Salt Lake Oasis, (2) the Reno Oasis, (3) the Snake River Plain, (4) the Salt River Valley, (5) the Imperial Valley, (6) the Columbia Plateau Apple Valleys, (7) the Columbia Basin Reclamation Project (Grand Coulee), and (8) the Rio Grande Project.

Great Basin at the foot of the Sierra Nevada lies a beautiful and productive oasis fed by streams from melting snow. It is separated from the Salt Lake Oasis at the eastern end of the basin by hundreds of miles of practically unproductive desert. The most fruitful part of the Reno Oasis, the Truckee confined to the valleys of the Humboldt, Truckee, Carson, and Walker rivers. Yet all this in the aggregate comprises less than one per cent of the area of the state. Elsewhere agricultural enterprises consist almost exclusively of grazing.

The Snake River Plain. Another important

Figure 13–7. Intensive farming in a portion of the Salt Lake Oasis, Utah. Water from streams emerging from the Wasatch Mountains sustains hundreds of small farms. The light-colored material in the middle foreground is a mud-rock flow brought down from a canyon during a heavy rain. Great damage was done to much valuable farm land. (Courtesy of U. S. Forest Service.)

Meadows, is sustained by waters of the Truckee River. Here is a checkerboard composed of hundreds of small farms, mostly 40 acres in size, on which are grown alfalfa, wheat, and vegetables. Dairying too is important. The largest project, the Newlands, was created by the United States Bureau of Reclamation.

The greater part of the irrigable land, and, therefore, of the agriculture of Nevada, is oasis in this region is the Snake River Plain. In many ways it is more productive agriculturally than the entire state of Utah. Nevertheless it is tributary to Salt Lake City. As compared with the Salt Lake Oasis, it lacks the productive nearby mines and possesses little focal quality with respect to transportation. It supports more than one half the population of Idaho. Into this area at the foot of the Grand Tetons come two forks of the Snake River pouring their waters through head gates into canals. The irrigable land totals about 1,700,000 acres or almost one tenth of the irrigated land of the United States. The chief crops are alfalfa and other feed crops, potatoes, sugar beets, dry beans, and wheat. Vegetables and fruit are important also — particularly near Ontario and Payette.

Some sheep and dairy cattle also are raised, the sheep being grazed in the national forests in summer and on the plain in spring and autumn. They are fed in oases in winter. Large numbers of lambs are fattened for market.

Most of the products when converted into a concentrated form have high value, a necessity in an area located far from large consuming markets. A notable exception is the potato, a product that is both perishable and relatively inexpensive. Because of its superiority to all other Anglo-American potatoes for baking, the Idaho potato (grown from St. Anthony to Boise and Nampa) is in demand almost everywhere in the United States.

The Salt River Valley. First of the major irrigation projects undertaken by the Bureau of Reclamation and one of the most economically successful in Anglo-America is that in the Salt River Valley. Twentieth-century engineers have built near the inner margin of the desert of south-central Arizona the large Roosevelt Dam, which has converted the upper valley into Roosevelt Lake and has turned the lower valley into a great citrus-, truck-, alfalfa-, and cotton-growing area. The site chosen was the narrow canyon of the Salt River just below the junction with Tonto Creek about 75 miles north of Phoenix. Behind the dam is impounded enough water to irrigate the fields for two years if not a drop of rain should fall. The dam supplies water for canals and laterals aggregating some 1,321 miles. Additional dams have been constructed for providing storage, chiefly for the development of power, thereby forming a continuous chain of lakes 60 miles long.

The valley, physiographically considered, is not a valley but a detrital plain — very flat and with alluvium 50 to 200 feet deep.

Centuries before white men arrived, Indians had farmed this area. According to archeologists they settled in the valley about 700 A. D., reached their peak in 1200 A. D., and disappeared about 1400. It is believed they abandoned this area because the soil became water-logged and, lacking pumps, they could no longer grow crops. So admirably planned and executed were some of their works that they would do credit to modern engineering. Since then the problem of wet land has been solved, the ground-water level being controlled by pumps.

Probably the main reason for the success of the Salt River Project is the long frostless season; 60 per cent of the land grows winter crops. Though agriculture is both intensive and diversified, a permanent system of farming has not yet evolved. At first alfalfa and dairying predominated; then Egyptian cotton became the leading crop as a result of high prices for long-staple cotton during the first World War. At present alfalfa occupies about half the cultivated area, though cotton, now short-staple or middling, remains important. Cantaloupes, watermelons, dates, and figs are produced in large quantities near Phoenix.

The future of this project and of the people who live in it will depend largely upon the care given to the watersheds. Unless trees and grass are planted and maintained as a check against soil wash, Roosevelt Lake will be filled with sediment in approximately 200 years. A series of successive dry years recently has worried the people of this area.

The Imperial Valley. From an economic standpoint the Imperial Valley, whose frost-free season is one of the longest in the United States, varying from 303 to 323 days, has a bright future. It occupies the cultivable part of the Salton Basin and first attracted settlement about 45 years ago.

The Inter-California Canal was built down the slope of the delta through a part of northern Mexico toward the Salton Sea (Figure 13–8), but the river during a flood cut around a head gate of the canal, enlarged the channel, and doubled the area of the Salton Sea. From then to 1935, Imperial Valley

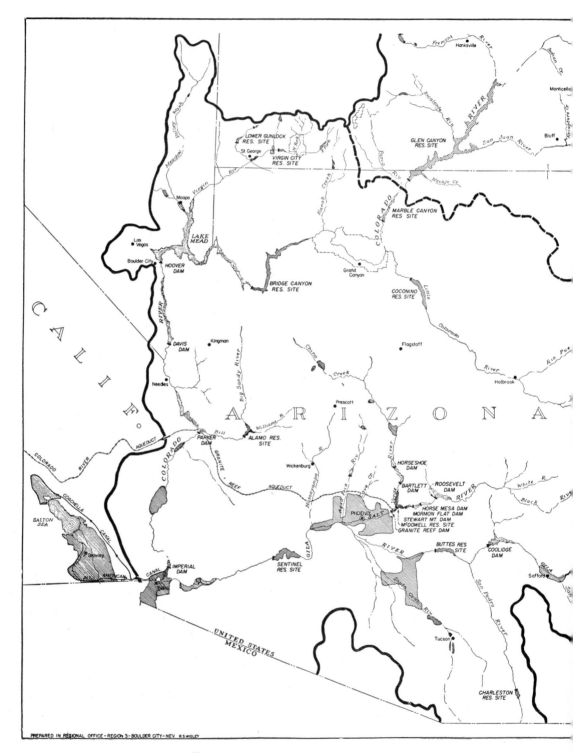

Figure 13–8. Lower Colorado River Basin.

EXPLANATION

Constructed Reservoirs

Reservoir Sites

Irrigated Lands

Constructed Transmountain Diversions

Possible Transmountain Diversions

UNITED STATES
DEPARTMENT OF THE INTERIOR
BUREAU OF RECLAMATION
COLORADO RIVER INVESTIGATIONS
LOWER COLORADO RIVER BASIN
GENERAL MAP

SCALE OF MILES

farmers lived in terror. The Hoover Dam Project, however, has changed all this, for the river is now kept under control. This dam, one of the highest in the world, has formed behind it an artificial reservoir, Lake Mead (Figure 13–9). The stored water is carried down the Colorado River and diverted at Imperial Dam, passing through desilting works (Figure 13–10), and carried to the valley through the All-American Canal. The All-American Canal was built some 80 miles across the most forbidding part of the Great American Desert so as to lie entirely within United States territory, and to increase the irrigable area of the Imperial Valley. It carries Colorado River water from 20 miles north of Yuma through sand dunes and across a desertic high tableland to the Valley. Drainage and salinity are ever present and are serious problems in the irrigated areas.

Most of the crops, with the exception of alfalfa, have a high value per acre and compensate for the high cost of water. Particularly important are the many early truck crops — carrots, lettuce, cabbage, cantaloupes, tomatoes, and peas. Dates, citrus fruits, flax, sugar beets, and cotton also are important. A leading money crop is the crisp head lettuce, which dominates the American market during the winter from December to March. So successful has this area become in the growing of this crop that it has practically ruined the production of lettuce in greenhouses along the southern shore of Lake Erie. Moreover, it constitutes an outstanding item of business of the Southern Pacific Lines — thousands of carloads a year. In recent years flax has ranked among the first two or three crops. Vegetable growing is reputed to be more highly mechanized here than in any other area in the world. With a natural environment much like that of the Nile Delta, the Imperial Valley produces high-grade long staple cotton. Despite its type of climate, the Imperial Valley leads all other California counties in the production of sugar beets. Alfalfa which yields ten tons per acre and five to seven cuttings in a single year, is fed to livestock, and is shipped out in the concentrated form of dairy prod-

Figure 13–9. Hoover Dam, with Lake Mead behind it, is one of the greatest of America's man-made wonders. Lake Mead is 115 miles long and up to eight miles wide. Some of its waters pour through giant turbines at the base of the dam to produce electricity for Arizona, Southern California, and Nevada. (Courtesy of U. S. Bureau of Reclamation.)

ucts and fat cattle and sheep. Herefords and Brahman cattle are now being cross-bred in an effort to get animals better able to withstand the mid-summer heat. The sheep are range animals brought here specifically to be fattened. The Imperial Valley has one of the West's most important livestock feeding industries.

Where water is to be had in sufficient amounts, two or more crops are grown on the same fields during the year — which is not common in the United States. In a recent year the Valley's agricultural production was valued at more than 125 million dollars with 16 crops averaging more than one million dollars each.

Farm labor is a problem over much of the **arid** Southwest and particularly of Imperial Valley. Only one aspect of this labor problem is discussed here — that of the "wetbacks." Wetbacks are Mexicans who cross the border illegally. While the name appears to apply only to those who wade across the shallow Rio Grande, it also includes those who climb fences or cut holes in them. At least half a million Mexicans move across the border each year.

These people work at substandard wages and most of them live under deplorable conditions. Their very presence constitutes an adverse economic and social condition. An investigation in Arizona disclosed filthy living quarters and dangerously contaminated water supplies. Many of the camps consist of crude shacks without sanitary facilities.

Congress has moved toward checking the flow of wetbacks by making it a felony to transport, harbor, or conceal them. It is realized that temporary alien labor is needed for harvesting certain crops, but it should be contract labor with a definite minimum wage. Accordingly, the United States and Mexican governments have signed a migrant-labor agreement permitting 100,000 to 200,000 Mexican nationals to enter the United States for temporary farm work.[19]

Columbia Plateau Apple Valleys. In the rain shadow of the Cascade Mountains lies a series of disconnected oases — Anglo-America's most famous apple-growing area — the Yakima, Hood River, Wenatchee, and Okanogan valleys. Sixty per cent of the irrigated land is in fruit, chiefly apples. Other important crops are alfalfa, asparagus, dry beans, grapes, hops, peppermint, potatoes, sugar beets, and vegetables, as well as soft fruits.

The Yakima Valley ranks high in agriculture in the State of Washington, in the Intermontane Region and nationally. A quality product, national advertising, and national and international markets are responsible. Yet this prestige has been attained solely from irrigation from the Yakima River and

[19] For a graphic and moving set of articles on the distressing plight of the Mexican "wetback" see the *New York Times* for March 25 through March 29, 1951.

its tributaries, which are in a region receiving only 7.5 inches of precipitation per year, less than one third of which falls during the growing season.

In the public mind Yakima and fruit are synonymous, despite the great importance of open field crops. Most orchards are planted on slopes to benefit from air drainage. Apples

alfalfa, and small grains. The animal industries, involving cattle and sheep, also have attained prominence in recent years. Many bands of sheep are grazed in the Cascade Mountains in summer and fed during winter in the valley. Much hay and grain and pasture are available.[20]

The Wenatchee Valley which is typical of

Figure 13–10. Desilting works at Imperial Dam on the Colorado River, 250 miles below Hoover Dam. Dotted with constellations of clarifiers, these still pools lose by gravity their heavy load of silt and then spill into the All-American Canal, starting an 80-mile journey to the Imperial Valley. (Courtesy of U. S. Bureau of Reclamation.)

occupy more land than any other fruit crop, though pears are very important. These two crops are grown mostly in the Upper Valley (upstream from Union Gap), a few miles southeast of the City of Yakima, and apricots, cherries, grapes, and peaches in the Lower Valley (downstream from Union Gap). There is less land favored by air drainage in the Lower Valley so that field crops are important — row crops (asparagus, corn, hops, peppermint, potatoes, and sugar beets),

all apple-growing districts in this region extends from the Columbia River to Leavenworth, a distance of about 22 miles. The part used for fruit varies from one to two miles in width but increases to six miles along the Columbia River at the city of Wenatchee.

The climate is highly favorable for apples:

[20] Richard M. Highsmith, Jr. and Elbert E. Miller, "Open Field Farming in the Yakima Valley, Washington," *Economic Geography*, Vol. 28, January 1952.

below zero temperatures are rare; the growing season approximates 200 days (apples *need* close to 150 frost-free days); and the high percentage of sunshine gives the fruit an attractive color. Most of the trees are grown on slopes to benefit from air drainage. Surveys made by the United States Weather Bureau show that on a frosty morning a rise of 50 feet on a slope will sometimes cause the temperature to be 30 degrees higher than at the base of the hill. The precipitation is both inadequate and badly distributed for tree growth without irrigation. The soils, while extremely varied, generally contain adequate nutriment, except nitrogen, for which deficiency alfalfa is grown. Most of the farms are small, 10 to 15 acres, and are operated by owners.

On the average, a train of 45 to 50 refrigerator cars, loaded with approximately 750 boxes of apples per car, leaves the Wenatchee Gateway every day of the year.

The Columbia Basin Reclamation Project (Grand Coulee Dam). During the Ice Age the course of the Columbia River was obstructed by ice, forcing the river to cut a new channel in the State of Washington some 150 miles from the Canadian border. When the ice receded northward, the dam disappeared and the river resumed its former channel, leaving the old channel abandoned. It is now known as the Grand Coulee. The Columbia River Basin, a flat land of some two and one-half million acres, with rich volcanic soil in an arid and semiarid area, became important for wheat and livestock around the turn of the century. But a slight increase in rainfall made a proportionately greater increase in yield and after a year or two of good crops on marginal land farmers started to plow and plant even poorer land. Then followed a period of below normal precipitation and many farmers went broke.

In the winter of 1933–1934, the federal government began construction on the Grand Coulee Dam, largest concrete dam in the world, aiming to create a new agricultural frontier and make irrigable some 1,200,000 acres of semiarid land in the Big Bend area of south-central Washington for the several hundred thousand "Okies," "Arkies," and others forced into migration by soil erosion. The Grand Coulee Dam was built on the Columbia River 92 miles west and north of Spokane and just below the head of the Grand Coulee (Figure 13–11). Here granite is exposed on both banks. Behind the dam lies Lake Roosevelt, a 151-mile long storage reservoir, impounding 10,000,000 acre-feet of water — enough to supply New York City for ten years. More than 4,000 miles of main and secondary canals have been constructed. The irrigated area is actually about 50 miles from the Grand Coulee Dam. Although a wide variety of crops is grown — alfalfa, dry beans, onions, other vegetables, sugar beets, potatoes, and grapes — irrigation from the canals did not begin until 1952 and the agricultural pattern is not yet developed. The dam supplies water for irrigation agriculture and power for manufacturing, transportation, and domestic use.

The Rio Grande Project. The Middle Rio Grande Valley, above and below El Paso, constitutes one of the oldest irrigated areas on the continent, having been developed by pre-Columbian Indians. Three centuries of Spanish dominance did not materially change the systems nor extend the area "under the ditch." When the land became a part of the United States, some improvements were made by private capital. Since the federal government did not own any land in the area, it was not interested in development even after the passage of the Reclamation Act in 1902. As more and more water was diverted from the Rio Grande, it became a dry stream immediately below El Paso. As a result, a considerable part of the total irrigated area — the Juarez Valley — was rapidly reverting to desert, and the Mexican government threatened suit unless their lands were provided with water and again made irrigable. After considerable negotiation, Elephant Butte Dam in southern New Mexico was constructed and a treaty signed guaranteeing the Juarez Valley 60,000 acre-feet of water a year delivered to the head of the International Diversion Canal. The Rio Grande Project then developed rapidly under federal auspices. Today it contains some 175,000 acres. At first it produced fruits and

Figure 13–11. General air-view of Grand Coulee Dam in Washington. Grand Coulee is the largest engineering work ever attempted by man. (Courtesy of U.S. Bureau of Reclamation.)

alfalfa almost exclusively, but its major crop now is long-staple cotton.[21]

Flood-water Farming. The third and least important type of agriculture from the standpoint of acreage, but the most unique

[21] Edwin J. Foscue, "The Mesilla Valley of New Mexico: A Study in Aridity and Irrigation," *Economic Geography*, Vol. 7, No. 1, January 1931, pp. 1-27.

among Anglo-American Indian forms of husbandry, is flood-water farming. This method differs from dry farming in that soil moisture is not conserved by disking after each rain; in fact, no method whatever is used to divert or convey water. The field is flooded but the sheet of water must not assume great velocity or cover the growing plants with too much detritus. It is practiced either on gentle slopes below rock or shale escarpments or in valley floors often inundated by sheet floods. Two crops only, corn and beans, are grown. In planting, the Indians dig a deep hole with a planting stick and drop the seed into the hole. They hardly disturb the ground.

Although a precarious type of farming, it has been followed by sedentary Indians, particularly the Yumans, since prehistoric times in the more isolated parts of Arizona and New Mexico. Five Yuman tribes still occupy parts of the Southwest, but the four which lived along the lower Colorado and Gila Rivers are now extinct.[22] When the Spaniards arrived, flood-water farming was changed, as a result of the introduction of livestock, from strictly subsistence farming to a phase of commercial farming. With modifications, flood-water farming may reclaim successfully a considerable acreage in the Southwest.

Grazing

In this region of rough terrain, light rainfall, sparse vegetation, and poor transportation, most of the land (if it is to be used at all), must serve as range for livestock (Figure 13–12). Probably not more than 3.5 per cent of the land between the Rockies and the Sierra Nevada–Cascades is in crops. Some cannot even serve as range; the ten-inch isohyet is said to separate grazing country from true desert. Disaster awaits him who settles in the latter. Grazing, however, is possible where the precipitation is less than ten inches providing the animals browse in winter when snow or rain occurs.

Ranches of 2,000 to 4,000 acres and more are usually necessary. The greater part of the land does not make even good range, much being so poor that 25, 50, and even 75 acres are needed to support one steer.

Obviously the pronounced differences in elevation cause differences in precipitation and in vegetation which, in turn, are reflected in the seasonal utilization of the range. Mountain pastures are strictly summer pastures; deserts are utilized mostly in winter when snowfall provides water for sheep and occa-

[22] E. F. Castetter and W. H. Bell, *Yuman Indian Agriculture.* Albuquerque: University of New Mexico Press, 1951.

Figure 13–12. A roundup in Arizona. The barren landscape is the result of overgrazing. The grass is cropped so short one year that it has no chance to make seed for the next. In pioneer days grasses grew luxuriantly here. (Courtesy of U. S. Forest Service.)

sionally for cattle. Oasis pastures and feed-lots are caring for more and more animals in winter.

Sheep. This region has been one of Anglo-America's leading sheep centers since 1893. Since sheep do well on rugged land and over a wide range of climatic conditions, their production has been especially successful in the sparsely populated arid West (Figure 11–10). Furthermore they relish the shrubby and wheaty types of forage, which horses and cattle do not like.

After 1870 the sheep industry expanded rapidly in the West. In early days the only expense was for labor and supplies, the only investment in the animals themselves and in a camp outfit. Expansion continued until the range became overcrowded and overgrazed. Acquisition of land for dry farming also reduced numbers, for whenever dry farming enters an area, sheep give way to cattle.

Ranches handling sheep are nearly always located near streams or perennial waterholes. A man with a couple of dogs can manage and keep in good condition about 3,000 sheep. The herder is with his flocks constantly, directing grazing, preventing his sheep from straying, and protecting them against the depredations of wild animals. He is aided by a camp tender who brings supplies and moves camp. Herding is a lonesome occupation, and before trucks became common, western states passed laws compelling herders to work in pairs. The sheep are raised for both wool and mutton, although emphasis is turning toward the latter.

Cattle. Although beef cattle can graze on rough land and sparse vegetation, as a rule they are raised in areas of better forage. In summer they are driven into large areas of abundant grassland and abundant browse in the mountains. In winter they are either driven to valley ranches and fed on alfalfa, beet pulp, and grain, or are shipped to California or the Corn Belt to be fattened. Historically in the West more livestock have been raised than could be fattened on the feed produced, whereas in the East the reverse was true; hence the importance of stocker and feeder shipments from the West to the East. However, since 1925 a larger

share of western marketings has been sent to western slaughterers. Ogden and Salt Lake City have become important stockyard and slaughtering centers. This is true particularly of Ogden because of its location at the junction of major railroads. Thus the line of east-west movement (the boundary to which western packer-buyers must come from coastal points to purchase their slaughter livestock) has gradually moved eastward.[23] The same trend holds for sheep and hogs.

Horses. Outside the irrigated districts, this entire region is a land of the horse. In the Navajo Country, a family's wealth, prestige and standing have depended on the number of horses owned. Actually there have been too many horses; they have prevented many of their Indian owners from having enough to eat. Accordingly, the federal government for a long time tried to convince the Indians that in order to save their fast-disappearing grass, they would have to sell some of their horses. Finally in 1939, thousands were sold. The aim is for better breeds and smaller numbers.

Goats. Angora and milk goats thrive in the high, dry lands of Arizona and New Mexico where Indians run them with their sheep. Goats do well where cattle would starve.

Mining — Copper, Silver, Lead, and Zinc

From the Wasatch to the Sierra Nevada and from the Columbia Plateau to the Mexican border, the region is dotted with communities located solely to tap the mineral resources — communities that enjoy a mushroom growth so long as the mines produce, but decline precipitously and become ghost towns once the ores are worked out (Figure 13–13).

In several of the states, particularly Nevada, prospecting for minerals was the major factor in settlement and early development. Moreover, the total value of minerals mined during the history of the Intermontane Re-

---

[23] Western Livestock Marketing Research Technical Committee, "Shifts in the Trade in Western Slaughter Livestock," *Agricultural Information Bulletin No. 14*, p. 2. Washington, D. C.: Government Printing Office, 1950.

Figure 13–13. Virginia City, America's first big silver-mining camp. Millions of dollars poured from the mines and the town boomed as few others have. At its height in 1880 Virginia City had a population of 10,917; now it has only 800. (Courtesy of *Dodge News*.)

gion still is said to be greater than that from any other single source.

The first prospectors, mostly gold miners from California, sought only placers. Later, however, they worked vein outcrops. The Intermontane West is no longer the land of the lone prospector with his lowly burro, pick and blankets, beans and bacon, searching for gold and silver. Rather is it the land of the large corporation taking great risks, investing fabulous sums of money, and employing eminent engineers and a large labor force. It is now concerned more with low-grade than with high-grade ores.

Copper mining is most important in this region but its status of relatively recent date depended upon the revolutionary developments in the science of metallurgy. There was no question regarding the reserves. The big question was whether the ore could be concentrated at a cost that would permit its sale. The operator had to make one of two choices — both necessarily bad — either (1) smelt almost the entire ore output, which means exorbitant fuel cost or (2) discard so much of the low-grade material as to make the whole mining process unprofitable. The problem facing porphyry copper was almost identical

with that facing taconite today. Porphyry copper was so named because it is finely dispersed in a hard igneous rock called "porphyry." Today such ore can be successfully concentrated even when there is less than one ton of copper in each 100 tons of copperbearing rock. This accomplishment has been one of the marvels of our time.

Some Major Districts in Utah. Figure 13–6 shows the concentration of mines near the vigorous agricultural settlements of the Salt Lake Oasis, the leading nonferrous mining area of the United States. Location here is highly significant, for every mine, regardless of size, is near good transport facilities. A deposit of equal richness located in some parts of Nevada, however, might be held back permanently by high transport costs. Bingham, Tintic, and Park City — the last just beyond the border in the Rocky Mountain Region — yield nine tenths of Utah's metals.

Bingham, lying in a canyon of the same name, in a low Basin Range about 30 miles southwest of Salt Lake City, is one of the world's best known and most profitable mining ventures. Historically, it is important because the first mining claim in the state of Utah was staked out there in 1863. Though several mines working copper, lead, silver, and zinc are located in Bingham, the most famous and most profitable is that of the Utah Copper Company. There actually the great electric shovels are tearing down an enormous mountain (1,400 feet high) of low-grade ore, 1.07 per cent metallic copper. The mountain is girdled with levels of terraces, tracked, and completely electrified (Figure 13–14). Laden ore-cars are delivered to the mountain base, made into trains, transported to concentration mills, and later to the Garfield smelter. So large is the reserve that mine and town reflect a permanency seldom associated with mining. Copper is also mined in Bingham by the leaching and precipitation process.

Tintic, wedged in the low East Tintic Hills, a southern extension of the metal-rich Oquirrh Range, 60 miles south of Salt Lake City, is an important silver-lead producer.

The first mining claim was made here in 1869, but because of poor transportation facilities, early development was retarded until railroads were projected into the area in the 1870's. In 1940 the district was depressed as were most silver-producing areas in Anglo-America. Like most mining towns, it has its ups and downs depending upon the demand and price of silver.

Some Mining Communities in Nevada. In 1859 silver was discovered in Nevada, a state differing from others in the West in that its economic life and very existence have been derived from mining. From 1875 to 1877, Nevada produced more gold and silver than all the rest of the United States combined. Near the western border of the desert lies *Virginia City,* formerly the greatest silver mining camp of all time and "a rip-roaring prodigy of the wildest days of the West." The ore was discovered by ignorant prospectors who, seeking only gold, had cast aside and cursed the blue-black rock which later assayed as high as $4,791 per ton.

As soon as the news spread, a rush set in. Tent houses and saloons sprang up like mushrooms. There was no economic basis for livelihood except mining: fuel and food had to be brought over the Sierra Nevada by wagon trains from California; even water was scarce.

Thousands of people — gamblers, prostitutes, millionaires, promoters, lawyers, doctors, bonafide miners, and even preachers — flocked there. For awhile the mines were valued on the stock exchange at 400 million dollars.

In 1877 the Comstock Mine produced ore valued at 36 million dollars. As time went on, mining had to be carried to greater depths, entailing serious heat and water problems.[24] The ground water pouring into the shafts sent overhead costs to such a point that even the better ore bodies could scarcely be mined at a profit. The water problem was finally solved in 1878 by building at a cost of four and one-half million dollars the nine-mile Sutro Tunnel. Temperatures rose to 120° F. and ice had to be taken below for miners and mules.

---

[24] When President U. S. Grant visited Virginia City and went down into the mine, he fainted dead away. When reviving he said: "That's as near Hell as I want to go."

Even so, four picked men in some stopes could not produce as much as a single miner in a cool drift. After two decades of large-scale mining the industry declined and Virginia City, which had attained a maximum population of 10,917 in 1880, had so wilted by 1950 as not to be included among the state's first 12 cities and towns. It exists now only because of the tourist business.

The Ely District, lying in eastern Nevada in the heart of the parched Great Basin, is the principal copper-mining area of Nevada. Its porphyry ores are very much like those at Bingham, the copper being disseminated in veins so small that crushing fails to separate the metal from the gangue. The mineralized zone is about nine miles long and one-half to one and one-half miles wide, the ore being found in the igneous rocks which break through the sedimentaries. Mining began with the discovery of gold and silver-lead ores in 1868-1869.

The town of Ely supported a population of only 3,558 in 1950, a drop of 14.1 per cent from 1940. The mines lie 140 miles south of Cobre on the Southern Pacific to which they are connected by the Nevada Northern Railway. The unproductive desert in the intervening land exerts a tremendous charge against the mines. This is in marked contrast to the situation at Bingham, which is close to the productive agricultural lands of the Salt Lake Oasis and hence benefits from transportation built and supported largely by farming.

Two new copper developments in Nevada are those by Anaconda Copper Company at Yerington, and Kennicott Copper Corporation at Ruth. At Yerington a huge overburden of some ten million tons covering the copper to a depth of 150 feet had to be removed by huge shovels. The ore is trucked out of the hole by a fleet of gigantic trucks each able to haul 25 tons in a single trip. The ore body now being mined is an oxide ranging up to one per cent copper. Below this body of ore, which extends to about 250 feet below the surface, lies a sulfide copper deposit whose copper content is approximately the same. At Ruth, ores averaging .83 per cent copper are being mined, a shaft having been sunk

1,700 feet deep. The "block caving system" of mining is employed here. This mine is a high-cost producer, yields only a small margin of profit, and depends upon a high price for copper to operate.

Some Arizona Highlands Mining Districts. The mines of the Arizona Highlands

Some of this copper is rich ore though there is also much of the lower-grade type. As elsewhere in the region, copper mining requires heavy capital investments. Arizona prospers and suffers according to the price of copper. The discovery of gigantic supplies in Chile, Peru, the Belgian Congo, and Canada results

Figure 13–14. Famous Utah Copper Company mine at Bingham, Utah. This is one of the world's largest and most interesting open-cut copper mines. The short, dark lines that appear on several of the terraces are trains carrying out the ore; from their

support approximately one half of the state's population, furnish the bulk of its railway tonnage, and provide the chief markets for most of its farm products. Moreover, Arizona is the first state in copper production. All the mines, of course, are not in the Highland Subregion, as for example, the Ajo District.

Since 1858 these mines have produced in excess of three billion dollars in metals, approximately 87 per cent of which was copper.

in the periodic closing down of numerous high-cost producing mines in Arizona. The critically short domestic copper output during the early years of the defense mobilization program has witnessed the birth of many mines, and the reopening of others which could not possibly operate during so-called "normal times."

Morenci, in the eastern part of the state, has been until recently the home of Arizona's largest copper mine. A low-grade ore body, it had been known for a long time but could not be worked profitably until the advent of modern technology. The Phelps Dodge interests have invested in excess of 30 million dollars to get at the 230 million tons of ore carrying only 1.06 per cent copper or about of its mines. The city boomed about 1900 and, though output rose and fell with the demand for copper, the district has been one of the nation's leading metal producers for more than 70 years.

The town itself is unique, houses clinging to the slopes tier above tier. It is the largest

minuteness in the photograph an idea may be had of the tremendous size of the mine. (Courtesy of Kennecott Copper Corporation.)

20 pounds to the ton. Open-pit mining is followed — gigantic electric shovels removing the ore and dumping it into trucks and trains.

Bisbee, located in the steepest part of the Mule Pass Gulch, is the center of one of the continent's richest copper-producing districts. It is located on the Southern Pacific Lines, which dominates rail transportation in the southern part of the region. Its ore is richer than that at Morenci. Mining is the sole support of Bisbee, whose history is the history town in the United States without house-to-house mail delivery. Despite its location in an area with an annual rainfall of only 18 inches, Bisbee has a small per capita water consumption (30 gallons per day). Consumption is restricted by the exceptionally high water rates which result from the fact that water must be pumped 9 miles against an elevation of more than 1,000 feet.

San Manuel, in Pinal County, a new development of Magma Copper Company, is considered to be the largest copper discovery in the United States in 20 to 30 years. The reserves of ore, averaging about 0.8 per cent copper, are estimated to be in excess of 500 million tons. The project includes an underground mine with an annual production of about ten million tons.

Mining — Additional Minerals

Metallic Minerals. *Iron Ore.* Although the Mormons discovered and worked iron ore near Cedar City more than a century ago, accurate information regarding the reserves and distribution was unavailable until quite recently. It was World War II that caused intensive research to be carried on in this mineral. Iron ore is widely distributed throughout the West — much more so than coking coal. Each state in this region has sizable reserves with relatively high iron content but the major deposits of the entire Intermontane Basins and Plateaus Region are in the Iron Mountain, Iron Springs, and Desert Mound areas of southwestern Utah. The total potential reserve here is placed at 500 million long tons and 100 million tons exceeding 45 per cent iron. Next most important are those in the Eagle Mountain district of Southern California.

The quality of the ore is high — in some respects superior to that of Eastern ores. The magnetite ores of Utah have a higher metallic content than those in the Mesabi and Birmingham areas, 56 per cent as compared with 52 and 36.6. The iron content of the Eagle Mountain deposits is 65.2 per cent. These ores are both hematite and magnetite. It is not anticipated that beneficiation of these ores will be necessary at any future time.

Utah, which ranks fourth in the nation in iron ore output, produces more than four million tons of ore annually. It supplies almost 60 per cent of all Western production. About half of this ore is consumed within Utah itself, about a fifth is shipped to blast furnaces near Pueblo, Colorado, and substantial quantities are sent to Fontana, California. Some is even shipped to Ohio, Illinois, and Pennsylvania. All the mines are open pits.

Uranium. The Intermontane Basins and Plateaus Region not only is the uranium center of the United States now, but promises to be for years to come. It also is the second largest source of uranium in the world. Colorado is the largest producer in the United States at present, but New Mexico and Utah and even Arizona are showing great promise. Trained geologists are literally combing the Colorado Plateau in search of uranium but the results are clouded with secrecy, due partly to national security measures.

This mineral, with a potential energy content three million times greater than that of coal, is widely distributed. Today its importance stems from its role as the principal ingredient in the manufacture of atomic bombs: it is a source of fissionable material that gives the bomb its explosive and destructive force. It is predicted, however, that by the end of the century it will have supplanted coal as a source of commercial power and that coal will be used chiefly as a source of organic chemicals.

Uranium occurs in several forms and is found in many kinds of rocks but a crumbly yellow substance, known as carnotite, is the source of most of it.[25] Deposits have been found in widely-spaced areas and new mines have sprung up in highly inaccessible and unknown places. Hundreds of prospectors, equipped with Geiger counters or scintillometers, are working alone, secretively, in an effort to "make a strike." Once the prospector has made his find, the ore comes under the jurisdiction of the Atomic Energy Commission to become part of the nation's stockpile for defense and scientific research.

Non-metallic Mineral Production. *Potash.* Potash, so indispensable to agriculture and industry, was not produced in the Western Hemisphere prior to the first World War. When the British blockade, however, shut off shipments to the United States, the government sought alternative supplies, procuring small quantities at Salduro on the Utah-Nevada border, from Great Salt Lake, from alkaline lakes in the Sand Hills of Nebraska, and from Searles Lake in the Mojave Desert

---

[25] "How Uranium Production Grows," *Mining World,* Vol. 13, July 1951, p. 39.

of Southern California. The end of the war found the United States with 128 potash plants in operation but with production costs so high that most of them could not survive. Searles Lake, remnant of an inland sea, is a salt deposit 12 square miles in size, containing a crystal mass whose surface is firm and compact. Brine is pumped from wells sunk into the lake and treated for potash. Until the more recent exploitation of the Carlsbad deposits in New Mexico, Searles Lake supplied 95 per cent of America's output. It continues, however, to produce, yielding 18,154 out of a national total of 1,264,119 short tons in 1950.

Phosphate rock.[26] The United States is believed to have 40 per cent of the known high-grade phosphate rock deposits of the world. The largest reserves in Anglo-America are in the West, partly in the Rocky Mountain Region and partly in the Intermontane Basins and Plateaus Region. The deposits, which occur over an area of some 100,000 square miles in Montana, Idaho, Wyoming, Utah, and Nevada, are divided into eastern and western portions with the dividing line extending from Helena through Salt Lake or coinciding roughly with the 111th meridian.

Despite the high quality of these deposits the actual tonnage exploited per annum is relatively small — amounting in 1950 to 783,209 long tons for the entire West and 573,044 long tons for the Intermontane Region and its mountainous fringe. This small production results from remoteness of the deposits from the large fertilizer markets in the Middle West, South, and Middle Atlantic States with resulting heavy transportation costs. Recently agronomists of Western beet-sugar companies discovered that proper applications of phosphate fertilizers increased sugar beet yields in alkaline soils of the Intermontane Region by as much as 16 per cent. This has created a considerable Western market for phosphate. Fortunately, too, sulfuric acid, a major raw material in the manufacture of commercial fertilizer, is available in requisite amounts and at reasonable cost as

a result of the smelting industry — particularly that phase treating copper ores.

There are now four major producers — three of which use open-pit mining methods and one underground methods. The deposits are of such high quality that they need little beneficiation. The most important mining operations are being carried on between Montpelier and Fort Hall, Idaho, at Conda, Idaho, and at Sage, Wyoming. At Conda underground methods are used.

Salt. Great Salt Lake is the major salt-producing area in the region. Yet, Utah produces less than one per cent of the national total.

Each spring the lake water is pumped into ponds on diked flats covering hundreds of acres. The density is so maintained that almost pure salt is precipitated in "garden ponds" and solids heavier than common salt in "settling ponds." In the autumn after the desert sun has evaporated the water, the salt is harvested by loosening it with tractor-drawn disc plows, piled near the railroad tracks with salt harvesters, and removed to a nearby refinery for purification and removal of moisture. Some 100,000 to 120,000 tons are produced annually and sold mostly in the 11 western states. The market for this low-priced and widely distributed commodity is determined by freight rate relationships between Utah and competitive areas. Utah production competes with that from Kansas on the east and California on the west. Utah utilizes about 20 per cent of its production. Seventy per cent of all Utah salt is used by the livestock industry.

Mineral Fuels. *Coal.* Fortunately this region is well endowed with coal. Among the states included, Utah ranks first both in reserves and production and in the importance of coal to the state's economy. Utah's 54 coal mines produced 6.1 million tons in 1951. Utah ranks ninth in coal production among American states and first among those west of the Mississippi River. All production is from underground mines.

Most (about 99 per cent) of the output is from two counties, Carbon and Emery — 77 per cent coming from Carbon County alone.

Utah coal is bituminous and subbitumi-

---

[26] "Symposium on Western Phosphate Mining," *Mining Transactions, AIME*, Vol. 184, August 1949.

nous, though only the former is mined. The Utah product has the highest heating value of any coal in the West.

Twenty-seven of the 54 mines are served by railroads and 27 by trucks. Most of the coal is marketed in Utah, Idaho, Montana, Nevada, Washington, Oregon, and California. Utah supplies California with blast furnace fuel. This coal, as well as that used in Utah's iron and steel industry is mined in the Castlegate-Sunnyside area.

New Mexico, too, has important coal production (more than one million tons), mostly in the northwestern part of the state near Gallup. Most of this is subbituminous in grade. However, the northern part of the state is part of one of the three coking coal producing areas of the West — the Trinidad-Raton area of Colorado and New Mexico.

Petroleum. Although the map of oil lands in this region is expanding and although the amount of drilling is increasing, the Intermontane Basins and Plateaus are but a minor producer — contributing less than 1 per cent of the national output. Utah, the largest producer, supplies eight per cent of the oil it refines.

Oil Shale (Figure 13–15). Some day oil shale must serve as a great source of petroleum. It is widely scattered over that part of the region in Utah south of the Uinta Mountains, in adjacent west central Colorado, and southern Wyoming (partly outside the Intermontane Region). Actually these shales contain not petroleum but kerogen which can be converted to crude oil by heating. At present it costs more to distill a gallon of gasoline from shale than to refine or polymerize it from crude oil. However, the United States Bureau of Mines has had an oil extraction plant since 1947 whose cost of operation is approaching the goal of commercial production.

Harnessing Water Power

Strictly speaking the water-power resources of intermontane Anglo-America are not particularly great since most of the region consists of basin and plateau country and of basin ranges — all too low to result in heavy precipitation. The existing water power is of two types: (1) that created on the borders by the precipitation falling in the Sierra Nevada, the Cascades, and the Rocky Mountains, and (2) that created by man-made dams of private industry and of the federal government — Hoover, Grand Coulee, McNary, Salt River, Strawberry, and others.

Grand Coulee. The Grand Coulee, on the Columbia River, is the largest hydro-electric plant in the world on the basis of both installed capacity and output, and accounts for 27 per cent of the total head on the Columbia from the Canadian border to the river's mouth. With its 2,700,000 H. P., it towers above all other outstanding world installations — Hoover Dam, the world's second largest (1,835,000 h.p.); Dnieprostroi, Russia (550,000); Wilson Dam at Muscle

Figure 13–15. A shale retort in Colorado dumps its load of spent, crushed ore after the oil has been extracted by heating. This type of retort, used now for experiments, is too slow for a potential shale-oil industry. Scientists are seeking a continuous process to handle millions of tons, and much progress was made during World War II. (Courtesy of *The Lamp*.)

Shoals (610,000); and Niagara (United States, 557,000; Canada, 1,048,000).

Hoover Dam. Located 30 miles east of Las Vegas on the Colorado River where it forms the boundary between Arizona and Nevada, the Hoover Dam shares with Grand Coulee the distinction of being man's most outstanding power achievement. Completed on March 1, 1936, it rises 727 feet above bed rock (Figure 13–9) and forms behind it Lake Mead with a capacity of ten billion gallons. Some of this power is sent as far as Los Angeles — 266 miles over deserts and mountains.

Manufacturing

The industries which have become located here result in large part from the region's isolation and have developed almost entirely (1) to meet the requirements of the local community, and (2) to convert bulky products of the field, range, and mine into concentrated forms for economical transportation to distant markets. Not a single city in the region can be considered a manufacturing city to the same extent as those of the American Manufacturing Belt.

The highest-ranking industries are smelting — ferrous and nonferrous — aluminum making, sugar refining, flour milling, canning, slaughtering, and meat packing. Lumbering is important locally.

Smelting: Nonferrous Metals. Smelting is the most important single industry in Utah. In fact, within a 30-mile radius of Salt Lake City is located the greatest concentration of nonferrous mining, milling, and smelting in the nation. It is reported that 16.2 per cent of the nation's copper-smelting capacity, for example, is located here. So many of the minerals produced are of such low-grade as to be unable to move to Pacific Northwest or Atlantic Seaboard mills without first being concentrated and smelted.

The Salt Lake area owes its importance to nearness to numerous productive metal mines and to a good supply of coal, excellent transport facilities, and ample labor. Though Salt Lake City is recognized as one of the world's major smelting centers, very little smelting, and no copper smelting, is actually done within the city because of space requirements, high taxes, and especially dust, smoke, and chemical fumes, which unless precipitated electrically, are often offensive, dangerous, and destructive. Five smelters and a number of concentration mills treat ores originating in Utah and in other states, and to some extent from foreign countries (Australia, Cuba, and Mexico). The Garfield smelter, largest copper smelter in the nation, treats principally the output of concentration mills at nearby Magna and Arthur. The Midvale Smelter treats lead concentrates and ores. Another plant just west of Garfield processes cobalt concentrates from Forney, Idaho, and contributes about 40 per cent of United States consumption. Other plants are operating at Tooele and Milford.

Their output consists of blister copper, lead bullion, and zinc oxide concentrates, products that are shipped to other areas for refining — for removing gold, silver, and other metals. Zinc concentrates are shipped outside Utah for smelting. It is significant that the total capacity in operations of milling and smelting is considerably in excess of the state's mine production.

Within the past few years, an electrolytic copper refinery was constructed at Garfield. It treats about half the state's output of blister copper, yielding a product 99.9 per cent pure. As a result of this plant, Utah now has a completely integrated copper industry. Smelting is also a major industry in Arizona, especially at Clarkdale, Douglas, Miami, Morenci, Hayden, and Superior, and in Texas in the El Paso area. El Paso and Inspiration also have refineries.[27] The El Paso plant, eight miles west of the city, is ideally located: it is on well-drained sandy soil with slope, there is ample room for expansion, and there is an adequate supply of water. The plant is constructed on four different ground levels. Unrefined copper is unloaded on the highest

---

[27] Whereas concentration mills and most smelters lie very close to the mines that support them, electrolytic refineries are located mostly on tidewater and 70 per cent of those of the United States between New York and Baltimore. These refineries are market-oriented in their location.

level and refined copper shipped from the lowest level. The only smelting in Nevada for many years was done in the Ely District at McGill, but now titanium metal is produced at Henderson, about 15 miles from Las Vegas. Power from Hoover and Davis dams is utilized.

Aluminum manufacture, a war-created industry, has become outstanding in the Columbia Plateau. Transmission lines fan out from the publicly-owned concrete giants at Grand Coulee, Bonneville, McNary, and elsewhere. In the Columbia River and its tributaries lurks nearly half the latent hydroelectric power of the United States. No four of our other rivers combined possess so much energy.

Availability of power in huge amounts and at low cost is vital to the aluminum industry, which is a hog for power. In fact, the aluminum industry is one of the few manufactural enterprises whose location is determined primarily by availability of large blocks of power at very low rates. In most industries power costs play but a small role in the total cost of production. The aluminum industry takes from one fourth to one half the energy output of the entire utility system, private and public, in Oregon and Washington. Columbia River industrial power rates are the lowest in the nation. In a recent year comparable prices were 2.5 mills per kilowatt hour at Bonneville, 3.4 in the TVA, and 7.3 in Boston. The aluminum industry obtains a significant part of its total power requirement at low rates for 'surplus' power sold on interruptible schedules, which permit service to be cut to the extent necessary to assure a firm supply to the high-rate users. The aluminum industry at times (in winter) thus has to reduce its consumption, for it is then that maximum demand occurs. Occasionally, too, the low head of water results from cold winter weather which permits but little runoff into streams. Interruptible power is low cost power provided when sufficient water is available for permiting full utilization of the hydroelectrical facilities. When the water supply is low, interruptible power is the first to be curtailed.

There is also an important aluminum ex-trusion plant at Phoenix, Arizona, which sends 70 per cent of its output to the aircraft industry.

Smelting: Ferrous Metals. Until the outbreak of World War II, this enormous region had only one small blast furnace two miles south of Provo, Utah. Under the urgent needs of war, however, the Defense Plant Corporation of the federal government decided to build the largest and the first completely integrated steel plant in the West at Geneva, Utah, near Provo. Constructed at a cost of more than 200 million dollars, it began production in December of 1943. The plant draws its iron ore 255 miles from the southwest, its coal 120 miles from the southeast, and its fluxing stone 35 miles from the south.

After the war this plant was sold to the United States Steel Corporation for $47,500,-000. Utah itself consumes little steel; the market is on the Pacific Coast, principally in the Los Angeles and San Francisco Bay areas of California, and in Oregon and Washington. In order to make the most of Geneva's capacity, the Corporation integrated the plant's production with that at Pittsburg, California, which has an important output of steel sheets and tin plate. Approximately one third of all the tin plate required by the American canning industry is used by canners west of the Rockies, together with those in Hawaii and Alaska.

The site of the Geneva plant is strategic. It assembles its basic raw materials at the blast furnaces economically, labor of high quality is in good supply, water of satisfactory grade is available at low cost and in enormous amount, and good rail and highway facilities are at hand. The only weakness is the limited home market.

The West had wanted an iron and steel industry for many years. Even after the termination of World War II, it was not certain that fabrication west of the Rockies could compete favorably with that in the East. It now appears that it can compete; favoring conditions are (1) security and social influences now operating toward decentralization of industry, and (2) increasing demand throughout the West for iron and steel in the oil industry, public utilities, construction, and the mining and milling industries.

Oil Refining. The north Salt Lake area, considering its small population, ranks very high in oil refining. Comprising four refineries, the industry has facilities for handling about 60,000 barrels of crude oil daily. About 40 per cent of the crude oil processed is converted into gasoline. A fifth refinery is located at Jensen in the Uinta area.

These refineries, which utilize Colorado (about 85 per cent), Utah, and Wyoming oil, not only provide Utah with 90 per cent of its gasoline requirements, but supply a considerable part of the market of the West (except for New Mexico). Idaho takes 78 per cent of these shipments. A finished-products pipeline extends from Salt Lake City to Pasco, Washington, through which various oil products follow one another in an unbroken stream without difficulty.[28] Another pipeline has been completed from Salt Lake City to Twin Falls.

Sulphuric Acid. One of man's most important industrial raw materials, sulphuric acid, is manufactured west of the copper smelter at Garfield. The annual output of 144,000 tons is consumed by the fertilizer, chemical, oil, cobalt, and copper-refining industries. This plant is well located with respect to raw materials sources, transport, and market.

Sugar Refining. Since the sugar beet is a major cash crop in the northern irrigated districts, although it is also grown in the Imperial Valley, sugar refining is an important industrial enterprise (Figure 3-7). Sugar beet areas invariably are characterized by scientific farming and reasonably prosperous farmers. Hand in hand with sugar beets goes the fattening of livestock, since tops, pulp, and residue molasses along with hay and grain can best be utilized in this way. In the past the West produced unfinished livestock, "feeders," which were sent into the Corn Belt for fattening. Today in all beet-sugar growing areas, large feeding operations are supported by the by-products of the beet industry.

[28] How these different products are sent through a single pipeline is discussed in *The Bulletin*, Standard Oil Company of California, April 1952, pp. 9-15.

The sugar beet industry of the Intermontane Region began in 1852 when Brigham Young sought to make his followers independent of distant sources of sugar. But the region's first successful enterprise got started in 1891 at Lehi, south of Salt Lake City. Today much sugar is refined in large factories located not more than 30 miles from the growers and the product is shipped as far east as Chicago.

Flour Milling. The importance in wheat production of the Columbia Plateau and of irrigated and dry-farmed southern Idaho and northern Utah has already been pointed out. Flour milling accordingly is of more than local importance. Large mills (those turning out more than 1,000 sacks daily) are located in The Dalles, Athena, Freewater, Helix and Pendleton, Oregon, and Cheney, Ritzville, Spokane, Wenatchee, and Waitsburg, Washington. In Idaho large mills are located in Burley, Pocatello, and Twin Falls. Of this group of cities and towns, only Spokane is a large milling center.

Although Utah has 45 mills, three (two in Ogden and one in Salt Lake) account for most of the production. Ninety per cent of the wheat utilized by the large mills originates in the northern Utah — southern Idaho area. The average protein content of this wheat is 11.5 per cent. Some Montana and Columbia Plateau wheat also is milled as a means of increasing or decreasing the protein and gluten content of the Utah-Idaho grain to meet the requirements of the various types of flour produced. Montana wheat, averaging about 15 per cent, has the highest protein content of any wheat grown in the United States, and hence is mixed with Utah-Idaho wheat to make a strong baker's flour. A small amount of white wheat from the Columbia Plateau is mixed with Utah-Idaho wheat to produce a low-protein cake and pastry flour. From 70 to 80 per cent of the flour produced by the large mills of Utah is shipped to California.

Canning. Where irrigation agriculture is important, farms small, population dense, and transportation good, the growing of vegetables and fruits is a major activity. Since the markets of the Intermontane Region can absorb only a part of the total production, despite the yearly consumption of 400 cans per family in the West, a great deal must be canned for shipment outside the area. To prevent deterioration, most canning is done within five or six miles of the farms which grow the fruits and vegetables. Accordingly, these rural workshops comprise a conspicuous part of the cultural landscape. Canning provides both the farmer and the laborer with an indispensable source of income. The farmer makes a contract with the canning company for his vegetables, the latter furnishing the seed and supervising the growing and harvesting of the crop. The crop is contracted for *before,* not *after,* maturity; in fact, it is bought *before it is planted.* Unlike vegetables the fruit crop is rarely contracted, the results of lack of uniformity, quantity, and national carryover.

The canning of fruits and vegetables is for the most part a small-scale industry, employing about 50 persons on the average and operating only about 120 days per year. Some, however, are very large. These canneries tend to locate where soil and climatic conditions favor specific crops.

In Utah are 31 canning factories, mostly in the Salt Lake Oasis, whose total pack exceeds 100 million cans. Shipments are made to 44 of the 48 states in the Union. Even California consumes much Utah canned corn and peas. More than 88 per cent of the total fruit and vegetable pack is consumed outside the state.

Peas head the list of vegetables, contributing 42 per cent of the total, but tomatoes, corn, and snap beans also are important. Cherries and apricots together constitute 85 per cent of the total fruit pack. Peaches rank third.

The Columbia Plateau Area ranks high in the canning of peas. Corn and snap beans also are canned. The canning industry here is only about 25 years old. The pea crop is not irrigated: peas usually use less moisture than wheat. From one sixth to one fifth of the national pea pack comes from six of the country's largest canneries on the slopes descending from the Blue Mountains extending from Dayton, Washington, to Athena,

Oregon. The West as a whole cans about a fourth of the total national pea pack.

Labor is scarce in the Columbia Plateau and therefore every operation is mechanized as much as possible. Since peas after threshing are highly perishable, both plants and field crews work round the clock during the canning season. Pea canneries must be located in the heart of a producing area and must be well served with good highways to permit rapid delivery of the peas from the farms. They are also nearly always located in towns large enough to supply most of the labor.

The Imperial Valley is noted for the canning of tomato products despite the fact that it has only one factory. In 1951 it grew 5,200 acres of cannery tomatoes.

The frozen-food industry is of great and increasing importance in Utah, Idaho, Oregon, and Washington. There is currently a trend among many canneries in these states to change from canning to freezing. Frozen products from these states are sent by rail and even by truck (dry-iced) to the eastern part of the country.

Slaughtering and Meat Packing. The Intermontane Region is outside the orbit of "big time" meat packing. Whereas the bulk of the livestock in the United States is produced west of the Mississippi River, the bulk of the meat is consumed east of it. In the past the predominant movement of livestock (except swine) from this region was eastward but this is not true now. Aside from the meat consumed within the region itself, the bulk of the surplus as well as of live animals moves to the Pacific Coast, particularly to California, to help provide meat for that state's rapidly growing population. About 60 per cent of the beef, 80 per cent of the pork, and 40 per cent of the lamb must be shipped into California either as live animals or as dressed meat to supply the demand. As Los Angeles and San Francisco-Oakland have grown, they have required more meat, and in order to get it, they have to pay more than Kansas City and other large packing centers. Hence, it has become more profitable than in the past to slaughter animals in the Intermontane Region and in California.

The big packers have been decentralizing

in recent years and are locating smaller establishments nearer the livestock feeding and fattening areas. Each state in this region has commercial slaughterers but the numbers vary widely.

Logging and Lumbering

In this region, only northern Arizona has forests containing saw timber; elsewhere trees are found only in the mountains which border the region — the Rockies, the Cascades, and the Sierra Nevada.

In northern Arizona the high plateaus support vast forests of virgin timber most of which (about 12 million acres) is within national forests. From time to time the Forest Service offers for sale blocks of ripe timber — considerable stands of western yellow pine and Douglas fir along with spruce and white fir. Approximately ten million board feet are cut annually though the forest could sustain double this amount for a century. The most important logging operations are concentrated in and around Flagstaff, McNary, and Williams.

Transportation

The frontier could not advance unbroken over the barrier of the Rockies, but carved channels through it on the lines of least resistance, notably the Oregon Trail (early 1840's) and the Santa Fe Trail (1821). These trails were destined to become major rail lines of industrial flow to the Pacific Coast.

Pioneer Trails. The *Oregon Trail*, paralleled by the later Mormon Trail, was the best known and the most used route to the Pacific. Each year, at the approach of spring on the Great Plains, hundreds of covered wagons prepared for the long trek to Oregon. This trail divided the American bison into northern and southern herds leaving the route bare save during seasonal north-south migrations.

The *Santa Fe Trail*[29] (1821), began at In-

dependence, Missouri, a short distance east of Kansas City, and extended some 850 miles to Santa Fe. Though primarily a trader's trail, it was nonetheless an important trailway for migrants from the East to the West. This trail contributed notably to the shrinkage of the Great American Desert and broke the policy permitting Indian occupation in the Southwest. In the early 1800's Santa Fe was one of old Mexico's leading commercial distributing centers as well as a point from which trails and highways moved down the Rio Grande Valley.

At first traders made only one trip a year, setting out in early summer as soon as the pasturage was promising. Later on, trade became so important that caravans set out every few days. A day's journey was usually about 15 miles. In 1866 approximately 3,000 wagons were working the Santa Fe Trail.

In 1950 an air line pilot rediscovered this trail first spotting it through clusters of snow that had frozen into the old wagon ruts, often six sets abreast and a full foot deep.

Pre-railroad Transportation. The *Pony Express* carried the first mail to California. It began in 1860, lasted only 16 months, and ruined its promoters.

The *Stage Coach* delivered mail and passengers. Some coaches drove day and night, but others halted at night to enable their passengers to rest.

The *Camel Caravan* was used to open up the Southwest along a route extending from Texas through southern New Mexico and Arizona to California. Camels were tried out during 1857-1858 by Edward F. Beale who reported them to be eminently satisfactory.

I look forward to the day when every mail route across the continent will be conducted and worked altogether with this economical and noble brute.

However, the experiment failed. Though the animal could carry heavy loads and was adapted to desert conditions, he required patient, careful handling which American mule skinners would not give. The completion of the first transcontinental railway in 1869 sounded the death knell of the camel experiment.

---

[29] The Santa Fe Trail lies entirely east of this region but it is discussed here with other trails because of its historic significance and because the Spanish Trail was a continuation of it.

Railroads. This region, more than any other, is dependent upon railroads, though only seven transcontinental routes cross it.[30] This paucity is striking, but if they get too close together, tapping the same trade territory, as do the Northern Pacific, the Great Northern, and the Chicago, Milwaukee, St. Paul, and Pacific at times, they cannot prosper.

Several of these transcontinental lines, however, prosper because they connect rich productive areas, which permit service to the "revenue vacuums" in between. All western railroads face two major problems: (1) much of the country is mountainous which results in high capital and operating costs, and (2) most of the flat country is so dry and sparsely settled as to yield a low traffic density.

Thus while the people who dwell in the region dispose of many of their products and bring in much of what they use by rail, the bulk of the traffic is supplied by the terminal areas, and the arid region functions primarily as a transit land. Most of the west-bound freight trains are made up of empty cars.

It was in this region on May 10, 1869, that the first so-called *transcontinental* railroad in the United States was completed — Union Pacific–Central Pacific. At Promontory, Utah, just north of Great Salt Lake, a golden spike was driven into a cross-tie to commemorate joining the rails of the Central Pacific (now the Southern Pacific) built eastward from Sacramento and of the Union Pacific built westward from Council Bluffs. Princely land grants, used as bait to stimulate rivalry between the two roads, hastened construction.

Roads. Good roads reflect rich lands and dense population for they are expensive to build and maintain and unproductive areas characterized by sparse population cannot support them. This region therefore, has relatively few superior roads, except those connecting the Atlantic and Pacific Coasts built by the federal government in co-operation with the several states. They are, therefore, the result of a remarkable national program,

existing primarily to serve the "automobile nomad" and bus and trucking interests.

While railroads carry the greater part of the interregional freight and much of the bulky products in intraregional trade, trucks are hauling an ever-increasing proportion of both.

Air Routes. Transcontinental air travel, especially that catering to passengers, grows daily and forms an important link connecting all of Anglo-America's regions. So far as this Intermontane Region is concerned, Salt Lake City is the focal point since it is the largest urban center. Lines from Butte, Portland, San Francisco and Los Angeles converge here for the assembly and interchange of passengers with the trunk route east to Chicago and New York.

Tourist Trade

The region under discussion is one of the most scenic in America with Bryce, Zion, and the Grand Canyon, Cedar Brakes, the Kaibab National Forest, the Petrified Forest, the Painted Desert, Death Valley, Hell's Canyon on the Snake River, and the Columbia River Gorge. Fortunately the United States government has preserved these scenic beauties and has made them a part of its national parks, monuments, and forests.

Several generations ago only the rich and the indigent could see their country, "the one in a Pullman, the other in a box car." The Automobile, however, has brought a large tourist income to these states which suffer from the "ups-and-downs" of mining. While most visitors spend only a few days in a given place, some settle down permanently.

The Grand Canyon of the Colorado. The Grand Canyon is a colossal chasm 250 miles long, 10 to 12 miles wide, and more than one mile deep, is too gigantic for the human mind to encompass. The visitor is "numbed by the spectacle . . . There is no measure, nothing which the eye can grasp, the mind fathom . . . Comprehension lies always just beyond his reach."[31] The Grand

---

[30] Actually only the Southern Pacific may be considered transcontinental because it reaches from the Pacific Ocean to the Gulf of Mexico.

[31] Department of the Interior, *National Parks Portfolio, The Grand Canyon of the Colorado River in Arizona*, p. 195. Washington, D. C.: Government Printing Office, 1931.

Canyon is the world's choicest exhibit of erosion – the result of cutting and grinding of fast-flowing mud- and rock-laden water, abetted by frost, wind, and rain. It presents the world's greatest geological timetable. The mile of rock from bottom to rim represents a period estimated at 700 million years. The whole panorama is a riot of colors from the mineral strains and mineral salts originally in the sediments. To be appreciated the canyon should be seen in the sunlight, moonlight, during a rain, and when the weather is cloudy. No color film, no brush, no pencil – no matter how inspired – can reproduce what one sees, and word pictures fall flat.

Bryce Canyon National Park. The Bryce Canyon in south-central Utah is a significant amphitheatre. The coloring is beyond description and the trails are comparatively easy to follow. No other national park appears so fantastic – its bizarre forms being slender, dainty, bulky, or grotesque. Moreover, these forms are of many colors, but essentially pink, red, white, orange, and purple. Bryce Canyon also tells a story of erosion. One stands on the rim of a precipice and looks down on a forest of tall and eratically carved stone spires.

Zion National Park. Lying a short distance from Bryce is Zion National Park, consisting of a narrow meandering canyon with vertical walls 1,000, 2,000 and 2,500 feet high and with a maze of side canyons. It is banded with white and many shades of red. Some consider it the most inspiring sight in the world. Entering it through a long tunnel, one suddenly comes out into the narrow towering canyon with its unbelievable colors. The Virgin River occupies the bottom of the valley.

The Outlook

Man has accomplished much in this restrictive environment. No one can stand on the steps of the State Capitol Building at Salt Lake City and gaze at the green island that is the oasis without being impressed. Nevertheless there is a limit to what human beings can accomplish against a stubborn and relentless nature. Since water, which means life, is scarce, and much of the terrain is rugged, the greater part of the region is destined to remain one of the emptiest and least used on the continent.

Agriculture should become more important, though too great dependence on outside markets is a retarding factor. For this reason the region must convert into concentrated form those products it cannot itself consume. Sugar beets in irrigated areas over much of the northern part of the region, though also in the Imperial Valley in the south, will continue to be an important crop, for they guarantee the farmers their "tax money." This will be true even if beet acreage declines in certain areas from time to time.

The United States Reclamation Service will probably continue to add to the irrigable area with enormous projects similar to the Grand Coulee, McNary, and Hoover dams. Throughout the entire region, however, more attention must be given to conserving water – especially storing for future use the spring floods of rivers. The government must not allow people to settle here unless it makes the land safe for settlement. One of the anomalies of the past was the Department of the Interior giving away Public Domain at the very time the Department of Agriculture was warning homesteaders of the dangers of dry farming. Any agricultural areas added in the future will be done so only at heavy cost.[32] The most recent large area to be added to the irrigable Intermontane Region is the Columbia Basin, the nation's largest reclamation project (Figures 13–16). About 70,000 acres a year is being brought under irrigation. Ultimately the area will have 12,000 to 14,000 farm units with new schools, churches, highways, shopping centers, and recreational facilities.

Grazing will improve, for nothing has been done since pioneer days to help the enter-

---

[32] The Great Basin had almost ideal terrain for pioneer irrigation, for its streams flowed toward interior drainage base levels and had lower courses in shallow valleys rather than deep canyons. This enabled water to be diverted by simple pioneer tools. The Colorado, the Green, and the Snake, all larger than Great Basin streams, flow out through great canyons from which pioneers could not divert water.

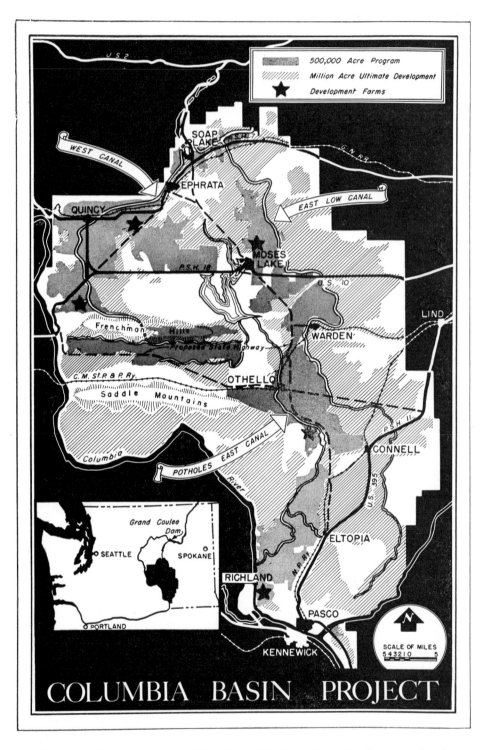

Figure 13–16. As a result of the Columbia Basin Project a huge sagebrush desert in central Washington is being transformed into a verdant and productive oasis at a rate of about 70,000 acres per year out of a total of 1,029, 500 acres. (Courtesy of U. S. Bureau of Reclamation.)

prise so much as the Taylor Grazing Act of 1933. Until its passage, the Public Domain was a "common" of some 165 million acres — a "free-for-all" grazing region mostly unfenced. The Taylor Act authorized temporary withdrawal of the Public Domain from homestead entry and provided for the formation of districts within which land can be leased to stockmen under fair regulations. Ultimately the carrying capacity of the entire range should increase.

Mining will become even more important than it now is. Continued exploration and new techniques in mining and treating ores will add discoveries (strikes), camps, and populations. This was the case in the 1940's and 1950's. The region fortunately has a great variety of minerals. Mining, however, is a robber industry and only one "crop" of minerals can be "harvested." Ultimately nearly all ores will be mined (Figure 13–17) and we shall be dependent for many of our minerals upon foreign countries. Mining

Figure 13–17. There are times when a cartoon can drive home a message better than any other medium. When, as depicted, "Uncle Sam" begins to see the bottom of the barrel, there can be no doubt that our situation in minerals is becoming critical. (Courtesy of *San Francisco Chronicle.*)

towns will be abandoned and the already appreciable list of ghost towns will grow. It is interesting to note that in 1870, Nevada, which is essentially a mining state, had half as many people as Utah, a predominantly agricultural state. But after the bonanza mines had run their course, the population over much of Nevada disappeared. In 1950 Nevada had 160,083 inhabitants and Utah 688,862.

The tourist trade should thrive and greatly expand as good roads are built with federal funds, as the American standard of living rises, and the average worker has more leisure time.

With huge power resources — hydroelectric, coal, petroleum, natural gas, and oil shale; with a wide variety of industrial minerals, forest, and agricultural products; with excellent transport facilities; and with an increasing population, manufacturing is growing in importance. Moreover, the possible danger of bombing has stimulated the decentralization of American industry and the Intermontane Region is benefiting. Even its iron and steel industry has proved that it is competitive.

In rural areas, particularly in Utah where the Mormon pioneers once sought to prevent mining and keep out outside interests, open forums are being held to show the farmers that an integration of heavy industry, mining, and agriculture is both possible and desirable, that the fears of the Church and of the farmers of "big business" are groundless.

A really enlightened policy should at last be used in working with the 420,000 American Indians, most of whom live in this region. Diseases, the language barrier, prejudices, and ignorance all have conspired to render their health and their general situation inferior to that of the white population. Their death rate is double that of the whites. Thousands are victims of poverty, malnutrition and inadequate medical care and many die each year from sheer neglect. During that part of the year when roads cannot be used at all, most of the 61,000 Navajos are without access to any kind of medical care. Many parts of the reservation are almost inaccessible at all times.

Where the Indian population is sizeable it should continue to increase and, if the present trend of aiding the Indian to live his own type of life continues, his lot should improve.

Finally, this region is one that has been mismanaged. Conservation of every single resource is badly needed. Only slight progress in this field has thus far been made.

Table 12

SELECTED CITIES AND TOWNS OF THE INTERMONTANE BASINS AND PLATEAUS

City or Town	Urbanized area	Political center	City or Town	Urbanized area	Political center
Albuquerque		96,815	Pasco		10,228
Bend		11,409	Pendleton		11,774
Boise		34,393	Phoenix	216,038	106,818
Caldwell		10,487	Pocatello		26,131
Douglas		9,442	Provo		28,937
El Paso	136,918	130,485	Pullman		12,022
Grand Junction		14,504	Reno		32,497
Idaho Falls		19,218	Richland		21,809
Klamath Falls		15,785	Salt Lake City	227,368	182,121
Las Vegas		24,624	Spokane	176,004	161,721
Lewiston		12,985	Tucson		45,454
Logan		16,832	Twin Falls		17,600
Mesa		16,790	Walla Walla		24,102
Moscow		10,593	Wenatchee		13,072
Nampa		16,185	Yakima		38,486
Ogden		57,112	Yuma		9,145

Selected Bibliography

"A Symposium: Resources for the Chemical Industry in the United States: 'The Far West,'" *Industrial and Engineering Chemistry*, Vol. 43, December 1951, pp. 2647–2693.

Harry Bernstein, "Spanish Influence in the United States: Economic Aspects," *Hispanic American Historical Review*, Vol. 18, 1938, pp. 43–65.

Herbert E. Bolton, *Coronado*. New York: Whittlesey House, McGraw-Hill Book Co., Inc., 1949.

Justinian Claire, "The Sheep Industry," Supplement to *Federal Reserve Bank of San Francisco Monthly Review*, September 1950.

Charles C. Carr, *Alcoa: An American Enterprise*. New York: Rinehart and Company, 1952.

G. F. Carter, *Plant Geography and Culture History in the American Southwest*, Viking Fund Publications in Anthropology, No. 5. New York: Viking Fund Inc., 1945.

Marion Clawson, "Water Laws," *Farm Policy Forum*, Vol. 2, October 1949

———, *The Western Range Livestock Industry*. New York: McGraw-Hill Book Co., Inc., 1950.

John D. Garwood, "An Analysis of Postwar Industrial Migration to Utah and Colorado," *Economic Geography*, Vol. 29, January 1953, pp. 79–88.

Irrigation Agriculture in the West, United States Department of Agriculture, Miscellaneous Publication No. 670. Washington, D. C.: Government Printing Office, 1948.

Tim Kelley, "The Taylor Grazing Act and the West," *Annals of the Association of American Geographers*, Vol. 39, March 1949, pp. 56–57.

"Man *vs* Mesquite," *Life*, August 18, 1952, pp. 69–72.

E. Louise Peffer, "Which Public Domain Do You Mean?" *Agricultural History*, Vol. 23, April 1949, pp. 140–146.

E. M. Spieker, *The Transition Between the Colorado Plateaus and the Great Basin in Central Utah*, Guidebook to the Geology of Utah, No. 4. Salt Lake City: Utah Geological Society, 1949.

14.

The Subtropical

Pacific Coast

THE most diversified region in the entire United States, one that is characterized by many different types of economic activity, is the Subtropical Pacific Coast. Agriculture is important in almost every segment with cotton, fruits, and vegetables being leading crops, and with livestock and dairying important in areas ill-adapted to cultivation. Actually California means different things to different individuals; and this is as it should be for actually there are many Californias — each having marked individuality — the result of its distinctive geographical conditions. In this book the entire state, with the exception of the Salton Trough, the Imperial Valley, and the Northern California Littoral, is considered under the heading of the Subtropical Pacific Coast (Figure 14–1). This division lends itself well to the regional approach:

1. Southern California (from Santa Barbara to San Diego and east to San Bernardino and Riverside).
2. The Great Valley.
3. The Sierra Nevada.
4. The Central Coast Ranges and Valleys, including the important San Francisco Bay Area.

While these subregions show marked contrast in relief, climate, soils, natural vegetation, and economic development, they are nonetheless so interrelated and so mutually interdependent as to constitute one major geographic region.

In each of these subregions the people are adjusting themselves in their own particular way and the state now ranks second only to New York State in total population. It would seem that if California can solve its water problem, it may eventually become first among the states of the Union in population. More of this growth in population results from heavy immigration than from a high birth rate.

Since there is not much that can be said about the state as a whole, the treatment here is largely by subregions.

Water: Great Problem of the Region

Water is considered by nearly all authorities on California and particularly of this region to be the number one problem. California fought several of the western states in order to effect federal construction of Hoover Dam on the Colorado River. Owens Valley

375

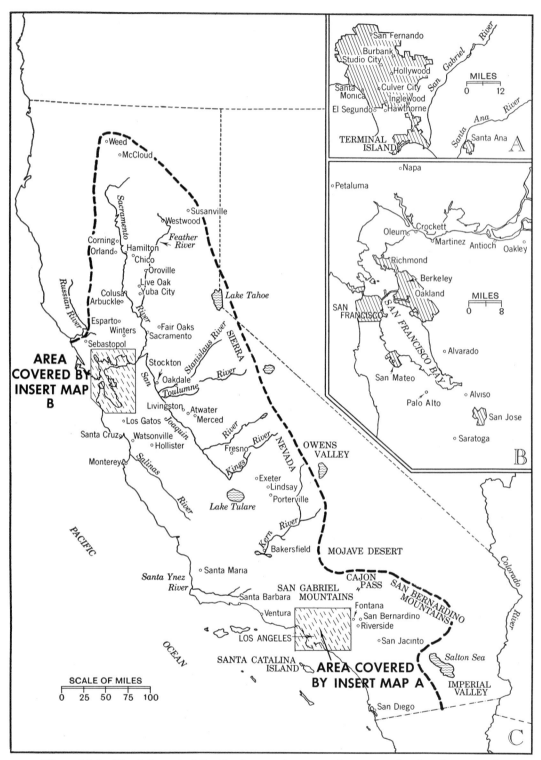

Figure 14–1. The Subtropical Pacific Coast. A region of citrus and other fruits, truck farming, market gardening, mixed farming, ranching, grazing, fishing, lumbering, mining; of petroleum, motion-picture, and aircraft production; and of commerce and resorts.

ranchers fought in real "wild West" fashion to prevent Los Angeles from using their water. They lost, however, for a Superior Court ruled that water must be used for the greatest good of the greatest number.

California receives sufficient rainfall as a state but the moisture doesn't fall in the right places at the right time in the right amounts (Figure 14–2). Thus if one compares a map showing where water is available with one showing population distribution, it becomes immediately apparent that man has not adapted himself to the pattern set by nature, for two thirds of the available water is in the northern part of the state, whereas two thirds of the population is in the southern half.

The problem is to get water from where there is too much to where there is not enough. Down through the years an effort has been made to do this. No state in the Union made such tremendous expenditures reaching out for water. Yet from some points of view California is water poor. It has taxed man's ingenuity seriously, having impounded surface waters, tapped underground sources, attempted to make rain by cloud seeding, and even experimented with methods of freshening sea water at low cost. However, man in California is removing water faster than nature is replenishing it.

In 1948 the Subtropical Pacific Coast experienced a serious water shortage. Many crops failed, large numbers of livestock died from thirst and some herds had to be moved to better watered areas, water for power was cut 20 per cent, and daylight saving time extended over the entire year.

Such a problem would be serious if only the natural increase in population had to be considered but California's population increase is far from normal. Population and manufacturing both are growing at rapid rates. Both, however, may be halted eventually by the paucity of water unless man can overcome the problem.

Assuming that population and industry both will continue to increase what will be done? Water resources will have to be allocated with priority to industry and domestic uses, in which case agriculture will decline. From a position of exporting surplus farm produce, the state may be forced to rely on agricultural producing areas in eastern United States.

Population:
Sensational Regional Growth

For 300 years the people of the United States have had a reputation for moving from region to region. As pointed out earlier, Americans began carving out their homes in the wilderness (the empty country between their settlements and the Pacific Ocean) and the process continued for three centuries. "Like locusts they swarmed, always to the west, and only the Pacific Ocean stopped them." The existence of an area of free land, its continuous recession, and the advance of settlement westward, explain American development.

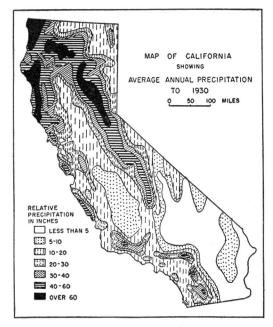

MAP OF CALIFORNIA
SHOWING
AVERAGE ANNUAL PRECIPITATION
TO 1930
0   50   100   MILES

RELATIVE
PRECIPITATION
IN INCHES
☐ LESS THAN 5
▦ 5-10
▦ 10-20
▦ 20-30
▨ 30-40
▤ 40-60
■ OVER 60

Figure 14–2. Rainfall in California. Note how the precipitation varies from heavy to very light. There is no "California climate"; there is a series of California climates. The word "climate" in California is a slogan applied largely to the area around Los Angeles and historically employed to attract tourists and settlers. (Courtesy of University of California, College of Agriculture.)

The 1950 Census discloses that the westward trek is stronger than ever and that California is the great Mecca. It is estimated that 26 states contributed an average of 10,000 migrants in a single year (1946) to California alone. The decadal growth of this state (both excess of births over deaths and immigration from other states) from 1940 to 1950, was 3,678,836 persons, giving the state a total population in 1950 of 10,586,223.

This trend in population growth is expected to continue as the industrial tempo is accelerated. The more reliable forecasts, while varying, foreshadow an increase of one to two million up to ten million or a total population for 1960 of between 12 and 14 million. The only retarding factor of any real significance seems to be the water supply.

The history of settlement in California has been characterized by a continuous movement in number and space marked by new forces finding expression in new forms of population distribution.

Southern California

This is the smallest of the subregions of the state but it is one of the most important areas and one of the most intensively developed in all Anglo-America. It has a true mediterranean subtropical climate. With the rapid growth of metropolitan Los Angeles and San Diego, the area has become highly urbanized and highly industrialized.

The boundaries of this subregion are natural — both physiographic and climatic. The east-west range of the San Gabriel and San Bernardino Mountains excludes winds from the continental interior and confines the mediterranean climate to a small strip of coast. The San Jacinto–Santa Rosa–Laguna Mountains to the southeast separate this subregion from the Salton Trough and the Imperial Valley, parts of the Intermontane Basins and Plateaus Region.

The Natural Environment

The most distinct feature of the terrain [1] is the east-west mountain range along the northern margin — the San Gabriel and San Bernardino Mountains. South of this rim of mountains lies the Los Angeles Lowland, which is subdivided into several smaller valleys such as the San Fernando and San Bernardino by a number of intervening ranges of hills.

Much of this lowland is covered with huge coalescing alluvial fans formed of material washed down from the mountains. These fans slope from altitudes of 1,000 to 2,000 feet at the base of the mountains to 300 to 500 feet a few miles away. The streams forming these fans are broad, stony washes, becoming surface streams only during times of flood. They provide, however, an important supply of ground water for the area's large-scale irrigation development.

Much of this basin is now occupied by the extensive urban area of Los Angeles and by intensively cultivated citrus groves. South of this area lies a narrow coastal plain that extends to the Mexican border. This narrow plain forms a continuation of the Southern California agricultural area.

The coastline of Southern California is marked by alternating low shelving beaches at points where the deltaic plains reach the ocean, and elevated beaches and bold promontories where the mountain spurs approach the coast. From 25 to 90 miles offshore lie a number of small rocky islands that are a definite part of the region.

The climate is a true mediterranean type, having a definite seasonal rhythm of rainfall. The precipitation (15 to 20 inches) comes almost entirely during the winter season. Desert conditions with a maximum of sunshine prevail during the dry and hot summers. Winters are mild and summers are hot, although near the Pacific Ocean the summer temperatures are modified by cool sea breezes. The high percentage of sunshine,

[1] N. M. Fenneman, *Physiography of Western United States*, pp. 493-510. New York: McGraw-Hill Book Co., 1931.

even during the winter rainy season, has attracted tourists as well as many important industries. Southern California vies with Florida in selling climate to the people of the rest of the continent.

The natural vegetation in this foothill and valley area consists largely of chaparral at elevations of 3,000 to 5,000 feet, with annual and perennial grasses forming much of the understory. Directly below on the lower slopes extend considerable dense thickets of chamisal. On the higher slopes where the rainfall is greater, there was formerly an open stand of coniferous forest. Lumbering was a fairly important enterprise in the San Bernardino and San Jacinto Mountains in early days.

Settlement

Little is known about the Indians who inhabited Southern California. Records indicate that the area was occupied by scattered small tribes in a low cultural stage. When the Spaniards arrived they subjugated the natives without difficulty.

The Spanish-Mexican Period (1542-1848). In September 1542, Rodriguez Cabrillo, the first European to visit the region, sailed up the west coast from Mexico and discovered San Diego Bay. After exploring the coast and offshore islands he claimed every harbor for Spain. Some years later (1602), a second expedition under Sebastian Vizcaino explored the coast northward as far as Monterey. Following this, however, no further explorations were made, and no settlements attempted in California for more than 160 years. Southern California seemed to offer little attraction to the adventurous gold-seeking *conquistadores*. Renewed interest was stimulated not by the possibilities of the region itself but by the rapid advance of Russian domination of the Pacific Coast south from Alaska. Although Spain considered the whole California area economically worthless, she felt that a buffer state should be established to prevent possible Russian encroachment upon her more valuable colony of Mexico. As a result, Spain renewed her interest in this region in 1769 through the establishment of a string of presidios and missions, followed later by the founding of pueblos or towns. The first mission was established at San Diego in 1769 and soon was followed by others. Later, towns were located near most of the missions.

Although some mineral wealth was found within the subregion, including quicksilver at Santa Barbara, little mining was practiced. The Spanish cattle brought in by the early settlers multiplied so rapidly that ranching became the chief occupation. Since there was no way to market cattle, they were slaughtered and the hides and tallow sold to New England traders, whose vessels put in at the ports of San Diego, San Pedro, and Santa Barbara. Though Spain prohibited this trade, she offered no substitute; hence the isolated colonists of Southern California continued to ship out animal products in exchange for manufactured goods brought in by Yankee clipper ships. Whaling vessels also visited the California ports to outfit for their long trips into the Arctic. During the last two decades of this Spanish-Mexican period (1828-1848), it is estimated that more than a million hides and more than 60 million pounds of tallow were exported from California.

The Early American Period (1848-1876). Toward the end of the period the Santa Fe Trail was extended to Los Angeles. Furthermore, Spanish-Mexican settlers in Santa Fe and Southern California had few contacts with each other. When this territory became a part of the United States in 1848, California's non-Spanish population was estimated at 380 out of a total of 6,000. The westward drift of settlement was moving toward California, but no great progress was made until gold was discovered near Sacramento in 1848. News of the strike spread rapidly, and soon the most spectacular mass migration in the history of the New World began.

Without gold, with poor harbors, and remote from routes of travel, Southern California had little chance to profit from this new migration. Eventually, however, some people failing to find gold, drifted southward. Through devious means many large *ranchos* were broken up and title to considerable land was obtained by these new American settlers. Cattle ranching continued dominant throughout the rest of this period.

In 1876 the Southern Pacific Railroad built a line from Oakland southward to Los Angeles, and five years later extended it eastward to New Orleans. In 1885 the Sante Fe Railroad completed its "transcontinental" line, making Los Angeles its Pacific terminus. These new connections with the outside world broke down the extreme isolation of Southern California — an isolation that had retarded its growth since the beginning of Spanish settlement.

The Commercial and Industrial Period (1876 to the present). Following the completion of the railroads, people moved into Southern California in great numbers and for two decades most of them went into agriculture. Other important enterprises, however, began about the same time. Oil was discovered in 1880, and the petroleum industry began its phenomenal growth. This was followed in turn by the motion-picture industry, tourism, the commercial growth of the port of Los Angeles, and quite recently by manufacturing. This modern period, which will be described in more detail, evolved so rapidly that Southern California outgrew all other areas of comparable size on the continent during the past century. Los Angeles County, for example, jumped in population from 2,785,643 in 1940 to 4,151,687 in 1950— an increase of 49 per cent.

Agriculture

Prior to the time of the 1849 gold rush, California agriculture, except for small irrigated areas near missions, was almost entirely pastoral. The great army of gold seekers, centered in northern California, created a demand for food at high prices and initiated a period of bonanza wheat growing. While most of this was confined to the Great Valley, some wheat was grown elsewhere including Southern California lands.

Ranching, however, remained dominant until the severe drought of 1862-1863 brought death by starvation to thousands of cattle and other range animals. Until that time, most of the land in Southern California was in large land holdings, *ranchos,* which had been granted to early settlers by the Spanish crown or the Mexican government. This disastrous drought practically wrecked the livestock industry, and forced many large landholders to sell at least a part of their acreage.

In the late 1860's, boatloads of prospective land-buyers went from San Francisco to Los Angeles. Land sales soon became so important that companies were organized to subdivide and sell ranches that had been acquired by foreclosure of mortgages. With the completion of railroads to Southern California, the land boom increased, and during the 1880's reached large proportions. Since the area was deficient in rainfall and most of the rain came during winter, many agricultural experiments were made. Among crops attempted were cotton, tobacco, and castor beans; even sericulture was tried. Unfavorable physical factors, coupled with high transportation costs to distant markets, caused these early experiments to fail.

Ranching, however, continued important, especially on the rougher hill lands, and today is surpassed only by irrigation farming.

On the drier bench lands along the coast, barley and beans are grown without irrigation. Though occupying considerable acreage, their value is of minor significance in comparison with that of the irrigated crops.

Irrigation was practiced on a small scale by the early Spanish settlers, each mission having its irrigated plots. The limited amount of surface water, however, precluded any extensive development until additional supplies could be developed from wells or could be brought in from the outside. Until the coming of the railroads in the early 1880's, few surplus crops could be sold outside the region and production was limited largely to the local market. Between 1850 and 1880, however, small shipments of fruits and vegetables were sent regularly by vessel from Los Angeles to San Francisco. The boom in irrigation agriculture started in 1880, and its importance has increased each decade since then. Irrigated lands have so encroached upon dry farming and ranching areas that today only the least desirable lands remain in lower-grade uses. It should be noted, however, that much land formerly irrigated has since been abandoned to non-agricultural uses because of the rapid growth of the Los Angeles and San Diego metropolitan areas.

The Irrigated Crops. In surveying agriculture in each of the subregions, it will be seen that most crops are irrigated. Yields under irrigation nearly always are high. It is not surprising to learn, therefore, that California's cash farm income has ranked first in every year since 1929 despite the fact that many other states harvest larger acreages.

Truck Crops. This subregion, along with the Subtropical Gulf Coast and the Imperial Valley, supplies most of the early truck crops for the United States. Although grown here under irrigation, the methods used in culti-

vation and production are similar to those described in the other areas. The Southern California Subregion ranks high in production of lettuce, tomatoes, cauliflower, celery, and carrots. Because of the great expansion of the citrus-fruit industry in this subregion, however, the Imperial Valley of southeastern California (Chapter 13) has been able to surpass it in the production of truck crops.

Citrus Fruits. While citrus fruits are grown over wide areas in California, by far the major production is confined to the Southern California Subregion, making it one of the leading producers of the continent. Oranges and lemons predominate although some grapefruit also is grown.

Extensive acreages of citrus groves dominate much of the landscape of Southern California (Figure 14–3), and no fruit district of the nation is more intensively cultivated or more productive. Since citrus fruits

Figure 14–3. Orange groves in Southern California, which has about three fourths of the state's trees. Southern California is one of America's principal sources of citrus fruits, especially oranges and lemons. (Courtesy of Sunkist Growers, Inc.)

are produced by irrigation, this has created a tremendous demand for water. Aside from the fact that the fruits are irrigated, in contrast to those of Florida, production methods in the two states differ little.

Because of the great distance of this subregion from the large consuming centers of the East, marketing procedures must be very efficient.

During the early years of the commercial industry, oranges were bought outright by dealers who then shipped them to wholesalers in the East. These dealers developed into large shipping and marketing concerns, and by the 1890's five or six such organizations practically controlled the business. These firms packed and marketed the oranges on a commission basis, consigning the fruit directly to commission merchants in the East.

Early attempts at co-operative marketing were unsuccessful. In 1893, however, some 60 orange growers organized a type of exchange which operated successfully for a while but was ultimately rendered impotent through loss of membership. Then came the Southern California Fruit Exchange, which, as an incorporated institution, established co-operative marketing of citrus fruit on a reasonably secure basis. Today this large organization, now called Sunkist Growers, Incorporated, functions for practically all citrus producers. Picking, packing, and shipping are now done by it, or under its supervision.

The Care of Orchards. Groves belonging to members of Sunkist Growers, Inc., average from 10 to 15 acres in size. Protection from frost is largely the responsibility of the individual owner, although the United States Weather Bureau co-operates by broadcasting daily the expected temperatures. Owners must be on guard at all times during the frost season. Many of them have installed automatic signal systems that sound an alarm at the approach of a critical temperature. Growers have learned to plant trees on slightly sloping hillsides to benefit from air drainage, but at times temperatures fall so low as to necessitate the use of orchard heaters and blowers (Figure 14-4).

Figure 14-4. Wind machines are beginning to replace the long-used smudge pots to protect the fruit from frost in California's citrus-growing areas. They mix the warmer air above the trees with colder air beneath them. One "air mixer" will protect 20 acres of citrus trees. (Courtesy of Sunkist Growers, Inc.)

Occasional hot dry winds, known as "Santa Anas," which blow into this subregion from the desert country to the northeast, inflict great damage on orchards. Although windbreaks have been used with some success, areas opposite canyon mouths, particularly Cajon Pass, are avoided by citrus growers because of the destructive force of these desert winds.

No citrus fruits are grown without irrigation. Intensively cultivated land in Southern California is directly proportional to the amount of water available. Water costs are high and most water is controlled by mutual organizations of users. Nearly three fourths of that used by citrus growers comes from wells. Orchards receive five to eight applications of water each year in addition to the scanty rainfall. Excessive irrigation in areas of poor drainage results in the accumulation of salts in the soil, which is detrimental to the citrus trees.

Picking and Packing the Fruit. When the fruit reaches maturity, the job of picking usually is turned over to a local packing unit, which harvests the fruit economically by using crews of expert pickers. The packing plant lays down strict rules: all pickers must wear gloves to keep their fingernails from injuring the fruit, and all must use special clippers for removing the fruit from the tree. Special picking bags and carefully designed field boxes are used, to assure a minimum of damage to the fruit. When the field boxes are filled they are taken by motor truck to local packing houses and the fruit is prepared for shipment. The organization provides the local packing houses with all supplies, such as wraps, labels, and boxes.

Other Irrigated Fruit and Nut Crops. *Peaches* are grown in a number of the valleys bordering the mountain zone. *Olives* are grown in portions of Los Angeles, Riverside, and San Diego counties, but production is of minor significance compared with that in the valleys to the north. *Avocados* have recently become quite important, and large farms or "ranches" have been established to produce them for the ever-increasing national market.

Almonds are produced to some extent in the northern part of this subregion, though the bulk of the output comes from the coastal valleys of central California and from the Sacramento Valley. Southern California, however, is the country's leading producer of *English* (Persian) *walnuts*, output being confined largely to Los Angeles, Orange, and Ventura counties.

The Southern California Subregion also produces large quantities of tomatoes, some of which are canned, and a sizeable early potato crop. The increasing urban population is creating a large local market for all kinds of foodstuffs.

Food Preparation Industries

California leads all states in the food preparation industries.[2] While canning is state-wide in its distribution because the ecological adaptations of many crops have quite definite climatic and soil requirements, there is nonetheless much concentration within a relatively few areas. This subregion is one of the areas of greatest concentration.

Food processing is conducted for the most part on a small scale compared with other outstanding branches of manufacturing. It could not, however, operate efficiently otherwise, for the sources of its raw materials are widespread and these materials are highly perishable. Moreover, the industry is seasonal — the actual operating period lasting for six weeks to six or eight months. In the southern coastal area, the canning season is long, whereas in the San Francisco Bay area, where the various products mature in a short period, it is short. The long growing season and the great diversity of crops enable the canneries to utilize to better advantage costly plant equipment and to operate over a long season. A large part of California's pack of canned foods is fruits: apricots, peaches, and pears account for about 97 per cent of the total fruit canned. The seasonal aspect of canning also demands a pool of potential workers, mostly women, interested in seasonal employment.

The quick freezing of food skyrocketed in growth in the past several years. Frozen foods compete seriously with canned, dried, and even fresh fruits and vegetables.

Possibly the most interesting phase of the frozen foods industry has been the freezing of citrus concentrate. In a few years it has had a terrific impact on the entire citrus industry. Traditionally, of course, California's orange growers marketed fresh fruit. The fine quality of the product assured financial success. But the meteoric rise of the frozen juice industry in Florida which in 1951 produced 85 per cent of the frozen orange juice forced California growers into the business. Recently, Sunkist Growers, Inc., which controls about 70 per cent of the State's orange crop, put out a concentrate under its famous *Sunkist* label. The cost of production is greater in California than in Florida. While labor is the big factor, tax costs are higher and irrigation is expensive. Florida in 1951

[2] For the geographic principles involved in the location of such plants, see Chapter 24, "Food Preparation Industries," in *California and the Southwest*, Clifford Zierer, ed. New York: John Wiley and Sons, 1956.

could break even on a can of juice at eight cents, whereas California had to get fourteen.

The Fishing Industry

Southern California is one of the important commercial fishing regions of the continent. The major fishing grounds extend from Southern California waters southward along the coast of Mexico, Central America, Ecuador and Peru. Most commercial fish are brought to Los Angeles and San Diego harbors.

The establishment of a sardine cannery at San Pedro in 1893 marked the beginning of commercial fishing. The year 1905 found a temporary scarcity of sardines, and the fishermen experimented with the canning of albacore (tuna). By 1909 the canning of tuna had become so profitable that the packing of sardines was temporarily abandoned. When other types of tuna were caught and canned after 1918, the commercial fishing grounds were extended into the waters off Lower California. San Diego, the nearest port, profited greatly from this new expansion of the fishing grounds. By 1923 Latin American waters were supplying nearly half of the tuna landed at Southern California ports. High license fees for fishing in Mexican territorial waters caused the construction of larger sea-going tuna vessels that could fish in offshore waters, thereby avoiding the payment of the Mexican fees. The development of these larger ships has so expanded the tuna fishing grounds that they now extend southward beyond the equator and westward as far as Hawaii. All of this catch is handled by San Diego and Los Angeles canneries. Some tuna caught off the coast of Oregon is canned in that state. Of the 111 million pounds taken in the peak year of 1930, San Diego handled about 60 per cent and Los Angeles the remainder.

The temporary stoppage of the European supply of sardines during the first World War led to the re-establishment of the sardine industry. Los Angeles soon became a major center and has maintained its importance even in competition with European supplies. More recently mackerel, a fish abundant along the Southern California coast through-out most of the year, is being canned especially during months when tuna and sardines are not available.

About 1930 a tuna-canning industry patterned after that of Southern California was developed in Japan, and in 1933 more than 600,000 cases of Japanese tuna appeared on the United States market, despite a 30 per cent *ad valorem* tax. The duty was soon increased to 45 per cent, but even that, as a result of the differential between American and Japanese labor, was not sufficient to bar Japanese competition. Furthermore, Japan, through a subsidy, was making it possible for her canned tuna to be delivered to markets on the Atlantic Coast at only five cents a case more than that of California fish. Despite apparent advantages Southern California seemed to enjoy in the tuna industry, Japanese competition was a serious threat to future expansion. Peru is now marketing canned tuna in the United States.

The United States tuna industry is not presently in a strong economic position because of foreign competition. In 1952, 75 per cent of this 80 million dollar industry with its 18,000 workers and hundreds of ships (almost all of it in Southern California), was idle. Of the 250 big tuna clippers sailing out of San Diego, 210 were tied up.

"Fish Harbor" is an artificial basin developed on Terminal Island at the time Los Angeles Harbor was being constructed. Here are located all of the fishing docks, canneries, and residences of most of the fishermen, who are largely Japanese, Yugoslavs, and Italians. Eight large fish canneries and associated oil and meal plants line the north side of the docks at Fish Harbor providing outlets for the catch. The west side of the harbor is lined with marine oil and gasoline stations and with ice and other supply plants for outfitting the fleet.

Because the fishing industry in Southern California is so new, vessels and equipment are very modern. With the construction of sea-going fishing ships to work the offshore and distant tuna grounds, modern Diesel-powered tuna clippers have been developed. These craft, built exclusively for catching tuna at sea by means of hand lines (Figure

14–5), are equipped to refrigerate the fish for several weeks while the vessel is away from port.

Tuna are caught largely from June to September, sardines between November and March, and mackerel largely in winter though to some extent throughout the year. This seasonal distribution provides all-year employ-

Figure 14–5. Hauling in tuna off the coast of Southern California. The tuna clippers operating out of San Diego and Los Angeles make trips as far distant as the west coast of South America. (Courtesy of San Diego–California Club.)

ment for the canneries and has made Los Angeles one of the best-organized fishing ports in Anglo-America.

Petroleum and Natural Gas

The Southern California Subregion contains some of the most productive oil fields on the North American continent, and, despite its small areal extent, the region accounts for approximately 16 per cent of the United States production. Two of the major California oil districts are located in this area, the Coastal district with more than 12 producing fields and the Los Angeles Basin with more than 14 fields.

Oil was discovered in the Los Angeles Basin as early as 1880 with the completion of the Puente Hills field, but despite miscellaneous drilling, no further important development occurred until 1902, when the Brea-Olinda field was brought in about seven miles west of the center of Los Angeles. Extensive drilling began throughout the basin, but, after reaching a peak in 1909, drilling declined until the close of the first World War. By that time rotary drilling was replacing that by cable tools, and deeper horizons could be explored. The big oil boom for Southern California came in 1921 and 1922 with the completion of three large fields at Huntington Beach, Long Beach (Signal Hill), and Santa Fe Springs. In 1936 these fields, the three largest in the Los Angeles Basin, contained one half the producing wells of the area. In 1939, seventeen years after they were brought in, they were producing more than 37 million barrels or nearly one third the total for the basin. Only the new Wilmington field (1937) of the Los Angeles Basin, and the Ventura Avenue field in the coastal district, surpassed these in production.

The Cuyama Valley field, found in 1948, was the first major discovery following World War II. It is difficult to place Cuyama in any of the recognized districts because it is really a sort of isolated field lying in the Coast Ranges about 50 miles southwest of Bakersfield, but definitely not in the San Joaquin Valley. In 1952 important discoveries were made also in the Ventura Basin.

Probably the most interesting aspects of the Southern California fields are those concerned with land utilization. In general, oil fields have been brought in on lands having little surface value. In the Los Angeles Basin, however, much of the land was under intensive utilization before oil was brought in. With rapid increases in land values due to the phenomenal growth of the City of Los Angeles, some of the less productive fields are being abandoned. Although some of the fields are in brush-covered hill lands, many are either in irrigated agricultural lowlands or in crowded urban territory. Those along the Pacific Coast compete with bathing beaches and in some cases have been forced out into the water. Nowhere else have oil wells had such keen competition for surface rights.

Clifford M. Zierer [3] classes the fields of the Los Angeles Basin into three types according to location: (1) hill districts, where fields have been developed on brush-covered hill lands devoted largely to grazing activities, (2) urban districts, where oil wells, drilled on building lots (50 by 120 feet or less in size), have resulted in the greatest crowding of derricks to be found anywhere, and (3) rural districts, largely irrigated and planted in citrus orchards or intensively cultivated truck crops. In the latter the oil fields have had to compete with high-value surface rights, and serious conflicts in surface development frequently take place.

Despite the tremendous production of oil in the Subtropical Pacific Coast Region, especially since 1920, the proved reserves in 1951 stood at 3,761 million barrels,[4] a figure surpassed only slightly by two other years — 1947 and 1948. Nonetheless in 1952 and 1953 the state has been importing petroleum from Indonesia, Venezuela, and elsewhere. Causes for this shift are the rapid increase in population with consequent heavy requirements for motor fuel, the Korean War, which required California, now producing 16 per cent of the nation's oil but being called upon to supply 50 per cent of the military needs, and the cutting off of oil production in Iran.[5]

Nearly all fields in the region are accompanied by considerable gas pressure, but the large urban market of metropolitan Los Angeles consumes practically the total production. Natural gas is now being piped into California from Texas and New Mexico.

Refining and Shipping Petroleum. Refining petroleum and the shipping of it are important industries in Southern California. Because of the chance distribution of the oil fields within a 25-mile radius of Los Angeles Harbor, most refining is done on the coast. Oil and refined gasoline, above the requirements of Southern California, have until re-

cently moved out of the port by tank steamer to Alaska, to the East Coast (via the Panama Canal), and to the Pacific Coast of South America. Prior to World War II, Japan received a large share of its aviation gasoline from Southern California refineries.

While Southern California still refines much petroleum, nearly all of the state's new refineries have been established in the Bay Area, particularly near Richmond, Martinez, Crockett, Oleum and elsewhere. The cracking plants are nearly all located in the Bay Area.

Manufacturing

This subregion, long famous for its agriculture and climate, is at present gaining fame for itself in manufacturing. Especially is this the case in the great conurbation that occupies the Los Angeles Lowland.

Among the principal industries are those engaged in food processing, in making aircraft, agricultural pumps and implements, food machinery, specialized mining and oil-well equipment, calculating machines, motion pictures, sportswear, refined oil products, furniture, synthetic rubber, rubber tires, electronics, cement, paint, iron and steel, and others.

The Motion-picture Industry. What Pittsburgh is to steel and Akron to rubber, Hollywood is to the motion-picture industry: it is the movie capital of the world. Nine tenths of the motion pictures made in the United States came from the Hollywood–Los Angeles area. One half of the studios are either in Hollywood or Los Angeles proper, though in recent years there has been some decentralization out of these centers and into Culver City, the San Fernando Valley (Burbank), Studio City, and Westwood. The principal attraction of the San Fernando Valley is availability of land in large tracts and at lower cost than in the older areas.

The Southern California Subregion, especially Los Angeles and its world-famous suburb Hollywood, produces two thirds of the motion-picture films of the world in some 75 studios.

The original studios were attracted to Southern California by the sunny mediterra-

---

[3] Clifford M. Zierer, "An Ephemeral Type of Industrial Land Occupance," *Annals of the Association of American Geographers,* Vol. 26, 1936, pp. 125-156.

[4] This estimate includes offshore reserves.

[5] "California Turns Oil Importer," *Business Week,* June 21, 1952.

nean climate and the great variety of scenery to be found within the immediate area — mountains, deserts, tropical vegetation, and seacoast. This early start enabled the area to retain the industry even after natural advantages were no longer so significant. Early photography required good sunlight, and before the advent of "sound-on" films, most pictures were taken in the open, which required periods of protracted sunlight with a minimum of rain that might damage the equipment. Today most movies are staged in studios, and since a large part of the lighting effect is produced artificially, Southern California sunshine is no longer a controlling factor. Nevertheless, the industry is firmly entrenched here.

The motion-picture industry has attracted tourists and job-seekers. Many of the latter have been "misfits" and frequently have been a severe drain on Los Angeles charities.

The Aircraft Industry. Part of the rapid development of this industry is due to World War II and the gigantic demand for military aircraft, but the industry was entrenched in Southern California before the outbreak of the war. The 1937 *Census of Manufactures* reported 24 establishments for California and only 17 for New York, which until then had been the leading state. Possibly nowhere else in the world is there so large an aggregation of airframe plants. Within a ten-mile radius in the Los Angeles industrial area are located the principal plants of four of the seven largest American aircraft producers.

The finished airplane is the result of the combined efforts of the three main groups of manufacturers: (1) engine manufacturers who construct the vital power plants which are to propel the machine; (2) manufacturers who provide literally thousands of parts and sub-assemblies for each airplane; and (3) manufacturers who build the frames of the airplanes and assemble into them the necessary engines, propellers, parts, and accessories. As a matter of fact, in all of California, there is not a single plant which can be considered completely integrated. In 1940 California had 44.1 per cent of the airframe production but only 33.3 per cent of the total aircraft production (airframe, engine, and propeller).

Yet Southern California ranked first in floor-space, in employment, in supply contracts, and in airframe production (Figure 14–6). The engine and propeller plants remain at or near their original sites in the East, where materials and skilled labor are at hand. California's favorable flying weather is no inducement to them.

Before the United States began to prepare itself for national defense, the aircraft industry was heavily concentrated in Los Angeles, Seattle, Baltimore, and Buffalo. After 1939, however, the business grew so fast and changed so much that statistics applicable to that year "are of interest only to the historian." For military reasons the total capacity of the industry on the coast fell from 77.3 per cent of the nation's total to 42.3 per cent. Los Angeles' share was reduced from 28.4 per cent to 11.8 per cent — a situation attributable to economic causes and to the desire to lessen the vulnerability of the industry to possible air attack.

Climate appears to be the most important single location factor affecting this industry. Snow and freezing temperatures are of very rare occurrence in Southern California and there is an abundance of sunshine. The mild climate is advantageous in four ways: (1) the good flying weather permits year-round flight testing of airplanes; (2) the warm and relatively dry climate permits the storage of parts and equipment out of doors; (3) mild temperatures reduce heating needs and consequently construction costs—an important factor where hangars covering millions of square feet are used; and (4) work may be carried on out of doors all year round, a factor of special importance because the final assembly process of airframe production requires a great amount of space owing to the huge wing span of modern planes (Figure 14–7). For these several reasons this operation should, if possible, be done out of doors to save the cost of constructing huge sheds.

The second most important location factor is availability of a large pool of skilled labor. Los Angeles and San Diego developed such a pool, and as a result, other airframe plants and allied industries established themselves nearby in order to draw on the supply. Thus

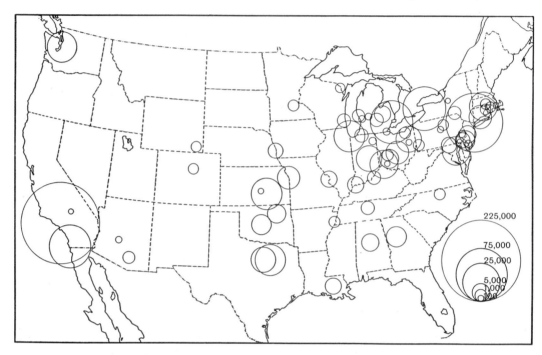

Figure 14–6. Aircraft industry of the United States, as indicated by total employment by metropolitan districts, cities, and towns. So rapid are changes in this industry that any statement of a statistical nature but a few months old is obsolete. The purpose of this map is to help the reader appreciate *where* this industry is located and most concentrated. (Map from William Glenn Cunningham, *The Aircraft Industry: A Study in Industrial Location.* Los Angeles: L. L. Morrison, 1951.)

in 1952 all but a small part of the labor force was in these two cities. Most of the important centers are now able to utilize such supplies. Skills take a long time to develop. The time required for and the expense of training inexperienced workmen and the high wage rates necessary to move skilled workers from already producing areas make difficult the task of locating in new areas to meet changed conditions. Many women are employed in this industry: one in five of all aircraft workers in the Los Angeles labor market area in mid-1952 were women and one in three in San Diego.

Taxation may be an important locational factor. The high taxes are proving an incentive for the decentralization of the airframe industry to communities surrounding the large cities, such as Santa Monica, El Segundo, Long Beach (Douglas), Culver City (Hughes), Burbank (Lockheed), Inglewood (North American), and Hawthorne (Northrop).

Other factors that have favored all districts have been (1) an early start; (2) ample space for the construction of huge plants and essential adjacent landing fields at reasonable cost (there has been a shift away from large cities for this reason); (3) low-cost fuel and power — natural gas and electricity; and (4) nearness to Air Force and Navy training and proving grounds. The aircraft industry is also being decentralized because of national security.

In 1953, Southern California accounted for approximately one third of total United States aircraft employment. And the aircraft industry provided directly for 26 per cent of all jobs in manufacturing in the Los Angeles area and for 75 per cent in the San Diego area. The production of aircraft and parts was by far the largest manufacturing enterprise in the subregion.

Iron and Steel. At Fontana, 50 miles inland from Los Angeles, is the only completely integrated iron and steel plant on the Pacific Coast. It emerged during World War II, when American railroads were laboring under the strain of supplying the terrific demands of the two-ocean war. There was urgent need for building ships on the Pacific Coast. The water route via the Panama Canal, however, was menaced by German submarines and the railroads could carry no more overland traffic. Henry J. Kaiser, who built the plant, wanted to locate it on tidewater, but naval security seemed to require that it be built inland. Nearness to market and easy access to tidewater were the dominant location factors. The plant, which cost originally about 100 million dollars, has been expanded and now includes several of the nation's largest blast furnaces, by-product coke ovens, open hearth furnaces, and other facilities.

The enterprise gets its fuel from Kaiser-owned coal mines in Utah some 800 miles away, its iron ore partly from mines 175 miles away in San Bernardino County and partly from mines in Utah; its limestone from a local quarry, and its scrap from the region at large. Los Angeles is the largest scrap source on the Pacific Coast. Water is purchased but is re-used by cooling. Since the plant is only 50 miles from the Los Angeles industrial area, it has a good market (Los Angeles normally constitutes 43 per cent of the Western steel market). In its proximity to market, Fontana differs from the Colorado and Utah industries. Indeed, it is well located for supplying the entire Pacific Coast.

In addition to the Fontana plant, there are in the Los Angeles area subsidiaries of some of the big eastern corporations. They are of a size and type, however, typical of those usu-

Figure 14–7. The aircraft industry needs plenty of room both inside and outside its buildings. In Southern California the industry found ample room. Note the new planes strung along the apron in right foreground. (Courtesy of Douglas Aircraft Company, Inc.)

ally found when dependence is preponderantly on local supplies of scrap.

Compared with Pittsburgh, Gary, Youngstown, and Birmingham, the California iron and steel industry is unimpressive but to the state itself, it means much. Moreover, the industry is growing rapidly.

Many persons wondered how the Western industry would fare after World War II. Fortunately, the freight-rate structure has been made more favorable and the government's recent concern over having its great iron and steel industry dispersed has played its part.

Sports Wear and Shoes. In certain lines of clothing, Southern California poses a real threat to both New York and Paris. Hollywood greatly influences style trends because of the popularity of the motion-picture stars. But it is in sportswear that the state, particularly Southern California, is surging ahead spectacularly. Californians are said to have "invented outdoor living." Assuredly, the climate does encourage living out of doors. Hence, designers make it a point to understand outdoor fabric requirements. The wools are a little thinner and the cotton a little heavier; silks and rayons are semitropical. Southern California also is a leader in bathing suits and play clothes.

There are some problems, however, chief of which is distribution. California cannot get its clothes into production and on to the store shelves as fast as New York. Labor costs, too, are higher. Moreover, the California market emphasizes quality rather than price and it originates styles rather than copies them.

In shoe manufacturing, Los Angeles is growing rapidly. Some 30 companies make all kinds of shoes and have a national distribution and even some international business. The economic geographic principles that operated in decentralization out of Massachusetts into the Middle West operate here — proximity to a big and prosperous market, high freight rates on shoes, nearness to hides and skins, and ability to meet emergency demands rapidly as a result of intimate knowledge of the needs of the local and nearby market.

Furniture. Southern California has a young, rapidly growing, and important furniture industry. In fact it has the only important such industry in the West. Los Angeles is the principal center, its advantages being progressive management, skill in design, workmanship and market analysis along with an important market. California consumes about ten per cent of all furniture and house furnishing retail sales of the entire country. Unlike the centers in the East and Middle West, furniture manufacturers here are not near their lumber, textile, and metal suppliers. California does have softwood and some hardwoods but the bulk of the latter must be shipped in.

Los Angeles is not hampered by tradition, its designers being willing to experiment. The impact of Hollywood on much of America's thinking has enabled Los Angeles to become a style center in furniture precisely as it has in the clothing industry. Particularly is it pioneering in outdoor furniture, and the new style concept of ease and sprawling comfort is making itself felt even in the indoor type of furniture.

In a national study of labor costs, it was found that the Los Angeles area paid the highest wages in the industry.

Other Industries. There are additional industries that are very important but cannot be discussed here. Of these rubber and rubber tires, mining and oil-well equipment, calculating machines, chemicals, automobiles, and photographic equipment, are prominent. In the manufacture of automobile tires, Los Angeles, with each of the "Big Four," maintaining large plants, stands second only to Akron, capital of this industry. As a motor car center, Los Angeles ranks second only to Detroit. The several assembly plants in 1948 turned out 650,000 cars. In 1948 Ford's West Coast purchasing program was operating at the rate of about 45 million dollars annually and with nearly 50 independent manufacturers participating. The manufacture of photographic equipment here was a natural response to the prominence of the motion-picture industry.

Resorts and the Tourist Trade

The Southern California Subregion, with

its mild, sunny climate, is an American "Riviera." Southern California offers the tourist mountains, beaches, citrus groves, offshore subtropical islands, a large city, and Hollywood. These draw visitors from all parts of the continent and the world, and the Los Angeles Chamber of Commerce, with its various allied organizations, does a good job in advertising the attractions of the subregion.

At first Southern California attracted people largely during the mild winter season. Although summers are relatively cool near the beaches, the inner parts of the Los Angeles Basin often record high temperatures, which, according to the natives are "unusual." The winter season is a festive occasion, with many pageants and entertainments, climaxed by the "Tournament of Roses" and the famous "Rose Bowl" football game at Pasadena on New Year's day.

Overcrowding by destitute "tourists," job-seekers, and movie-aspirants has caused the state of California to try to keep out additional migrants of that class.

To provide for the legitimate tourist trade, Southern California has many large resort hotels in the mountains, along the coast, and on the offshore islands, and has so improved its highway system that all parts of the state are easily accessible by hard surface roads. Railways and airways have contributed greatly to the development of the resort business by providing swift transportation from distant centers of the East. The new Diesel-powered trains on the Santa Fe and the Union Pacific railroads make the trip from Chicago in less than 40 hours, and the transcontinental airlines place Los Angeles only about ten hours from New York.

It is the automobile tourists, however, that come in greatest number. The number of persons entering Southern California in passenger cars bearing out-of-state license plates in 1951 was 1,876,000 and in 1952 2,280,000. This latter figure for this subregion is approximately 54 per cent of the total number of persons entering the state.

The Central Valley

The Central Valley Subregion consists of a broad trough lying between the Sierra Nevada and the Coast Ranges and averages about 50 miles in width and more than 400 miles in length (Figure 14–8). It is outstanding agriculturally, ranking as the largest single concentration of fruit farms and vineyards in the United States. It is also the largest continuous block of agricultural land in California.

The Natural Environment

Structurally the Valley is synclinal, having been warped downward when the Sierra Nevada and the Coast Ranges were uplifted. The long period of erosion that followed this uplift caused the trough to be filled by great quantities of sand, silt, and gravel washed down from the mountains. In places the alluvium has a known thickness of more than 2,000 feet. The Valley is divided into three drainage basins; the Sacramento Valley in the north, the San Joaquin in the middle section, and the Tulare Lake Basin, an area of interior drainage, in the extreme south. The Sacramento River flows through the northern half of the Great Valley and the San Joaquin flows north through the southern half. They converge near San Francisco Bay emptying into the Pacific Ocean through the only large break in the Coast Range. Their delta comprises one of the state's leading truck farming and horticultural areas (Figure 14–9).

Climatically the area has mild, rainy winters and warm to hot summers. Local variations occur, however, where elevation produces a modification of the general climatic type. The climate is often called the "hot summer" mediterranean climate. Lying between the Coast Range and the Sierra Nevada, most parts suffer from a deficiency of rainfall. The precipitation decreases rapidly from more than 30 inches in the north to less than 6 inches in the extreme south. The maximum falls in winter. So far as tempera-

THE PROBLEM

SACRAMENTO VALLEY While two-thirds of the Central Valley's water supply originates in this section, the Sacramento Valley contains but one-third of the agricultural lands Stream flows reach their crests in late winter and spring, allowing the greater percentage of valuable water resources to waste unused into the Pacific Ocean and occasionally causing destructive floods In summer low river stages often are inadequate to meet irrigation needs, and prevent river navigation for any considerable distance upstream from Sacramento

DELTA REGION This fertile farming area is threatened by the inflow of salt water from San Francisco Bay during the late summer months when fresh water in the Sacramento and San Joaquin Rivers reaches low stage and is insufficient to repel the incursion of salt tides As a result, thousands of rich, irrigated acres face permanent damage and the cities and industries of the Delta and northern Bay areas suffer for lack of adequate fresh water supply

SAN JOAQUIN VALLEY This section of the Central Valley contains two-thirds of the agricultural lands, but is provided by nature with only one-third of the water supply During the summer, when irrigation reaches its peak there is not enough water to meet crop needs A large portion of these lands are irrigated by pumping and the overdraft on subsurface supplies resulting from expansion of agriculture has caused a serious water deficiency Thousands of acres already have been abandoned because of the lack of water, and many additional thousands of acres are similarly threatened Located in this section are many thousands of acres of dry land which can be made productive by an assured irrigation supply.

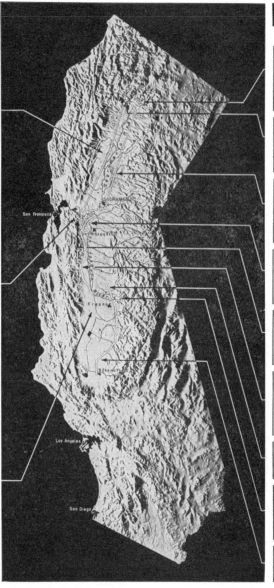

THE SOLUTION

SHASTA DAM — stores Sacramento River water for use downstream and for transfer into the San Joaquin Valley It also controls floods, provides water for navigation and generates electric power

KESWICK DAM - reregulates the water released through Shasta Power Plant for irrigation and other uses downstream It also has a power plant and facilities for fish conservation

TRANSMISSION LINES — convey electric power from Shasta and Keswick Power Plants for the operation of project pumping works and for sale to irrigation districts, municipalities and other agencies

DELTA CROSS CHANNEL — carries Sacramento River water across the Delta to Tracy Pumping Plant and furnishes a fresh water supply to repel salt water intrusion

CONTRA COSTA CANAL - brings irrigation to the farms of Contra Costa County and supplies fresh water to the towns and industries on the south side of Suisun Bay

DELTA - MENDOTA CANAL — carries Delta Cross Channel water from Tracy pumps southward along west side of San Joaquin Valley to Mendota to replace San Joaquin River water diverted at Friant Dam

MADERA CANAL - diverts water north-westerly from Friant Dam for irrigation of lands in Madera County

FRIANT DAM - stores San Joaquin River water for diversion through the Madera and Friant - Kern Canals onto the thirsty lands of the San Joaquin Valley. It also provides flood control

FRIANT - KERN CANAL — diverts water southward from Friant Dam for irrigation use in Fresno, Tulare and Kern Counties

Figure 14–8. The Central Valley of California.   (Courtesy of U. S. Bureau of Reclamation.)

ture is concerned, the valley is characterized by mild winters with a long growing season, and very hot summers; daytime temperatures ordinarily exceed 100° F.

The soils in the Great Valley consist of immature alluvium materials deposited by the torrential flood waters of the rivers. Continuous deposition of alluvium prevents most of the valley from attaining soils with mature profiles. Nevertheless it is the alluvial fans that serve as the foundation for the productive agriculture.

In the southern part of the Valley near Tulare Lake, alkaline conditions make large areas unsuited to irrigation agriculture, although several thousand acres have been reclaimed by an elaborate system of pumps and drainage ditches which impound the flood waters for irrigation during the dry season. Along the lower course of the Sacramento–San Joaquin rivers, much land is waterlogged and hence is unsuited to cultivation. On the whole, however, most of the Great Valley is covered with rich alluvium that provides excellent plant food for agri-

Settlement

Although a slow infiltration of English-speaking settlers into this subregion occurred during the first half of the nineteenth century, the total non-Spanish population was small. Remoteness from populous centers and the

Figure 14–9. The delta cross-channel canal carries Sacramento River water across the delta for transfer into the San Joaquin Valley and furnishes a fresh water supply to repel salt water intrusion. (Courtesy of U. S. Bureau of Reclamation.)

culture, and this, together with the abundance of irrigation water, makes these areas among the most important farming sections of the entire continent.

Because of the low rainfall, nearly all of the Great Valley was originally a grassland, with tall grasses and scattered oaks in the northern better-watered section and bunch grass and desert vegetation in the drier southern part. The largest area of open grassland in the state lies along the edge of the Central Valley. Chaparral occupies considerable areas in the hills.

vast undeveloped landholdings of the Spaniards served to retard any rapid westward drift to California. The discovery of gold in 1848, however, touched off the spark that sent hordes of people from everywhere in a mad dash for California — particularly this area.

The Gold Rush. In January 1848, shortly before the signing of the treaty closing the Mexican War, James W. Marshall discovered flakes of gold in the river gravels of one of the canyons of the Sierra Nevada. During the following summer, news of the discovery spread to the coast of California and to Oregon, and from both places hundreds of men rushed to the Sacramento area. The stampede caused San Francisco to be almost deserted, and for a time the local newspaper was suspended. Before winter the news of the great gold find had spread to the East and to northwest Europe, and before the end of 1848 the real rush had set in. During one month in the spring of 1850, 18,000 people were estimated to have gone overland to California. By the end of that year the state's population was 92,000; ten years later it had risen to 380,000. The "Forty-niners" suffered untold hardships on their way to the "gold diggings," but nothing daunted them.

The Period Following the Gold Rush. Gold mining continued important for some years after 1848, but the more easily worked stream gravels were soon exhausted and the majority of individuals either had to find other occupations or move to new mining areas elsewhere in the West. The discovery of gold in the Rockies of Colorado and of silver in Nevada took a large number of miners eastward. Many of the people, however, who had moved to California realized its potential worth as an agricultural area and began to secure land from the old Spanish *ranchos* that were being broken up and sold. Remoteness from large centers of population made it impossible for these areas to produce farm products for the outside market, but they had a decided advantage for supplying California. Subdivision of the great ranches into small tracts brought many new home-seekers to California, particularly after the close of the Civil War, and soon the Central Valley became an outstanding wheat-producing area. With the completion of the first "transcontinental railroad" in 1869, providing a greater outlet for agricultural surpluses, the Valley blossomed forth as one of the great "bonanza" wheat-growing areas of the nation.

Agriculture

Agriculture was relatively unimportant for years after the Gold Rush. The reasons for this were (1) that most of the adventurous people who came to the mining region had little or no farming background or even interest; (2) there was little inclination to farm so long as hopes were good for making a "strike" in mining, (3) uncertainties of land titles arising from existent grants, and (4) the large extent of swamp and overflowed land in parts of the area — for example in the lower Sacramento Valley.

Even the climate was different. The rain came during the winter. So great a departure from the climate of the East and Middle West, according to the Commissioner of Agriculture, subjected "the culture of the soil to novel conditions, unsettling old traditions, and defying some of the most tenaciously held lessons of experience in the older parts of the country." No wonder agriculture was slow in getting a foothold in the Great Valley.

Offsetting the dry season of summer was the possibility of irrigation, especially on the east side of the valley, for many rivers flowed westward from the Sierra Nevada.

Wheat was the first great crop of the Valley. It could be planted in the winter and harvested in the dry summer and the grain could even afford transport to distant domestic and even to export markets. The crop was grown on large farms averaging 400 acres, though one ranch on the west bank of the Sacramento had 50,000 acres under cultivation in 1880. Barley also became an important winter crop. It was widely used as feed for draft animals and particularly for the pack trains.

Irrigation in the Central Valley. In the 1880's when irrigation began to be practiced in this subregion, much land that previously had been used for ranching or for growing wheat or other small grains was placed "under the ditch." Prior to that time the courts of California had upheld the "doctrine of riparian rights," for the waters of the Valley, which allowed the owners of land bordering streams to maintain the flow of water in those streams in undiminished volume. This doctrine, designed for a humid country, was unsuited to a land where the chief purpose of water was to be for irrigation, and it had the effect of granting a large supply of water to certain overflow lands that did not need it and prohibiting the use of water on good irrigable lands not adjacent to streams. Within recent years, however, the courts have ruled that even riparian landowners are entitled to only a "reasonable use" of stream waters and that the surpluses may be diverted. Following the peak year of grain production in the Great Valley (1885), irrigation has increased steadily. The irrigated lands of the Valley represent more than 65 per cent of the total for California.

The Central Valley Project. Almost from the beginning of irrigation in the Great Valley, need was felt for some central control of irrigation waters, so that the heavy winter precipitation on the Sierra Nevada could be better conserved for summer use. Some fifty active irrigation districts have distributed waters to more than two million acres of irrigated lands. On some of the major streams, such as the Toulumne, the Stanislaus, and the Merced, large storage reservoirs have been constructed, but still no unified project had been completed. In 1920, Robert B. Marshall worked out an elaborate plan for the co-ordinated exploitation of water resources of the Great Valley. Although the plan was rejected, it created interest in a Central Valley Project. The California legislature began an investigation; plans were issued in 1923 and revised in 1925, 1927, and 1930. The plans were replaced by a final one presented by the state engineer, Edward Hyatt, and ultimately adopted, with minor changes, by the state legislature.

The present Central Valley Project (Figure 14–8) has two main purposes: (1) the supplying of water to the dry southeastern San Joaquin Valley and (2) the prevention of salt-water encroachment in the delta area. Actually there is enough unused water to meet present needs in full and to provide for further growth. The shortage results from the failure to save flood waters. An annual average of about 20 million acre-feet of water flows unused into the Pacific Ocean from the streams of the Central Valley.

The big overall problem is that two thirds of the water but only one third of the irrigable farm lands are in the Sacramento River Basin, whereas one third of the water but two thirds of the irrigable farm lands are in the San Joaquin River Basin.[6]

The initial problem of the project provides for the irrigation of 500,000 acres of new land and for furnishing water for about 500,000 acres of cultivated lands badly in need of supplemental supply (Figure 14–10).

The ultimate program of the Bureau of Reclamation is to utilize fully and efficiently all the water resources of the Central Valley. The master plan contemplates 48 dams and 20 large canals, powerhouses and other works, and would double the Central Valley's irrigated area. The total program ultimately would provide water for 3,040,000 acres of land not now irrigated and produce 8 billion kilowatt-hours of power a year.[7]

Crops

Cotton. Cotton production expanded rapidly after 1925 in the San Joaquin Valley, which is today one of the nation's outstanding cotton-growing areas. In addition cotton is now the most important single crop in the State.

Most of California's cotton acreage is in the Central Valley, particularly in the middle and southern portions. So important has the crop become that it has changed the system of farming in many parts of the valley since it has been more profitable than fruits, vegetables, and even dairy products. It has replaced much irrigated pasture formerly used for sheep. The major factors controlling the localization of cotton are the climate, the availability of irrigation water, and the value of competing crops. The long, hot, growing season, the freedom from rain during picking, and the flat land are additional favorable factors, as is the absence of the cotton boll weevil, and until 1951 of the pink bollworm.

The invasion of the Valley by the pink bollworm is the most serious insect threat so far experienced by California cotton growers. Unlike the cotton boll weevil, the pink boll-

[6] Bureau of Reclamation, *Central Valley Project, California.* Washington, D. C.: Government Printing Office, 1950.

[7] Bureau of Reclamation, *Central Valley Project, California.*

Figure 14–10. The Friant-Kern Canal is 153 miles long and diverts water southward from Friant Dam for irrigation use in the southern San Joaquin Valley. (Courtesy of U. S. Bureau of Reclamation.)

worm thrives under arid conditions. Unfortunately, no chemicals have yet been found which eradicate the pink bollworm although DDT is of some value in the battle.

This subregion grows exclusively an upland type of cotton known as Acala 4–42, which was developed specifically for the San Joaquin Valley climate and soil by a scientist of the United States Department of Agriculture Experiment Station near Shafter. It is a relatively long-staple variety and yields heavily — 650 pounds to the acre (in 1951) as against 285 pounds for the national average. Because of its superior quality (it has a uniform length of fiber, fewer kinks, and good spinning qualities) and the early recognition of the advantages of specialization in one variety, legislation at the request of the growers themselves, makes it unlawful to grow any other variety in the counties from San Joaquin to Kern.

The crop is harvested by both hand pickers and mechanical pickers. Hand picking is cleaner but more expensive. So far hand pickers have to follow up the machines. Since cotton must not be picked when wet, because it balls up and grades low, mechanical pickers start working a field only after the dew is off and they stop before the dampness of evening commences. As to comparative costs of picking, it is estimated ten dollars per 100 pounds for hand picking and five for mechanical picking.

Until recently nearly all the labor force was migrant. Now part of it is being settled at least for the four or five cotton months; then it moves into the fruit and field crop areas as the several crops come in season.

Grains and Other Field Crops. *Alfalfa,* the chief hay crop of the subregion, accounts for more than 80 per cent of the production of all hay crops. It is grown mainly under irrigation. Because of the long growing season, alfalfa is cut from three to six times annually. It is grown for hay, seed, alfalfa meal, and pasture, and is a principal legume grown for soil improvement. Its high nutritional value makes it the preferred roughage for dairy cows. Its wide adaptability accounts for its widespread distribution throughout the area.

Ladino clover is the basic legume in California's 600,000 acres of irrigated pasture. The crop is grown mostly in the Sacramento and northern San Joaquin valleys, where it thrives on the heavy clay or loam soils. It does well on shallow soil underlain by a tight layer of clay or a hardpan. It is both productive and palatable, fast growing and long-lived. It does well on soils too shallow for such deep-rooted crops as alfalfa, sugar beets, and tree fruits.

Sugar beets.[8] The first really successful sugar beet factory in the Southwest was begun in 1879 at Alvarado; nine years later a second factory was built at Watsonville. California leads the nation in sugar beet production and the principal growing area, though by no means the only one, centers in the Sacramento and the northern and central San Joaquin valleys including the delta. Beets are raised on thousands of farms, on many of which other crops cannot be grown to advantage because of less tolerance to alkali.

The beets are grown under contract with sugar refining companies of which there are three operating in the Valley. A single plant usually contracts for about 20,000 acres of beets. Assuming a yield of 20 tons to the acre, such a factory processes 400,000 tons of beets annually.

At harvest the beets are dug in accordance with a company schedule and shipped to a designated factory by truck or rail or to a loading station for shipment to the factory. Beets can be transported only about 30 miles because of their considerable weight

and bulk in proportion to value and their perishability.

Wheat, once the most important crop in the Valley, declined rapidly in importance between 1899 and 1909, partly because of the use of the better lands for more intensive crops and partly because of the depletion of soil fertility from continuous cropping. High prices for wheat during World War I caused a revival in production, but today wheat occupies a relatively small acreage. The crop is both dry-farmed and irrigated. California wheat is "soft wheat" and hence commands no premium price.

Barley grows in the same lands as wheat but is better adapted to the dry climate of the Great Valley. Areas of heaviest production are found in the northern part of the San Joaquin Valley and in the Sacramento Valley. In the latter, particularly, it is both dry-farmed and irrigated. Barley now greatly exceeds wheat in acreage because it usually yields enough more per acre to offset the price advantage of wheat. Most of the crop is used for feed, and about one fourth is exported or used locally for malting. Very little barley is exported.

Rice is grown in some 290,000 acres (1949) mostly in the counties of the Sacramento Valley, which is the northern segment of the Great Valley. The crop has been grown on a commercial basis since 1912. Factors conducive to production are a plentiful supply of relatively cheap water, heavy clay soils highly retentive of water, good drainage, and high summer temperatures. Additional factors are the long, warm growing season and the freedom from rains during harvest. The heavy soils are of limited value for other crops. Hence the number of crops which can be rotated is small. These crops consist primarily of Ladino clover, which is well adapted to heavy, adobe soil, beans, and wheat. A common rotation is rice, beans, wheat, beans, and rice.

Rice is seeded on the watered fields by airplane almost to the exclusion of drilling it on land, the reasons being that (1) it is a fast method, (2) slightly less seed is required, and (3) less attention need be de-

---

[8] Despite California's importance in sugar beet production, only a few of the salient conditions are presented here because the crop has received adequate attention in previous chapters.

voted to the preparation of the seed bed (Figure 14–11).

The crop is irrigated and kept flooded until before harvest, water having the following functions: (1) it supplies the plant water for normal life processes, (2) it helps control weeds, and (3) it regulates and makes more uniform the temperatures affecting growth. California rice is grown on

Figure 14–11. Seeding rice on water by airplane in the Central Valley. The fields are flooded before planting in order to kill the weeds. (Photo by John Black and Associates.)

a large scale, and labor saving implements are employed at every stage.

Grapes. Although grapes are grown widely over the state, it is the Central Valley, particularly the San Joaquin segment, that ranks first. The grape's essential requirements are dry, hot summers and cool, wet winters (or irrigation for supplementing rainfall) and freedom from killing frosts.

California grapes are classified according to use as raisin, table, or wine grapes, and their geographical distribution based upon these uses is not identical. Some grapes are suitable for more than one purpose. Thus the Malaga is used as a table grape, for wine,

and in some years for raisins; the Muscat is used for making both raisins and wine and locally as a table grape; the Thompson (Sultanina), leading table and raisin variety, is regularly used for making wine.

The wide distribution of areas suitable for grapes for one use or another augurs well for the future of the industry. The availability and cost of labor, however, have become real problems. Several of the larger growers, accordingly, are violating Old-World tradition and are planting their vines widely enough apart to permit small powered cultivators to replace men with hoes in weeding and cultivating.

Citrus Fruits. Some citrus, particularly oranges, is grown on the piedmont slopes of the Central Valley but the area is not outstanding since its production represents less than one fourth of that of the state. Navel and Valencia oranges are grown in the San Joaquin Valley in the Porterville and Lindsay districts. Since the navel is more tolerant of high summer temperatures and less susceptible to frost in winter than the Valencia, it is better suited to the Central Valley.

Deciduous Fruits and Nuts. The Central Valley is one of the world's outstanding areas of deciduous tree-fruits and nuts. The soils are deep and retentive of moisture, there is adequate water for irrigation, the winter temperatures are sufficiently low to break the rest period of the trees, there is little danger from late spring frosts, and the growing season is long and hot. The crops belong to two climate zones; the *temperate*, consisting of peaches and apricots, and the *subtropical*, consisting of figs, walnuts, and almonds. Local differences in climate and soil greatly affect the distribution of these crops.

Peaches, grown primarily in the Great Valley, are concentrated along the east side of the San Joaquin Valley in the vicinity of Fresno and Merced, where they are grown almost entirely under irrigation. In the Sacramento district, however, large peach orchards thrive without irrigation. Although California ranks first in the United States in the production of peaches, little of the crop is marketed fresh; most of it is canned and dried. The clingstone varieties are grown for canning; the freestone for canning, drying and fresh consumption.

The long period of bright, sunny days, the low humidity, and the high summer temperatures in the Central Valley are excellent for peach growing. Diseases and pests are well controlled.

Apricots are grown in the Central Valley but are important only in selected areas. Since the tree is quite tolerant of soil conditions, its distribution is controlled largely by climate. Since the tree tends to bloom early and since spring frosts may occur in the Valley, sites must be carefully selected.

Olives. California grows 99 per cent of the American crop of olives and production is virtually confined to the Central Valley. In the Sacramento Valley, olive plantings are concentrated near Oroville, Corning, and Fair Oaks and in the San Joaquin Valley in the Lindsay-Exeter district. In the San Joaquin Valley olive trees frequently serve as border plantings around citrus and deciduous fruit orchards, where they act as windbreaks, dust screens and ornamental borders.

The olive is well suited to the Valley, for it can withstand much heat and aridity. It is susceptible, however, to damage by freezing temperatures. It can do well on soils too poor for other tree crops. For the most part the crop is irrigated. Fortunately for California, the olive is free from the insect infestations common to Mediterranean lands. This permits the olives to be picked ripe and most of the crop is marketed in this form.

Figs are widely distributed over the southern half of California, but commercial production is centered largely in the Central Valley, particularly in the San Joaquin segment. The fig tree needs a long, warm growing season, low humidity, and hot summers. Killing spring frosts and cold winters are detrimental.

Nut crops. Both almonds and walnuts are commercially important in this subregion, but almonds are far more important. Almond production centers mainly in the Sacramento and northern San Joaquin Valleys with 50 per cent of the bearing acreage in the former (mainly around Chico, Live Oak, Yuba City, and Fair Oaks on the east side and in the Orland, Arbuckle, Esparto, and Winters district on the west side) and 22 per cent in the latter (Oakly, Oakdale, and Atwater-Livingston districts). Successful culture is attuned to the long, warm growing season, absence of damaging spring frost, and the adequate supply of irrigation water. The great demand for shelled and salted almonds combined with a high tariff on imported nuts enables California to be a huge producer.

Although California supplies more than 90 per cent of the English walnut crop of the nation, most of it is grown outside the Valley. Some walnut production takes place, however, in both the San Joaquin and Sacramento valleys. This crop does best where the growing season is long but where summer temperatures are not excessive as they often are in the Central Valley. Excessive heat sunburns the nuts.

Vegetables. Asparagus, beans, tomatoes and potatoes all are very important in the Central Valley; most other vegetables, however, are of only secondary importance.

Asparagus is a major crop in the Delta of the Sacramento and San Joaquin rivers; in fact more than 90 per cent of the state's total acreage is here. Geographical conditions are particularly favorable in the Delta: the soils, a mixture of muck and alluvium; temperatures modified by the sea breezes through Carquinez Strait; and a plentiful supply of irrigation water.

Field beans production is outstanding from Merced County north to Tehama County. The extreme heat of the southern San Joaquin Valley rules out bean production there. The varieties grown are limas, pinks, blackeye, cranbury, Mexican red, red kidney, and bayo.

Potatoes, because of their low value per unit of weight and their perishability, should be grown relatively near their market. Since California now ranks second in population among the states of the Union, an appreciable market is at hand. Nevertheless potatoes are among the less important of the state's row crops. The largest white potato acreage (about a third that of the state but about half the production) is on the San Joaquin Delta. The crop is grown under large-scale methods.

Kern County grows more than 75 per cent of the state's *early* potatoes. California specializes in early potatoes — those that can be marketed in May and June. The yield is more than twice that of other late spring potato-growing states. Of the two million acres devoted to potatoes in the United States only 15 per cent grows early varieties and California has 40 per cent of this acreage.

Tomatoes are a major crop in California. In fact 31 per cent of the national acreage in 1951 was in California and the Central Valley is one of the principal growing areas. In the valley, because of its long growing season, tomatoes mature before the really high temperatures begin.

The crop is grown both for the fresh market and for canning. During a recent year 79 per cent of the total pack of California canned vegetables consisted of products from tomatoes.

Mechanization of Agriculture

The open, relatively level floor of the Central Valley along with the relative scarcity of farm labor, stimulate the wide employment of labor-saving machinery.

Because of the climate and the kinds of crops grown, however, the problems are not precisely like those in other agricultural areas. It is not surprising to learn, therefore, that Californians are noted for their versatility in solving peculiar crop problems through the use of special inventions. The combined harvester-thresher was being used on the big Central Valley farms as early as the 1880's. During World War II, when field labor was particularly scarce, a number of "dirt farmers" in the Central Valley developed machinery adapted to their own special products. One farmer developed a machine for shaking walnuts off the trees. Another device is the sloping catching frames which are placed under the trees for collecting and delivering the fruit to field boxes. Vacuum and brush pickups even gather the nuts from the ground. Recent contributions are a green asparagus harvester, tomato picking aids, a mechanical apricot cutter, a hay-making machine which lifts hay to the wagons, a sugar

beet harvester, and a weed cutter. Airplanes now seed from the air 90 per cent of the California rice crop; they also fertilize and spray much of the rice. Pneumatic shears are now used for pruning. Cotton is mechanically chopped, onions harvested, and adobe lumps sorted out of beans by machinery.

Livestock

During the period of Spanish settlement huge tracts of land were granted to the colonists for ranches. Cattle ranching, although the leading activity during the entire Spanish-Mexican period, as a result of the abundance of native grasses and the mild climate, was never especially profitable. With the increase in the demand for foodstuffs following the discovery of gold, the better lands in the Central Valley were plowed up and planted to cereals — particularly wheat. Hence cattle and sheep ranching were crowded onto the poorer hill lands of the coast or into the drier parts of the San Joaquin Valley.

Beef Cattle. The distribution of beef cattle is fairly wide throughout the state, though the Central Valley is the leading area. The cattle are marketed at lighter average weight than was the case in the past and feeding in the area is now well developed.

Dairy Cattle. Widely distributed over the state also, are the dairy cattle, but the Central Valley is outstanding. The huge output of alfalfa serves as the principal roughage. The Holstein breed predominates. Most of the Valley milk is sold as whole milk or cream for manufacturing, though some market milk is sent to Valley cities, to those in the Bay Area, and to metropolitan Los Angeles.

Sheep. In sheep, California ranks next to Texas and Wyoming, with approximately six per cent of the nation's total. Sheep, though widely distributed over the State are most highly concentrated with about 85 percent in the Central Valley and the North Coast. The pattern of distribution changes very slightly from decade to decade. Sheep raising is prosecuted under both farm and range conditions, the former being most highly developed in the lower Sacramento Valley; here the flocks are maintained during summer and fall primarily on native pasture, volunteer grain fields, grain stubble, and beet tops. The foothills bordering the Valley provide winter grazing and lambing grounds for thousands of head of range ewes. As feed in the Valley dries up, many sheep men in the Sacramento and in parts of the San Joaquin Valley truck or ship their stock into the high pastures of the Sierra Nevada. Many sheep are moved into the Sacramento-San Joaquin Delta each fall for feeding.

Changes, however, are occurring in the sheep business: much land formerly devoted to sheep raising is now being used for crops because the latter are more profitable. Skilled sheep labor is both scarce and expensive; grazing in the national forests has been reduced and wool prices have fluctuated widely. Nevertheless there is much land in the state that can be utilized more profitably by sheep than by anything else.

Petroleum and Natural Gas

The San Joaquin Valley petroleum district, like the region's other two, lies in the south-ern part of the state.[9] All four comprise only 3.63 per cent of California's area and yet it is reported that no area of equal size in the world approaches their record of distribution. The San Joaquin Valley district, comprising more than 23 fields (Figure 14–12), is by far the largest of California's oil-producing areas. It also ranks first in estimated proved reserves, first in estimated ultimate production, second in past production, and third in average estimated ultimate production per acre. Although some of its fields are definitely declining, for example, Coalinga and Kettleman Hills, such important discoveries were made in the southern part of the district in 1952 as to cause re-examination of the south and west slopes of the Valley. Bakersfield is the big center of this district.

In natural gas California is one of the nation's four leading states. Though gas was first brought in at Stockton in 1864, it was

[9] For excellent and authoritative maps of California's oil and gas fields see State of California, Department of Natural Resources, *Geologic Formations and Economic Development of the Oil and Gas Fields of California,* Bulletin No. 118, San Francisco, 1943, pp. 265; 274.

Figure 14–12. Derricks and wells in the Sunset-Midway oil field of the San Joaquin Valley, looking northwest. (Courtesy of Spence Air Photos.)

not until 1937 that the business really became outstanding with successful production at depths in excess of 10,000 feet. Despite heavy production in the Stockton district and elsewhere within the Subtropical California Region, receipts from Texas via pipeline continue to increase sharply.

Manufacturing in the Central Valley

There is considerable manufacturing in the Central Valley but until recently nearly all of it was concerned with the processing of the products raised there — cotton ginning, cotton oil processing, flour milling, beet sugar refining, meat packing, rice milling, the drying of raisins and other fruits, and wine making. Several of these industries are presented here.

With the federal government stressing the dispersion of industry over the nation, the Valley is aggressively seeking other types of manufactures and is meeting with considerable success. One example is that of International Harvester Company of America's new 3 million dollar plant for producing heavy duty equipment for use in the specialized agriculture of the Far West.

Sugar Refining. California is the only state to refine both beet and cane sugar (Figure 3–7). It has already been pointed out that California ranks first in production among the 22 beet growing states, its share being about 30 per cent. A beet sugar factory, in order to operate profitably, must process in the neighborhood of 400,000 tons of beets annually, which means contracting for about 20,000 acres of beets. It must also have access to a large supply of good water — 200,000 to 400,000 gallons per hour — at moderate cost. Each factory draws upon a restricted area of beet land and operates seasonally. Most of the factories are located in the northern part of the Central Valley (Figure 3–7).

Wine Making. Grapes are grown in 47 of the 58 California counties and 40 per cent of the crop enters the wine industry.[10] Many of the vineyards are enormous, the largest oc-

cupying some 5,000 acres. Almost 20,000 California farmers grow grapes and it is reported that one out of every 75 Californians draws his livelihood from grapes and wine. Grapes beget wineries and hence maps of the two coincide remarkably well.

California, with 400 wineries located mostly in eight different areas, manufactures 90 per cent of the total commercial wine made in the United States. It produced 175 million gallons in 1946 and 125,000,000 gallons in 1950.

Almost every known variety of grape and wine type finds a congenial *milieu* somewhere in the state. The temperature and rainfall maps largely tell the story of wine varieties and specialties, though altitude and soil types also play a role. These last two factors are so variable, however, even among neighboring vineyards, that they cannot be discussed in so short a chapter.

The Drying of Raisins. The nation's raisin production is confined mainly to the San Joaquin Valley and Fresno is synonymous with raisins. This area yields about half the world output. Annual production varies widely according to price and market; in some years 400,000 tons will be dried and in another 170,000 tons. Though some raisins are dehydrated, probably 85 per cent are sun-dried. When the fruit has attained a sugar content of about 25 per cent some time during the latter half of August, the clusters of grapes are hand picked and spread on wooden and paper trays between the rows of vines, where they are allowed to dry for about 10 to 15 days.

Livestock Slaughter and Meat Packing. Considering the West as a whole, it is a surplus cattle-sheep region. California, however, is a deficient area; if Oregon, Idaho, Nevada, Utah, and Arizona all were to ship their combined surpluses into California, the State still would be a deficit area. Approximately 60 per cent of the beef, 40 per cent of the lamb, and 80 per cent of the pork must be shipped in as live animals or as dressed meat.[11]

Western states that formerly sent their live-

---

[10] Because the methods of making wine are so similar, this discussion is applicable to the entire state, not just the Central Valley.

[11] Edwin C. Voorhies, "The Sheep and Wool Industry," *California Agriculture* (California College of Agriculture), Vol. 5, January 1951, p. 2.

stock East now send most of it to California. The increased meat requirements have made it necessary for California packing house buyers to go farther and farther East to satisfy their demands.

Slaughtering is widely distributed throughout the state but the greatest concentration of plants is in the Central Valley, the San Francisco, the Los Angeles, and the San Diego areas.

The Sierra Nevada

From some points of view the Sierra Nevada is the least important of the four subregions (Figure 14–1). Population is much smaller than elsewhere and economic opportunities are fewer. Mining, logging, grazing, and recreation are the leading occupations. Of these mining is declining in importance. Transportation is a big problem, particularly in winter.

The Natural Environment

The Sierra Nevada constitutes a huge mountain block 50 to 80 miles wide and 400 miles long. It was formed by a gigantic uplift which tilted the block westward. The eastern front is marked by a bold escarpment which rises 5,000 to 10,000 feet above the alluvial-filled basins of the Intermontane Region to the east, and this bold escarpment marks one of the most definite geographic boundaries on the continent. The western slope, although more gentle, is deeply incised with river canyons and has been greatly eroded by glaciers, forming such magnificent canyons as those of the Yosemite and Toulumne.[12]

The summits of the Sierra Nevada have suffered severe glacial erosion and consist of a series of interlocking cirques. Complex faulting, mountain glaciation and stream erosion account for most of the details of the mountain mass. Some of the block-faulted valleys contain lakes, the most noted of which is Lake Tahoe. Since the crest of the Sierra Nevada is toward the eastern margin of the region, and since the rain-bearing winds come from the west, practically all of the precipitation falling upon the mountains flows down the gentle western slope into the Central Valley providing it with water for irrigation.

The Sierra Nevada, because of its great elevation and because it presents a formidable barrier to the rain-bearing winds from the Pacific Ocean, has a heavy precipitation on the western slope, while the eastern, rain-shadow side is comparatively dry. Although some rain falls throughout the summer, the maximum precipitation comes as snow during the winter season. The western slope receives the heaviest snowfall of any part of the United States, the average being more than 400 inches a year. Heavy snows tend to emphasize the barrier nature of the Sierra Nevada and have caused great expenditures in money to transportation lines operating across them.

On the western slopes of the Sierra Nevada dense forests of conifers dominate the landscape. These include ponderosa (yellow pine), Douglas fir, lodge-pole pine, sugar pine, and sequoia, and constitute some of the most magnificent forests of the continent. Higher up on the slopes the large trees give way to smaller dwarfed varieties and ultimately on the highest summits to tundra vegetation.

As a result of man and some of his practices such as destructive logging, accidental and willful fires, and excessive grazing, there is progressive deterioration from higher and more valuable to less valuable types of woodland, chaparral, or sage brush.[13]

The Economy

Lumbering and the Forest-products Industries. The middle portions of the Sierra

[12] Wallace W. Atwood, *The Physiographic Provinces of North America*, p. 441. Boston: Ginn & Co., 1940.

[13] H. L. Shantz, *The Use of Fire as a Tool in the Management of the Brush Ranges of California*. Sacramento: California State Board of Forestry, January 1, 1947.

Nevada are covered with dense stands of conifers, including western yellow pine and sugar pine. Hence California is an important lumber-producing state.

Logging and lumbering began with the development of mining. For a long time the chief uses for wood products were for mine props, cross-ties for railroads, and construction timber for dwellings and other buildings in the mining camps. Logging operations in those days were extremely wasteful and doubtless much more timber was destroyed through fire and careless logging methods than was actually utilized.

With the development of the national forests, much of the formerly cut-over and burned-over land was withdrawn from logging activities, though a large part still remains in the hands of major lumber companies. The establishment of the national forests in the Sierra Nevada was partly to reestablish forest stands for future lumbering industries, but chiefly to protect the watersheds of the numerous streams that provide waters for irrigation, domestic use, and power. These national forests also serve as important recreational centers for the entire region, and they provide summer pastures for a large range livestock enterprise.

Since the snows in the mountains are extremely heavy, most logging activities are confined to the summer months. Logging camps, temporary settlements that are moved from season to season, are usually located in remote areas. When logs can be moved out of the forests, they are brought to such lumber towns as Westwood, McCloud, and Weed, where they are converted into lumber. California, particularly metropolitan Los Angeles with its tremendous demand, is deficient in lumber supply. Hardwoods for furniture and cabinet purposes must be brought in from other regions since the Sierra Nevada forests are primarily coniferous.

Sunkist Growers, Inc. owns and operates a large lumber mill at Susanville which is designed primarily to produce shook for Sunkist orange, lemon, and grapefruit packing boxes. Although this mill provides the greater part of the boxes, additional supplies must be purchased on the open market. During a re-

cent year the box factories of the corporation handled 43 million feet of lumber; to transport the manufactured product, 4,300 railroad cars were needed.

The forest-products industries of the Sierra Nevada are of much importance to the region, but they occupy a place of minor significance as compared to the great lumber-producing areas in the Pacific Northwest or the South.

Mining. Mining made "California" a name known to almost everyone — really put the region "on the map." In recent years, however, mining has been largely overshadowed by agriculture, manufacturing, and tourism, despite the fact that the state continues to be rich in minerals.[14]

Gold still is mined on a limited scale in the Sierra Nevada, but in value the yellow metal is now surpassed by several other minerals. It is interesting to note that California produces commercially more than 60 minerals — a greater number than any other state. The amount of each mined in some cases is small but all contribute to continue mining as an important economic enterprise with an annual production exceeding 20 million dollars. The majority but by no means all of the minerals are mined in the Sierra Nevada.

Grazing. There are four life zones in California [15] (Figure 14–13). Generalizing, it may be said that the Lower Sonoran in the Central Valley is confined to areas below 500 feet. It consists of scattered desert shrubs and a few species of annual and perennial grasses. The Upper Sonoran lies immediately above the Lower Sonoran at elevations up to 3,000 to 5,000 feet. It includes the foothill and valley lands where the precipitation is slightly higher and the temperature somewhat lower than in the zone below. Chaparral is common. Native and introduced annuals predominate. The Transition Zone, occupying a narrow elevational range between 2,000 and 5,000 feet just above the Upper Sonoran, contains the commercial timber of the subregion.[15]

---

[14] Olaf P. Jenkins, *The Mother Lode Country* (Centennial Edition) State Division of Mines, Bulletin 141, Sept. 1948, p. 17.

[15] Arthur W. Sampson and others, *California Grasslands and Range Forage Grasses*, Bulletin 724, California College of Agriculture, May 1951, p. 13.

Rainfall here is higher and temperatures lower than in the zone below. The Boreal, a relatively small zone [16] lies above the Transition Zone at elevations above 5,000 feet. Here the snowfall is high and temperatures low. Grazing is limited to a short midsummer and late summer period. Sheep graze it most advantageously.

In order to obtain maximum utilization of the range, the typical practice is to graze the animals in the Lower Sonoran and lower

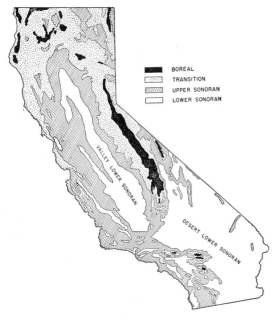

BOREAL
TRANSITION
UPPER SONORAN
LOWER SONORAN

Figure 14–13. Vegetation life zones of California. Map after Dr. Joseph Grinnell.)

reaches of the Upper Sonoran during winter and as late in spring as the forage remains succulent, and then move them into the Transition Zone and finally into the Boreal Zone in summer and early autumn. This practice, known as "transhumance," is followed particularly by those stockmen who own or lease private lands in the high mountains or obtain grazing permits from the Forest Service to run stock in the national forests. Both cattle and sheep are raised in the mountains.

Recreation. The great extent of the Sierra Nevada, 50 to 80 by 400 miles, their height, the deep canyons, waterfalls, lakes, fish laden streams and lakes, forests, historical interests (ghost towns) and good roads have made the mountains a great attraction for tourists and vacationists. In the Sierra Nevada are located some of the nation's most famous national parks. Among these are Sequoia, famous for its magnificent grove of giant sequoia trees, and Yosemite, for its spectacular glacial scenery and waterfalls. These parks, together with the Lake Tahoe district and other famous resort centers, attract thousands of tourists during the summer season. In recent years a sizable winter-sports business has been developed. The Sierra Nevada may be classed as one of the continent's outstanding recreational areas and the continued growth of its resort industry seems assured. Because of location, however, it will tend to serve mainly a West Coast clientele and can never rival the highlands of the Northeast in volume of business.

Water Power

The large extent of the Sierra Nevada, its great height, and the heavy snow pack, result in considerable water-power capacity being available to the region. To the natural factors man has added dams and reservoirs. Water power from the Sierra Nevada plays a relatively large part in the electric energy supply of central and northern California. Among the most recent to contribute hydroelectric power are the Feather River and the Central Valley projects. Yet population and manufacturing are increasing at so fast a pace that water power cannot be expected to keep up with the demand for energy. Indications are that fuel-based energy is destined to play an increasingly important part in the electric power supply. In Southern California its proportion for new fuel plants runs close to 75 per cent. Fuel-based electric energy has recently overtaken that from hydroelectric plants.[17]

---

[16] The term "Boreal" is used here to include the Canadian, Hudsonian, and Alpine-Arctic Zones.

[17] "Western Power and Fuel Outlook," *Supplement to Monthly Review,* Federal Reserve Bank of San Francisco, November 1950, p. 5.

The Sierra Nevada in Winter

From time to time spells of winter weather in the Sierra Nevada become so "unusual" that they cause the entire nation to focus attention on man's struggle with the mountains. Thus in January, 1952, heavy snows halted all surface transportation. Drifts 50 feet deep and an overall snow pack of up to 188 inches buried all the highways. Reno was virtually isolated for days. Trains, buses, trucks, and automobiles were brought to a standstill. U. S. Highways 40 and 50 over Donner and Echo Summit passes were closed for days at a time. This snow storm was possibly the worst in 50 years. The Western Pacific Railroad Company spent about $10,-000 a day just for labor for clearing its tracks over a short distance. Southern Pacific Lines' crack streamliner, *City of San Francisco*, became stalled and was unable to move for several days (Figure 14–14). The storms in the mountains caused the Southern Pacific a loss approaching two million dollars. Pacific Gas and Electric Company estimated damage to its installations from the storm at one million.

Figure 14–14. Rampaging nature! The Southern Pacific's westbound streamliner *City of San Francisco* shown here was stalled with 222 passengers for 80 hours in the heavy snowdrifts 15 miles west of Donner Summit in the Sierra Nevada, January 1952. There were two weeks of almost continuous snowfall. Snow packed at average depths of 18 feet at Donner Summit. Drifts 20 to 30 feet deep were common. (Courtesy of *San Francisco Chronicle*.)

The Central Coast — Including The San Francisco Bay Area

The Central Coast is one of the most highly diversified, productive and outstanding areas of the state. Farming, mining, logging, fishing, manufacturing, just about everything is done somewhere in this subregion.

The area consists of the Coast Ranges and their valleys. Only the central portion, however, is considered here — that extending from northern Sonoma County, about 80 miles north of San Francisco, to San Luis Obispo County, about 260 miles to the south (Figure 14–1).

The Natural Environment

The Coast Ranges lie west of the Central Valley and tend to run parallel to the coast. Their nearly even crests average 2,000 to 4,000 feet above sea level. Severe faulting throughout the ranges has resulted in numerous intervening valleys that have been eroded by small streams. The entire mountain mass is divided into fault blocks that are tilted in different directions. Along the coast, ancient shore terraces (in places as high as 1,500 feet above sea level) show that much of the area has been uplifted. More recently a moderate amount of localized sinking has allowed the sea to break through some of the fault valleys of the outer coastal range and submerge the lower valleys of the streams. Golden Gate and San Francisco Bay were formed by this type of subsidence.

On the whole the subregion is characterized by mild winters and warm to hot summers, with the maximum precipitation in winter. Great warmth and dryness characterize the interior portions.

The Coast Ranges receive more moisture than the Central Valley and are somewhat cooler in summer, but, since few of the summits exceed 2,000 feet in elevation, they do not get the heavy precipitation of the Sierra Nevada. Certain portions, however, such as the Santa Cruz Mountains receive very heavy rainfall.

Along the coast a distinctive variation of the Central California climate exists in what is known as the "Fog Belt" — an area characterized by mild winters and cool summers with a maximum of fog during the summer season.[18] Because of the prevalence of fog, the summer maximum temperature occurs in August and September, but throughout the entire area cool summers are characteristic. Rainfall comes largely during the winter season.

The vegetation in this belt of foothill and valley country consists largely of grass, both native and introduced annuals. There is evidence supporting the claim that before grazing became extensive here, the plant population consisted largely of palatable perennial grasses. These apparently were transformed by overgrazing, droughts, and introduction of mediterranean plants.

In the "Fog Belt" the Coast Range supports considerable coniferous forest growth. Oak is quite common on the lower slopes (Figure 14–15) and in the rainier and foggier parts, such as in the vicinity of Santa Cruz, considerable numbers of the large redwoods appear; small groves occur locally elsewhere, also. North of San Francisco Bay, along the northwest coast, lies the world's greatest redwood forest but that area falls within the North Pacific Coast Region (Chapter 15).

The soils are variable because of differences in parent material, climate, age, and location. Residual soils are found in the hills, transported soils in the valleys. The former, lying atop bedrock and usually not more than three or four feet deep, are little used except for fruit trees on occasional foothills.

Irrigation is not feasible on most such slopes because of cost and physical difficulties and the soils are too shallow for dry farming. For the most part, if put to agricultural use at all, they are used for pasturing range livestock; their carrying capacity averages one animal unit[19] to every 5 to 20 acres.[20]

Figure 14–15. Thousands of beef cattle graze the hillsides and ranges of Santa Clara Valley. Pictured is a roundup at a ranch in the southern portion of Santa Clara County. The vegetation in the photograph is typical for the area — grass and open oak forest. (Courtesy of San Jose Chamber of Commerce.)

The soils, particularly in the Russian River, Santa Clara, Salinas and Santa Maria valleys are fertile. If soils alone were involved, production could be greatly increased, but the big problem is water. There appear to be no large opportunities for development of irrigation here.

Agriculture

Conditions of natural environment vary so widely in this subregion that there is much specialization. Sonoma and Marin counties

---

[18] R. J. Russell, "Climates of California," *University of California Publications in Geography,* Vol. 2, No. 4, 1926, p. 82.

[19] An animal unit is a measure of livestock consumption of feed. It is the amount of forage required to maintain for a period of one year, 1 cow, steer, horse, or mule, 5 hogs, 7 sheep or goats, or 100 poultry.

[20] Arthur Shultis, *Farming in California, Circular 173,* College of Agriculture, May 1951, p. 16.

on the north are among California's leading dairy areas, producing fresh or market milk for the San Francisco Bay Area. Petaluma in Sonoma County is among the nation's leaders in commercial poultry raising and the near-by Sebastopol area is famous for its fresh berries and apples. The Napa Valley farther east produces wine grapes, prunes, and other crops.

The valleys in the San Francisco Bay Area, particularly the Santa Clara, are the heart of prune, apricot, almond, pear, and walnut growing and even rank high in production of wine grapes, vegetables, and field crops. The same area is also one of the world's leading flower-growing areas. Among the more favorable factors are the high percentage of possible sunshine, the mild winters and the low cost of heating greenhouses. The chief obstacles have been the salinity of the soils and the great distance from Eastern markets with resultant high shipping costs. Most of the flowers, which are sold in the East, are shipped by air.

The Pajaro Valley (in which Watsonville is located) is probably California's most famous late apple growing area and it is important also for artichokes, strawberries, and other crops.

The Santa Maria and Santa Ynez valleys to the south are large producers of vegetables and flower seeds.

Along the Pacific in this subregion are outstanding vegetable-growing areas — those yielding cool-climate varieties such as lettuce, artichokes, peas, and Brussels sprouts.

Three valleys in the subregion are discussed in some detail, though many others would be if there were ample space.

The Salinas Valley. Largest in Central California is the Salinas Valley, the north end of which is nationally famous for carrots and lettuce (Figure 14-16); it also grows large acreages of white beans, sugar beets, and strawberries. In the hotter and drier southern end, field crops and livestock are important; here even beef cattle are being raised on high-value lands of irrigated pastures.

At present lettuce is making the Salinas Valley known throughout the United States as the "Salad Bowl." Here close to the Pa-

Harvesting lettuce in the field. The heads are placed in cartons of the dry-pack machine and then hauled to the vacuum-cooling plant by truck. (Courtesy of Cochran Equipment Company.)

cific Ocean with the proper proportion of warm sun to cool fog, on level terrain and in fertile soil, lettuce is grown commercially nine months of the year — April through most of December. To a certain extent it may be said that lettuce has been tailored to the valley rather than that geographic conditions here are ideal for the crop. This is not to say, however, that natural conditions are not highly propitious. This valley grows mostly spring and fall lettuce but also some summer lettuce. During this period, from April to December, it produces about half of all the lettuce consumed in the country with shipments running up to 300 cars per day. This valley normally grows about 70 to 80 per cent of the California interstate shipments. The Imperial Valley, only other major California producer, grows only winter lettuce; during the rest of the year its climate is too hot for this crop. From time to time there is overproduction. Then in order to stabilize prices, large areas are plowed up.

All the lettuce is irrigated, the water supply coming from wells used to tap natural reservoirs. With three crops a year, water requirements are high — as much as six acre-feet.

The Santa Clara Valley. The Santa Clara Valley embraces the southern arm of San Francisco Bay between the Coast Ranges — the Diablo Range on the east, the Santa Cruz on the west. Hollister is commonly considered to be at about the southern boundary of the valley.

Since San Francisco is very near and San Jose is in the valley, the occupance is industrial, commercial, and agricultural. In fact this valley is one of the choicest agricultural areas in Anglo-America.

From a frontier Spanish-Mexican livestock ranging area, the Santa Clara Valley went through a wheat-growing stage when the crop was grown for gold miners. Now a fruit- and vegetable-growing stage prevails and the valley ranks as a foremost horticultural area (Figure 14-17).

Fruit is grown intensively on the valley floor but the surrounding ranges are much less intensively utilized. This is most notice-

able in summer when the valley is green and the lower mountain slopes yellow-brown.

The valley bottom north of San Jose consists largely of prune orchards. In some places these are broken by vineyards, or by orchards of pears and apricots and even fields of alfalfa, tomatoes and broccoli. Santa Clara ranks high in vegetable production, particularly tomatoes, and is one of the state's six leading tomato growing counties. Additional crops are peas, spinach, cauliflower, and beans.

The reasons for concentration of horticulture in the Santa Clara Valley are the same as those for concentration of agriculture in the whole state — mild winters, long growing season, abundance of sunlight, and water for irrigation. Water is the critical problem in the Santa Clara Valley now.

Santa Clara County ranks first among all California counties in the production of prunes and apricots and it ranks near the top in that of pears. Most of the prunes are dried, but only about 20 per cent by the sun, the rest being mechanically dried. It is believed that dehydration will eventually become the accepted method of drying for all fruits except apricots and raisins, because it results in cleaner, higher quality fruits at lower cost, and less labor is employed. It also reduces the drying time. The part of the state's apricots that is dried is sun dried. From 17 to 32 per cent of the apricots grown are canned as is about half of the Bartlett pear crop. The largest and most specialized Bartlett pear canning area in the United States is the Santa Clara Valley. Whereas other pear-growing areas seldom can more than 25 per cent of their Bartlett crop, the Santa Clara Valley cans nearly 100 per cent.

Since World War II, the population in Santa Clara Valley has increased greatly and much horticultural land is being taken out of agricultural use for suburban dwelling. In the past few years more than 10,000 acres of Class I and II land have been converted from agricultural to urban use. Many persons who work in San Francisco live as far south as San Jose, Los Gatos, and Santa Cruz and commute daily. This results from their desire to avoid the fogs which, during summer,

Figure 14–17. Apricot trees in bloom on hillsides of the Santa Clara Valley. Because of the trees' susceptibility to spring frosts, sites must be carefully selected. Hence plantings tend to be concentrated on the higher lands to insure good air drainage. The hillside trees are not irrigated. (Courtesy of Henry Washburn, Santa Cruz, California.)

regularly hang over the central Bay Area but seldom penetrate the Santa Clara Valley. Many wealthy retired families live along or in the foothills of the Santa Cruz Range as far south as Los Gatos.

There is still considerable grazing in the foothills of and in the Coast Ranges themselves in this subregion (Figure 14–15). It is estimated that ranches totaling more than one-half million acres extend the length of the eastern foothills of the valley.

The population, agriculture, and industrial growth of the Santa Clara Valley in the final analysis will depend upon the water supply, which in turn will depend upon the measures which the occupying group takes to guarantee for the future an adequate and economical water supply.

The Napa Valley. Nestling between two of the parallel Coast Ranges north of San Francisco Bay is small, beautiful Napa Valley. Its deep alluvial valley soils are intensively utilized for tree crops, particularly prunes, and vines.

Napa Valley is one of the famous wine districts that fan out around San Francisco. Here the temperatures are cooler than in those areas to the east and south. Most of the grapes are grown on hillsides without irrigation (Figure 14–18). The fruit grown here develops a higher acidity — a quality desired for making table wines. Many of its wineries are set in the valley among acres and acres of grape vines. Napa is famous for its red and white dry table wines and for its dessert wines.

Manufacturing

The San Francisco Bay Area is one of California's two leading industrial areas but it is greatly overshadowed by Los Angeles in this respect. Only in canning and shipbuilding does it rank first and even shipbuilding is a "war baby" industry that booms only in time of war. However, the San Francisco Peninsula is rapidly becoming one of the nation's leading manufacturers of electronic equipment.

Forty canneries are supplied from the rich and productive Santa Clara Valley and from servicing the food processing industries.

Many of the new factories established in the Bay Area came as a result of World War II and are branch plants of national concerns with main offices in the East.

Manufacturing plants employing more than 100 persons each are widely dispersed from San Francisco eastward to Antioch and southward to San Jose (Figure 14–19). Most of them are located along the main railways,

Figure 14–18. Vineyard of wine grapes in Napa Valley, north of San Francisco. The northern coastal valleys, of which Napa is one, are climatically ill-adapted to growing raisin and table grapes but yield excellent grapes for wine. (Courtesy of Wine Institute.)

the delta lands of the Sacramento and San Joaquin rivers. Some of the largest canneries have introduced equipment for food freezing in their effort to lessen the seasonal nature of the business and to retain their supply of labor. In addition to the canning, freezing and drying of fruits and vegetables, there is considerable processing of such exotic products as cacao, coffee, copra, and cane sugar. Several large tin-plate, glass, and paper container plants have located in the area for which keep to the tidal shores of the Bay, where the land is level and cheap and where disposal of industrial waste is easy. Water for some purposes is also available in quantity. The majority of the largest plants, those employing 500 workers and more, are in the East Bay counties — Alameda and Contra Costa.

Among the outstanding industries in the Bay Area are oil refineries (Figure 14–20), chemical and munitions plants, a cane sugar refinery (the only one on the West Coast), meat packing establishments, tanneries, steel mills, electronics plants, food machinery factories, electrical equipment plants, a helicopter plant, and cement, ceramics, fibre glass, chemical and salt works.

The Outlook

The future of this region, which as has been pointed out includes all but the wettest and driest parts of California (Figure 14–2),

Figure 14–19. Industries in the South San Francisco area are with few exceptions relatively unimpressive as to size. They are, however, numerous. Their distribution is determined largely by transport — both railway and highway. Farther south is the peninsula's heavy-industry center. Note the Bayshore Freeway in the center of the photograph. (Courtesy of *California Highways and Public Works.*)

The future growth of industry in the Bay Area is threatened by diminishing reserves of petroleum and natural gas, by power shortages in years of nearly normal rainfall, and by the high cost and limited amount of available fresh water.

seems bright. Rich in climate — possibly the most highly publicized in the world — as well as in the bases for a thriving agriculture and, with a rich heritage in forests, minerals, and scenic attractions, it is not surprising to learn that California's population is growing at a more rapid rate than that in any other American state. In fact, every census since 1849 has shown California outstripping the nation as a whole in population growth. Probably better than any other state, it exemplifies that perpetual internal migration that makes the American people the most mobile in the world. This tremendous and sustained trek seemingly will not be stayed. The state gained 2,320,000 residents during the World War II period.

Year after year, California ranks as the leading agricultural state and several of its counties are in the vanguard in national standing. During the last great war, it contributed one eighth of the total necessary agricultural production. In product after product California takes agricultural leadership; for example in 1951 it produced one out of every three tons of truck crops canned and frozen in the entire nation.

More and more the agriculture of this region will be devoted to the production of specialized fruit and truck crops and to dairy products. General farming will shrink to small proportions.

Subtropical California is one of the most highly urbanized regions in Anglo-America; eight out of every ten persons residing there live in cities and metropolitan areas and of these eight, seven are dwelling in Los Angeles County, the San Francisco Bay Area, and San Diego County. All are on or very near tidewater. In few regions is there such pin-point crowding in so few urban areas.

Manufacturing is increasing rapidly. In

Figure 14–20. Oil refinery at Richmond in the Bay Area. In operation since 1902, this is one of the best located as well as one of the largest oil refineries in the world. (Courtesy of Standard Oil Company of California.)

several lines, such as aircraft construction, processing of fruits and vegetables, and in the making of motion pictures, this region has no peers. And in numerous others — electronics, oil well equipment, automobile assembly, rubber goods and tires, agricultural machinery and implements, oil refining, clothing, chemicals, and even iron and steel — the growth is phenomenal. In government arms spending, California in 1952 ranked second and close on the heels of New York (6.2 billion dollars and 17.2 per cent). This has been chiefly in aircraft contracts.

The idea behind manufacturing here is to make mostly those items that will be used by the residents of the region — items bought elsewhere until quite recently. It is true, however, that some companies that located here during the war left for places having cheaper labor, cheaper and better water, and lower freight charges.

How far can this growth in population and manufacturing go? In 1950 the population reached ten and one-half million; it is estimated conservatively that the figure will reach 12 million by 1955 and 14 million by 1960. The governor of the state predicts a population of 20 million within the lifetime of many of those now comprising the population.

Some students do not believe that most California industry is as scientifically located as that in many parts of the American Manufacturing Belt. They call attention to the fact that the great growth in both population and industry has occurred in the two metropolitan nodes that are separated by nearly 400 miles of relatively inhospitable coast and that all must be explained less in economic terms

than in "ballyhoo." In this region, they say, is to be found uncompromising faith in the ability of man to mould nature to his ways, that serious deficiencies do exist in such basic raw materials as coal, iron ore and water, to mention but three.

Yet manufacturing continues to grow and confound the prophets. In fact the rise in industrialism from 1904 to 1939 increased eight times and the state now produces well over five per cent of the nation's fabricated goods. Nonetheless the picture should be reviewed realistically; California is isolated, the market still is relatively small and water is both scarce and costly. However, it appears to the authors that this region has broken for all time the shackles that made it a mere economic outpost of the East. There is good business to be done in the West today and it is economic to manufacture there. Hundreds of Eastern concerns are finding it profitable to establish branch plants in this area. And many new Western businesses are being established. More water is needed and something must be done to solve this problem. However, the region is young, imaginative, fearless and optimistic and much research is being carried on at enormous cost. More dams are being built to save flood waters from the Sierra Nevada; more is being learned about underground waters; studies are being made to find economical ways of freshening sea water. One of the most exciting water projects is the so-called "Reber Plan" for saving fresh water now going to waste in San Francisco Bay.[21]

[21] Chester F. Cole, "A Solution to Some San Francisco Bay Area Problems — The Reber Plan," *Journal of Geography*, Vol. 48, March 1948, pp. 112–120.

Table 13

SELECTED CITIES AND TOWNS OF THE SUBTROPICAL PACIFIC COAST

City or Town	Urbanized area	Political center	City or Town	Urbanized area	Political center
Alameda		64,430	Compton		47,991
Alhambra		51,359	East Bakersfield		38,177
Bakersfield		34,784	Fresno	130,592	91,669
Berkeley		113,805	Glendale		95,702
Beverly Hills		29,032	Huntington Park		29,450
Burbank		78,577	Inglewood		46,185

City or Town	Urbanized area	Political center	City or Town	Urbanized area	Political center
Long Beach		250,767	San Diego	432,974	334,387
Los Angeles	3,996,946	1,970,358	San Francisco		775,357
Lynwood		25,823	San Francisco–Oakland	2,022,078	
Monterey		16,205	San Jose	176,473	95,280
Oakland		384,575	San Leandro		27,542
Palo Alto		25,475	San Mateo		41,782
Pasadena		104,577	Santa Ana		45,533
Pomona		35,405	Santa Barbara		44,913
Redondo Beach		25,226	Santa Cruz		21,970
Redwood City		25,544	Santa Monica		71,595
Richmond		99,545	South Gate		51,116
Riverside		46,764	Stockton	112,834	70,853
Sacramento	211,777	137,572	Vallejo		26,038
San Bernardino	135,770	63,058			

Selected Bibliography

H. Foster Bain, *A Pattern for Western Steel Production*, U. S. Bureau of Mines, Information Circular 7315. Washington, D. C.: Government Printing Office, 1945.

Ruth E. Baugh, "California: A Type Study of a State," *Education*, Vol. 69, September, 1948, pp. 16–23.

M. K. Bennett, "Climate and Agriculture in California," *Economic Geography*, Vol. 15, 1939, pp. 153–164.

Bureau of Agricultural Economics, *The Effect of the Central Valley Project on the Agricultural and Industrial Economy and on the Social Character of California*, Berkeley: 1945.

"Commercial Fisheries of the Pacific Coast States and Alaska," *Federal Reserve Bank of San Francisco Monthly Review*, September and October 1948, and January 1949.

L. A. Crawford and Edgar B. Hurd, "Types of Farming in California Analyzed by Enterprises," *College of Agriculture Bulletin 654*. Berkeley: University of California Press, 1941.

William Glenn Cunningham, *The Aircraft Industry: A Study in Industrial Location*. Los Angeles: L. L. Morrison, 1951.

Howard F. Gregor, "A Sample Study of the California Ranch," *Annals of the Association of American Geographers*, Vol. 41, December 1951, pp. 285–306.

Harold A. Hoffmeister, "In Defense of the Sugar Industry of the Western United States," *Yearbook of the Association of Pacific Coast Geographers*, Vol. 10, 1948.

Claude B. Hutchison, *California Agriculture*. Berkeley: University of California Press, 1946.

O. P. Jenkins, *Geologic Guidebook Along Highway 49–Sierran Gold Belt, The Mother Lode Country*, Department of Natural Resources, Bulletin 141. San Francisco: 1948.

O. P. Jenkins and others, *Geologic Guidebook of the San Francisco Bay Counties*, Division of Mines, Bulletin 154. San Francisco: 1951.

Carey McWilliams, "Look What's Happened to California," *Harper's*, Vol. 199, October 1949, pp. 21–29.

H. F. Raup, "The Delayed Discovery of San Francisco Bay," *California Historical Society Quarterly*, Vol. 27, No. 4.

"Salute to the Golden State," *Engineering and Mining Journal*, Vol. 149, January 1948.

Raymond Schuessler, "Air Pollution in Our Chemical Age," *Think*, Vol. 17, December 1951.

G. E. Stedman, "Cokes Utah Coal in Pacific Coast By-Product Ovens," *Steel*, January 25, 1945.

Max Stern, "California's Next 100 Years," *Atlantic Monthly*, Vol. 184, September 1949, pp. 53–57.

Western Livestock Marketing Research Technical Committee, *Shifts in the Trade in Western Slaughter Livestock*, Agriculture Information Bulletin, No. 14. Washington, D. C.: Government Printing Office, 1950.

15.

The North Pacific Coast

THE North Pacific Coast Region occupies the northwest coastal fringe of Anglo-America between the crest of the Cascade Mountains in Oregon and Washington, the Coast Ranges of British Columbia and Alaska on the east, and the Pacific Ocean on the west. It is nowhere more than 150 miles wide, but it has a length of more than 2,500 miles (Figure 15–1). Despite its great latitudinal extent, conditions throughout the region are somewhat similar as a result of the dominance of the temperate marine climate. Similarity is also evident in the rocky coast, and the moist, forest-covered slopes.

The Terrain [1]

The entire region is dominated by mountains. These vary in height from the comparatively low coastal ranges of northern California, Oregon, and Washington, to the higher ranges of the Cascade Mountains with their superb volcanic peaks of Mount Jefferson, Mount Hood, Mount Adams, Mount St. Helens, Mount Rainier, and Mount Baker, and to the great alpine ranges of British Columbia and Alaska surmounted by Mount McKinley (elevation 20,300 feet), the highest peak on the North American Continent.

[1] Wallace, W. Atwood, *The Physiographic Provinces of North America*, pp. 452–472, 481–486. Boston: Ginn and Co., 1940.

416

The coastal ranges within the United States portion of this region comprise a series of somewhat distinct mountain areas. They include the Coast Ranges of northern California, the Klamath Mountains which tie these ranges to the southern Cascades, the Coast Ranges of Oregon, the Olympic Mountains of Washington, and the mountains of Vancouver Island.

The California Coast Ranges consisting of folded and faulted structures, have an even, though discontinuous crest line. The entire mountain mass is divided into a series of blocks that are tilted in various directions. The streams that break through these ranges follow structural valleys. The mountains frequently project out into the ocean forming bold rocky headlands.

The Klamath Mountains appear as a dissected plateau with an average summit level of 2,000 to 4,000 feet. The stream canyons that radiate from the Klamath show the influence of glaciation in their upper reaches.

The Oregon Coast Range which extends northward from the Klamath almost to the mouth of the Columbia River, is dissected by the deeply entrenched Rogue and Umpqua rivers and by several smaller streams that flow across this mountain mass to the Pacific Ocean. The gaps through the mountains facilitate travel between the coast and the interior

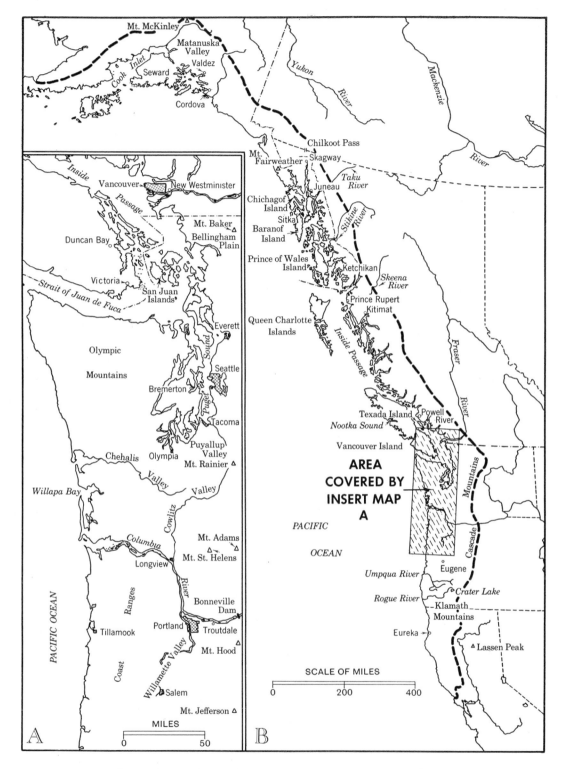

Figure 15–1. The North Pacific Coast. A region of lumbering, fishing, farming, manufacturing, resorts, and commerce.

417

valleys but do not seriously affect the barrier nature of the Coast Ranges so far as climate is concerned.

In Washington the Olympic Mountains, with their somewhat uniform summit level, appear to be the remnant of an old erosion surface that has been greatly carved by glaciation. Mount Olympus (elevation 8,200 ft.), the highest peak in the range, rises as a monadnock above the other peaks. Because of the extremely heavy snowfall in these mountains, some small glaciers still exist near their summits.

The Cascade Range, extending from Lassen Peak in northern California to southern British Columbia, is divided into a southern and a northern section by the deep gorge of the Columbia River. The relief features of the southern part are due largely to upbuilding, while those of the northern part have been carved out of the uplift mass by streams and glaciers. One of the most interesting features of the southern Cascades is Crater Lake, which occupies the crater of an extinct volcano. Toward the northern end of this section, Mount Hood (elevation 11,225 ft.), a nearly perfect volcanic cone rises sharply above the general level of the Cascades. The Columbia River crosses the entire Cascade Range through a deep gorge (Figure 15–2), indicating that the stream is antecedent, although its course may have been determined to some extent by faulting. All of the northern Cascades, composed largely of a huge granitic mass, has been severely eroded by glaciers, and within this area are numerous small active mountain glaciers today.

Between the Cascades to the east and the Olympics and Oregon Coast Ranges to the west lies the structural trough of the Willamette Valley and Puget Sound. The trough was formed by the sinking of this land mass at the time the Cascades were elevated. In glacial times a large lobe of ice advanced down Puget Sound and was instrumental in forming that body of water. The Willamette Valley today is a broad alluvial plain 15 to 30 miles wide and 125 miles long, while the Puget Sound lowland is somewhat smaller in area, since a large part of it was submerged. North of Puget Sound glacial erosion and

Figure 15–2. The Columbia River Gorge east of Portland. This gap through the Cascade Range provides the best route of travel to the east from the North Pacific Coast. (Courtesy of the Union Pacific Railroad.)

submergence formed the "Inside Passage."

North of the international boundary, the mountains that correspond to the Cascades are known as the Coast Ranges. They average 100 miles in width, have a length of nearly 900 miles, and have been eroded severely by mountain glaciers. Deep canyons of the Fraser, Skeena, Stikine, and Taku rivers have cut across the range, forming features similar to the Columbia Gorge. The outer belt of mountains, which corresponds to the Oregon Coast Ranges and the Olympics, is sometimes referred to as the Vancouver system. These mountains constitute a series of discontinuous islands including Vancouver, Queen Charlotte, Prince of Wales, Baranof, and Chichagof, and unite again with the mainland in the great Mount Fairweather Range. Between these islands and the mainland lies the Inside Passage, the submerged counterpart of the Willamette-Puget Sound trough.

Northwest of the Mount Fairweather-Chilkoot Pass district, the Alaska Range and the Coast Range extend westward and ultimately blend into one, constituting the Alaskan Peninsula. Between the Alaska Range and the

Coast Range lies the Susitna-Matanuska Valley, the only lowland area of any extent in this northern part of the region. The Alaska Range with Mount St. Elias, Mount Logan, and Mount McKinley presents some of the most superb mountain scenery on the continent.

Climate

In an area so dominated by mountains, marked vertical differences of temperature are expected; however, uniformity of lowland temperatures is characteristic of the North Pacific Coast Region. Temperatures range from 38° to 67° in central Oregon and from 33° to 55° along the coast of Alaska. In some interior valleys, however, such as the Matanuska, the average winter temperature drops to about 16°. Practically all valleys of this region have a growing season in excess of 100 days. The most distinctive feature of the region is the complete change in climatic conditions from winter to summer.

The seasonal distribution of precipitation is uniform throughout the region; it is frequently stormy from September to May and nearly rainless in summer.

From September to May, gigantic cyclonic storm systems, which migrate eastward across the Pacific basin, bring simultaneous precipitation for 1,000 miles north and south along this coastal region. Mountainous terrain influences the areal distribution of precipitation, southwest slopes receiving copious rainfalls while northeast sides are much less wet. The southwest exposure of the Olympic Mountains, saturated in winter, has an annual total of 150 inches, the maximum for the United States. In contrast, the northeast side of these mountains, only 75 miles away has an annual rainfall of 16 inches which, without the aid of irrigation, is too little for good pastures.

Modified by the terrain, the east-west precipitation pattern falls into four easily recognizable belts: (1) the coastal strip with abundant rainfall and little snow, (2) the windward side of the Coast Range with excessive precipitation, (3) the leeward side of the coastal mountains and the interior trough with only a moderate rainfall and rare snows, and (4) the western slope of the Cascades with nearly 100 inches of precipitation — mainly winter snows.

The winter season is cloudy, monotonously mild, and protected from chilling continental winds by a double barrier of mountains to the east.

Summer, the almost rainless season, is characterized by mild temperatures, light surface winds, coastal fogs, and low clouds. Throughout the region the average number of clear days is less than 100.[2]

Natural Vegetation and Soils

Except in some of the interior valleys, the heavy precipitation throughout this region makes it a land of forests. In the northern California Coast Ranges and in parts of the Klamath, the dominant tree is the redwood, and within this area may be found some of the most magnificent forests of the world. Along the coasts of Oregon and Washington and in the Cascade Mountains, the Douglas fir is dominant, constituting one of the major lumber trees of the continent. Other trees within this area are the western hemlock, western red cedar, and Sitka spruce. In the Canadian and Alaskan sections, Sitka spruce is the leading tree. The forests of this region are almost exclusively coniferous.[3]

A marked contrast in natural vegetation exists between the Willamette Valley of Oregon and the Puget Sound area of Washington. In the former the barrier nature of the Coast Range tends to produce a low summer rainfall, while in the latter the rainfall is slightly heavier in summer because the gaps in the Coast Range allow more rain-bearing winds from the Pacific to enter the valley. The slightly cooler temperature of the Puget Sound Valley also causes it to be somewhat more humid. As a result, the native vegetation of the Willamette Valley was largely prairie

---

[2] Douglas B. Carter, personal communication.

[3] H. J. Andrews and R. W. Cowlin. *Forest Resources of the Douglas-fir Region*, p. 3. U. S. Department of Agriculture, Miscellaneous Publication No. 389, Washington, D.C.: Government Printing Office, 1940.

grass, while that of the Puget Sound area was a dense stand of giant Douglas fir trees with limited expanses of prairie. This contrast in vegetation types profoundly influenced the settlement of the two areas. Much of the region consists of rough mountainous terrain. Good soils are confined largely to the valleys and are not especially fertile. The Willamette Valley, with its predominance of prairie soils, is by far the most important agricultural section.

Occupance of the Region

In the United States portion of the North Pacific Coast, white settlers found numerous small Indian groups in the river valleys and coastal areas who derived most of their livelihood from fishing and hunting. In Canada and Alaska the Haida and Tlingit Indians represented a more advanced stage of culture, living along the shore of the Inside Passage and depending largely upon coastal waters for their food. They built large dugout canoes from native cedar trees, and became skilled woodcarvers, as shown by their totem poles (Figure 15–3) designed usually to show the genealogy of each family. In California, Oregon, and Washington, Indians are now insignificant in number, although some of them still carry on fishing activities or are seasonally employed in canneries, mills, and in the fruit harvest. In Canada and Alaska, however, they have remained about as important as they were before white settlement. Today Indians constitute a sizable portion of the population of southeastern Alaska where they are employed in salmon fishing and canning.

Early Exploration. The voyages of Vitus Bering between 1728 and 1742 led to the advance of Russian trappers and fur-traders southward along the Alaskan coast, In 1774 the Spaniard Juan Perez sailed as far north as latitude 55° and laid claim to Nootka Sound (latitude 49°). Another important voyage was that of the English Captain Cook in 1778, who explored the coast between latitudes 43° and 60° N, and further complicated the claims to this strip of coast. In 1792 a New England trading vessel reached

the mouth of the Columbia River and established a fourth claim to the region. Thus by the end of the eighteenth century four nations, Spain, Russia, Great Britain, and the United States, had explored and claimed in whole or in part the Pacific Coast of North

Figure 15–3. Tlingit totem poles of Beaver and Eagle at Saxman, Alaska. These poles, each a standing beaver in human form, were carved for a Tongass Tlingit house. (Reproduced with permission of the National Museum of Canada.)

America from San Francisco Bay to western Alaska. Permanent Spanish settlements were never established very far north of San Francisco Bay, but by 1800 Russia was entrenched on Baranof Island in southeastern Alaska, and had its seat of colonial government at Sitka. Further settlements were made to the south, but agreements were signed with the United States and Great Britain in 1824 and

1825 limiting the Russians to territory north of the 54°40′ parallel. Spain abandoned her claim to Nootka Sound and all land north of the Columbia River. This left the Oregon country, between the Spanish settlements in California and the Russian settlements in Alaska, to the United States and Great Britain. British claims were based partly on the voyages of Captain Cook but more on the explorations of the Hudson's Bay Company, which had sent expeditions into the area via the Saskatchewan River, the Selkirk Rockies, and the Columbia River. The claims of the United States were based primarily upon the discovery of the mouth of the Columbia River by an American sea captain and later upon the explorations of Lewis and Clark, who reached the coast in 1805 via an overland route.

Later Settlements. Spain made no further attempts at colonization in the North Pacific and Russia was content to establish additional settlements in southeastern Alaska north of the 54° 40′ parallel. Great Britain and the United States, however, became active in the settlement of the disputed territory between Spanish and Russian America. Following the Lewis and Clark expedition, the American Fur Company in 1810 established a trading post at Astoria at the mouth of the Columbia, but this settlement was seized by agents of the Hudson's Bay Company during the war of 1812. The British Fort George and Fort Vancouver, on the lower Columbia, dominated the area until 1818, when an agreement was reached for joint occupance by English and American traders.

At first the only Americans who reached this far-off land were a few trappers and traders, but in the early 1830's New England colonists came overland via the Oregon Trail, and soon a mass migration began. The great trek along the Oregon Trail took place in the early 1840's. These pioneers, determined to establish a Pacific outlet for the United States had as their "battle cry" the slogan "Fifty-four forty or fight." Most of them located in the prairie land of the Willamette Valley of Oregon, and by 1845 there were 8,000 Americans in the Oregon Country. In the settlement of the "Oregon Question" in

1846, the United States got the lands south of the 49th parallel, except for Vancouver Island, and Great Britain got the land between there and Russian America. However, the final status of the San Juan Islands, now a part of the State of Washington, was not decided until 1872.

Influence of the California Gold Rush. Most of the early settlers were in the Willamette Valley, and some of the young men of that area were among the first to move southward to the California "gold diggings" when the discovery became known. The Willamette Valley, however, being in an excellent position to provide grain and other foodstuffs for the mining communities at favorable prices, soon became the chief source of foodstuffs. The Oregon Donation Land Law of 1850 further attracted settlers by giving 640 acres to a married man and 320 acres to a single man if he would settle in the area by December of that year. Neither the Puget Sound area nor the coasts of Canada and Alaska profited from the Gold Rush, because at that time their agricultural lands which could produce the greatly needed foods had not been developed.

The Transfer of Alaska. After furs became depleted in the 1840's, the Russians began to lose interest in their far-off American possession. Although they had leased or sold some of their posts to the Hudson's Bay Company (Wrangell in 1840), they were loath to sell Alaska to Great Britain because of the Crimean War, and therefore offered it to the United States. The purchase was made in 1867 for the sum of $7,200,000, or less than two cents per acre. Except for a few fur trappers, however, citizens of the United States showed little interest in this vast northern territory until the end of the century, when gold was discovered in the Klondike district of Canada and at Nome.

The Coming of the Railroads to the Pacific Northwest. The Puget Sound country was still remote from populous centers of the continent and, until the completion of the Northern Pacific Railroad in 1883, its only outlet for bulky commodities of grain and lumber was by ship around Cape Horn. Nevertheless a number of small sawmills were erected in the area between 1840 and 1850 to export lumber to the Hawaiian Islands and later to supply the mining camps of California. In 1893 the Great Northern completed its line across the mountains to Puget Sound, and some time later the Chicago, Milwaukee, St. Paul and Pacific Railroad built into the region. Meanwhile the Union Pacific established direct connection with Portland, and the Southern Pacific linked Portland with San Francisco. These rail connections made possible the exploitation of the great forest resources, which became important about the beginning of the present century, and contributed also to the industrial development and urban growth of that part of the region.

Influence of the Klondike Gold Rush. When gold was discovered in the Klondike in 1897 and at Nome in 1898, a stampede began that closely rivaled the California rush of 1849. The most direct route to the Klondike field was by boat through the Inside Passage from Seattle to Dyea and later Skagway, thence over Chilkoot Pass or White Pass to the headwaters of the Yukon River, and finally by river boat or raft about 500 miles downstream to Dawson — a long, hard, dangerous trip. When gold was found in the beach sands at Nome, the trip was made entirely by ship, but in each case Seattle profited by being the nearest port having railroad connections with the rest of the United States.

The Pacific Coast of Canada. Although settlements were established on Vancouver Island in 1843, little development took place in the British part of this region until the completion of the Canadian Pacific Railway to Vancouver in 1885, and later the building of the Grand Trunk Pacific (now the Canadian National) Railway to Prince Rupert in 1914. These two ports serve western Canada, but the former is by far the more important.

Ethnic Groups. Between 1900 and 1920 more than 100,000 European immigrants — Scandinavians, Germans, Finns, Swiss, and Hollanders — came to the Puget Sound area and the lower Columbia River Valley. In addition to those born in Europe, an equal number of American-born Europeans from the immigrant colonies established earlier in the Corn Belt, the Upper Lake States, and the northern Great Plains, came to this region. Some immigrants were attracted to western Washington and Oregon by the climatic similarity of the area to northwestern Europe, but most of them migrated across the continent in search of new land and new opportunities.

Since the Willamette Valley had been occupied previously by native American settlers, the wave of north European migrants moved into the lowlands of western Washington. The Bellingham Plain, the Skagit Delta, and certain minor valleys west of the Cascades attracted Scandinavians, Germans, and Hollanders, noted for their dairying, poultry raising, and bulb growing. Lynden, near the Canadian border, is a compact Dutch settlement specializing in butter, poultry, and bulbs. The Tillamook area of western Oregon over a half century ago attracted Swiss dairymen who laid the basis for the most profitable cheese-making industry in western United States.

The fishing industry at Astoria is dominated by Finns and Norwegians who own and operate the fleet. The Ballard district of Seattle, base of a large fishing fleet, a large mill, and most of the tug fleet, has the greatest concentration of Scandinavians in the North Pacific Coast Region. North of the Columbia River Scandinavian groups constitute a larger percentage of the total population than anywhere in the United States except Minnesota.[4]

Agriculture

The North Pacific Coast is still largely in timber — relatively little of the land being suited to agriculture. Dairying, the dominant farming activity of the region, accounts for a large part of the agricultural land in pasture, with hay and oats occupying more than half of the land in crops.

Since most of the region consists of high mountains, steep slopes, and heavily forested terrain, the many rich valleys of limited

[4] Burton L. Anderson, personal communication.

capacity are dwarfed by the immensity of the coastal mountain region. Some of the more important agricultural areas that contain most of the crop land, are: (1) Umpqua and Rogue River valleys of southwestern Oregon, (2) the Willamette Valley, (3) the Cowlitz and Chehalis valleys and the lowlands around Puget Sound in Washington, (4) the Bellingham Lowland, (5) the lower Fraser Valley of British Columbia, (6) southeastern Vancouver Island, and (7) the Matanuska Valley of Alaska. Of these, the Willamette Valley, having more than two million acres in crop lands, is by far the largest and best developed. The least developed of all is the recently colonized Matanuska Valley of Alaska.

Early Agricultural Development. The Willamette Valley was settled rapidly after the acquisition of the Oregon country in 1846, though a large number of agricultural colonists had occupied the area prior to that date. The valley, protected to some extent from the rain-bearing winds from the Pacific Ocean, was a grassland which appealed to the early settlers. They recognized in the area a type of farming land similar to that which they had left in the Middle West, and soon, practically all of the prairie lands were pre-empted and planted in grains. The California Gold Rush, with its great demand for foodstuffs, encouraged the farmers of the valley to grow grains and other agricultural products. When railroads were built into this valley in the 1880's and 1890's, a wave of new settlers arrived, attracted by the generous offers of land. Since most of the Willamette Valley prairies had been occupied prior to the advent of the railroads, the new settlers had to make farms by cutting the forests. Many of them had cleared forest lands in the East, but the gigantic size of the trees and the difficulty of stump removal in the North Pacific Region discouraged them. However, nearly four million acres in the Oregon-Washington part of this region has been transformed into agricultural land, by logging and subsequent clearing.

The Present Agricultural Situation. Although some grain is still grown in the Willamette Valley, and to a lesser extent elsewhere, the agriculture of this region is of two dominant types, dairying and fruit production. Dairying is by far the most important activity although poultry production and the raising of beef cattle and sheep assume some importance. In the dairy industry this region, especially the Puget Sound section, resembles New England in that most of the fluid milk is designed for the large urban markets near by.

Fruit crops occupy a smaller acreage than pasture or grain but have a greater value than either. The Willamette Valley specializes in filberts, apples, prunes, small fruits (berries), and cherries. Apples, the most widely distributed, are also grown in large quantities in the Fraser Valley of British Columbia and on the southeastern part of Vancouver Island. Prunes and cherries are largely confined to the Umpqua and Willamette valleys. Salem, in the Willamette Valley, is one of the largest cherry-canning centers in the United States. Strawberries, raspberries, blackberries, and loganberries are grown extensively throughout the region, but the major production is confined to the Willamette Valley.

The region is well suited to certain kinds of vegetables, particularly cabbage, kale, and mustard, but most of these are grown for local consumption. It is also an important producer of potatoes and hops. Local areas around Portland, the Puyallup Valley, and Bellingham Plain, and southeastern Vancouver Island have specialized in flower bulbs. The more northern agricultural areas of British Columbia and Alaska practice subsistence agriculture almost entirely.

Agriculture in Oregon and Washington. The older settled parts of the Willamette Valley and the Puget Sound Lowlands present an agricultural picture of a mature cultural landscape such as can be found in few places in the West. In the Willamette Valley one can drive for miles on excellent highways, past fruit farms (prunes, cherries, berries, and hop fields), small fields of wheat and oats, and excellent pastures (Figure 15–4). The Willamette Valley, occupied by farmers of the third or fourth generation on the same farm, is the old, long-settled, pros-

Figure 15–4. The Willamette Valley of Oregon extends for 140 miles southward from the Columbia River. This scene is in the area south of Salem. (Courtesy of the Oregon State Highway Commission.)

perous heart of Oregon that grows most of the fruit, berry, vegetable, and grain crops of the North Pacific Coast Region.

In the Puget Sound Lowlands, many of them diked or drained lands, are located the finest dairy and pasture lands of the entire region. Market gardening is an important agricultural activity that has increased in ratio with the growth of the large urban centers; it should increase in importance. The vegetable acreage includes peas, beans, cabbage, cauliflower, spinach, sweet corn, rhubarb, and tomatoes as the chief crops. Vegetables are grown in this area for use in the local urban markets, but the surplus is shipped to other parts of the United States. The quick freezing of field peas has caused a marked expansion in pea acreage.

Of the numerous speciality crops grown within this subregion, three deserve special mention: (1) the hop industry of the Willamette Valley, (2) the bulb industry of the Puget Sound Lowlands, and (3) the pea industry of the Bellingham Plain.

At one time the Willamette Valley was the major producer of hops in the United States but in recent years it has been surpassed by the Yakima Valley area on the eastern side of the Cascade Mountains. Yields in the Willamette Valley are lower than in the Yakima Valley but the total area in hops is still large. The sprinkler type of irrigation used in the Willamette Valley, although the most effective method in rolling lands, aids the spread of mildew which is detrimental to the vines. Since the hop yards in this area are relatively small (25 to 50 acres) and are frequently only a phase of diversification on larger farms, mechanization of harvesting such as is practiced on the larger Yakima hop farms is not profitable; therefore, most of the hop cones are picked by hand.[5]

Although large quantities of flowers are grown in the vicinity of Portland, and the extensive fields of gladiolas add materially to the scenic beauty of the area, the major commercial bulb industry is located in three areas of the Puget Sound Lowlands: (1) the Puyallup Valley (Figure 15–5), (2) the Bellingham Plain, and (3) the Fargo Lake area near Vancouver, Washington. Most of the bulb growers in these areas came directly from Holland or are of Dutch ancestry. The areas with a mild, humid climate, favorable soils, and a ready local market in the large cities of the Northwest provided the ideal setting for the bulb industry. Tulip and narcissus bulbs are dominant and are used in the greenhouse forcing trade. Although sold lo-

cally, from 150 to 175 carloads of bulbs are shipped to eastern United States each year largely through the efforts of the Puget Sound Bulb Growers Exchange.[6]

In the Pacific Northwest peas constitute one of the leading specialty crops. Because of the perishable nature of threshed peas, canneries must be located in the producing areas. Within this region the first real production (1923) was at Friday Harbor in the San Juan Islands. Additional canneries were soon opened on the Washington mainland and on the coast of British Columbia and the canning business became large. The usual yield of shelled peas is about one ton to the acre. Although it has only about one third the food value of alfalfa, the pea vines are fed as silage to dairy cattle. In recent years freezing has tended to replace canning, and

[5] Elbert E. Miller and Richard M. Highsmith, Jr., "The Hop Industry of the Pacific Coast," *Journal of Geography*, Vol. 49, 1950, pp. 63–77.

[6] J. P. Galvin, "The Bulb Industry of Western Washington," *Economic Geography*, Vol. 20, 1944, pp. 19–24.

Figure 15–5. An extensive field of daffodils in the Puyallup Valley near Orting, Washington. The majestic snow-capped summit of Mt. Rainier is in the background. (Courtesy of the Washington State Advertising Commission.)

a few freezing plants in western Washington now handle the entire pack.[7]

Agriculture in British Columbia. Most of the agricultural areas of British Columbia are concentrated on the delta of the Fraser River or on southeastern Vancouver Island. In these areas general mixed farming and dairying are carried on; there are also many specialty crops — fruits, berries, vegetables, and flowering bulbs. The leading agricultural industry of the Lower Fraser Valley is the production of whole milk for the Vancouver market. About 40 per cent of the farm land is in native pasture and an additional 34 per cent is in grain, most of it being fed to dairy cattle and to poultry. Vegetables and small fruits are raised on the lowland soils while orchard fruits are confined to the upland areas.

The southeastern lowlands of Vancouver Island contain about 80,000 acres of cultivated land. These lands are not continuous but are confined to deltas and to lake plains. Temperatures are similar to those of the Fraser Delta, but the rainfall is considerably lower. In addition to dairying, poultry raising, and the cultivation of fruits and vegetables, this area has specialized in the growing of spring flowers such as daffodils and narcissi for the eastern Canadian market. Since most of the coastal region of British Columbia is mountainous and incapable of being farmed, the remaining arable lands comprise less than 20,000 acres scattered in many small isolated valleys on the mainland and on some of the islands. Most of these areas produce mainly subsistence crops.[8]

The Matanuska Valley of Alaska. The Matanuska Valley, a fairly extensive, well-drained area of reasonably fertile silt-loam soils, lies at the head of Cook Inlet about 125 miles inland from Seward, Alaska. The area of the Valley which can be tilled is estimated at 48,357 acres but less than one fifth of it is cleared and under cultivation.[9] Some set-

tlement occurred in the Valley about 1910, and a few pioneer farmers of that period raised hay, grain, and root crops with reasonable success. The United States Department of Agriculture established an experiment station at Matanuska as early as 1915, but no further government aid was given until 1935, when the Federal Emergency Relief Administration sent 895 colonists from Michigan, Wisconsin, and Minnesota, who had been on relief.[10] Many of these farm families were unsuited for agricultural pioneering and in time were returned to the States; in 1950 there remained 187 individual farm units in the Valley.

The farms of the Valley, averaging about 40 acres (Figure 15–6), have been cleared by tractors and other machinery. Two years after improvement some of the lands produced as much as six tons of hay per acre. Other crops included spring wheat and barley (raised for feed), peas, root crops, strawberries, and garden vegetables. These were sold primarily to the small urban market at Anchorage. A canning plant and a co-operative creamery located at Palmer provides an outlet for the surplus. In spite of this, however, large quantities of imported canned milk are sold in Palmer in the heart of the Matanuska area.[11] With limited level land and a very short growing season, the agricultural possibilities of coastal Alaska can never be great.

Lumbering and the Wood-products Industries

The North Pacific Coast Region with its temperate marine climate contains possibly the most magnificent stand of timber in the world. The trees decrease in size from the

[7] Otis W. Freeman, "The Pacific Northwest Pea Industry," *Economic Geography*, Vol. 19, 1943, pp. 118–128.

[8] Donald Kerr, "The Physical Basis of Agriculture in British Columbia," *Economic Geography*, Vol. 28, 1952, pp. 229–239.

[9] *Some Economic Aspects of Farming in Alaska with Chief Attention to the Matanuska Valley*, pp. 27–28. U. S. Department of Agriculture, Bureau of Agricultural Economics. Washington, D. C.: Government Printing Office, 1950.

[10] Kirk H. Stone, "Populating Alaska: The United States Phase," *Geographical Review*, Vol. 42, 1952, pp. 384–404.

[11] Wilford J. Eiteman and Alice Boardman Smuts, "Alaska, Land of Opportunity — Limited," *Economic Geography*, Vol. 27, 1951, pp. 33–42.

Figure 15–6. The Matanuska Valley is the most important farming area in Alaska, producing about 60 per cent of all crops grown and marketed in the territory. (Courtesy of the Alaskan Agricultural Experiment Station.)

giant redwoods of northwestern California and the large Douglas firs and Western Red cedars of Oregon, Washington, and British Columbia, to the smaller varieties of spruce, hemlock, and fir along the coast of Alaska. Originally probably 95 per cent of the region was covered by these great forests.

Except for the lumbering operations in the California redwood forests and smaller logging and pulpwood cutting in the forests of the Canadian and Alaskan sections, the major lumbering and wood-products activities coincide with the Douglas fir forest subregion in Oregon and Washington. Because of the importance of this subregion, and because more complete data are available for it than for the other forested parts of the North Pacific Coast, it will be used to illustrate the development of the lumbering and wood-working industries of the region.

The Douglas fir subregion is exceeded in acreage by nearly every other commercial forest area on the continent, but it surpasses any of them in saw-timber volume because of the large size of the trees and the density of their stand. Ease of logging and transportation in the Puget Sound area and along the lower course of the Columbia River attracted the lumberman as early as the middle of the nineteenth century. Today the old-growth Douglas fir forests are largely depleted and have been succeeded by dense stands of regrowth, including red alder as well as young firs. In the less accessible parts of the subregion, however, excellent stands of timber are still found and under sustained yield management they could last for many years. Fires such as the one at Tillamook, Oregon, in 1933, which destroyed 380 square miles of forests have taken a heavy toll. Every effort is being exerted to reduce the hazard, including prevention measures both public and private, as well as better fire-fighting techniques. While this forest subregion contains

a number of commercial trees, the Douglas fir outranks all others. Practically all trees are conifers, the hardwoods occupying a place of minor importance.

The Douglas fir has a greater saw-timber volume than any other tree-species on the continent (Figure 15–7), the size of the individual trees and the density of the stand being exceeded only by the sequoias. Douglas fir attains its best development in western Oregon, Washington, and British Columbia, and constitutes more than 60 per cent of the saw-timber volume of this subregion. Sawlog-size trees range in diameter from 16 to more than 100 inches, and the volume stand per acre is from 10,000 to more than 175,000 board feet. The average per-acre volume for Douglas fir is about 60,000 board feet. Douglas fir is marketed throughout the world, the wood being widely used for structural timbers, flooring, doors, factory lumber, piling, ties, and plywood.

Western hemlock ranks next to Douglas fir in importance and constitutes nearly a fifth of the total saw-timber volume of the subregion (Figure 15–8). The wood is light, straight-grained, and nonresinous. Because of the ease with which it can be worked, western hemlock is used extensively for paper pulp, common lumber, box-shook, and flooring.

Sitka spruce, although limited in extent within this subregion, is highly prized because of its special qualities, being light in weight, tough, nonresinous, and easy to work. The chief uses today for Sitka spruce include box-shook, ladder stock, basket and crate veneers, and paper pulp.

Western red cedar, is a light, easily split wood which is extremely resistant to decay. Its chief use is for shingles but it is also used for sills, siding, posts, and telephone poles.

Port Orford cedar, localized in a small area in southwestern Oregon, sells at a high price for certain special uses including boat building, venetian blinds, and battery separators. The amount reaching the market is limited.

Figure 15–7. This mammoth Douglas fir began growing about the year 900 A.D. It has a diameter of 15 feet, 6 inches, and a height of 210 feet, and is estimated to contain 105,650 feet of usable lumber. (Courtesy of Crown Zellerbach Corporation.)

Figure 15–8. Douglas fir and hemlock growing together in heavy stands in the mature forests of western Washington. (Courtesy of the Weyerhaeuser Timber Company – Lee Merrill, photographer.)

White fir, grown at higher altitudes than Douglas fir, is becoming increasingly valuable. Although smaller in size, it can be used for small dimensional timbers and is well adapted to the manufacture of wood pulp.

Ponderosa and white pines are not characteristic of the Douglas fir subregion, but occur in commercial quantity in the Klamath Mountains. In southwest Oregon they assume a place of importance. The wood is used chiefly for sashes and doors, but is also used for box-shook and common lumber.

Hardwoods occupy a minor place among the commercial species of this subregion. Red alder and bigleaf maple are the two basic species and are used for furniture manufacturing and for fuel wood.

Logging and Sawmill Operations. The first sawmill in the Douglas fir subregion was erected by the Hudson's Bay Company in 1827 near Fort Vancouver on the Columbia River. Lumber was exported to Hawaii, and later, quantities were shipped to San Fran-

cisco and the California gold fields. Between 1850 and 1900 many sawmills were established to supply the rapidly expanding world market.

The lumber industry of the continent has been migratory. As each timbered district was depleted, the industry was forced to move to a locality more remote from the consuming centers. When the lumber industry came from the Lake States and later from the South (Chapter 7) to the Pacific Northwest, it moved into the last timbered frontier. Today this region and the South together produce most of the forest products of the continent. Not only does distance from market affect the industry in this region but the gigantic size of the trees, particularly the Douglas fir, has forced the development of many new logging methods.

Today the logging industry is highly mechanized. Giant Diesel-powered tractors with specially designed hoists, "snake" the logs out of the forest (Figure 15–9). These

Figure 15–9. Loading a log truck by power shovel equipped with heel boom. Trucks have largely replaced railroads in lumbering operations in the North Pacific Coast Region. (Courtesy of the Weyerhaeuser Timber Company—Lee Merrill, photographer.)

are then hauled by large trucks or by rail to the sawmills, or to streams where they can be floated to the mills. In British Columbia the common system of logging is the "sky-line," which utilizes two strong spar trees several hundred yards apart, with a cable fastened between them high above the ground. A traveling carriage runs along the cable or sky-line and from it a steel rope is fastened to the logs. The logs, with one end elevated are dragged to the head spar tree. By the use of sky-lines, logs can be taken from mountainous forests more cheaply than by any other method.[12]

Some sawmills are located in remote forested areas, but the major ones are on deep water where logs can be rafted to the mill and the finished lumber can be exported. One of the most important tidewater mill centers in the region is Longview, Washington, on the Columbia River. Built by a major lumber company it is an example of a planned wood-products city and port.

Since the opening of the Panama Canal in 1915, the North Pacific Coast Region has been favored by cheap water rates to the great consuming markets of the Atlantic Coast and to Northwestern Europe. The peak shipment was reached in 1928, when nearly two billion board feet of lumber were sent through the canal to the Atlantic Coast, 376 million feet of which came from British Columbia.

The Douglas fir subregion, produces approximately 30 per cent of the total lumber cut, more than 90 per cent of the shingles, and more than 20 per cent of the wood pulp of the United States.

While this production is scattered, it is most heavily concentrated along the Lower Columbia Valley, in Portland, in southwest Oregon at Eugene and Coos Bay, around Puget Sound, and in the Grays Harbor district. The older Canadian center is at New Westminister on the Fraser River, and a newer one at Duncan Bay on Vancouver Island.[13] Lumber mills occupy extensive tracts around Puget Sound and huge log rafts may be seen in many of the smaller inlets (Figure 15–10).

Forest-Products Industries. The manufacture of pulp and paper is rapidly becoming a leading industry. Although a considerable quantity of pulp is exported, the paper mills of the subregion are consuming an ever-increasing quantity in the manufacture of kraft paper and newsprint. Hydroelectric power is sufficient for the development of a sizable paper industry, and there is a steady export to other domestic areas. The British Columbia section has a number of paper and pulp mills in the vicinity of Vancouver, and newsprint is being manufactured at Powell River and Port Alice to the northwest.[14] A pulp mill has been established recently near Ketchikan in southeastern Alaska.[15] In the production of pulp and paper, other areas along the Inside Passage such as the Tongass National Forest could become important, since they have the chief prerequisites for the industry — an abundance of suitable spruce and hemlock, a wealth of potential water power, ample water supply for washing the pulp, and a tidewater location for shipment.

A 1951 addition to the wood-working industries of the North Pacific Coast was the new 300-ton-a-day pulp mill of an American company at Prince Rupert (Figure 15–11), Located on the Canadian National Railway and on a completely sheltered harbor, the plant is designed to provide high-grade cellulose for acetate yarn. The government of British Columbia has granted the perpetual right to cut all the timber the mill will need from a tract of land larger than the state of Rhode Island.[16]

The veneer and plywood industry is also expanding, with Eastern companies establishing new plants in the North Pacific Coast Region.

[12] A. W. Currie, *Economic Geography of Canada*, p. 278, Toronto; The Macmillan Co. of Canada, Ltd., 1946.

[13] Woodrow R. Clevinger, personal communication.
[14] A. W. Currie, *Economic Geography of Canada*, p. 284.
[15] Kirk H. Stone, "Alaskan Problems and Potentials," *The Journal of Geography*, Vol. 50, 1951, p. 183.
[16] Richard Austin Smith, "The Celanese Adventure," *Fortune*, August 1952, pp. 101–105 and 135–142.

Forest Conservation

If careful logging practices are followed, if forest fires are reduced, and if reforestation is practiced in the cut-over lands, this forest region should continue to produce an important part of the continent's wood products, and the industries here should not suffer the decline that has characterized other forested

cated to perpetual forest production.[17] Encouraged by low tax rates, these privately owned forests are carefully managed for maximum fire protection and regrowth. The tracts, which are located in the Coast Range and hilly portions of the Puget-Willamette trough, are already producing increasing volumes of pulp wood, poles, small timbers, and Christmas trees.

Figure 15–10. The Weyerhaeuser sawmill at Everett, Washington, as seen from the log pond where the logs are sorted for grade, size, and species. The once familiar waste burner is gone from the scene because modern manufacturing uses every log. (Courtesy of the Weyerhaeuser Timber Company — Lee Merrill, photographer.)

regions. This is the last timbered frontier on the continent. It must be used wisely if woodworking industries are to continue to be important.

Tree Farms. Much of the cut-over land of western Oregon and Washington has regenerated a new 30 to 50 year old Douglas fir cover. Large tracts, adding up to more than 2,500,000 acres in Washington alone, have been organized into tree farms dedi-

A continued volume of high-grade lumber and plywood production which requires large logs is increasingly dependent on the public timber sales of the Forest Service and the Bureau of Land Management of the federal government. These agencies in addition to the National Park Service and the Bureau of Indian Affairs now control over 75 per cent of the remaining virgin forest in Oregon,

[17] *Seattle Times,* Editorial, November 16, 1952.

Figure 15–11. Aerial view of the new Columbia Celanese plant on Watson Island near Prince Rupert, British Columbia, showing the mill in its fjorded coastal setting. (Courtesy of the Canadian National Railways.)

Washington, and Alaska. Similarly, most of the British Columbia timber is owned by the Canadian government. Mature timber in selected national forest areas is auctioned off for removal by private firms. Both selective cutting and clear cutting are practiced to insure minimum damage to the national forest as a whole.

A maturing public consciousness within the region concerning the vital problem of perpetuating the basic forest economy, followed with application of the most modern and foresighted principles of conservation, promises to continue it as a ranking producer of Anglo-America's wood products.[18]

The Fishing Industry

The North Pacific Coast is one of the major

18 Woodrow R. Clevinger, personal communication.

fishing regions of the continent (Figure 4–8) and ranks in total catch with the banks fisheries of the North Atlantic. Unlike those of the latter, however, most fish along the North Pacific Coast are taken in coastal waters or in the lower courses of streams where most of them are canned. Salmon is the major species caught, although in recent years halibut and herring have increased in importance.

Salmon Fishing. For a long time salmon has been the chief food of the Indians living along the North Pacific Coast. The first attempt by white man to preserve salmon was made in 1834, and the first canned salmon was packed in 1866 along the Columbia River. From these meager beginnings the salmon fishing and canning industry has grown so that today it represents one of the major activities of the region. Five species of salmon are caught in the coastal waters of this region. These are: (1) the chinook or king, (2) the sockeye or red, (3) the humpback or pink, (4) the silver or coho, and (5) the dog or chum salmon.

Some king salmon attain weights of 80 to 100 pounds. The meat of this fish commands the best prices on the market either canned or fresh (frozen). The king salmon range the entire length of the North Pacific Coast but are most abundant in the streams of Oregon and Washington. Second in importance is the sockeye salmon. Although smaller, sockeye provide most of the canned salmon. They are found in great abundance all along the coast from northern Washington to the Bering Sea, and are the chief fish caught in the Inside Passage of British Columbia and Alaska. The other varieties, although important, do not rank with these first two. An interesting description of the life history of the Pacific salmon is given below.

All species of Pacific salmon are anadromous, that is, the adults migrate from the ocean into fresh-water streams to spawn. They proceed up rivers, such as the Columbia, until they arrive at the same tributary where they themselves began life some years before. Very few stray to other streams. The female salmon deposits her eggs in a nest, or redd, which she digs in the gravel of the stream or shallow lake-shore waters. In the process of egg laying, the fertilized ova are covered with successive layers of gravel to a depth of several inches. The time required for the eggs to hatch depends on the temperature of the water. Newly hatched fish live in the gravel of the redd and gradually absorb the food in the abdominal yolk sac. At the end of this period, usually in the late winter or early spring, they struggle up through the gravel and begin to seek food. How long the young fish stay in fresh water varies considerably with the species, but eventually they migrate downstream to the sea, where they remain from 1 to 3 years and grow rapidly. When they approach sexual maturity, they return to fresh water to spawn and thereby complete the cycle. All Pacific salmon die after spawning.[19]

---

[19] Clifford J. Burner, "Characteristics of Spawning Nests of Columbia River Salmon," *Fishery Bulletin 61*, p. 97, Fish and Wildlife Service, Washington, D. C.: Government Printing Office, 1951.

Depletion and Conservation of Salmon. The chief cause of the depletion of the salmon-runs in the western streams is man himself. Destruction of the salmon has come through (1) over-fishing in rivers and oceans, (2) damming up streams, (3) pollution of spawning grounds, and (4) occasional destruction of salmon in irrigation ditches. The Columbia is still the most important river in the United States for salmon, but it has shown a decline from its peak year in 1895. The construction of the Bonneville and Grand Coulee dams across the Columbia River may ultimately diminish the 10 million dollars-a-year Columbia River industry. A fish ladder has been built at Bonneville Dam to allow the salmon to pass around this man-made barrier (Figure 15–12). The Fraser River in British

Figure 15–12. A fish ladder at Bonneville Dam on the Columbia River. (Courtesy of H. B. Carr, U.S. Fish and Wildlife Service.)

Columbia had a very destructive landslide that partly blocked it in 1913, the very year that the large run was ascending. Most of the fish never reached the spawning grounds, and as a result salmon-runs in that stream have never been so large since. Artificial propagation is now helping to keep the streams stocked with young salmon.

Methods of Fishing. The chief methods of catching salmon are by gill nets, purse seines, and floating and stationary traps. Formerly the fish wheel was used to some extent along the Columbia River, but this device is now unlawful. Indians still net salmon along some of the streams, but the total taken in that manner is not large. Gill nets and seines account for most of the catch. The gill nets are stretched across that part of the stream where the salmon are ascending, the fish becoming entangled in the nets.

In the deeper waters of the Inside Passage, most salmon are caught in floating or stationary traps. The stationary trap, which is the more common, consists of a number of piles driven into the deep water. Around the piles, below water level, is stretched wire netting, which directs the migrating fish toward the center or heart of the trap. In the center is a movable netting, called a "brailer," that allows the fishermen to lift the trapped fish out of the water and dump them into a boat or scow (Figure 15–13). From the trap they are transported immediately to the cannery.

Salmon Canning. Canneries are located on tidewater, readily accessible to fishing boats and tenders and also convenient to ocean shipping for marketing the canned product. Many Alaskan canneries are isolated and in use only during the summer season; yet these small canneries, whose only access to the outside world is by steamer or airlift, account for more than half of the annual pack. A cannery location requires plenty of fish, a safe ship landing, and an abundance of pure fresh water. The heavy precipitation throughout this region, particularly in Alaska, provides an abundance of fresh water from the many mountain streams. The cannery is usually built out on piles to assure deep water for the ships and so that the fish refuse can be dumped into the water and be carried away with the tide. Some canneries employ

Figure 15–13. Brailing a floating salmon trap in southeastern Alaska. Salmon are caught in traps as they approach rivers to spawn. (Courtesy of U. S. Fish and Wildlife Service.)

as many as 300 workers in the summer and in winter maintain only a caretaker or two.

As soon as fishing boats or scows bring their catch to the cannery, the fish are unloaded mechanically into bins. Streams of fresh water are played on the fish to remove all dirt and slime. Next they go to the dressing machine, known as the "Iron Chink," which cuts off the head, tail, and fins, scoops out the entrails, and removes the scales. Formerly this was all done by hand. After being washed again and inspected, the salmon pass through a series of revolving gang knives, which slice the fish into proper sizes. Other machines fill and seal the cans, which are fed into the cookers. In the most modern canneries, practically every operation is done by machine. Tins from Seattle arrive at Alaskan canneries in collapsed form which takes little space in the hold of the ship, and machines ream out and assemble the can.

The bulk of the canned salmon is marketed through Seattle to the large consuming centers of Anglo-America and abroad. Seattle ships more canned salmon to foreign countries than do all other American ports combined.

Although most of the salmon are canned, large quantities are now being marketed fresh, salted, smoked, or "mild cured." Fresh salmon sold through Seattle are worth a million dollars a year.

While salmon are commercially the most important fish in the North Pacific waters, large quantities of halibut, herring, pilchard, and tuna are also caught. In addition, a sizable shellfish industry (particularly oysters) has developed in recent years.

Halibut, by far the most important of the other commercial fish and one of the standard food fishes of America, is a large deep sea flounder which weighs up to 200 pounds. Unlike salmon, they live and spawn in deep waters. The eggs then rise to near the surface and drift with the currents. The small fish, when hatched, work toward the shallow waters near the shore. Halibut spawn more than once in their life cycle but do not enter fresh water streams. They are caught in deep water either by baited hooks, or by power-trawling. After many years of declining halibut catches, this American-Canadian fishery was strictly regulated on a quota basis, and has been stabilized at a productive level.

Halibut are marketed as fresh (frozen) fish, and the chief landing ports are Prince Rupert and Seattle. From there they are sent by fast rail service to all parts of Anglo-America. Today many freezing plants on the West Coast ship only the choicest parts of the fish eastward, thereby saving freight costs on the bones and other non-edible parts. A recent demand for halibut liver oil, which is high in vitamins A and D, has caused the growth of a subsidiary industry that brings halibut fishermen an additional income.

Tuna (albacore), the newest of the commercial fish along the northwest coast, are caught with short rods from fishing boats using lures or bait. Tuna are canned chiefly at Astoria, near the mouth of the Columbia River. The canning method differs from that for salmon; tuna must be cooked first, then packed in cans, and finally steamed in order to sterilize the pack.

Other edible fish caught in the offshore waters of this region include the herring, pilchard, Bering Sea codfish, sole, and other bottom fish. Astoria, Grays Harbor, Seattle, and Prince Rupert serve as the home ports for most of the fishing boats.[20]

Oysters are the most important of the shellfish taken in Northwestern waters. A million-dollar industry using modern cultivation methods has developed mainly in and around Willapa Bay. This bay, with its 100 square miles of shallow tidal flats, offers excellent conditions for growing the Pacific oyster. Eighty per cent of the oysters in the region come from the Willapa district, reaching the market either fresh or canned. The other important shellfish caught in Pacific Northwest waters are clams, crabs, and shrimp.

Mining

Until the discovery of gold in the Klondike

---

[20] For a general discussion of all Pacific Northwest fisheries, including those of British Columbia and Alaska, see *The Pacific Northwest*, Otis W. Freeman and Howard H. Martin, editors. New York: John Wiley & Sons, 1953.

and in the beach sands at Nome — both areas outside this region — little interest was shown in minerals as the mountains of the North Pacific Coast seemed poor in metallic wealth, and the dense vegetation discouraged systematic exploration. Even as late as 1880, some years after the United States purchased Alaska, the gold production of that territory amounted to only $20,000.

With the great discoveries in the interior toward the close of the nineteenth century and with later discoveries along the coast, the total Alaskan output has surpassed 650 million dollars, placers accounting for nearly two thirds of the total. Practically all placers are in the Yukon Valley but along the coast are several lode-mining districts.

The most important gold-mining district in this region, which lies in southeastern Alaska, produces about one-third of the total output of lode gold and nearly all of the silver, copper, lead, and zinc of Alaska.[21] For many years the largest single producer has been the Alaska-Juneau Gold Mining Company at Juneau, which, through complete mechanization of the mining process and the use of cheap hydro-power, has been able to extract low-grade ore at a profit. In recent years, however, this mine has been inactive except for small quantities of lead, gold, and silver obtained from cleaning up the mill and reworking the old tailings from this mill.[22]

Some production came from small mines in the vicinity of Ketchikan. Metallic mining is carried on also in the British Columbia section of this region, but production there is not large.

A second important mining area in coastal Alaska is the Cook Inlet-Susitna district, which operates dredges and portable washing plants, and produces small quantities of gold. In the Matanuska Valley of this district is one of Alaska's two important coal fields, but as yet there is a limited demand for coal in this remote land.

To the northeast lies the Copper River mining area, which has been an important producer of copper, silver, gold, and lead. For a long time the Kennecott Copper Corporation at Kennecott produced large quantities of copper ore which were shipped to the smelter at Tacoma. The known copper-ore reserves, however, seem to be exhausted, and in 1939 production was abandoned.

The southern section of this region produces only minor quantities of minerals, although coal deposits are found in the Puget Sound district and on Vancouver Island. Considerable quantities of iron ore have been produced on Vancouver Island in the vicinity of Quinsam Lake and on nearby Texada Island. Most of this ore (130,000 tons a month) has been shipped to Japan in recent years, but British Columbia is making plans to develop its own integrated steel industry at Vancouver, and is considering restricting exports.[23]

Manufacturing

Aside from the food- and wood-processing industries already mentioned, manufacturing in the North Pacific Coast Region must of necessity be limited because of the lack of variety in raw materials, the limited local market, and great distances from other large markets. The following industries, not listed in the above group deserve further consideration: (1) copper smelting, (2) aluminum reduction and refining, (3) aircraft manufacturing, (4) shipbuilding (both commercial carriers and Naval vessels) and (5) woolen textile manufacturing.

The Tacoma Smelter. This smelter, largest combined smelter and refinery for copper in the United States, represents one of the most important electro-metallurgical developments of the region. Although gold, silver, and copper are produced at this plant, copper is most significant. Some ore moves to this smelter and refinery from Lake Chelan and from the Rocky Mountain Region, but most of it comes by ship from the west coast of South America.

---

[21] Alfred L. Ransome, "The Mineral Industry of Alaska," *Minerals Yearbook, 1949*, p. 1361. Washington, D. C.: Government Printing Office, 1951.

[22] Ransome, "The Mineral Industry of Alaska," p. 1361.

[23] *Engineering and Mining Journal*, April 1952, p. 148.

The Aluminum Industry. In 1940, a large plant was built by Alcoa on the Columbia River near Vancouver, Washington, for the electrolytic conversion of alumina into metallic aluminum. This was soon followed by the construction of a reduction plant at Longview, Washington, by the Reynolds Metal Company through a substantial loan from the United States Government. In addition a small plant was established at Tacoma by the Olin Corporation, and the government completed a large plant at Troutdale, Oregon, a short distance below Bonneville Dam. In the post-war period, the Kaiser interests secured control of the Tacoma plant, and the Troutdale plant was leased to Reynolds by the United States Government.[24] Alumina is being produced largely on the Gulf Coast from South American bauxite and shipped to the Northwest by rail. This new industry to a great extent is due to the heavy demands being made by airplane factories for metallic aluminum. Cheap electricity and local war-time demands for aluminum in the aircraft industry attracted these plants to the Pacific Northwest, but some economists fear a power shortage in the area. The six northwest aluminum plants (four in this region and two at Spokane and Wenatchee in the Intermontane Region) consume a fifth of all the electricity generated in Idaho, Oregon, and Washington. The Northwest, although a region of great hydroelectric potential, develops power shortages during dry years in spite of the large amount of electricity generated at Grand Coulee, Bonneville, Rock Island, and other dams. The area also suffers from high transportation costs since producers must bring alumina at least 2,800 miles to cheap power and send aluminum 2,500 miles to market.[25]

At Kitimat, some 400 miles northwest of Vancouver, British Columbia, a new aluminum reduction plant and town is being built by Aluminum Limited of Canada, at an estimated cost of 550 million dollars. This plant, located in the desolate mountain fastness of the coastal area is scheduled for completion in 1954. Its location is primarily based on cheap electricity which will be produced by damming up mountain streams in the coastal range east of Kitimat, and dropping the water through a ten-mile tunnel some 2,500 feet into a powerhouse which will be built entirely within the side of the mountains. Transmission lines will carry the power fifty miles to the tidewater aluminum plant at Kitimat. Bauxite will be brought to the plant by ocean carriers from Jamaica.[26]

The Aircraft Industry. The aircraft industry is represented in this region by the giant plant of the Boeing Aircraft Corporation at Seattle. During World War II the Boeing plant specialized in the production of the large four-motored passenger craft and heavy bombers. Although some retrenchment took place at the close of the war, Boeing soon began the commercial production of its double-deck *Stratocruiser*, which is now being used by many of the overseas air lines. This 75-passenger plane is an outgrowth of wartime experience in building the famous B-29's and C-97's. Seattle now has a skilled labor reservoir of aircraft workers. Since the aircraft industry was discussed in detail in the Los Angeles area (Chapter 14) no further description will be given here.

The Woolen Textile Manufacturing. This industry is centered largely in the Willamette Valley. The wool for the mills comes from the surrounding territory. About one fourth of that produced in the Northwest goes to the mills in Portland, causing that city to rank as an important wool center for the continent.

Shipbuilding. Shipbuilding is located largely on Puget Sound and along the Columbia River. It became important during the first World War, and was revived during World War II. Both wooden and steel ships are built, the raw materials for the steel ships coming from outside the region. At Bremerton the United States Navy has one of the largest shipyards on the continent.

24 Erich W. Zimmerman, *World Resources and Industries,* pp. 725-727. New York: Harper and Brothers, 1951.
25 "The Great Aluminum Farce," *Fortune,* June 1951, p. 176.
26 "The Great Aluminum Farce," p. 98.

Hydroelectric Power and Industrial Development

No discussion of manufacturing in the North Pacific Coast Region would be complete without some consideration of hydroelectric power and its effect upon present and future industrial development.

Because of the mountainous terrain and heavy rainfall, the region has one of the highest hydroelectric potentials of any part of Anglo-America, but until the recent construction by the United States Government of the Grand Coulee Dam in the Intermontane Region (Chapter 13), and the Bonneville Dam across the Columbia River in the water gap through the Cascade Mountains a few miles east of Portland, no large power installations had been made. The Columbia is one of the most dependable of rivers but it varies greatly in volume and becomes abnormally low during years of drought.

The Bonneville Dam, completed in 1938 at a cost of more than 100 million dollars, has a generating capacity of 518,400 kilowatts and produces approximately one sixth of the total hydroelectric power in the Columbia River Basin. This dam, together with others scheduled for completion upstream on the Columbia-Snake system, can provide much additional power for the industries of the region, but the demand for electricity must not exceed the minimum annual supply. If Congress continues to support construction of dams, production of hydroelectric power should catch up with demand. Only then will the further expansion of industry depending upon electrical energy, be on a sound basis.

Resorts and Tourism

The North Pacific Coast is one of the continent's most scenic regions, and is rapidly becoming one of its major playgrounds (Figure 15–14). Remoteness from large population centers as well as the inaccessibility of many of the scenic spots, has retarded the development of resorts. Construction of new highways and, to a lesser extent, the extension of air and steamship service, has greatly stimulated travel. The United States section is the best-developed, having three national parks, Olympic, Mt. Rainer, and Crater Lake, and several national monuments, state parks, and other recreational areas. The Canadian section and the Inside Passage of southeastern Alaska rank among the world's most scenic areas with their spectacular mountains, glaciers, and fjords that are easily accessible by ocean and coastwise steamers. Along the coast of southern Alaska, however, is found the continent's most magnificent scenery, culminating in the majestic peak of Mt. McKinley (elevation 20,300 feet), and set aside for the public in the Mt. McKinley National Park. Although most tourists come during the summer season, the recent development of winter sports in the Cascade Mountains of Oregon and Washington has greatly increased the year-round volume of business.

Transportation

Despite the mountainous terrain, most parts of the North Pacific Coast are well served by railways, highways, airways, and seaways. Water transportation is still of major importance, as shown by the large ocean ports of Portland, Tacoma, Seattle, and Vancouver, which export great quantities of lumber and wood products. The British Columbia and Alaska sections are even more dependent upon water transportation although Alaska is connected with the United States by a highway, and the British Columbia coast is served by the two Canadian transcontinental railways.

Railroads. The southern part of the North Pacific Coast Region in Oregon, Washington, and British Columbia, is well served by seven major transcontinental railroads, and a number of smaller feeder lines. The transcontinental lines are: (1) the Southern Pacific, from New Orleans via Los Angeles and San Francisco; (2) the Union Pacific from Salt Lake City and the East, (3) the Chicago, Milwaukee, St. Paul, and Pacific from Chicago, (4) the Northern Pacific from Minneapolis, (5) the Great Northern from Minneapolis, (6) the Canadian Pacific from Winnipeg and Montreal, and (7) the Canadian National from Winnipeg and Montreal. The five United States lines have their western termini at Portland or Seattle, while the two Canadian transcontinental roads use Vancouver and Prince Rupert as their Pacific ports. In Alaska three short lines run back in Oregon and Washington are excellent. These roads have been of great value in reaching remote areas not touched by railroads, they have served not only to get out large quantities of timber but have also stimulated the tourist trade by providing

Figure 15–14. Lake Tipsoo and Mt. Rainier in the Cascade Mountains of Washington. This is one of the most scenic areas of Anglo-America and it is visited by many tourists from all over the world. (Courtesy of the Washington State Advertising Commission.)

from the coast to connect (1) Skagway with the headwaters of the Yukon River, (2) Cordova with the Kennecott District, and (3) Seward with Fairbanks. This last named railroad is owned by the United States government.

Highways. Almost all parts of the United States section and southern Canada are served by highways but north of Vancouver there are as yet few and in most cases they are poorly developed. Most of the highways easy access to numerous wilderness areas of superb scenery.

Airways. Most centers of the Pacific Northwest are served by airways, which also provide connections with Canadian territory and Alaska. New flying fields built in the Alaskan coastal districts during World War II are providing isolated areas with rapid transportation to the United States. The Seattle-Tacoma International Airport is the major point of departure for trans-Pacific flights, either via Hawaii, or to Alaska and via the Great Circle route to Japan.

The Outlook

Today the leading occupations of the region are lumbering and allied wood-products industries, general agriculture (especially in the broad Willamette Valley), specialized agriculture (dairying, fruit growing, poultry farming, market gardening), fishing, a limited amount of mining, and a growing array of metallurgical industries. Abundance of hydroelectric power tends to offset the lack of mineral fuel. Much of the terrain is still in forests — virgin or second growth. The Puget Sound area supports several large urban centers with a combined population of more than a million people. The cities of this region are primarily trade centers with their future partly dependent upon intercoastal and transpacific commerce.

This is primarily a region of extractive industries. The natural resources which once seemed almost limitless — timber and fish — are now being more carefully managed, and all activities dependent upon them should, therefore, be able to continue indefinitely. Agriculture is limited in area, but through specialization and intensification has become increasingly more valuable to the regional economy. Future expansion will be largely urban.

Practically all of the Canadian and Alaskan parts, will remain primarily a wilderness dominated by a few extractive industries.

Table 14

SELECTED CITIES AND TOWNS OF THE NORTH PACIFIC COAST

City or Town	Urbanized area	Political center	City or Town	Urbanized area	Political center
Aberdeen		19,653	New Westminster		28,639
Anchorage		11,254	North Vancouver		15,687
Astoria		12,331	Olympia		15,819
Bellingham		34,112	Petersburg		1,619
Bremerton		27,678	Portland	512,643	373,628
Cordova		1,165	Prince Rupert		8,546
Corvallis		16,207	Salem		43,140
Eugene		35,879	Seattle	621,509	467,591
Eureka		23,058	Seward		2,114
Everett		33,849	Sitka		1,985
Juneau		5,956	Tacoma	167,667	143,673
Ketchikan		5,305	Vancouver (B.C.)	530,728	344,833
Longview		20,339	Vancouver (Wash.)		41,664
Medford		17,305	Victoria		51,331
Nanaimo		7,196	Wrangell		1,263

Selected Bibliography

Otis W. Freeman, "The Pacific Northwest Pea Industry," *Economic Geography*, Vol. 19, 1943, pp. 118-128.

Frances M. Hanson, "Recent Developments in the Pacific Northwest," *Journal of Geography*, Vol. 48, 1949, pp. 248-252.

Gordon W. Hewes, "The Fisheries of Northwestern North America," *Economic Geography*, Vol. 28, 1952, pp. 66-73.

Richard M. Highsmith, Jr., and John L. Beh, "Tillamook Burn: The Regeneration of a Forest," *The Scientific Monthly*, Vol. 75, 1952, pp. 139-148.

Richard M. Highsmith, Jr., and Elbert E. Miller, "Open Field Farming in Yakima Valley, Washington," *Economic Geography*, Vol. 28, 1952, pp. 74-87.

Tim K. Kelley, "A Program for Stabilizing the Fishery of Washington," *Economic Geography*, Vol. 23, 1947, pp. 256-260.

A. W. Kuchler, "The Broadleaf Deciduous Forests of the Pacific Northwest," *Annals of the Associa-*

tion of American Geographers, Vol. 36, 1946, pp. 122-147.

Hoyt Lemons and Rayburn Tousley, "Washington Apple Industry: Its Geographic Basis," *Economic Geography*, Vol. 21, 1945, pp. 161-182.

Elbert E. Miller and Richard M. Highsmith, Jr., "Geography of the Fruit Industry of Yakima Valley, Washington," *Economic Geography*, Vol. 25, 1949, pp. 285-295.

————, "The Hop Industry of the Pacific Coast," *Journal of Geography*, Vol. 49, 1950, pp. 63-77.

Roberts Milnor, "The War's Impact on the Mineral Industry of Washington," *Mining and Metallurgy*, Vol. 25, 1944, pp. 411-414.

Kirk H. Stone, "Aerial Photographic Interpretation of Natural Vegetation in the Anchorage Area, Alaska," *Geographical Review*, Vol. 38, 1948, pp. 465-474.

Rayburn D. Tousley and Hoyt Lemons, "Washington Apple Industry: Economic Considerations," *Economic Geography*, Vol. 21, 1945, pp. 252-268.

16.

The Yukon-Kuskokwim Basins

Almost continental in magnitude, the Yukon-Kuskokwim Region is one of the most sparsely populated, least known, and least developed areas in Anglo-America (Figure 16-1). It has suffered and has been largely neglected because of misconceptions and apathy on the part of the people in both Canada and the United States. Such disparaging epithets as "Icebergia," "Seward's Folly," "Uncle Sam's Icebox," and "Walrussia" contributed to give the Alaskan segment a bad reputation as a land of ice and snow, unfit for the habitation of any human beings other than a few miserable Indians and Eskimos. And surprising as it may seem this misconception is still widely prevalent.

The discovery of gold in the Klondike and the defense program enabled the region to be at least temporarily rediscovered.

Yet, in spite of neglect and ignorance, the Yukon-Kuskokwim Basins form one of Anglo-America's more colorful regions. There are few persons who do not thrill to the names of Dawson, Klondike, Whitehorse, and Fort Yukon. The popular writings of Jack London, Rex Beach, Joaquin Miller, and Robert W. Service, which deal with man's battles against a hostile nature, have become a part of America's folklore.

The Yukon-Kuskokwim Region lying in the basins of the Yukon and Kuskokwim rivers, extends from the Alaska Range on the south to the Brooks Range on the north, and from the source of the Yukon in Canada to the Bering Sea. Because the Seward Peninsula lacks the Yukon Basin's extremes of temperature and supports no agriculture, it is considered a part of the Tundra rather than of this region.

The Physical Setting

From a location that was extremely poor, unimportant, and definitely in a "back eddy," the Yukon Basin as a result of proximity to the Soviet Union has become one of the most important locations in the world (Figure 16–2). A look at a population map of the world discloses several immutable facts of geopolitics: (1) the great northern land masses ring the Arctic; (2) nine tenths of the two and one-half billion people of the earth and most of the raw materials and industrial potential and hence of the military power are located on or north of the 35th parallel; and (3) the shortest or great circle routes between the "heavy weight" powers all cross the Arctic. The Yukon-Kuskokwim Basins thus possess a highly strategic location. This new concept, the "polar concept," assumes that if another war is touched off the Arctic and subarctic regions will provide the pathways for the initial and perhaps the decisive blow. At the Diomedes, Soviet Siberia and Alaska are only two and one-half miles apart and it is only about five minutes jet fighter time from Russia's Siberian Anadair air base to Alaska. Situation might then prove to be this region's dominant asset; on the contrary it could also be a weakness depending upon the military might the United States has there.

Unless America is strong in the Yukon country, the region will be vulnerable either across Bering Strait or over the North Pole. Should Alaskan air fields fall to an enemy, the latter's bombers might inflict damaging blows against American industry. The vulnerability of the Boeing airplane plant in Seattle no doubt weighed heavily in the transfer of part of the company's capacity to Wichita, Kansas. The Hanford atomic

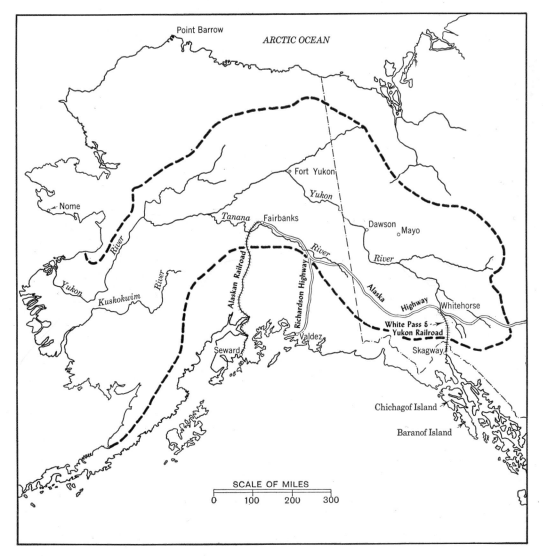

Figure 16–1. The Yukon–Kuskokwim Basins. A region of mining, hunting and fishing, trapping, subsistence farming, and military preparedness.

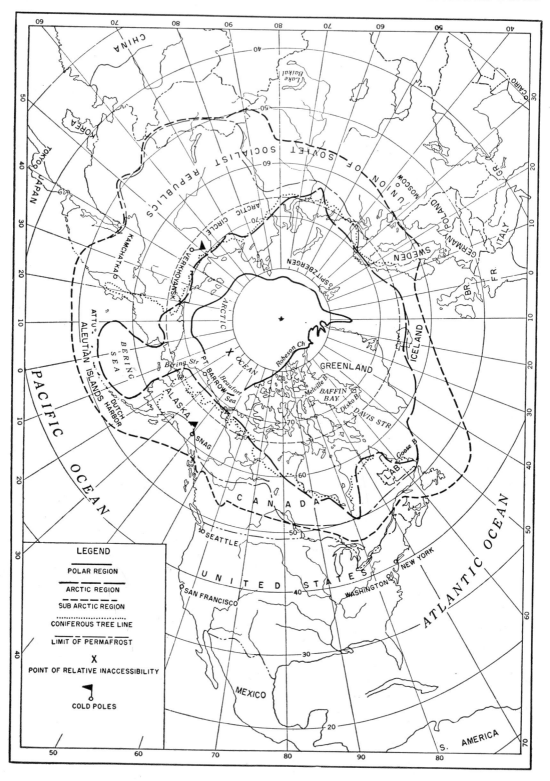

LEGEND

POLAR REGION

ARCTIC REGION

SUB ARCTIC REGION

CONIFEROUS TREE LINE

LIMIT OF PERMAFROST

X
POINT OF RELATIVE INACCESSIBILITY

COLD POLES

plant in eastern Washington, the aircraft and other industries of California, the vital industries of the Middle West, and even the highly strategic "Soo" locks would be vulnerable.

The development in the Yukon today owes its importance to the strategic factor as much if not more than to the economic.

For the most part the climate is decidedly continental, being characterized by extremes of temperature from summer to winter and by light precipitation. Summers are short and hot, winters long and cold. The average temperature of the three warmest months is about 57°F. The early part of June and last of August are critical periods, for frost is likely with resultant crop damage. The average January temperature is about 20°F. below zero and the average for July 60° above, an annual range of more than 80°. Periods of extreme cold, however, seldom last long. The lowest temperature on record is –76°F. at Tanana south of the Arctic Circle, and the highest 100°F. at Fort Yukon north of the Arctic Circle. The range of temperature is smaller near the Bering Sea, where winters are less cold and summers less hot. The growing season varies from 80 to 90 days, though the 18 to 19 hours of daylight in summer partly compensate for this short period and for the rather low heating power of the sun's rays.

The average annual precipitation varies from 10 to 12 inches, about three fifths of it falling during the period May through September. About one fifth falls as snow. Ordinarily only June and July are snowless. The snow cover amounting to about 24 inches is quite evenly distributed; there is little drifting because of the low velocity of surface winds. The rigors of winter have serious economic effects, the entire work cycle being determined by the weather.

The terrain of the region near the main river consists mostly of dissected, rolling, flat-topped hills whose summits show marked uniformity of elevation over a wide area. Known as the Yukon Plateau, it has an average elevation of 2,000 to 3,000 feet and is rimmed by mountains on the southwest, east, and north. In the Yukon Valley from Whitehorse to Circle, mountains lie along the river banks or at no great distance from them so that only the narrow river terraces give any promise of possible cultivation. Near Circle on the great bend in the Yukon are the marshy flats which continue downstream to Fort Hamlin. In the Tanana Valley area there are two main types of land — the terraces or bench lands and the bottom lands or flats. Each type has its distinctly different features of microclimate and consequent difference in crops.

For many miles along its lower course, the Yukon is virtually at sea level and hence the land is marshy. An additional cause of poor drainage and hence of ponds, marshes and lakes is the fact that the permanently frozen subsoil over much of the region prevents normal soak-in. In the 60-mile wide Yukon Delta, the water is so shallow and the distributaries so numerous that seagoing vessels cannot enter.

Soil. Since detailed soil studies have been made in but a few places, only broad generalizations regarding soils are possible.[1] Most of the soils in the Tanana Valley are water-sorted sediments and are cold and poorly drained. The poor drainage results from permafrost, which is usually 12 to 36

[1] C. E. Kellogg and I. J. Nygard, *Report on Exploratory Investigations of Agricultural Problems of Alaska*, U. S. Department of Agriculture, Miscellaneous Publication No. 700. Washington, D. C.: Government Printing Office, 1949.

————, *Exploratory Study of the Principal Soil Groups of Alaska*, U. S. Department of Agriculture, Monograph No. 7. Washington, D. C.: Government Printing Office, 1951.

Figure 16–2. *Facing page:* The Yukon-Kuskokwim Basins as well as the Tundra Region possess a highly strategic location on the direct great circle air routes between populous industralized Anglo-America and Eurasia. This area is now the front line of defense. Note also the southern boundary and the enormous area characterized by permafrost. About one fifth of the land area of the world is believed to be underlain by permafrost. (Courtesy of *The Military Engineer*.)

inches below the surface under a natural vegetative cover of moss, thick turf, and peat, which shields the soil from maximum penetration of heat by shading, by decreasing air circulation, by retaining moisture in and just above the soil, and by intercepting rain. The C horizon may be completely frozen in places.

When cleared, this soil in the Fairbanks area develops into a gray-brown to dark yellowish-brown fine sandy loam. The well-drained and relatively warm wind-laid deposits of the Fairbanks soil series comprise a satisfactory soil for agriculture. Unfortunately it is given to erosion once the natural vegetation is removed.

Black soils especially are important, for they best absorb solar energy. Thus the summer temperature of black soils of the bottom land is higher than that on the grayish soils of the benchlands. Hence crops in such soils grow faster and mature in a shorter period, provided the permafrost line is not near the soil surface.

Permafrost. In this region, permafrost or perennially frozen ground, occurs everywhere but it is not continuous as in the Tundra Region to the north (Figure 16–2). Permafrost is in delicate equilibrium with several other elements of the natural environment, hence if distributed, the landscape becomes modified. Whether permafrost is a negative or a beneficial factor in agriculture depends on the particular local permafrost conditions and the climatological factors relating to heat exchange.

Natural Vegetation. The natural vegetation consists largely of light forest growth of white spruce, cottonwood, balsam, poplar, and Alaska white birch on the benchlands and on the better-drained valley floors. The ground cover comprises dwarf heath shrubs, mountain cranberry, mosses, dwarf dogwood, and bluegrass. White spruce with a shallow and flexible root system is the tree species best suited to soils with permafrost. Black spruce, larch, and white birch have shallow but not as flexible root systems and are less frost tolerant. Living roots cannot, of course, either penetrate or occupy permafrost.

In the Tanana Valley, black spruce, dwarf birch and dwarf willow, Labrador tea and mountain cranberry grow on the cold poorly drained lowlands. Everywhere the type of vegetation has strong indicator value as to soil and drainage conditions.

Vegetation in winter may be subjected to severe water loss through exposure to dry winds at the very time the roots are encased in frozen soil and hence cannot absorb water. Tree growth is slow and trees seldom exceed six inches in diameter. Desiccating winds during the long cold winter are believed to limit tree growth on frozen ground. It is for this reason that the tree line extends farthest north in sheltered valleys. Towards the northwest the trees thin out and finally disappear in the tundra. Grass and tundra dominate the lower valleys near the Bering Sea.

Native Animals. The animal most closely associated with this region (excepting the Bering Sea littoral) and the one most highly valued is the caribou. Migrations of caribou, which travel in large herds, are much like those of the bison on the American Great Plains before they were exterminated in the 1880's. Each summer the caribou start north, crossing the Yukon between Selkirk and Circle, and return later to their winter quarters near the Alaska Mountains or between the St. Elias and Coast Ranges. Caribou meat furnishes the principal item in the diet of the natives and the skin makes ideal clothing for the far north. Unfortunately caribou are being depleted rapidly, though large numbers still persist.

Moose and black bear are plentiful. The marauding wolf, traveling alone or in pairs in summer but in packs in winter, kills annually thousands of reindeer and caribou. Among the smaller animals are the marten, mink, marmot, ground squirrel, Arctic hare, and snowshoe rabbit — the last two changing color from brown in summer to white in winter. In summer millions of ducks and geese make their nesting grounds on the Yukon Flats. Finally there are the billions of gnats, black flies, and mosquitoes which thrive in this region of poor drainage and high summer temperatures. Travelers insist that the mosquito is the curse of the Yukon; that they can overcome with a fair degree of satisfaction all the other obstacles — the vast stretches of swamps, the isolation, and the bitter winter cold. The mosquito retards immigration and lowers the quality of work. Farmers and miners must wear head nets and canvas gloves during May, June, July, and August. So greatly do mosquitoes torment cattle that some farmers prepare smudges in their pastures to enable the animals to get relief.

Settlement

The Yukon and Kuskokwim basins have never been colonized in the traditional way. The economic background of every white settlement has been the demand from distant areas for the furs and the gold which this region could supply. Obstacles to sedentary living are: (1) the long, bitterly cold winters, (2) the pestiferous black flies, gnats, and

mosquitoes, (3) the high-cost transportation creating almost prohibitive prices, (4) the limited market for farm products, and (5) the isolation. This last is the most important. Can this difficulty ever be reduced? It is the starting point of all studies of the region. The problem involves not only the isolation of the region from the *ecumene* of the United States and Canada, but of the different settlements from one another.

The population of the region by white peoples has ebbed and flowed. Obviously the loss was great after the Gold Rush. Then a gain was recorded until the interlude of World War I brought a drop. In 1920 came a small increase which has persisted up to the present time.

Most of the people are tied to lines of transportation — rivers, railroads, roads, and airfields (Figure 16–3). General accessibility is

Figure 16–3. Fairbanks, metropolis of the Yukon–Kuskokwim Basins, had less than 6,000 inhabitants in 1950. It gives little promise of ever becoming a large city. (Courtesy of White Pass and Yukon Route.)

a prime requisite for permanence of settlement: lacking it all other apparent advantages are useless. The density of population per square mile in this region is less than in the state of Nevada.

Since the number of white women is considerably smaller than the number of white men, interbreeding occurs and, as a result, every fourth Alaska native is of mixed blood.

In the entire region only Fairbanks, Dawson, and Whitehorse may be classed as significant permanent white settlements. A map showing the paucity of significant settlements is accordingly impressive. The discovery of gold brought what centers there are into being and dredge mining continues to be the primary function of the first two, though they are classed functionally as agricultural and military settlements also. In all probability it is only when a center has such a combination that it becomes permanent. Whitehorse owes its existence to transportation advantages at the crossroads of north-south and east-west traffic.

There is considerable instability in the farm population. A large proportion of the present homesteaders will not successfully fulfill the homestead requirements and hence will lose the land. In the Fairbanks area 90 per cent of the privately owned land has been thus relinquished.

Most settlers do not stay. To make a go of settlement in this region requires courage and capital. Courage alone is not enough: roughly $200 an acre is required for buying equipment and for building a house and for living until the land begins to produce. Many, victims of their own imagination, fail because they came to the northland with a glamorous viewpoint about the frontier and with romantic notions about pioneering. They had probably seen too many motion pictures of the "Far North." Experience taught them the country was not the way they had imagined it. Others, of course, fail because of lack of capital and lack of courage.[2]

The number of Indians and Eskimos is very small, for game does not exist in adequate

---

[2] "Alaska Awaiting Annual Migration," *The New York Times*, March 9, 1952.

numbers to sustain primitive man in appreciable numbers.

Eskimos. In former times, the Eskimo of the lower Yukon and Kuskokwim valleys lived wholly off the region, illustrating superbly man's capacity to adjust himself to nature. They now barter furs for flour, tea, sugar, canned goods, woolen clothing, and other products and are quite dependent upon the white man. While they are remarkable in transition, there is little chance they can endure in the white man's civilization which, in one generation, has swept them into a new world. They have little resistance to the contagious diseases that invariably go with the advance of civilization.

Indians. Indians are widely but thinly distributed over the region. They are Athapaskans and Kutchins — regarded by some authorities as the last wanderers to cross Bering Strait from Asia (Figure 16–4). They are constantly on the move because of their unceasing quest for food. Seldom is it possible to obtain sufficient game in any one place to sustain them for more than a few weeks. Originally they knew nothing about agriculture, living entirely on the fish and game they caught and the berries they gathered. They preferred the meat of the caribou, whose skin they required for clothing.

Economic Pursuits

Mining. The rich gold placers discovered in the Klondike brought a feverish stampede of about 80,000 persons to the region in 1898. Most of these knew nothing about this north country but they were willing to exchange a few weeks, a few months, or perhaps even a few years of hardship and adventure for a fortune. The trail, nearly 600 miles long, was a bitter and dangerous one, leading over notorious and dangerous Chilkoot Pass and later the less difficult White Pass, Dead Horse Gulch, the rock desert, and the Miles Canyon Rapids. Unlike the American West the Yukon had no "oases" — places where the weary might rest and refresh themselves. *But gold was there!* Production reached ten million dollars in 1898 and 16 million in 1899. Relatively few individuals, however, found prospecting profitable and by 1910 many of those still alive had returned to the United States.

More than a billion dollars worth of minerals, three fourths gold, has been removed from this region. Gold is taken both from

At first the ground was thawed with wood fires, then with steam engines. Today cold water is used. In this method pierced pipes, spaced 16 to 32 feet apart, are driven deep into the ground and cold water forced through them. The water seeps to the sur-

Route of Earliest Indians?

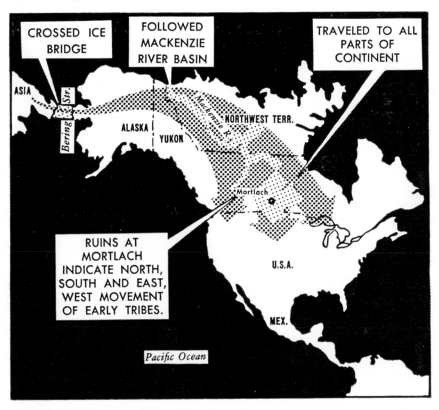

Figure 16–4. The probable route of the first Indians into Anglo-America was over the 50-mile ice bridge across Bering Strait. (Courtesy of *News Map of the Week, Inc.*)

placers and veins, though the Yukon is essentially one of gravel mining. The first miners separated gold from sand and gravel with a pan, rocker, or cradle. So slow were these methods, however, that a prospector could work only about two cubic yards a day. Then came the sluice box with its string of boxes into which gravel was shoveled and through which a stream of water was sent. Unfortunately much of the gold lay in frozen ground which could not be worked until thawed.

face and is used again. Sixty to 120 days are thus required to thaw the gravels.

After the more accessible and richer gravels were worked and prospecting became less profitable, large-scale corporate enterprises purchased the better holdings. Much of the placer mining today is done by huge dredges, which cost several million dollars and can remove as many as 10,000 cubic yards of gravel per day (Figure 16–5). Engineers determine in advance the quantity of gold, computing the profit so that there is hardly more risk involved than in any other business. Thus most gold mining in the region today is carried on by a few companies owned largely by nonresidents who employ little labor in proportion to the value of their product. Prospecting is done chiefly

ing, and limited railroad mileage keep production at a low figure. It is important locally, however, for transportation costs are high and the winters bitterly cold. Most of the coal mined is used by the Alaska Railroad and a gold-dredging concern near Fairbanks.

Figure 16–5. The tailings of gravel left by gold dredges resemble gigantic caterpillars. These million-dollar machines dig as deep as 60 feet below the bottom of a stream to find the type of alluvial or free gold that drew thousands into the region in 1898. Permafrost is the biggest problem facing the dredge operators. (Courtesy of White Pass and Yukon Route.)

with airplanes, which can cover the same territory in a fraction of the time required on foot or by canoe and can do so without battling swamp and muskeg, black flies, gnats and mosquitoes.

In addition to gold, the mining of base metals is growing in importance. Mayo is the center of a mining area yielding silver, lead, tungsten, and a small amount of copper. Coal of inferior quality is widespread, but the small population, lack of manufactur-

Mining in the region as a whole has been declining in importance since World War I. Occasionally it recovers slightly only to sink again into lower producing levels. But since only 49 per cent of Alaska has been mapped geologically by reconnaissance methods and less than one per cent in detail, it seems that mining still has a future.

Trapping and Fishing. Before white men reached the Yukon country the Indians lived chiefly on salmon which they caught in the streams while these were enroute to spawn. The catch was smoked and much of it cached above ground beyond the reach of dogs and wolves. The Eskimos killed walruses, seals, and whales and carried on some fishing.

With the coming of the white man, trapping became important. Following the purchase of Alaska by the United States, virtually all the Americans and probably most of the Russians who stayed on, were employed in fur trading. They traded flour, sugar, tea, and other items to the Indians for peltries. Despite the fact that trapping and fishing continue to be the chief activities of the Indians who live in the region, the enterprise yields at best only a precarious living, for fur-bearing animals are not numerous and trapping is not really profitable.

The methods followed are the traditional ones. In summer the Indians remain near the settlements along the principal streams. When the trapping season opens in autumn, they move into the interior.

Fur trapping differs from farming, which is highly localized, by being widely scattered.

This enterprise has declined to a secondary position. With greater regulation on the part of the governments, and by keeping white men away from the areas surrounding native villages, the industry might be revived, for the natural habitat is not unfavorable. The long cold winters give the animals thick coats.

In the Canadian part of the region the Hudson's Bay Company, oldest company in Anglo-America, still operates through its chain of fur posts and the fur trade is still an important part of its business.

Forest Industries. Forest industries were not important in the past, are unimportant now, and offer little promise for future development. The cold, long winters, short summers, and light precipitation conspire to keep the trees small. They might be used for pulpwood were there not so many regions better located and with superior growing conditions.

Most of the cut is for fuel for river steamers and mining operations, or for domestic firewood and for sawmills at Fairbanks and a few other points. Everywhere the timber is for local consumption.

Agriculture. Farming began here around 1900 for producing food for prospectors. Most of the first farmers were men who became disillusioned as gold miners and therefore turned to agriculture. Since transportation costs on all food items from the United States were high, a good profit could be made on their commodities in the mining camps, and in Dawson and Fairbanks.

Agriculture is unimportant now and will probably continue so into the remote future. This status results not only from the natural environmental conditions, which force man to utilize every ounce of ingenuity he can muster, but also from the small market and the great distance and poor transport facilities to markets. The region is definitely noncompetitive as a source of agricultural products for all but the small local market.

Farming is highly localized and its pattern is spotty. Fairbanks is the dominant center and yet there are only 30 to 40 farming families and only 2,400 acres of cleared land.[3] About 70 per cent of the cleared land is on the higher terraces and benchlands; here grains and vegetables do best. The remaining 30 per cent is in the lowlands and is used principally for pasture and silage crops. Some good farm land is located along the Alaska Highway west of Whitehorse and between Selkirk and Dawson.

The crops are essentially of the hardy type grains (oats, barley, rye, and wheat), root crops (potatoes, beets, radishes, carrots, and parsnips), and vegetables (peas, cabbages, and lettuce).

Vegetables were the first crops to be introduced into the region and they continue to be the most important. About 90 per cent of the farmers are engaged in vegetable growing. The local market for vegetables has never been met. The local annual food crop is estimated to be worth $150,000 whereas the value of food imported into the Fairbanks area is in excess of one million. Potatoes comprise the leading vegetable crop.

---

[3] E. Willard Miller, "Agricultural Development in Interior Alaska," *Scientific Monthly*, Vol. 72, October 1951, p. 248.

Scientists are at work selecting adaptable crops, the growing period of which may be shortened to fit them to the short growing season. Basil M. Bensin,[4] noting that snow along the railroad tracks melted much sooner than elsewhere and realizing that this resulted from the fact that the black coal dust (lignite is soft and gradually disintegrates into small particles after being exposed to the air for some time) absorbed heat from the faint spring sun, planted beans and squash in dusted rows whose soil temperature was two to four degrees higher than the undusted rows. He thus was able to plant crops several weeks earlier. He also developed a "frigid wheat" and the fastest growing barley in the world. He believes that his barley may play as important a role in the Yukon Basin as corn has in the American Corn Belt Sub-region of the Agricultural Interior. This, however, does not seem to be borne out by the facts. Since the completion of the railroad from Seward to Fairbanks, grain has been imported from the United States. The Yukon area cannot compete and the commercial production of wheat and barley has now virtually ceased. Today oats ranks first in importance among the grains. The crop is cut green for use as feed. Hay is not an important crop because August is the wettest month and grass will not dry in the fields. Hence silage crops are grown.

Agricultural labor is scarce and therefore expensive. The farmer must compete with the mining industry and with the military construction program, which obviously is almost impossible.

Dairying on a small scale is being tried in the environs of Fairbanks. The two commercial dairies in the area produce about one million pounds of milk, but maintaining the herds during winter is so costly that there appears to be no future for the business. In 1950 it was estimated that it cost between $45,000 and $50,000 to establish a modern 12 cow dairy.

Kirk H. Stone, in referring to northern lands, generally asserts that new settlements can hardly be expected to become permanent if they are to depend solely upon agriculture.[5]

Recreation. This region has access to superlative facilities for recreation in one of the few remaining so-called primitive regions accessible to Canadians and Americans.

At present little use is being made of these facilities because of (1) small population, (2) isolation, (3) vast distances, (4) pestiferous insects, and (5) the great cost of everything people need. The trip is now definitely beyond the reach of the average American and Canadian family.

Transportation

So large, isolated, and relatively unproductive is the Yukon-Kuskokwim Region that it has only six outlets: (1) the Yukon and its several navigable tributaries, (2) the White Pass and Yukon Railway, (3) the Alaska Railroad, (4) the Richardson Trail, (5) the Alaska Highway, and (6) the airways.

Waterways. The *Yukon,* chief highway of this tremendous land, is navigable for river boats to Whitehorse, a distance of about 2,200 miles during some three months of the year. The *Tanana* is navigable to Fairbanks by small boats specially built to go against its swift current. The *Kuskokwim* is navigable for 650 miles during some four months. Unfortunately the numerous distributaries of the delta and the badly shifting channel almost preclude ocean-going vessels from entering the Yukon. All river transportation comes to a complete standstill during the long cold winters.

Railways. The total mileage in the enormous area of Alaska and Canada's Yukon Territory is small,[6] but railways play a vital role. The *White Pass and Yukon Railway* was built in 1898 during the feverish boom days of the Klondike. It is 111 miles long and extends from Skagway up over White Pass to Whitehorse. Upon its completion freight rates, which had fluctuated from 30 cents to a dollar per pound, dropped to four and three-

---

[4] Agronomist, Alaska Agricultural Experiment Station, College, Alaska, personal interview.

[5] Kirk H. Stone, "Populating Alaska: The United States Phase," *Geographical Review,* Vol. 42, July 1952, p. 404.

[6] Most of this mileage is in the North Pacific Coast Region (Chapter 15) and not in the Yukon-Kuskokwim Basins.

fourths cents. The *Alaska Railroad,* extending 470 miles from Seward to Fairbanks, was built by the United States government to help develop and settle interior Alaska. It was completed in 1923. This route has greatly stimulated mining in its tributary area and, in turn, mining supplies the larger part of the traffic.

Probably no new railways will be built, certainly not at public expense. Even extensions should be made only after careful planning and after a definite need has been shown. Probably no railroad in this region can pay its own way year in and year out, though in some years the Alaska Railroad has made expenses.

Roads. The small population, the enormous distances, and the prevalence of much swampy surface mean great expense in building and maintaining good roads. Hence this region is almost empty of roads. The *Richardson Highway,* extending 371 miles from Valdez on Prince William Sound to Fairbanks in the interior, was the chief means of access, especially in winter, prior to the building of the Alaska Railroad. It was a trail in 1907, became a wagon road in 1910, and was improved for automobile traffic during the 1920's. It reaches from sea level to an elevation of 3,310 feet and then descends into the beautiful Tanana Valley. The *Steese Highway,* 160 miles long, is really a prolongation of the Richardson Highway from Fairbanks on the Tanana to Circle on the Yukon. Extending farther north than any other road in the region, it penetrates some of the outstanding and most highly mechanized gold-mining districts of Alaska. Recently constructed roads now connect Whitehorse with Dawson and Dawson with Mayo.

The *Alaska Highway,* extending 1,523 miles from Dawson Creek in British Columbia's Peace River country to Fairbanks, was built in 1942 as a wartime project by the United States. It opened up some previously untouched areas in Canada's northeastern British Columbia and southern Yukon as well as some in Alaska — a corridor northward through the wilderness (Figure 16-6). It is a 26-foot gravel-surfaced road with moderate grades and curves and traverses an almost entirely unsettled area — one inaccessible to river transport. The highway was built when it was feared the Japanese might prevent use of the Inside Passage by the United States at a time when machinery, food, and all heavy freight moved to Alaska by vessel. It also connected a series of airports previously constructed by the Canadian government between Edmonton and Alaska.

Airways. Aviation has become the chief solution to the transportation problems of the Yukon Basin. The airplane is the cheapest means of long distance travel and seems ideally suited to the small population scattered over this enormous region. Alaskans use planes as Americans use automobiles and buses. This is apparent from the fact that the number of passenger miles flown there annually is 15 times that of the United States on a per capita basis. The air cargo business, per capita, is 100 times greater. In fact, it was not until aviation tapped the region that it was really opened up. Large-scale construction of railroads and roads cannot be undertaken by private enterprise. Only governments can sponsor nonprofitable lines. Moreover, the rivers are not navigable in winter. In the Yukon are most of the large-producing placer camps but they are badly isolated, the operating season is short, and many workers leave camp when the freeze-up begins in autumn returning only when work begins in spring. Accordingly a rapid economical method of transportation such as the airplane provides is of inestimable value. Prospectors can now be flown annually to their destination whereas most of the season was lost in traveling to and from their workings in the old days. Trips that used to require months by the old fur traders are now covered in a few hours by air. Vilhjalmur Stefansson asserts that an Eskimo can go from Fairbanks to Nome more cheaply by airplane than he can by his own dog-sledge. The cost of food for himself and his dogs and of lodging during the trip is far greater than the price of an airplane ticket.[7]

----

[7] Vilhjalmur Stefansson, "The American Far North," *Foreign Affairs,* April 1939, Vol. 17, No. 3, p. 517.

Outlook

This enormous region is today supporting a population of less than 50,000. The whites are largely engaged in mining, transportation, and defense construction; the Indians and Eskimos in fishing, trapping, and hunting, though increasing numbers of natives improve their financial condition in a reasonably brief time.

In spite of the fact that crops can be grown over a considerable part of the region, not more than 500 acres are actually in production. This results from the short growing season and the unreliability of production, the shortage and high cost of labor, and

Figure 16–6. A segment of the 1600-mile Alaska Highway. This road, built during World War II, is not purely a product of military emergency with no peacetime future. Each year it is more widely used. (Courtesy of Bureau of Public Roads, U. S. Department of Commerce.)

are being lured to the defense industry by high wages.

The region appears to be essentially a reserve for the future, a region where only whites of the pioneer type — people willing to risk all to find something better — will venture. It is a paradox that Americans, who have been the greatest frontiersmen on earth, have thus far neglected Alaska. But a subsistence-farming existence without near neighbors and without roads, schools, churches and motion-picture theaters does not attract the average Anglo-American. Settlers avoid going to distant lands, especially unfriendly ones, unless they can appreciably difficult marketing problems. A director of one of the Alaskan industrial schools says:

The Government, through the Alaska Railroad, is carrying on a colonization movement to settle the fertile valleys of this territory. To me, who has spent two summers here among the dense clouds of mosquitoes which infest the interior regions from early spring until fall, this attempt at colonization with outsiders (people from the States) seems futile. A large per cent of these colonists will not remain after the first summer. Why overlook the material for colonization right at hand? Why not encourage the natives to take up agriculture as a means of livelihood? We all know that fishing and trapping are decreasing rapidly every year and cannot be depended upon any longer as the means of support. The boys and girls who have lived all their lives in this mosquito-infested region are accustomed to conditions. They will continue to live here.[8]

Before agricultural settlement in this region is encouraged, more should be known about the potentialities. Isaiah Bowman pointed out more than two decades ago that the thrust of culture into vacant lands has invariably been without guidance since the facts were not known. Whether it has been the valley of the Yukon, the basin of the Amazon, or the Great Plains of Anglo-America, the venturing farmer has had to be his own scientist.[9]

Gold mining, the dominant activity today, appears to be the most promising enterprise for the future, though ultimately it must die. It has been greatly aided by improvements in transportation — railways, highways, and airways. It will continue to be a large-scale enterprise inviting much capital, however, only so long as satisfactory profits are available. More and more minerals may be found, but how important mining will become will depend not only upon the presence of minerals but also upon how profitably they can be mined and transported. Remoteness and poor transport (except for products having high value per unit of weight or bulk) hang like the sword of Damocles over this region. The lone prospector has almost given way to the dredge and most miners today are salaried employees of large syndicates.

The grazing of reindeer by Eskimos for subsistence is possible over a considerable part of the region. In 1939 as a result of the Third Deficiency Act, the reindeer of white owners were purchased, making the reindeer industry exclusively native. For many years the presence of large herds of reindeer owned by whites using the same ranges as those animals owned by Eskimos had led to serious overgrazing and had created misunderstandings, one result of which was to discourage Eskimos from keeping reindeer. The industry, now exclusively native, should eliminate controversies, re-establish an interest in reindeer among the Eskimos, and build up the herds, thereby insuring the natives a supply of food and clothing at all times.

Since the natives have been declining numerically as a result of white contact and competition, the United States and Canadian governments must adopt policies to protect them from outside influences. Only the aborigines can form the foundation of future development, for only they are constitutionally suited to the country. The Bureau of Indian Affairs is launching a program to capitalize the native virtues and simultaneously orient the aborigines for living successfully in contact with white. Native culture must not be permitted to decay and perish.

As more is learned about Arctic weather and climate, cities such as Fairbanks and Dawson may attain international importance as centers on airways using great circle routes. At present, however, no principal commercial airways go over the North Pole. By late 1952 the Armed Services in three years had spent close to half a billion dollars in Alaska, much of it in this area, with no end in sight. Such expenditures and increased population impose a big responsibility on the region. Certainly the Yukon-Kuskokwim basins cannot safely plan their future on a foundation of defense expenditures. The region must create and produce. But how — and what? The answer is not yet forthcoming. Finally it seems that the Yukon country will not change greatly in the future. In addition to the factors, already presented, that retard development and settlement — isolation, remoteness, insects, climate, poor soils, and limited transport — there is the fact that a colonial psychology rules the region: 98 per cent of the land is held by the governments. Since this situation does not encourage settlement, it appears that the Yukon River (and its basin) will continue to be the "life artery to [but] a handful of forgotten people."

---

[8] H. Dewey Anderson and Walter C. Eells, *Alaska Natives, A Survey of Their Sociological and Educational Status*, p. 401. Stanford, California: Stanford University Press, 1935.

[9] Isaiah Bowman, "Planning in Pioneer Settlement," *Annals of the Association of American Geographers*, Vol. 22, 1932, p. 96.

Table 15

SELECTED CITIES AND TOWNS OF THE YUKON–KUSKOKWIM BASINS

City or Town	Urbanized area	Political center	City or Town	Urbanized area	Political center
Dawson		783	Nome		1,876
Fairbanks		5,771	Whitehorse		2,594
Fort Yukon		446			

Selected Bibliography

William S. Benninghoff, "Interaction of Vegetation and Soil Frost Phenomena," *Arctic*, Vol. 5, 1952, pp. 34-44.

Basil M. Bensin, "Agroecological Analysis of the Crop Plants Root System in the Tanana Valley Region of Alaska," *Bulletin, Ecological Society of America*, Vol. 27, April 1946.

W. C. Bethune, *Canada's Western Northland*. Ottawa: Department of Mines and Resources, 1937.

A. W. Currie, *Economic Geography of Canada*. Toronto: The Macmillan Company of Canada, Ltd., 1946.

Wilford J. Eiteman and Alice Boardman Smuts, "Alaska, Land of Opportunity – Limited," *Economic Geography*, Vol. 27, 1951, pp. 33-42.

S. C. Ells, "Alaska Highway," *Canadian Geographical Journal*, Vol. 28, 1944, pp. 104–119.

J. Douglas Gibson, *Canada's Economy in a Changing World*. Toronto: The Macmillan Company of Canada, Ltd., 1948.

G. W. Gasser, "Agriculture in Alaska," *Arctic*, Vol. 1, 1948.

Ernest Gruening, "The Political Ecology of Alaska," *Scientific Monthly*, Vol. 73, December 1951, pp. 376–386.

E. Willard Miller, "Agricultural Development in Interior Alaska," *Scientific Monthly*, Vol. 73, October 1951, pp. 245–254.

T. L. Péwé, "Permafrost and Geomorphology in the Lower Yukon River Valley," *Geological Society of America Bulletin*, Vol. 58, 1947.

Donald F. Putnam, editor, *Canadian Regions: A Geography of Canada*. Toronto: J. M. Dent and Sons, Ltd., 1952.

W. A. Rockie, "What of Alaska?" *Soil Conservation*, January 1946, pp. 147–153.

Kirk H. Stone, "Populating Alaska: The United States Phase," *Geographical Review*, Vol. 42, 1952, pp. 384–404.

Griffith Taylor, "Future Population in Canada: A Study in Technique," *Economic Geography*, Vol. 22, 1946, pp. 67–74.

"The Arctic: It Has Become the Key to World Strategy," *Life*, January 20, 1947, pp. 55–61.

U. S. Department of the Air Force, *Climatic Atlas for Alaska*, Report No. 444 and Supplement. Washington, D. C.: Government Printing Office, 1943.

17.

The Tundra

THE Tundra,[1] one of the larger regions in Anglo-America (Figure 17–1), is the most sparsely populated, the least productive economically, and certainly the least promising so far as man's future occupance is concerned. In few parts of the earth is nature more unyielding or more niggardly, and nowhere else are people's ways of living more closely attuned to the physical environment. Huge areas of land, some as large as western European countries, never have been explored by white men. The Tundra Region is primarily the land of the Eskimos; yet they have established themselves permanently only in small numbers.

Parts of this region have long been known to white men. Five centuries before Columbus reached the New World, Norsemen had visited the coast of Labrador. Eric the Red, who first colonized Greenland near the close of the tenth century, recognized the unattractive appearance of the landscape in giving Greenland its name, "for," he said, "that

might attract men thither when the land has a fine name." [2] Thus along with the hot dry deserts, the rainy tropics, and the lofty mountains, the tundra is one of the least desirable places for settlement. The few white inhabitants have gone to the Tundra Region to get furs, exploit minerals, convert the natives to Christianity, or to represent their respective governments. Cities and towns as we think of them in the United States are non-existent, though a dozen settlements in west Greenland would rate as large villages. In the more remote areas a settlement nucleus may not include more than two or three families.

The Tundra Region includes the part of Anglo-America that extends from the Bering Sea on the west to the Atlantic Ocean on the east and from the Great Northern Forest or *taiga* on the south to the icy Arctic Sea on the north (Figure 17–1); it includes also the vast Arctic archipelagos north of the Canadian mainland and the island of Greenland. The region thus comprises parts of Alaska, Canada, and Greenland.

There is considerable ignorance of the Tundra Region. More first hand information has been learned about this region in the past decade than in the preceding century. Prob-

---

[1] Greenland, though Danish, is included as part of Anglo-America in this book. When Germany occupied Denmark on April 9, 1940, the United States and Canada became apprehensive regarding Greenland, which could be of inestimable value to Germany as a base for submarines, surface craft and aircraft, and for weather forecasting. The United States proclaimed its firm determination to prevent transfer of any geographic region in the western hemisphere from one non-American power to another.

[2] Isobel W. Hutchison, "Flowers and Farming in Greenland," *Scottish Geographical Magazine*, July 1930, Vol. 46, No. 4, p. 216.

ably the most important concept is that there is not one region — an Arctic or a Tundra — but there are many and that few if any statements apply to all of them.

There are permanently ice and snow covered areas, such as the northeastern part of the Canadian Arctic ... and the vast Greenland Ice Cap. There are areas where most of the snow disappears in the short summers and the *tundra* vegetation becomes visible, with its characteristic abundance of flowering plants. Some areas are rolling grasslands, others are moss- and lichen-

winter temperatures as low as those characterizing certain stations in North Dakota and Montana. Extremes become greater south of Point Barrow since the country increases in altitude and is more remote from the ameliorating effects of the ocean. Thus the temperature range at Allakaket, 350 miles to the south, is much greater; whereas the lowest and highest temperatures at Point Barrow are −56° and 78° respectively, those at Allakaket are −79° and 90°. Winters every-

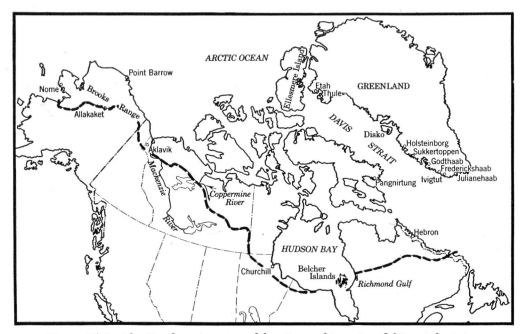

Figure 17–1. The Tundra. A region of hunting and trapping, fishing and mining.

covered, still others are bare rock outcrops. In some parts, the ground will thaw out to a depth of three or four feet, in others to only three or four inches. Beneath lies the permanently frozen earth called *permafrost*. There are also wide variations from place to place in the precipitation, but characteristically it is on the low side ... There are even wider variations in the length of the growing season.[3]

Except in books the tundra is not a land of perpetual ice and snow. Winter temperatures are low, though higher than in the taiga to the south. Point Barrow has yet to record

where in the Tundra Region are long and summers short except on the periphery of the oceans. The growing season at Point Barrow is only 17 days, whereas at Allakaket it is 54 and at Fairbanks (outside this region) it is 89. There can be two to four months without snow. The growing season in the area north of the Brooks Range in Alaska is less than 40 days.

The precipitation is light, varying over most of the area from 5 to 12 inches, with the maximum in summer. At Point Barrow snow begins falling by the middle of August. In the Canadian Arctic most of the snow

[3] "Resources of the Arctic," *Focus*, Vol. 2, February 15, 1952, p. 2.

falls in October and November. Air at low temperatures cannot carry much water vapor and the precipitation falls mostly as a fine dry snow or sleet. The amount is small and the number of days it occurs few.

Winds, especially in winter, are very strong and frequently howl day after day. They greatly affect the sensible temperature; thus on a quiet day a temperature as low as −30° is not at all unpleasant if one is suitably clothed; but on a windy day a temperature of zero, may be quite unbearable.

The periphery is greatly influenced by the ocean; thus the Polar Sea is 15° to 25° warmer in winter than lands to the south and it is correspondingly less warm in summer.

North of the Arctic Circle the climatic phenomenon of greatest significance to human beings is the seasonal changes in the length of daylight and darkness. The sun may remain continuously above the horizon for more than one day — even as long as five months at the northern extremity of Ellesmere Island, 83° N. latitude.

The strip of Labrador coast is much the same over a distance of 600 miles, latitude playing a minor part. The Labrador Current, carrying floes and bergs, causes the immediate coast to be barren and bleak. If the altitude remains the same, vegetation increases with distance from the ocean. There is no such thing as our summer; frost may occur in every month.

The climate of the Arctic is especially worthy of note because the source of much of the weather affecting southern Canada and the northern half of the United States is there. In winter, cold air masses from the Arctic Ocean move up the Mackenzie Valley and towards Hudson Bay. These cold air masses come into conflict with warm air masses from the tropics producing cyclonic storms, which travel across Canada and the United States from west to east.

The Physical Setting

Terrain. It is extremely difficult to generalize on the terrain of such an extensive region. The surface features of the polar lands include all varieties of relief, from low, swampy coastal plains to high ice plateaus and glaciated mountains.[4] Vast lowlands, monotonously flat and poorly drained, are especially extensive.

Most streams have tortuous courses, and estuaries characterize their northern reaches. Near the coast many split into distributaries. Innumerable lakes dot a large part of the mainland and the southern part of the Arctic Islands. Some of the lakes are small, some large. The east coast and much of the plateau consists of bald rock — a result of over-riding by glacial ice. Greenland, coastal Labrador, and the eastern archipelago have fjorded coasts. Off many of the coasts lies a fringe of rounded islets — *skerries*.

Soils. The tundra has few well-developed soils. Most of them are closely related to bog soils. Because of former glaciation there is a considerable accumulation of morainic materials and rewashed glacial deposits. Much of the Shield lacks soils altogether except in the valleys.

Permafrost. Where long cold winters exceed the summer thaw, large areas of permanently frozen ground known as *permafrost* occur. A layer of top soil, which annually freezes and thaws to a depth varying from a few inches to several feet lies above it. Below it the ground is permanently frozen. The *permafrost* may be several hundred feet thick; the depth to which the soil annually freezes and thaws depends upon exposure to sun and wind, the water content of the soil, the type of soil, the snow cover, and the type of vegetation.[5]

Natural Vegetation. The uninformed regards the Arctic as a cold and forbidding place perpetually covered with ice and snow, where no plant life can exist. Yet actually as far north as land reaches, grow numerous species of flowering plants, besides lower forms of plant life, such as mosses, lichens, algae, and fungi.

Most of the Arctic region as here considered refers to that part of Anglo-America

[4] J. Lewis Robinson, *The Canadian Arctic*, Department of Mines and Technical Surveys, Geographical Branch. Ottawa: 1951.

[5] S. M. Muller, *Permafrost and Related Engineering Problems*, Special Report, Strategic Engineering Study No. 62, U. S. Army, Washington, D. C.: Government Printing Office, 1945.

Figure 17–2. A small spruce tree growing in a sheltered spot north of Dismal Lakes, Canada. The spruce grows farther north than any other of the arborescent conifers. It is the wind rather than the absolute cold that determines the northward extension of tree growth. (Courtesy of A. E. Porsild.)

lying north of the tree line — north of the taiga or great northern coniferous forest belt. The line on the map separating the tundra from the forest is actually a zone within which the trees gradually become smaller and more scattered until, when the death struggle takes place, they disappear altogether (Figure 17–2). It coincides rather closely with the 50° isotherm for the warmest month. This line in most instances lies south of the Arctic Circle — reaching the 60th parallel on the east side of Hudson Bay.

Whether the taiga moves farther north or the tundra migrates farther south seems to depend more upon the velocity of the north winds than upon any other circumstance. That wind rather than absolute cold seems to influence the northward extension of tree growth appears to be proved by the

fact that as far north as spruce grows it produces an abundance of seed, at least in normal seasons.[6]

In areas having higher summer temperatures the forest encroaches upon the tundra. Thus in the valley of the Mackenzie the forest straggles to beyond the Arctic Circle — almost to the 70th parallel. An additional factor appears to be that during the last 30 or 40 years annual temperature records have shown an upward trend in the winter months.

The really characteristic vegetation of this region then is tundra; here is a great variety of plants and grasses, with lichens, called reindeer moss, especially being evident. The plain west of Hudson Bay, the rolling upland south of Amundsen Gulf, and the lowland of central west Baffin Island are the most extensive areas of tundra vegetation. Here lichens are the dominant plants forming the principal food supply of the caribou herds that migrate over the region (Figure 17–3).

In summer the tundra is virtually a swamp and a real barrier to transportation; in winter when frozen over, it facilitates human movement.

The vegetation has great value in this region because all land animal food depends upon it — being either directly assimilated by the larger and smaller herbivorous mammals or indirectly by all flesh-eating predators.[7]

Native Animal Life. Native animal life is far more abundant than one might expect. Among the most characteristic mammals are the Arctic hare, Arctic fox, caribou, ermine, lemming, muskox, and wolf. The lemming, never found outside the tundra, lives solely on grass roots and stalks, mosses, and reindeer lichens. The caribou and muskox, at home on the tundra, graze throughout the year — pawing the light snow cover away in winter. With its shaggy long coat of hair the caribou thrives even during the severest gales. The Arctic fox (white and blue) ranges as far south as the lower end of Hudson Bay but never leaves the tundra. The polar bear lives along the coast and on the ice-floes where it can fish and kill seals and walruses.

---

[6] A. E. Porsild, "Plant Life in the Arctic," *Canadian Geographical Journal*, March 1951.

[7] Robinson, *The Canadian Arctic.*

Birds, extremely numerous in summer, arrive by the thousand to breed in the seclusion and security of the tundra. They are also attracted by the prolific insect life. The snow owl, ptarmigan, gerfalcon, raven, and snow bunting are year-round habitants.

Marine life is more abundant than land life, for the sea teems with small forms such as crustacea which attract mollusks and fish. Most characteristic of the larger sea animals are the seal, walrus, whale, and sea elephant. The region has some fish life, but commercial fishing has taken place in only a few places, notably off western Greenland. The principal fish caught are cod, herring, and Arctic char.

Because of the abundance of poorly drained land, insects find this region a paradise during the short summer season. The only exception is the northern archipelago and the sea coast. The only way reindeer herders have of escaping from them during June and July is to move the reindeer to the coast where the cool winds afford some measure of relief. During the "big trek" from Alaska to Canada, when mosquitoes and warble flies descended on the reindeer, the animals bolted to the ocean to benefit from breezes and the soothing effect of salt water. In only a comparatively small number of areas are there hills sufficiently high to enable reindeer to escape the flies; accordingly reindeer herding in Canada within the Arctic Circle will always be limited to the sea coast and its immediate hinterland.[8]

---

[8] Erling Porsild, "The Reindeer Industry and the Canadian Eskimo," *Geographical Journal*, Vol. 88, July 1936.

Figure 17–3. Typical Arctic tundra near Point Barrow, Alaska. The white stake is about eight inches tall. (Courtesy of Ira Wiggins.)

Economic Activities

Fishing. Fishing on a subsistence basis is important both in summer and winter. The Eskimos use leisters, harpoons, hooks, and nets. The leister consists of a pointed middle prong and two elastic side prongs of antler, which are barbed to hold the fish. It is fitted to a long wooden shaft. Inland tribes on the "Barren Grounds" and in the Colville River area in Alaska employ the harpoon. When this method is used the Eskimo from a small snow hut watches for the fish through a hole in the ice. The most important method of fishing through the ice is with a jig, an unbarbed iron hook set in the under edge of an oval bone sinker. Deep-sea fishing is carried on only in the outer regions — Alaska, and Greenland-Labrador, where cod and halibut are present in great numbers. Cod are caught with a jig and halibut with a special kind of composite hook. However, much of this fishing is commercial, modern methods being used. Only the commercial fishing off the Labrador coast and Greenland are considered in this chapter, since commercial fishing in Alaska is discussed in Chapter 15.

Coast of Labrador. Fishing is the only economic enterprise of note in this segment of the region, entire communities depending almost wholly upon it. Actually the people have but one idea, one interest — fish. This is natural where the sea is rich in plankton and fish, and the land exceedingly poor in agricultural possibilities. Coastal Labrador lacks most of the qualities that make life easier in other parts of the world, and hence opportunities for making a living are indeed limited. If fish were not abundant there would be no people.

Fishing is carried on only in summer — the season beginning in late June. Trap nets 320 feet long, 50 feet wide, and 45 feet deep are set in the sea like huge boxes. A heavy catch is procured until winter abruptly terminates the season. Labradorians (*Liviyers*) and a few thousand Newfoundlanders fish in these cold waters, the latter coming in boats of all sizes. Although the *Liviyers* (Newfoundlanders by birth but Labradorians by adoption) work hard, remoteness from markets retards their progress.

Greenland. Commercial fishing on the south and west coasts became important in 1916 as a result of the decline in the number of seals in South Greenland and the increasing effect of the warm current off Greenland. The Danish Government rendered considerable aid to the fisheries. It established and supervised fishing stations; it aided in selling the fish; it sent experts to organize and conduct the industry along modern lines; and it procured for the native a more favorable income from his fish.

Formerly the Eskimos fished almost exclusively from *kayaks* (Figure 17–4) and by means of hand lines. Now they employ European boats — even motorboats.

The principal fish caught are cod, Norway haddock, Atlantic salmon, caplin, and Greenland shark. The catch is taken to stations and canneries in the Holstensborg, Sukkertoppen, Godthaab, Frederickshaab, and Julianehaab districts where fish are prepared for export. In 1948 the world's largest shrimp beds were found at Disko Bay. Especially flourishing at this time is the cod

Figure 17–4. The Eskimo kayak does in the water what the swallow does in the air. Among aboriginal craft, only the canoe of the South Sea islander equals the graceful, slender kayak. The waterproof dress worn by the Eskimo is tied tightly around the boat to exclude all water. (Photo by Highton. Courtesy of Federal Works Agency.)

fishing off the southwest coast of Greenland — a situation largely attributable to the warming up that the area has been experiencing possibly due to a northward extension of the Gulf Stream. Today the cod is at home in the waters of west Greenland as far as 73° N. whereas in 1900 it seldom was encountered beyond 64° N. Furthermore, comparable migrations have occurred with herring, haddock, and halibut in the more open waters of the North Atlantic.[9]

Hunting. Since edible plants are largely absent, the Eskimos, who constitute nine tenths of the population, are hunters. Upon the success of hunting and some fishing depends their comfort, health, happiness, and life itself.

Sea hunting. Nowhere on earth are there more skillful sea hunters than the Eskimos. They know the intimate habits of all animals. The most valuable animal of all is the seal, which provides shelter, clothing, food and fuel. Kayaks are used exclusively in sea hunting.

Ice hunting for seal, white whales, and polar bear takes place only when the ice is firm. The meat of the seal supplies the Eskimos with their staple food item. The haired skin is used for clothing and the dehaired skin for water-proof boots and kayak covers. Formerly the seals were harpooned; now they are shot and then harpooned.

Walrus, which congregate on islands off the coasts in late summer and on newly-formed sea-ice in autumn are hunted, but the meat is less popular with the Eskimos than is that of seals. Much is fed to dogs.

Polar bears are sought on moonlight nights in winter and in the dazzling sunlight of spring. The meat is used largely for dog feed, the fur for bedding and robes.

Land hunting. Land hunting, though not so necessary as that on sea and ice, is, nevertheless, important. Caribou, hare, fox, and birds provide sleeping bags, stockings, furs, and birdskin underwear. Bear skin is used for pants by the Polar Eskimo. The meat of these animals also adds variety to the Eskimo's diet.

Trapping. The principal means of liveli-

9 "Resources of the Arctic," p. 2.

hood of the Canadian Eskimos is trapping. Fur traders have induced the Eskimo locally to trap for skins as well as for meat, clothing, and shelter. This has led to some overexploitation locally of certain animal resources, chiefly the white Arctic fox, which for the most part is the only animal that is commercially exploitable, though about a thousand Eskimos are also engaged in trapping muskrat in the delta of the Mackenzie River. In a few parts of the region, outsiders are carrying on commercial trapping near native villages. Accordingly some trapping areas in Alaska have been so badly exploited by white men that the natives must migrate or starve. Whites are not permitted by law to trap in the Canadian tundra. The region is a preserve for Eskimos.

Commercial trapping also ties the Eskimo to the white man's world on which he depends both for necessities (traps) and luxuries (phonographs). Whereas formerly the Eskimo hunted caribou and seals for clothing and meat, he now frequently traps, getting his clothing and food from the trader. Sometimes unsuccessful or unskilled Eskimo trappers in Arctic Canada go on relief — trading goods being paid for by the government. Even more important is the family allowance of five to eight dollars per month per child payable to them as to other Canadians. In Greenland, the natives trade blubber and skins which they really need for themselves, for coffee, dried peas, flour, rice, sugar, and tea — European foods for which they have acquired a taste. The Danes discourage such trade, however.

Grazing. Throughout Anglo-America as a result of the depletion of the native food supply by the whites, the respective governments are attempting to transform the natives from hunters into graziers. Observing that Siberian Chukchee Eskimos kept reindeer as insurance against famine during the periodical depletion of wild life and sea food, two Americans, Sheldon Jackson and Michael Healy, purchased reindeer in Siberia and employed Lapp herders to instruct the Alaskan Eskimos, who were then appreticed for four years in the care of reindeer. At the end of their apprenticeship

each owned a herd of approximately fifty. Actually the animals require little care, for they need no shelter and secure their own feed (Figure 17–5). They must be herded, however, to prevent straying and to protect them against predatory animals, particularly wolves.

Anglo-America today has more than half a million reindeer. So long as white men and Eskimos used the same ranges there was serious overgrazing and there were numerous misunderstandings. Accordingly the United States government purchased all the reindeer owned by non-natives and now prohibits ownership except by Eskimos in Alaska.

The Big Trek. About 1928 the Canadian government, noting that the supply of game for its Eskimos was fluctuating and being favorably impressed by the American experiment in Alaska, contracted for the delivery of 3,000 reindeer from Alaska to Kittygazuit, east of the delta of the Mackenzie. It was believed that with these as a nucleus a considerable portion of northern Canada might be stocked in due time. The drive, estimated to take from 18 to 24 months for a distance of about 1,600 miles, actually required five years and the distance covered was 2,500 miles. Herders and animals suffered untold hardships — avalanches, exposure to frost, snow slides, storms, fogs, intense cold, attacks by wolves, bears, and insects, and shortage of food. Though 2,370 animals were delivered, it is estimated that only ten per cent of them actually started in Alaska.[10] The rest were born enroute.

The experiment near the Mackenzie River Delta has faced many difficulties, however, and the enterprise cannot yet be considered truly successful. The Eskimo, a trapper for centuries, is reluctant to become a herder. He is at heart a hunter and the only labor in which he delights is the chase. Moreover, the reindeer herds are located in one of Canada's best muskrat trapping grounds.

It should be realized that the entire tundra is not used for grazing reindeer. Nor is it all suitable. Much is rocky, a large proportion of the surface is covered with lakes, and

[10] Ovid M. McMillion, "Reindeer Trek," *Journal of Geography*, Vol. 38, 1939, p. 140.

Figure 17–5. Reindeer being driven into a corral at Egavik, Alaska. In the tundra of Arctic Alaska, where pastures consist mostly of mosses and dwarf willows and where winter nights are long, horses and cattle cannot be raised. Accordingly, the reindeer substitutes for them. (Courtesy of U. S. Indian Service.)

mosquitoes and flies definitely limit much of it.

Attempts to introduce reindeer into Labrador and Baffin Island have met with no success. In Greenland about 260 reindeer were introduced into the Godthaab area in 1952, and, if successful, the experiment will be extended to other areas. A small number of cattle have been kept since 1782 and sheep have been raised successfully since their introduction in 1906. In the Julianehaab area of southwestern Greenland are now some 20,000 sheep. Sheep must have shelter in winter and must be fed cured native grasses, willow, turnips and dried fish.

Minerals and Mining. Considerable mineral wealth is known to exist in this region and possibly new strikes of sensational importance may be made in the future. Transportation difficulties, the curse of the tundra,

have retarded commercial mining. Much of this region has never been prospected and there is very limited information regarding huge areas. Aviation more than anything else is opening up the Canadian and Alaskan mineral fields; airplanes can reach the most remote districts in a day or two and can transport supplies to sections which prospectors previously considered too remote. The helicopter, too, is proving highly valuable for prospecting. A map of commercial mining in Anglo-America shows only a small amount of activity in this region. It is known that there is considerable petroleum in northern Alaska. The United States has set aside in northern Alaska the Naval Petroleum Reserve, a tract of about 35,000 square miles. Coal also is widely distributed. In the Alaskan part of the region, more than a dozen beds of subbituminous and bituminous coal ranging from 4 to 20 feet in thickness are known and coal-bearing rocks have been found through a belt of country 100 miles wide and 300 miles long. This coal supply should prove of inestimable value locally because of the absence of other fuel. Some gold and silver, antimony, tungsten and asbestos have been located.

Soft coal is mined and used in settlements in northeastern Baffin Island. There is also considerable coal on the west coast of Greenland, and while the quality is not good, some is mined commercially and distributed along the coast in summer.

In the Canadian tundra iron ore is known to be present in the Belcher Islands, the Richmond Gulf area, and on the east side of Hudson Bay. Along the south and east coasts of Baffin Island deposits of mica, graphite, and garnet have been found. Native copper has long been known to be present near the mouth of the Coppermine River. Most of these deposits are not at present of economic value.[11]

The only deposit of commercial cryolite in the world is being worked in southern Greenland at Ivigtut. The mine, a great quarry mostly below sea level, is one of the most northerly on earth, its royalties providing the colony's chief revenue. Mining is carried on throughout the year. Ivigtut is a well-equipped mining center, many of the Eskimo miners living in steam-heated houses. Danish labor is used for mining all minerals except coal, the government allowing the natives to dig coal for their own use.

Agriculture. Since the Tundra Region has a short growing season, much of it only 40 days, and since the soils for the most part are shallow, acid, and poorly drained, commercial agriculture is impossible. The late Wilfred Grenfell believed that the Labrador climate would never permit cereal production in sufficient quantity to supply the needs of the people.[12] In certain highly

favored localities in the Canadian Arctic hardy vegetables are grown under glass. In coastal Labrador cabbage, beets, and lettuce are also grown, provided seeds are started indoors while snow still covers the ground. In Greenland root crops such as turnips, radishes, and potatoes are successfully grown as far north as 66° 15'. Umanak claims to have the most northerly garden in the world. Here broccoli and radishes, turnips and lettuce do fairly well.

Trade. Trade is relatively unimportant in this sparsely populated region where the majority of the inhabitants live outside a money economy. In Arctic Canada the Eskimos trade mostly with the historic Hudson's Bay Company, exchanging furs (chiefly white fox), ivory, and fish for tokens for which they get guns, ammunition, knives, needles, thread, cloth, tea, coffee, tobacco, and even lumber, iron, kerosene, and stoves. An exception until 1950, when private enterprise got started, was the trade in Greenland where a Danish state monopoly existed and where trade consisted of an exchange of products on a cash or credit basis.

Transportation

One of the biggest hurdles to economic development in this region is transportation. The tundra is almost impassable in summer except by canoe and pack dog (Figure 17–6)

Figure 17–6. Train of pack dogs in the tundra in summer. Good dogs will pack 30 to 35 pounds, but when the weather is hot and flies bad, the work is very hard on them. (Courtesy of A. E. Porsild.)

---

[11] J. Lewis Robinson, "Mineral Resources and Mining Atcivity in the Canadian Eastern Arctic," *Canadian Geographical Journal*, August 1944.

[12] Sir Wilfred Grenfell, "The Problems of Labrador," *Canadian Geographical Journal*, Vol. 7, 1933, pp. 202-203.

and in winter save by dogteam (Figure 17–7). Railroads and roads are almost nonexistent for they could not pay in so thinly populated a region. Villages on the sea are accessible to small ocean-going vessels for a few weeks each year (the open season on the coast near Point Barrow, Alaska, is practically limited to the month of August). Only products of high value in proportion to bulk or weight

water shipping period of late summer, trappers are employing airplanes to bring out bales of prime furs during winter when the highest prices prevail. However, freight charges and passenger fares are high.

What remoteness means can be appreciated by calling attention to the fact that the scattered settlements of the eastern Canadian Arctic comprising some 7,000 Es-

Figure 17–7. The system of hitching and driving the dogs fan-fashion, each dog with his own trace back to the sledge, is a direct response to the conditions of environment. The sea-ice over which the trail generally leads is in many places too tough and broken to permit driving the dogs tandem, either singly or in pairs. (Courtesy of American Museum of Natural History.)

such as furs and gold can stand transport very far by sledge or canoe.

The airplane is breaking down the region's isolation by reducing travel time from weeks to hours. Areas formerly too far away for mining are now within easy reach. The airplane carries the miner, his equipment and mining machinery, as well as mail, medical supplies, and food. It also establishes gasoline caches. Maps accurate to minute detail are now being made from aerial photographs. Moreover, rather than wait for the open-

kimos and 150 whites have their hard and lonely routine broken only once a year when a government patrol boat brings supplies that must last for an entire year. The ship, which travels 10,000 miles during the short summer, remains at each point of call for only a few hours or at most a few days.

The Hudson Bay Railway, 510 miles long, extending from The Pas, Manitoba, to Churchill on Hudson Bay, passes through a flat country, broken by lakes and rivers. The terrain offers few construction difficulties except where spongy soil requires heavy ballast. The deep harbor at Churchill is one of the few shelters for deep-sea vessels along the shallow west coast of Hudson Bay.

The railway was built by the Canadian government for political rather than strictly economic reasons. Prairie Province wheat farmers demanded the construction of this line, declaring that the depression following the first World War was caused and prolonged by high freight rates.

The Saskatchewan wheat belt, which uses the route most, is much closer to Liverpool via Churchill than via Montreal. The navigation season via the Hudson Bay Route, however, is short, being free from ice for only about three months — from the end of July to late October. Fog, too, is bad but no worse probably than on the coast of Nova Scotia.

The railway is of strategic rather than economic importance. The principal shipments to Churchill consist of wheat which may be stored there in large elevators. Mining now provides most of the local traffic south of the tundra.

The People

It is impossible to generalize on the population of this tremendous region. The three most important groups are the Eskimos, the whites, and the mixed bloods. The Eskimos, who live along the Arctic coast of Alaska and Canada, from the Bering Sea to coastal Labrador and Greenland, are scattered over so large an area that the Tundra Region is one of the world's most sparsely populated areas. The Canadian Eskimos, who number only 9,000, occupy an area of more than 800,000 square miles which gives them an approximate density of one Eskimo for each 100 square miles. Since most Eskimos dwell on the coastal periphery, however, the average is about five miles of coast line per Eskimo [13]. The whites are thinly scattered over the region and occupy Hudson's Bay trading posts, isolated government radio and meteorological stations, mission stations, and schools. Many, of course, especially in

[13] J. Lewis Robinson, "Eskimo Population in the Canadian Eastern Arctic," *Canadian Geographical Journal*, Vol. 29, August 1944.

Alaska and Canada, are not permanent residents. Often a "settlement" in actuality is no more than a cluster of buildings around a trading post. In all Greenland there are only a few hundred whites; in Arctic Canada not more than 200, and in Alaska about 2,000. Mixed bloods comprise the greater part of the "Greenlanders" who are part Eskimo and part European. The mixed bloods are increasing notably also in the Alaskan segment and in the far western part of the Canadian Arctic. Only in Greenland is there any considerable expansion in the population. Whereas the island had 11,500 inhabitants in 1900, today it has roughly 22,600 natives and 1,100 non-natives.

The Eskimo. The Eskimos, fur-clad hunters of the north, girdle Polar Anglo-America. The Polar Eskimo of northwestern Greenland, the most northerly people in the world, were completely separated from their nearest neighbors when first discovered by John Ross in 1818. They had lived in isolation so long they had forgotten their origin and believed themselves to be the only people in the world. The Caribou Eskimos, who occupy an interior area west of Hudson Bay are the only group who do not live on the seacoast. Some of these have never visited the coast and some adults have never seen a seal.

Nowhere else on earth are human beings faced with so severe and grudging an environment, and yet the Eskimos have learned how to endure and enjoy the "unspeakable tedium of the long winter." To them the Arctic is home — the earth's most favored place and they have no desire to go elsewhere.

The Eskimo's contact with white men: gain or loss? All Eskimos have now had contact with white men — those in southern Greenland for centuries and those of the Canadian Western Arctic since early in this century.

They have rapidly adopted the white man's tools and civilization but at great cost. They are losing mastery over their environment and it seems unlikely that they could subsist as did their fathers. They are now utterly dependent for some essential foods, weapons, and tools. The white man's high-powered rifle has upset the balance of the game supply. The white man has also encouraged the Eskimo to kill for furs rather than for food, clothing, and shelter, which has resulted in overexploitation of some animal resources.

Then there is the matter of crossing of breeds. Today the pure-blood Eskimo is extremely rare. In Alaska racial diffusion has been increasing with greatly accelerating speed. In Greenland there is a strong admixture of Eskimos and Danes. Mixed bloods are found in Canada, though the proportion is smaller than elsewhere in the Tundra Region. Whether ultimately this racial blending will be for good or ill is a controversial question on which anthropologists and sociologists do not agree.

The Eskimo would no doubt be much better off today if the white man had not invaded his land. The picture, except for Greenland, is quite dismal: the game has been decimated, new diseases have been introduced and are spreading, thereby threatening the very survival of the people in some areas. Modern medical techniques have been introduced in some areas, however. The native's economy is in a stage of transition, and many Eskimos are on relief. Education and paternalistic treatment offer little hope. Since they are the only people who are at home in this *milieu,* Canada and the United States should do what Denmark has done — accept them as equals and as partners, for they are among the real assets of the Arctic.

The future of the Eskimo. Despite paternalistic considerations shown the Eskimos by the several governments, these folk cannot long endure a civilization that is sweeping them out of a past 10,000 years away. They cannot compete with the white man; they are deteriorating from the use of European food; and to some extent they are dying off from introduced diseases such as measles, small-pox, tuberculosis, and syphilis. Dentists who have examined the teeth of meat-eating Eskimos find few dental caries, but in the teeth of those who eat the food of the white man, they find much tooth decay. The Eskimos also find it difficult to resist the white man's temptations, and moral degeneration has set in.

It should be said to the credit of Denmark that under her intelligent and progressive guidance, every precaution has been taken to protect the Eskimos in Greenland. New laws allow for gradual opening up of the island and it is to become a part of Denmark with representatives in the Danish Parliament.

The island is closed to all but certain Danish officials and to scientists vouched for by their own governments and approved by the Danes. Accordingly, the natives increased in numbers, improved in health, and gained in wealth. Greenland became the outstanding example of progressive government in polar lands.

The White Man. Norsemen under Eric the Red reached Greenland in 986 with 14 ships and about 400 people. A republic was maintained from 990 to 1261 — 271 years. These immigrants survived as Europeans as late as 1520 and then disappeared as though the earth had swallowed them up, leaving no authentic records. Recent research indicates that they merged with the Eskimo population, and that they were absorbed, not lost. After all it was better for a Norwegian girl to marry an Eskimo and live than it was for her to stick to her European culture and die.[14]

Most of the whites who live in this region today are government officials, scientists, aviators, missionaries, and fur traders, except for the miners at Ivigtut.

Villages, Settlements, and Hudson's Bay Company Posts

Settlements (often called "villages") in the Tundra Region usually mean a cluster of a few igloos, tupeks, or houses. In Canada a settlement may include a store or a Hudson's Bay Company post, a school house, Anglican mission, radio station, weather station, and homes.

The characteristic abode of the Eskimos prior to the coming of the white man was the permanent village located at some spot on the coast or on a river bank of a coastal

14 Vilhjalmur Stefansson, *Unsolved Mysteries of the Arctic.* New York: The Macmillan Co., 1939.

stream suitable for hunting and fishing. The major location factor was proximity to navigable water containing sea mammals. The sealing economy thus placed a premium on scattered small settlements. The fishing economy encourages a few large settlements; so does the need for education, health services, etc. The tendency in Greenland today is toward large settlements and the abolition of little hamlets. The hostility of interior Indians (Alaska and Canada) also influenced the Eskimos to settle in the Tundra Region.

Political Geography

Anglo-America's Tundra Region, despite its sparse population and comparative lack of development, has since World War II assumed new importance. Sharing with the Soviet Union the major part of the polar region the tundra, in the new Air Age, becomes Anglo-America's first line of defense against transpolar attack (Figure 16-2).

The strategic importance of Alaska, northern Canada and Greenland were not widely and fully appreciated until World War II. Yet General William Mitchell stated in the chambers of the House Military Affairs Committee on February 13, 1935 that "Alaska is the most important strategic place in the world."

Today there can be no doubt regarding the correctness of Mitchell's thinking as to Alaska's strategic significance. Its importance was emphasized by the decision of the Air Force to transfer part of Boeing's production of bombers from Seattle to Wichita. Part of this decision resulted no doubt from the fact that Seattle is more easily vulnerable than Wichita but part also resulted from the fact that it was not believed to be a wise thing to make both the B-47 (medium bomber) and the B-52 (heavy bomber) in a single plant. In fact the Air Force Secretary at the time said it would be a mistake to build them both in any one plant regardless of location.[15] Besides the Boeing plant, the Hanford atomic plant in eastern Washington, the great concentration of manufacturing in

the Los Angeles and San Francisco areas, are also vulnerable via Alaska.

Referring to the strategic situation of the Arctic, General Carl A. Spaatz, the world's most experienced air man, said, "The airplane can cross the polar sea and bomb enemy industrial areas. Through the Arctic every industrialized country is within reach of our Strategic Air Force. America is similarly exposed. Whoever controls the Arctic air lanes controls the world today."

It is not surprising in the light of the new concept of the Arctic that Canada and the United States now have a Permanent Joint Board on defense for considering the defense of the northern half of the Western Hemisphere. This was a move in answer to critics that Anglo-America is "wide open at the top."

Possibly the most strategic part of the Anglo-American tundra is Greenland because it lies athwart great-circle routes between the United States and northern Eurasia. During World War II, the United States had several air bases on the island. In September, 1952, the Danish and United States governments announced the establishment of the Thule [16] Air Base — a full-scale, year-around base for big bombers built at a cost of 263 million dollars and only 900 miles from the North Pole. This base thus "looks over the top of the world and down into Russia, whose industrial heart is only 3,000 miles or five hours flying time in a jet bomber.[17] The geopolitics of the Anglo-American Arctic are more than of academic interest and significance. They are vital to the very existence of these nations. But as Stefansson has remarked, the problems of the North have never been understood for they are not problems of the past but of the future.[18] A polar world must postulate one world!

The Outlook

The region's future will continue as a land

---

[15] "Battle of Seattle," *Business Week*, September 24, 1949, p. 22.

[16] Thule takes its name from classical references, Ultima Thule legendarily being the "farthest land in the world."

[17] "Birth of a Base," *Life*, Sept. 22, 1952.

[18] Vilhjalmur Stefansson, *The Northward Course of Empire*, New York, 1922.

of great distances and few people, where nothing more than a scanty livelihood is obtainable by trapping, hunting, fishing, or grazing. Cities in the true sense will, as now, be non-existent.

Agriculture may increase somewhat, locally, as a means of supplying more food to small insular concentrations of population. This will, however, be only in the more favored locales. For the Tundra Region as a whole no radical departures in agriculture and stock raising are to be expected. Trapping will continue to be important.

The entire region, of course, has gained new prominence because of its strategic value in the present Air Age. The Tundra Region lies athwart polar air routes. Thule is only 2,752 statute miles from Moscow, 3,199 from Omsk, 3,367 from Stalinsk, and 4,115 from Vladivostok. Over this region the route from California to Denmark is 1,600 miles shorter than via New York City. Scandinavian Air Lines started to survey this very air route in 1952 and a successful flight was made from Los Angeles to Copenhagen via Edmonton and Thule. Colonel Bernt Balchen, veteran authority on polar aviation, speaks of the huge new air base at Thule as being, "in the center of the world of the air age." Also travel to remote areas, which used to require months, has been greatly shortened. Any place is now only a matter of a few hours away. It is no exaggeration to say that transportation was advanced by half a century as a result of World War II and the need

for aviation. But military and even commercial airways can scarcely be expected to account for more than a small number of spots in this empty, desolate, treeless land, where life is hard and lonely and where pioneers have to accept a lower standard of living. Except for a sprinkling of these (about 200) most still occupy the narrow population belt along the United States-Canadian border. Few Americans live permanently in the Alaskan tundra. Even Denmark has sent not more than a thousand of her people to Greenland.

The recent history of the Eskimos unfolds step by step as one proceeds in Canada from the taiga into the tundra. Among the southern Eskimos can be seen what lies in store for the group as a whole. Perhaps the mixed blood is the solution as the mestizo is in many countries in Latin America.

Certainly more attention and more intelligent attention will be given to this region and to the natives than has been true in the past. Especially does this apply to problems of health and education and work. Also all three nations should capitalize on the talents of the Eskimos. The natives could man weather stations, service and drive tractors, snow-mobiles, and even aircraft, and they could function in the armed services.

Geopolitically speaking one thing is certain; the needs of military defense have forced and will continue to force the United States, Canada, and Denmark to work more closely together in the North.

The Ice Cap

Greenland, the world's largest island and definitely a part of Anglo-America, is a great plateau 1,800 miles long and 800 miles wide at its greatest breadth.[19] Nine tenths of it, or an area five times the size of the United Kingdom, is an ice desert. This ice cap discharges to the sea through narrow valley glaciers. Fjords characterize the plateau margin. Near both the eastern and western coasts are to be found fairly high mountains but over much of this interior plateau the

surface is flat with few minor irregularities. Greenland experiences bitterly cold temperatures, among the strongest winds in the world, and the northern parts of it experience much darkness in winter.

The ice cap has no permanent inhabitants and is utterly lacking in utility, offering no prospects for the future. Its location on the great circle route, the most direct air route between America and Europe, gives it some potential geographical value for airplane landing fields. There are some problems,

[19] Recent research indicates that the ice cap may consist of several islands.

however: what might otherwise constitute ideal landing fields for ski-equipped aircraft, are handicapped by changing surface conditions and by the high elevation of most of the ice cap — more than 90 per cent of it lies above 4,000 feet.

Selected Bibliography

"Canada Counts Its Caribou," *National Geographic Magazine,* Vol. 102, August 1952, pp. 261–268.

M. J. Dubar, "Greenland During and Since the Second World War," *International Journal,* Spring 1950.

Geographical Branch, Department of Mines and Technical Surveys, *An Introduction to the Geography of the Canadian Arctic,* Canadian Geography, Information Series No. 2, Ottawa: 1951.

F. Kenneth Hare, "The Labrador Frontier," *Geographical Review,* Vol. 42, 1952, pp. 405–424.

Richard Harrington, "Coppermine Patrol," *Canadian Geographical Journal,* Vol. 41, 1950, pp. 257–269.

H. W. Hewetson, "What Are the Possibilities of Settlement in Canada's North Land?" *Public Affairs,* Vol. 10, 1946.

R. M. Kark and others, "Observations on a Mobile Arctic Force. The Health, Physical Fitness and Nutrition of Exercise 'Musk Ox,'" *Journal of Applied Physiology,* Vol. 1, July 1948–June 1949.

Trevor Lloyd, "Canada's Strategic North," *International Journal,* Vol. 2, 1947.

———, "Progress in West Greenland," *Journal of Geography,* Vol. 49, 1950, pp. 319–328.

L. B. Pearson, "Canada Looks 'Down North,'" *Foreign Affairs,* Vol. 24, 1945–1946, pp. 638–647.

William E. Powers, "Polar Eskimos of Greenland and Their Environment," *Journal of Geography,* Vol. 49, 1950, pp. 186–192.

"Resources of the Arctic," *Focus,* Vol. 2, February 15, 1952.

J. Lewis Robinson and M. Josephine Robinson, *The Geography of Canada.* Toronto: Longmans, Green and Company, 1950.

18.

Anglo-American Co-operation

ANGLO-AMERICA is an aggregation of complementary regions shared primarily by the United States and Canada. It is significant that within 200 miles of the common border are the continent's leading cities, their *ecumenes*,[1] their richest and most productive mines, and their most fruitful fields.

Canada's terrain, however, is so effectively fragmented as to cause the country to be harassed by sectionalism. The Shickshocks of eastern Quebec wall off the Maritime Provinces; the rocky hills, lakes, and streams of the Canadian Shield separate the St. Lawrence Valley from the Prairie Provinces, and the Rocky Mountains divide the prairies from the lands of the Pacific. Thus the grain of the continent extends north and south, whereas the international border has been drawn east and west. The geographic regions which cross this political boundary vary in minor ways on each side, but these differentiations, with the exception of French Canada, are limited to differences in architecture and secondary cultural items.

Factors Encouraging United States-Canadian Co-operation

Natural Environment. So identical are

---

[1] The most populous region of a state, particularly that part most closely knit by communication lines.

472

the natural environment factors on the two sides of the international border that there is a close affiliation between the two peoples. The Maritime Provinces form a unit with New England, as does the Shield of western Ontario with Michigan and Wisconsin, the Prairie Provinces with Montana and the Dakotas, and British Columbia with the American Pacific Northwest. It is thus apparent that much of the international boundary is indifferent to nature — to mountains, drainage basins, lakes, and rivers.

Proximity of the Canadian population to the United States (70 per cent of the Dominion's inhabitants live within 100 miles of the international boundary) is a major factor leading to close co-operation, for economically and socially Canada is the narrow belt bordering the United States. Furthermore, the peoples in these two countries were neighbors long before the American Revolution. Outside the *ecumene*, Canada is largely a wilderness of forest, muskeg, and tundra inhabited by small numbers of Indians and Eskimos and widely scattered white trappers, traders, loggers, and miners. Canada's two transcontinental railways operate close to the international frontier. The physically natural routes in most cases were with or through the United States. Where nationalistic insistence confined rail routes to Canadian terrain, as across the wilderness north of Lake Superior, construction was costly and the lines operated at little or no profit for a long time. In such cases the nation had to pay the bill. There is now considerable local freight from and to the pulp-towns and mines.

Juxtaposition also facilitates a constant exchange of cultural ideas through the medium of the press, magazines, radio and television, motion pictures, sports, higher education, lectures, and travel.

Similar Economies. Since the natural environment in southern Canada and northern United States is roughly similar, the economies of the two nations are similar. Both are world leaders in the production of wheat and other small grains, flax, copper, lead, zinc, gold, silver, lumber, fish, fruits (particularly apples), tobacco, and dairy products. Both countries are industrialized, though not to the same degree. Each year, however, Canada becomes stronger industrially. From an overwhelmingly agricultural nation Canada has evolved into one of the world's great industrial countries with both raw materials and plant capacity. As her manufacturing enterprises expand, Canada becomes less and less dependent upon England and more and more dependent upon the United States. The United States, on the other hand, depends upon Canada for many raw materials, especially woodpulp, asbestos, copper, titanium and uranium, and very soon she will be importing large tonnages of iron ore.

Canada has become the acknowledged leader of the so-called Middle Powers. She has become the third trading nation of the world. Moreover, she is the only nation besides the United States wealthy enough to contribute men, money, and materiel to the North Atlantic Treaty Organization.

Common Standard of Living. Probably nowhere else in the world is the standard of living so high and in such contrast to that characterizing Asia, most of Latin America, and even continental Europe. The American tourist traveling through Anglo-Canada feels at home as does his Canadian neighbor in the "States." Neither is considered a foreigner in the other's country. This part of Anglo-America, then, is on the same social level. Never would Canadians be willing to accept the lower standard of living characterizing continental Europe, an argument against which neither sentiment nor politics can prevail.

Similar Cultural Background. Similar cultural background is one of the strongest factors bearing on international unity. Regardless of how far a people may go from the original home, the national roots are difficult to escape. The Canadian and the American,[2] unlike the Mexican and the American, speak the same language. They are derived from identical colonial stock (true of only loyalist stock). They have the same habits of thought, religion, and political traditions; they enjoy the same inheritance of the English Common Law; therefore, these people understand each other well. Moreover, when the United States purchased Alaska from Russia in 1867, Anglo-America became assured of English-speaking domination. The French influence, however, is far more distinct in Canada. Rights of religion, civil law, and language guaranteed to the French by the British in the Quebec Act of 1774 have hindered to some degree the development of a true Canadian unity.

Type of Human Migration. Settlement of Anglo-America was not in the form of two parallel streams north and south of the intangible political boundary; it was rather a single tide. The people moved wherever they wished responding only to the economic conditions and political events of their day and disregarding the wholly artificial international boundary.

Thus to the people of these two countries, land and opportunity exerted a stronger pull than allegiance to a flag or questions of political jurisdiction. The history of the continent presents a picture of one body of Anglo-Americans migrating to make the best

---

[2] There is much objection to calling only the citizen of the United States an American, the argument being that anyone dwelling in the Western Hemisphere is an American. Academically this is true, but except for Latin American countries, usage recognizes as Americans only citizens of the United States.

livings they could.[3] Canadians tended machines in the factories of New England, cleared forests in the Upper Lakes area, broke sod in the American prairie, helped build towns and cities from New York to California, and aided in organizing and building the web of railroads centering on Chicago. Americans helped to log much of the Canadian forest, locate and develop the mineral wealth, plow the land (especially the prairie since Iowa and Illinois farmers knew how to subdue the tough sod); they also played an important role in the completion of the Canadian Pacific, the first transcontinental railway. And they are contributing much to the industrialization of the country.

Immigration to the United States of talented and skilled people is today one of Canada's major problems. Canadians are attracted to the south by higher wage scales, research and study facilities, and opportunities in the entertainment and artistic world. In 1951, 20,000 of the 26,000 who emigrated from Canada went to the United States while 12,000 Americans moved to Canada. Many of these were skilled workers.

If Canada has any single vital shortage it is in population. Her rapid industrialization has doubled the ratio of workers to farmers; hence she is eager for more people. The immigration policy is designed to encourage foreigners to settle and build up the expanding Canadian economy. As this volume goes to press Canada is attempting to get 20,000 Britishers to settle in Canada. While the immigration policy favors the British on paper, actual immigration since the termination of World War II has consisted in large part of displaced persons. In the past Canada has found it easier to attract immigrants than to retain them. This problem, however, depends in large part on the prosperity of the country.

Investments. Investments in a foreign country may or may not create a better relationship between two nations. American investments in Canada, however, definitely

have promoted good will. Furthermore, lacking them, it is doubtful whether many of Canada's natural resources could have been developed without sacrificing standards of living. American business has about 8 billion dollars invested in Canada — more than in any other single country. Canadians have about a billion dollars invested in the United States. Many American corporations built branch factories in Canada in order to serve the important Canadian market and circumvent the high tariff which Canada has imposed as a means of providing revenue for the government and employment for its people. American investors control some 2,500 Canadian plants that account for one quarter to one third of Canada's total manufacturing. Some plants are run almost entirely from the American head office, while others are autonomous companies which enter into direct competition with the parent. Canadians are also expanding and investing in new industry with the result that though foreign capital has been flowing heavily into the country, the percentage of foreign ownership of Canada is declining.

Americans have been encouraged to invest in Canada because of favorable Canadian governmental policies. Corporation profits are taxed at a lower rate in Canada than in the United States. After World War II, a temporary tax measure was introduced that permitted certain enterprises to depreciate their equipment much faster than usual. As Canadians have increased in numbers and in wealth, there has been a greater market for goods. Recent discoveries of rich natural resources have also stimulated American investments.

Travel and Transportation. Travel enables Anglo-Americans to erase sectional lines and build up a unity of thought and feeling. Business and recreation induce tens of millions of crossings of boundary lines each year. Canada's attraction for American tourists has been called a capital example of the law of compensation. Where the physical environment permits only small numbers of people to earn a living, many at least can play. Even the Canadian winter has become

---

[3] Marcus L. Hansen and John B. Brebner, *The Mingling of the Canadian and American Peoples*, p. 245. New Haven: Yale University Press, 1940.

a tourist asset. Tourism is now the Dominion's fourth largest industry.

One of the best indications of the closeness of the two countries is the continent's 300,000 miles of railway closely interwoven at the border through 50 gateways. The New York Central enroute from New York City and New England to Chicago offers the choice of going north of Lake Erie through Canada or south of it through American territory. The Canadian Pacific crosses Maine and the Canadian National most of the New England states. The Grand Trunk Railway (now a part of the Canadian National) began as a means of uniting the provinces but built its first main link to Portland, Maine. It pressed on to Chicago in 1880. This enabled it to participate in the traffic from the Middle West to the Atlantic Seaboard. It could also send wheat during winter to ice-free ports in the United States and take back manufactured products from New England to western Canada. In short the Grand Trunk denied the reality of the United States-Canadian boundary. In all probability Canada could not exist as a nation unless her trade was made to conform to the political reality of east-west confederation and away from the natural north-south axis. The reality of this statement is seen in the national policy that encourages long-haul low-cost movements.

The Canadian National Railways, successor to the Grand Trunk, consider their Chicago-Atlantic Seaboard traffic most important to their system. More than 15 per cent of Canada's total freight tonnage is derived from foreign connections destined to foreign points.

Nowhere else in the world is there anything to compare with this intimacy of border contact. Through-traffic for domestic consumption or to and from nations across the seas flows as freely over the international border as from state to state or province to province. Interesting indeed is the fact that Canadian railways are members of The American Association of Railroads. Moreover, increasing numbers of people from the Middle West have been using Montreal and Quebec as their seaport enroute to Europe. Thousands of Americans also travel on the

Great Lakes aboard Canadian steamships. Many Canadian motorists reach their own West via Chicago and St. Paul-Minneapolis, although the most popular route is via Sudbury-Soo-Duluth.

Trans-Canada Airlines, a government corporation, was created in 1937 and operates more than 16,000 miles of air routes, including routes to American centers. Certain reciprocal air rights were guaranteed by the Canadian and American governments when both countries became members of the International Civil Aviation Organization with headquarters in Montreal.

Trade. Canada's economy depends upon foreign trade, exports being its lifeblood. Trade between contiguous important countries invariably is large. Hence the United States and Canada have become each other's best customers. In 1951, their total trade reached five and one-tenth billion dollars when 69 per cent of Canada's imports came from the United States and 59 per cent of Canadian exports went to the United States. The United States sends iron and steel and their products, coal, petroleum, cotton, citrus fruits, and vegetables to Canada for which the latter exchanges lumber, newsprint, wood pulp, minerals (especially asbestos, copper, nickel, platinum, and uranium), furs, fish, wheat and chemicals.

The United States, Great Britain, and Canada must keep each other in mind in working out their mercantile calculations, so interdependent are they. Though Canada's trade with the United States is considerably greater than with Great Britain, the latter's market is of outstanding importance, especially for the exports of the Prairie Provinces and British Columbia. Canada's welfare depends upon international free trade or at least freer trade in wheat, a result of the fact that her Prairie Provinces became a gigantic wheat field prior to and during the first World War, when she could sell all the wheat she raised. Since Great Britain is the world's largest market for wheat getting into international trade, the importance of this trade is obvious.

United States tariff barriers have at times affected adversely an untrammeled exchange of goods but in retaliation the Ottawa Agreement of 1932 gave preferential tariff treatment to all Empire countries. In 1939, however, the United States made a trade agreement with Canada, which greatly accelerated and increased commerce between the two countries.[4] After World War II, further trade agreements were made.

There has been a decline in trade between Canada and Great Britain. From 1935-1939, 18 per cent of Canadian exports went to Britain, but in 1950, the percentage was down to 13. Now Canadians are apprehensive lest they become economically tied to the United States, whose tariff policies are subject to capricious changes. Hence as more products become available for export, Canada constantly seeks new markets.

The International Boundary and Common Problems

When two nations are separated by so artificial a boundary as that between Canada and the United States, there are necessarily common problems, many of them acute. If these are solved for the common good, the two countries are brought closer together. Canadians had little to say in drawing up the boundary between Canada and the United States. American officials dealt with British rather than Canadian representatives and the British, in their desire to avoid war with the United States, sometimes disregarded the interests of the Canadians. Nevertheless, settlement of the boundary was accomplished without blows.

Other problems have arisen between the contiguous countries. Treaties have been drawn up concerning fishing rights, fur seals, wild life, and radio channel allotment. In 1909 the International Joint Commission was set up under the Boundary Waters Treaty. Its powers are so great and the sentiment behind it in both countries so sincere as to make it one of the world's leading international bodies. Following are two good

examples of cases coming under the jurisdiction of the Commission.

1. The Trail Smelter, located in the Columbia River Valley of British Columbia some ten miles north of the international boundary, was producing some 250 million pounds of sulphur per annum, nine tenths of which it discharged into the atmosphere as sulphur dioxide gas. Because of the narrow river gorge and the prevailing winds, lateral distribution of the fumes was prevented. These were accordingly carried southward some 42 miles into United States territory to burn the natural vegetation and crops of Washington farmers. Upon complaint of the farmers, the matter was turned over to the International Joint Commission for investigation and a unanimous decision reached whereby $350,000 was paid as compensation to cover damage up to January 1, 1935. Since then the fumes have been collected in a special plant and used as the base for a chemical fertilizer.

2. There is also the case of the power dam at Grand Falls, New Brunswick. Since the St. John River forms the International boundary above the dam and since the latter would affect water levels there, permission had to be secured from the International Joint Commission prior to construction.

United States–Canadian Pacts for Defense

In 1940 the United States and Canada established a permanent Joint Defense Board to achieve close military and economic co-operation. This was a big step in American foreign policy and was undertaken primarily because (1) Great Britain was imperiled and the two Anglo-American countries felt it was a common peril, and (2) realization on the part of the United States that the shortest distance between the powers is by air "across the top of the world." A. Lawrence Lowell said in 1939 that no hostile army could land in Canada without getting into a war with the United States and that a cession of Canadian territory to a foreign nation is unthinkable.[5]

---

[4] The *Fortune* Survey, polling a cross section of the public in both countries, found sentiment overwhelming for the free movement of goods between the United States and Canada.

[5] A. Lawrence Lowell, "Frontiers of the United States," *Foreign Affairs*, July 1939, Vol. 17, No. 4, p. 665.

In 1947, it was declared that "in the interest of efficiency and economy, each government [must] continue to collaborate for peace-time joint security purposes." [6] An example of such collaboration is to be found in the airplane industry. Canadair in Montreal, connected with the Electric Boat Company, American builder of submarines and PT craft, builds sabrejets and the twin-engined T-36 transport trainer for the United States Air Force. Jet engines, radar, and some other instruments are delivered from the United States. De Havilland Aircraft of Canada makes the Beaver plane for its southern neighbor.

The armed forces of both countries have participated together in land, sea, and air exercises. In the Canadian northland, Americans have learned of some of the difficulties of Arctic warfare. A Military Co-operation Committee, made up of representatives of the branches of the service from each country, co-ordinates many activities.

In 1949, Canada and the United States became members of the North Atlantic Treaty Organization, binding themselves together in another defense agreement. When war broke out in Korea, Canada followed the United States in sending aid there.

A joint United States-Canada Mobilization Planning Committee formulated principles accepted by both governments in 1950.

Our governments shall co-operate in all respects practicable, and to the extent of their respective powers, to the end that the economic efforts of the two countries be co-ordinated for the common defense and that the production and resources of both countries be used for the best combined result.

The Canada–United States Civil Defense Pact signed in 1951 stipulates that activities be co-ordinated to protect persons and property from the result of an enemy attack as if there were no border.

Growing Spirit of Nationalism in Canada

The closeness of Canadian-American rela-

tions should not be construed as meaning that Canada is moving inevitably and happily into union with the United States. Said Mr. Lester B. Pearson [7] in 1949 before an American audience:

We are content with our position of independence inside our Commonwealth of Nations. We may, of course, be wrong, but somehow or other we feel that our political and social and legal institutions are better for us than yours would be. We move at a somewhat slower tempo in Canada and we like it that way.

It took many years for Canada to work out its political maturity with Great Britain. Before Confederation, Canada gained control of its tariff policy (in 1859), but it was not until after World War I that Great Britain relinquished determination of Canadian external affairs. The Imperial Conference of 1926 defined the new autonomy. With reference to Great Britain and the Dominions, it was stated: They are autonomous communities within the British Empire, equal in status, in no way subordinate one to another in any aspect of their domestic or external affairs . . . The next year, the first Canadian legation was opened, and it is significant that the site was Washington. Canada severed more ties with Britain by abolishing, in 1947, the right of appeal to The Judicial Committee of the British Privy Council. Canada's highest court is now within Canada. In 1952, for the first time a Canadian-born assumed the position of Governor-General. One bond is yet to be broken: Canada cannot amend her constitution, the British North American Act, without British approval. However, any amendment proposed to the British Parliament would be passed by that body without a division.

Canadians feel an inner necessity to assert their independence from Washington fully as much as from London. Said an unidentified member of Canada's Department of External Affairs, "We can't jump from an imperial frying pan into an American fire." And the *Economist* carried the statement:

The Canadian anxiety is that, having escaped from British tutelage, they will be thought to

---

[6] W. R. Willoughby, "Canadian-American Defense Co-operation," *The Journal of Politics*, November 1951, pp. 675-697.

[7] Secretary of State for External Affairs.

have fallen under that of the United States. It is from Washington, fully as much as from London, that the Canadians feel an inner necessity for independence.[8]

Canada's economy is now so strong and her future so promising that she faces the world with confidence. She has started out independently to construct the vast enterprise of the St. Lawrence Seaway.

The Massey Report. A manifestation of Canadian concern with national development is the Massey report. The Royal Commission on National Development in the Arts, Letters, and Sciences, under the chairmanship of Mr. Vincent Massey, investigated the position of cultural and educational facilities in Canada and published its findings in 1951. In surveying Canadian achievements and deficiencies, it was concluded that an effort must be made to resist the somewhat absorptive capacity of the nation to the south. In seeking to maintain a balance between British loyalties and sensitive responses to American influences, Canadians have adopted and adapted, but created little of their own. The present Canadian desire is to show the world that Canada has something distinctive to contribute to civilization.

Canadian Grievances Against the United States. Exceedingly irksome to Canadians is the typical American tendency to ignore Canada, to take her for granted, or to think of her as merely an unincorporated state of the American union. Mr. Pearson remarked:

We are not willing to be merely an echo of somebody else's voice . . . It would also help if the United States took more notice of what we do, and indeed occasionally of what we say.[9]

Canadians have been critical of some American foreign policies, particularly in the Far East. Again Mr. Pearson expressed his country's point of view when he said:

Our preoccupation is no longer whether the United States will discharge her international responsibilities, but how she will do it and how the rest of us will be involved.[10]

Certain economic policies of the United States have not helped to foster good will. Mercurial changes in tariff policies, such as the recent increased tariff on cheeses, Congressional refusal to permit American stockpiling of Canadian aluminum, and the long delay in approving the Seaway have displeased the nation to the north.

General American ignorance about Canada and her political status is particularly disturbing to a nation that is in the throes of nationalistic sentiment. Not long ago, an American Representative seriously proposed that the United States take over Canada from England in payment for the British loan. True Anglo-American solidarity will come only with mutual confidence born of understanding.[11]

Anglo-America —
Stronghold of Democracy

If democracy in its broadest sense is to survive, it will be primarily through the efforts of Anglo-America, most of all the United States.

The democratic testament is one lesson that America has to teach the world. A second is a new reading of nationalism. Some day and somehow, the peoples must discover a way to brigade themselves for peace . . . the United States was the conscious work of men's hands and a task which has once been performed can be performed again. She is the supreme example of a federation in being, a federation which recognizes the rights and individuality of the parts, but accepts the overriding interests of the whole.[12]

Canada, too, has inherited from the past this faith in democratic self-government and along with the United States her large and diverse regions are successfully working out complex problems with a minimum of friction.

---

[8] "Canada as a World Power," *Economist* (London), June 30, 1951, p. 1543.

[9] From a speech delivered April 10, 1951, before the Empire and Canadian Clubs of Toronto.

[10] From Pearson's speech, April 10, 1951.

[11] Alfred Leroy Burt, *A Short History of Canada for Americans.* Minneapolis: University of Minnesota Press, 1942.

[12] John Buchan, "My America," *Pilgrim's Way,* pp. 275-276. Boston: Houghton Mifflin Co., 1940.

The Anglo-American

Though nationalism is strong on both sides of the international border, loyalty to the United States or to Canada should never crowd out pride in descent from the blended peoples who created the common Anglo-American heritage.[13]

An Anglo-American is the result of a collection of national groups of diverse origins that has become absorbed by the land of their adoption and held together by common interests.

An exception to this mixing are the French Canadians who are concentrated largely, though not entirely, in the Province of Quebec. They comprise a considerable element — possibly four fifths of Quebec's population and one third of the nation's total of 14 million. They have been the nearest thing in Anglo-America to the European peasant. They did a great deal of the agricultural pioneering and are still doing some of it in parts of the Clay Belt and in the remoter hill country where they continue as subsistence farmers. A considerable number have settled north of the English Canadians in Ontario, where the land is not good for agriculture but where the French Canadians are more easily satisfied than the British. Many also work in the mines and pulp mills. The French Canadians made good pioneers because they could endure hardships and privations and because they had much ingenuity and self-reliance.

By and large, however, they are no longer subsistence farmers; today they must be considered cash-crop, government-subsidy farmers. No longer do they use obsolete and crude farm implements; to an increasing extent they use modern mechanized techniques. In short they do not differ appreciably in their economic life from the farmers of southern Ontario.

Their ways of life definitely are changing. Especially is this true among the young people, who have left the country-side by the thousand: almost everywhere in French Canada depopulation is occurring.[14] Almost half the French Canadians now live in big industrial cities — more than one million in Montreal itself. French Canada is now experiencing the impact of twentieth-century industrialism on a tremendous scale. According to F. Kenneth Hare the people of French Canada are in more rapid transition than any others he has met. For a long time it was believed these people were not susceptible to change — that their cultural integrity was as steadfast and granite-like as that of the Mexican. Now we know that once they are removed from the influences of their culture, they experience as little difficulty in merging into the general Anglo-American culture as any element not born into it.

Canada as a result of the French Canadians is bilingual. Some people consider the use of two languages to be a major force working against national unity. Others do not. Some of the latter group believe that Canada has a unique opportunity of achieving in Anglo-America something comparable to the achievements of the Swiss. Whatever the situation one thing is certain — the French Canadians will not abandon their language!

The French Canadians have long been opposed to English ways, viewing with suspicion the increasing powers of the national Parliament which, they fear, may take from them those things for which they fought for nearly two centuries. They have, however, been guaranteed recognition of their language as an official language on an equality with English in the Province of Quebec, and for all proceedings in the federal Parliament and in federal courts all over Canada; they have also been granted the right to a Roman Catholic school system under the control of the Roman Catholic part of the Quebec population. Actually the British Government, after losing the Thirteen Colonies, in an effort to secure the loyalty of the new French-speaking subjects, granted them very explicit guarantees.

In order to survive, however, any government in Ottawa must have considerable support from French Canada. The French Canadians, conscious of their minority position,

---

[13] Marcus L. Hansen and John B. Brebner, *The Mingling of the Canadian and American Peoples,* p. xi. New Haven: Yale University Press, 1940.

[14] F. Kenneth Hare, McGill University, Montreal, personal communication.

are inclined to function as a unit in national politics and to support whichever national party gives most attention to their particular claims. *True Canadian unity*, however, can come only when the nation bases its foreign policy entirely on its own needs as an Anglo-American State. In his very enlightening book, *Canada*, Alexander Brady calls Canada a country of two nations and says that it cannot hope for more than a super-nationality.

Probably the strongest force in French Canada is the Catholic Church.

Although the idea of a voluntary annexation of Canada was apparently terminated by the Anglo-American Conference of 1871, there are still Americans and Canadians who think that some type of absorption is inevitable. These, however, do not represent public sentiment in either country.[15] Certainly Canada shows no desire for political union and the United States none for forcing a merger. Regardless of how intermeshed their economic and strategic relations become, they show no indication of coming closer to political union. In solving their various and sundry problems the Canadians will wish to do it themselves and they will wish to remain Canadians. There is no reason why Canada should not move in the orbit of the United States and at the same time retain her identity.

Canada and the United States, Neighbors

Twice hostile American armies invaded Canada to free (really absorb) it. In the controversy over the boundary between southeastern Alaska and Canada, the American slogan became "54–40 or fight." Between 1782 and 1925 the United States–Canadian boundary was the object of negotiation at least 17 times, though only details were considered. Most of these misunderstandings resulted from errors made when European monarchs drew ambitious lines upon the inaccurate maps of their day.

The boundary today, however, stands as

the most notable "unarmed frontier" and the "safest borderline" on earth. In the present state of international relations, with the entire world being menaced by tyranny, nothing could be more significant than this unarmed border. That the peoples on either side of the international boundary will continue to drift back and forth seems assured.

Canada has developed a nationality of her own, though Englishmen call it "American" and Americans call it "British." Actually it is a concoction of both with a dash of something else that has made it neither, but rather "Canadian."

Regardless of what happens in the world today, the United States and Canada must and no doubt will act as a unit, for it seems that the interests of both nations can best be served if Canada remains Canada and the United States remains as she now is, a strong, sympathetic neighbor. Moreover, because she is joined by geography to the United States and by political ties to Britain, Canada is in a most enviable position to link them.

Foreign observers occasionally assert that Canada is merely a satellite of the United States. This is not true. Canada is, and is determined to remain, a separate entity. She still looks to London and Washington but focuses her attention mainly on Ottawa.

It has been pointed out that the regions of Canada are really prolongations of those from the United States — and that they have more in common with their complementary parts south of the border than they have with one another; that the peoples of these international (geographic) regions feel at home on either side of the border; that whereas Canada is in many ways as *Anglo-American* as the United States, she still is nevertheless "ineradicably British."

Canada represents politics at war with geography. She is geographically an integral part of the American continent. . . . But politically she belongs to a system mainly European and her economy has been organized not on a north-south but on an east-west axis.[16]

Canada has struggled hard to overcome the

---

[15] *Fortune's* 1942 poll found sentiment among leaders and the general public on both sides of the border opposed to a Canadian-American union.

[16] John MacCormac, *Canada: America's Problem,* p. 215. New York: Viking Press, 1940.

obstacles imposed by her physical geography (1) by confederation, (2) by building a transcontinental railway system, and (3) by sustained faith of nationalists who have considered her place within the British Empire a more important asset than union with the United States. Indeed the persistence of loyalist sentiment in Canada is one of the least understood things in the United States.[17]

In the past, there have been disagreements between Canada and the United States about boundaries, fishing rights, and economic policies. Americans have looked upon Canada as the outpost of the European power against

whom they fought to win their independence. At times Canadians have seen the United States as a potential threat of forcible annexation and even now many are wary of American economic and cultural influences. Cultural annexation is a recurring theme in Canada. However, the long tradition of arbitration and negotiation that has grown up between the two countries, accompanied by a spirit of good will and co-operation, will help them to solve successfully the majority of any future problems that may arise, however difficult they may be. Both countries see the hand-writing on the wall: the need for preserving freedom and the cold facts of economics have conspired to make the two nations interdependent partners.

[17] Robert Falconer, *The United States as a Neighbor from a Canadian Point of View*. New York: Cambridge University Press, 1925.

Selected Bibliography

American Academy of Political and Social Science, *Features of Present-Day Canada*, Robert H. Coats, ed., Annals, Vol. 253. Philadelphia: The Academy, 1947.

Alexander Brady, "Canadian-American Relations," *International Affairs*, Vol. 28, 1952, pp. 190–195.

J. Bartlet Brebner, "A Changing North Atlantic Triangle," *International Journal*, Vol. 3, 1948.

Wilfred Eggleston, "Canadian Geography and National Culture," *Canadian Geographical Journal*, Vol. 43, 1951, pp. 254–273.

James A. Gibson, "Canadian Foreign Policy: A Forward View," *International Journal*, Vol. 4, 1949.

Daniel W. Hoan, "The St. Lawrence Seaway — Navigational Aspects," *Canadian Geographical Journal*, Vol. 36, 1948, pp. 52–69.

Gilbert R. Johnson, "United States–Canadian Treaties Affecting Great Lakes Commerce and Navigation," *Inland Seas*, Vol. 3, 1947; Vol. 4, 1948.

A. Mitchell, "Canada as a World Power," *American Mercury*, Vol. 63, 1946, pp. 48–55.

Lester B. Pearson, "Canada and the North Atlantic Alliance," *Foreign Affairs*, Vol. 27, 1949, pp. 369–378.

Walter N. Sage, "Canada: The Neighbor to the North," *Pacific Historical Review*, Vol. 20, 1951, pp. 111–121.

B. K. Sandwell, "Population: A Canadian Problem," *Queen's Quarterly*, Vol. 54, 1947.

Paul F. Sharp, *The Agrarian Revolt in Western Canada. A Survey Showing American Parallels*. Minneapolis: University of Minnesota Press, 1948.

Mason Wade, *The French-Canadian Outlook: A Brief Account of the Unknown North Americans*. New York: Viking Press, 1946.

Appendix A

The Physical Background of Anglo-America

ANGLO-AMERICA lies entirely north of the Tropic of Cancer and largely south of the Arctic Circle, and thus is almost completely within the middle latitudes. The land mass also fronts on both the Atlantic and the Pacific Ocean and is thus in a favored position to play a dominant role in world trade. In addition, its great size causes it to have a wide variety of land forms, climatic types, vegetation associations, and soils.

Because of its structural axes, North America is wedge-shaped, with its widest part to the north. In the center of the continent between the Appalachian Mountains and the Rocky Mountains lies an extensive plain that is drained to the south by the Mississippi River and its tributaries, to the northeast by the St. Lawrence, and to the north by several streams that flow into the Arctic Ocean, such as the Nelson and the Mackenzie. East of the Appalachians is a fairly extensive coastal plain that is crossed by many short but economically and historically important streams such as the Potomac, the James, and the Roanoke. A similar condition exists along the Gulf Coast both east and west of the Mississippi drainage. In the western part of the continent the several basins and ranges that constitute the Cordilleran System

482

tem so completely dominate the area that there are no extensive plains and few major streams — in fact, a considerable part of this area has interior drainage. On the Pacific slope are several important coastal valleys that are drained by such streams as the Sacramento-San Joaquin, the Columbia, and the Fraser.

The Physiographic Regions

Anglo-America contains a number of major physiographic regions and subregions (Figure A–1), most of which are found within the United States, although a few appear only in Canada. The map here presented is based primarily upon the classification of regions as worked out by N. M. Fenneman[1] for the United States portion and by W. N. Thayer[2] for the Canadian portion. Wallace W. Atwood[3] has published a map for the entire continent in his volume, *The Physiographic Provinces of North America,* to which the

[1] N. M. Fenneman, "Physiographic Divisions of the United States," *Annals of the Association of American Geographers,* Vol. 18, 1928, pp. 261-353.
[2] W. N. Thayer, "The Northward Extension of the Physiographic Divisions of the United States," *Journal of Geology,* Vol. 26, 1918, pp. 161-185.
[3] Wallace W. Atwood, *The Physiographic Provinces of North America,* Boston: Ginn & Co., 1940.

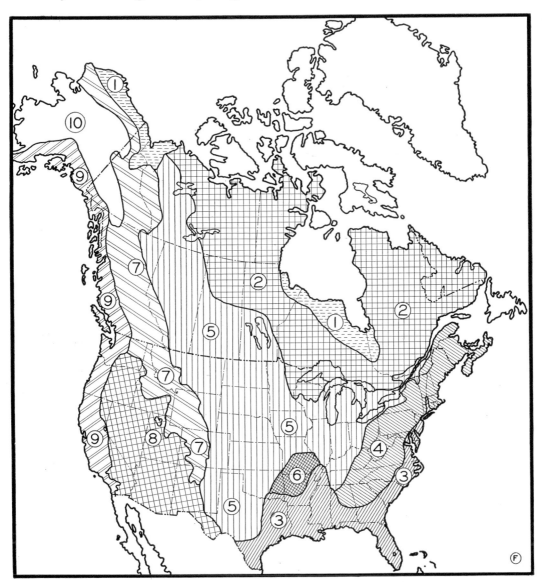

Figure A–1. The Physiographic Regions of Anglo-America: (1) Arctic Slope, (2) Laurentian Plateau, (3) Atlantic and Gulf Coastal Plain, (4) Appalachian Region, (5) Interior Plain, (6) Interior Highlands, (7) Rocky Mountains, (8) Intermontane Province, (9) Pacific Coast Region, and (10) the Yukon Basin. (After Fenneman and Atwood.)

reader is referred for more detail regarding descriptions of the physiographic provinces.

Climate

The latitude of Anglo-America is an important factor in the seasonal distribution of pressure and winds. Since the whole area lies north of the Tropic of Cancer, it has no large tropical regions. Poleward, the continent extends beyond the Arctic Circle, but the major part lies between the Tropic of Cancer and the Arctic Circle.

Types of Climate in Anglo-America. There are almost as many classifications of climate as there are climatologists. While all classifications are fundamentally the same, minor variations and complex nomenclature may confuse the reader. Unfortunately, no standard classification such as Fenneman's for physiographic regions has been adopted for climates. In this volume the major climatic classifications are given by means of four maps (Figures A–2, A–3, A–4, and A–5), and an outline of the types of climate found in each of the classifications. In this way it is felt that a student may approach the climatic diversification of Anglo-America from the point of view of the climatic classification

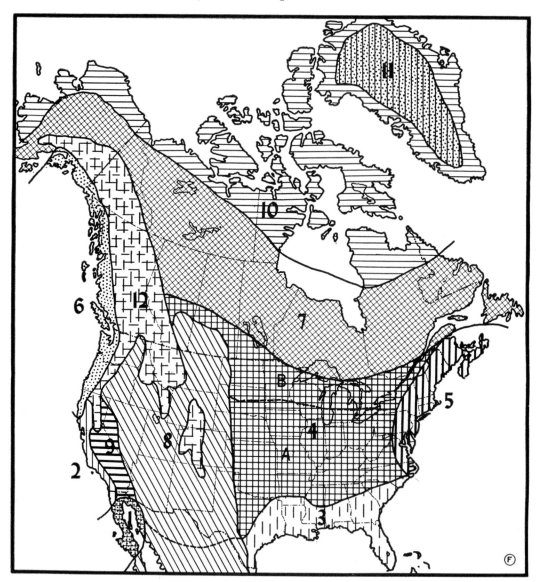

Figure A–2. Climatic Regions of Anglo-America according to the Bengtson and Van Royen Classification. Regions shown are as follows: (1) Warm Desert, (2) Mediterranean Subtropical, (3) Humid Subtropical, (4) Humid Continental, (5) East Coast Continental, (6) West Coast Marine, (7) Subpolar, (8) Middle Latitude Steppe, (9) Middle Latitude Desert, (10) Tundra, (11) Ice Cap, and (12) Mountain Climates.

most familiar to him, and hence not be required to learn a new system. For further details on each classification see the original sources.[4]

Natural Vegetation

Anglo-America's natural vegetation is divided into three classes — forests, grasslands, and deserts.

The *forests* are grouped into six zones: (1) the Great Northern, or taiga, (2) the northern hardwoods, (3) the southern hardwoods, (4) the southern pine, (5) the Rocky Mountain, and (6) the Pacific Coast.

The taiga, composed largely of coniferous trees growing under extremes of temperature in a region where the precipitation is largely in the form of snow, occurs in only two places: (1) on the North American continent, in Canada and northern United States, and (2) in Eurasia from Sweden to Kamchatka. Because of the longer growing season, large trees are found along the southern margin of this forest. They are dominantly conifers with wide annual growth rings, the result of rapid growth during the short but warm summer season. At the northern margin, the trees resemble those found at timber line on high mountains.

Three belts of forested land extend southward from the taiga. One prong follows the Appalachian Mountains and adjacent lowlands, another the Rocky Mountains, and a third the Sierra Nevada. The easternmost (Appalachian) prong has three subdivisions: the northern hardwoods, the southern hardwoods, and the southern pine. Between these types no sharp lines can be drawn, since the characteristic species of trees in each mingle near the boundaries. The northern mixed forest of New England, New York, and Pennsylvania comprises a birch, beech, maple, hemlock association; it also includes other trees such as spruce and pine. The southern hardwood forest extends from Pennsylvania to northern Georgia and Alabama. Its northern part is dominated by oak, hickory, and maple while its southern part contains gum and cypress, mixed with conifers. In the southern pine forest, conifers are found on the upland and hardwoods in the bottomlands. There are no pure stands of hardwoods.[5] The nearly pure stands of pine formerly present in the southern forest have been almost destroyed by logging and lumbering. On the southern tip of Florida is an area of mangrove swamp.

The Rocky Mountain and Pacific Coast prongs are largely mountain forests. In the Southern Rockies trees grow only in the uplands, but in the Northern Rockies some of the lowlands also are forested. In the Rocky Mountain forest, Engelmann and blue spruce are common, with western yellow pine covering the lower slopes. Aspen, the first tree to occupy an area after a fire, is one of the few deciduous trees. Because of rugged terrain, this forest has not been exploited to any great extent. Most of the stands are incorporated in national forests. The forest's worst enemy is fire, an especially serious danger after a period of drought. Open spaces — parks — have grass and are used for grazing. Except for piñon and juniper on the higher

---

[4] Nels A. Bengtson and William Van Royen, *Fundamentals of Economic Geography*, 3rd ed., pp. 82-87. New York: Prentice-Hall, Inc., 1950.

Vernor C. Finch and Glenn T. Trewartha, *Elements of Geography: Physical and Cultural*, 3rd ed., pp. 129-133. New York: McGraw-Hill Book Co., 1949.

W. Köppen and R. Geiger, *Handbuch der Klimatologie*, Vol. 1, Part C. Berlin: 1936.

C. Langdon White and George T. Renner, *Human Geography: An Ecological Study of Society*, pp. 36-39. New York: Appleton-Century-Crofts, Inc., 1948.

[5] The terms "hardwoods" and "softwoods" are the most generally accepted popular names for the two classes of trees, the *Angiosperms* and the *Gymnosperms*. Most Angiosperms, such as oak, hickory, sugar maple, and black locust, are notably hard woods and many Gymnosperms, such as pines and spruces are rather soft woods. But there are a number of outstanding exceptions. Basswood, poplar, aspen, and cottonwood, all classified as hardwoods, are in reality among the softest of woods. Longleaf pine, on the other hand, is about as hard as the average hardwood, although it is classified as a softwood. The most accurate popular descriptions for the two groups are "trees with broad leaves" for the Angiosperms, and "trees with needles or scale-like leaves" for the Gymnosperms (from Forest Products Laboratory, *Technical Note 187*, Madison, Wisconsin).

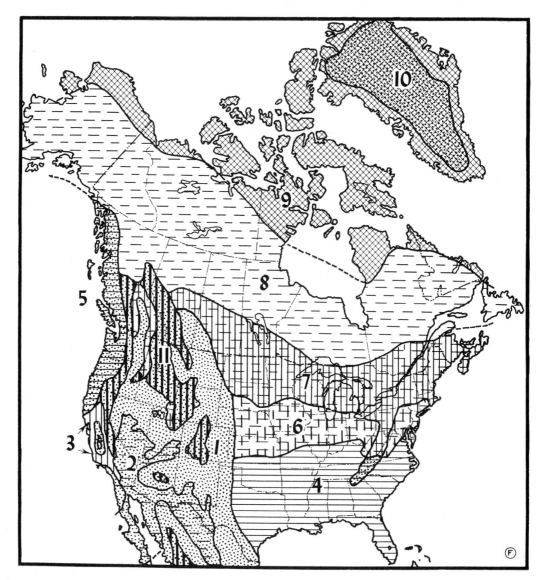

Figure A–3. Climatic Regions of Anglo–America according to the Trewartha System. Regions shown are as follows: (1) Middle Latitude Steppe, (2) Middle Lattitude Desert, (3) Mediterranean or Dry-Summer Subtropical, (4) Humid Subtropical, Warm Summers, (5) Marine West Coast, Cool Summers, (6) Humid Continental, Warm Summers, (7) Humid Continental, Cool Summers, (8) Subarctic, (9) Tundra, (10) Ice Cap, and (11) Undifferentiated Highlands.

ridges, and the somewhat extensive ponderosa pine forests of the Colorado Plateau, the area between the Rocky Mountains and the Sierra Nevada is lacking in trees.

The Pacific Coast forests are largely softwoods. In Washington and Oregon, the Doug-

las fir is dominant, growing seven to eight feet in diameter and 200 feet high. In northern California and in the Sierra Nevada the redwood and sequoia trees often attain a diameter of 15 feet and a height of 300 feet.

Grasslands usually are found in areas

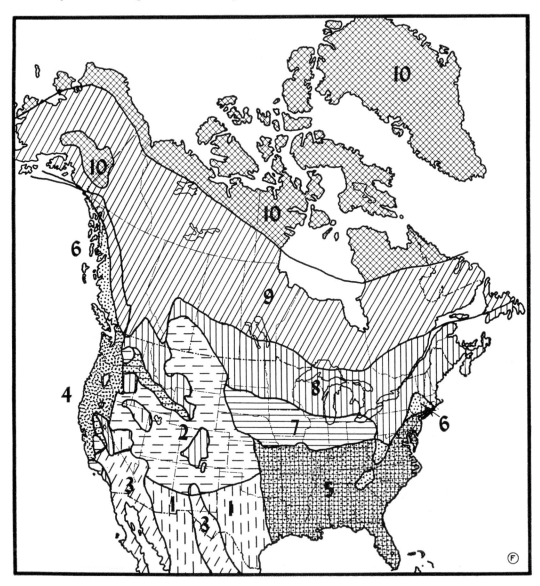

Figure A–4. Climatic Regions of Anglo–America according to the Köppen System. Regions shown are as follows: (1) BSh, (2) BSk, (3) BWh, (4) Csb, (5) Cfa, (6) Cfb, (7) Dfa, (8) Dfb, (9) Dfc, and (10) ET and EF.

where the rainfall is insufficient for trees, most of them never having had any other type of vegetation. Sometimes grass is a climax vegetation but more often as in southern Texas, it is replaced by a thornbush forest. Where grass is tall, it is called "prairie"; where short, "steppe." Some characteristic species of the steppe are blue stem, buffalo, grama, and wire grasses. Toward the desert margin the short grass vegetation grades into bunch grass.

The *tundra* is clothed with a spongy mass of mosses and lichens — a special pseudo-grassland.

Deserts are too dry for much vegetation, but some of their characteristic plants are sage brush, mesquite, cactus, and creosote bush. The salt desert is nearly barren.

Soils

Soil [6] is more than merely the covering of the bedrock. A true soil must have remained in place long enough to develop a mature profile consisting of the A–, B–, and C–hori-

[6] For a more complete study of the soils of the United States, see *Soils and Men, 1938 Yearbook of Agriculture,* pp. 1019-1161, Washington, D. C.: Government Printing Office.

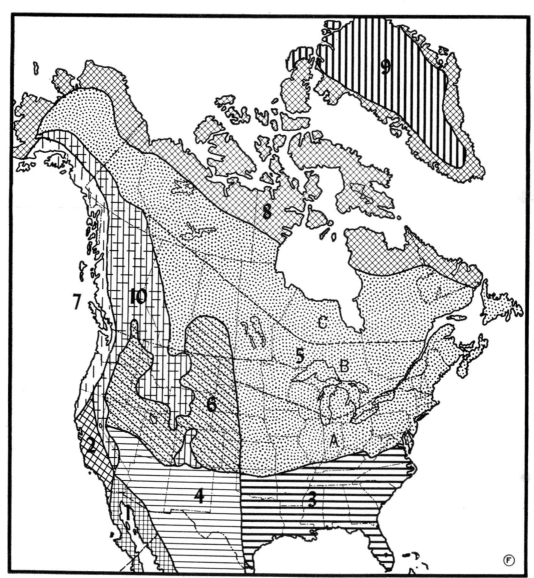

Figure A–5. Climatic Regions of Anglo–America according to the White and Renner System. Regions shown are as follows: (1) Arid Tropical, (2) Mediterranean Subtropical, (3) Humid Subtropical, (4) Dry Subtropical, (5A) Humid Continental — Long Summers, (5B) Humid Continental — Medium Summers, (5C) Humid Continental — Short Summers, (6) Dry Continental, (7) Temperate Marine, (8) Subpolar, (9) Polar Ice Cap, and (10) Highlands Whose Climates Vary With Altitude.

zons. The surface of the soil (A–horizon) is composed largely of organic material (humus) contributed by the native vegetation which gives it color; the C–horizon or parent material is dependent largely upon the type of bedrock; but the B–horizon is the distinguishing factor. The division of soils into humid and arid groups is made on the basis of the minerals contained in the B–horizon. Characteristic minerals of the B–horizon are calcium carbonate and aluminum and iron salts; calcium carbonate is soluable, and aluminum and iron compounds insoluble. In humid soils lime has been leached out, the

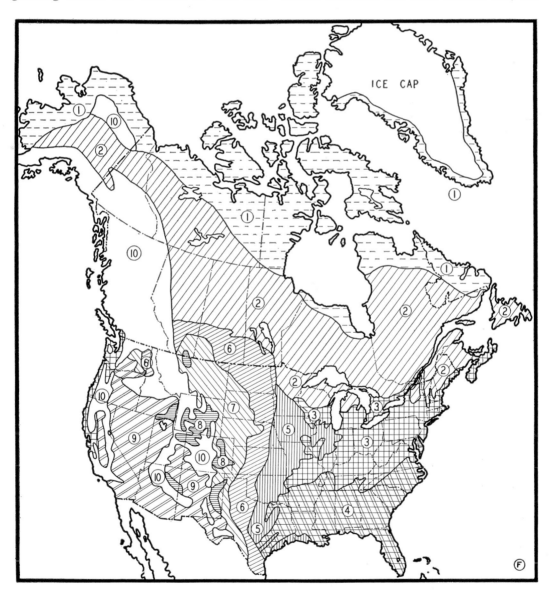

Figure A–6. The soil regions of Anglo–America. The major soil types shown are: (1) tundra soils, (2) podzols, (3) gray-brown podzolic soils, (4) red-and-yellow soils, (5) prairie soils, (6) chernozems, (7) chestnut-brown soils, (8) dark-brown soils, (9) gray-desert soils, and (10) soils of mountainous areas. (After Marbut and others.)

iron (ferric-oxide) producing a bright red color. In arid soils the calcium is present with the iron in the ferrous state. From the mineral composition of the B–horizon, arid soils are called *pedocals* and humid soils *pedalfers*.

Near the line of 20 inches of rainfall, or the hundredth meridian, is a transition between the humid east and the arid west. In the humid east the main zonation of the pedalfers depends on the length of the growing season, since rainfall is sufficient for forests everywhere except along the western margin, where the prairie soils are found. From north to south lie the belts of podzols, gray-brown podzolic soils, and red-and-yellow soils. The degree of leaching is progressively greater from north to south because in the South,

where the soil is not frozen in winter, leaching continues throughout the year. On the western margin of the pedalfers lie the prairie soils that form a transition between the pedalfers and the pedocals (Figure A–6).

In the West, the soil belts run predominantly north and south, as they result from decreasing precipitation toward the west. The easternmost soil of the pedocal group is the black *chernozem*. Next is the dark brown soil and finally the gray desert soil. In the Pacific Coast valleys, with their abundant rainfall, the soils are similar to those of the humid East. It is almost impossible to trace soil belts west of the Rockies. Large areas in the Rocky Mountains do not have true soils.

Appendix B

Occupance and Land Use of Anglo-America

Until recently, little concrete evidence has been offered to support the view that man might have been present in Anglo-America during the glacial period. Discoveries in southwestern United States suggest that man lived contemporaneously with such animals as the imperator elephant and the Pleistocene horse — animals which became extinct in Anglo-America during the glacial period. The natives found by the early explorers from Europe and erroneously called "Indians" were new-comers to Anglo-America — having reached the Atlantic coast only a comparatively short time before they were discovered. In many cases they had not had time to make any permanent adaptation to their environment. It is usually assumed that the Indians came via the Bering Sea or the Aleutian Islands, and that the northeastern part of the continent was the last region reached by them. This may help to explain why the settlements in the Southwest or in Mexico and Central America were more advanced than those of the Northeast. Other factors, however, that retarded the development of the Indians were paucity of protected habitats (except in southwestern United States), lack of domesticated animals other than the dog, and unfamiliarity with metals other than gold, silver, and copper.

Although the Indian was well adapted to his habitat, the land remained sparsely populated. When the white man arrived, Anglo-America was comparatively empty. It is reliably estimated that New York City has today living within it more than ten times as many people as did all of what is now Anglo-America when Columbus arrived (1,150,000). Of this number, 846,000 were within the limits of the present United States, 220,000 were in Canada, 72,000 in Alaska, and more than 10,000 in Greenland.[1]

Many scholars believe the small Indian population to have been a result of their cultural stage (hunting and fishing), which allowed only two to eight persons per square mile. Others think incessant warfare followed by unrest and famine and ineffectual political organization, might have been the cause. Still others make much of the conservative food habits whereby the Indians in their diet demanded a very high proportion of meat and fish. One authority thinks agriculture

---

[1] Mathew W. Sterling, "America's First Settlers, the Indians," *National Geographic Magazine*, Vol 72, 1937, pp. 535-539.

was of little importance in the East. On the other hand, there are those who believe that the majority of prehistoric aborigines, at least in that part of Anglo-America comprising the United States, were sedentary farmers and not roving hunters. They insist that the European never grasped the idea that there was not a typical Indian — that where the natural environment was favorable he accomplished much; where unfavorable, little. Had physical conditions been everywhere uniform, the distinctive cultures of different parts of the continent might not have developed.

The major Indian cultural groups found in Anglo-America include the Algonquin, the Iroquois, the Muskhogeans, the Caddoans, the Sioux, the Athapascans, and the Haida and Tlingits. In addition there were numerous minor cultural groups varying in development from the advanced civilizations of the Hopi and Zuñi to renegade tribes such as the cannibalistic Karankawans of the Texas Gulf Coast.

The Conflict Between the White Man and the Indian

White man subdued the Indian in a comparatively short time. One factor in this struggle was the contrast in cultural development. The European was using iron and steel while even the most highly civilized natives were still in the Neolithic stage. The white man also had the horse and other domesticated animals while the native had only the dog. When he came to the New World he had to combat few new diseases; on the other hand, he introduced several. Measles and smallpox killed the natives in great numbers and accounted in large measure for the victory of the white man. It seems evident that most tribes had been in Anglo-America only a comparatively short time and had not completely adapted themselves to the new environment when the Europeans came. From every point of view the white man had the advantage.

The Indian made many contributions to agriculture. In the New World the most valuable discoveries were not gold but new foods. Among the food plants domesticated and developed by them and given directly or indirectly to the white man corn or maize stands first. The Indian also contributed the white potato, tobacco, many kinds of beans, peanuts, pumpkins, squash, the sweet potato, tomatoes, and other foods.[2]

Many crops introduced from Europe grew well in Anglo-America. All cereals found favorable habitats. Only the Mediterranean grape, which was accustomed to dry summers, failed in the eastern part of the New World, because the heavy summer rains encouraged the growth of a fungus. A native grape, the Concord, however, was successful. In southern California the Spaniards had no difficulty in growing the Mediterranean grape because there it found a climate similar to that of its original habitat.

By fair means or foul, the white settlers killed off or pushed back the Indians. Today the remnants of most tribes in the United States live on reservations scattered throughout the West, and on a few reservations in the East.

Exploration and Early Settlement

In ancient times European culture reached its highest development along the shores of the Mediterranean Sea. During the Middle Ages the main cultural centers moved into Western Europe. However, several of the old Mediterranean cities, such as Venice, Genoa, Florence, and Constantinople (Istanbul), maintained their supremacy, their importance resulting from trade with the Orient. In the fourteenth century Venice and Genoa became the main *entrepot* ports for Oriental goods. When Constantinople was captured by the Ottoman Turks in 1452, trade routes to the East were closed. This caused the Italian cities to decline commercially.

The Portuguese, under the patronage of Prince Henry the Navigator, had explored the west coast of Africa even before the fall of Constantinople, and had rediscovered certain Atlantic islands. Columbus, a native of Genoa, sailing in the interest of Spain, crossed

---

[2] For an interesting discussion of this topic, see Carl O. Sauer, *Agricultural Origins and Dispersals*, pp. 40-61. New York: American Geographical Society, 1952.

the Atlantic in 1492 and landed in the West Indies. Depending on an ancient Ptolemaic map, he underestimated the distance from Europe to Asia and at first thought he had reached India. Probably he realized his mistake on one of his three subsequent voyages. The quarrel between Portugal and Spain over their conflicting interests in the New World was settled by the Treaty of Tordesillas in 1494. Meanwhile England sent out the Cabots, who discovered Newfoundland and the Gulf of St. Lawrence and claimed that territory for England. Later Jacques Cartier, sailing under the flag of France, reached the Gaspé Peninsula. It was not until the close of the sixteenth and the beginning of the seventeenth century, however, that these two nations made any further attempts to acquire colonies in North America. The French then explored the main rivers including the St. Lawrence and the Mississippi, while the English confined themselves to settlements on the Atlantic Coast and in the West Indies.

Cabeza de Vaca, after being shipwrecked on the Texas coast, wandered across the Southwest as far as Arizona, then turned southward down the west coast of Mexico. Coronado traveled through Arizona and New Mexico, Texas and Kansas, and then returned through the Southwest to Mexico. Having failed to discover the "fabulous" Seven Cities of Cibola, he considered the expedition a failure.

At about the same time, an expedition under Hernando DeSoto advanced northwestward from Florida, and crossed the Mississippi River to the south of the present city of Memphis. DeSoto went as far west as the Ozarks, but upon returning from that area he died and was buried in the Mississippi. In spite of the extensive explorations of the South and Southwest, Spain made no definite claims to the area because her explorers found no gold. Thereafter, her interests were concentrated largely in Mexico and South America.

The French came to Canada, dominated the St. Lawrence Valley, then the Great Lakes area, and ultimately claimed all lands drained by the Mississippi River and its tributaries. The English, reaching Anglo-America later, settled only on the east coast. Each country ignored the claims of the others, all the grants to the English colonies reading "thence westward to the Pacific." The Finns and Swedes, who had settled in Delaware, were absorbed by the Dutch, who in turn were incorporated into the English colony.

The Negro Slave

Soon after the first white settlers occupied the land of Tidewater Virginia there arose the problem of labor for clearing the forests, cultivating the soil, and harvesting the crops. Since land was free, no white man would consider working for another when he could have his own land, and the Indian of the Atlantic Coast could not be enslaved. At first indentured servants — white men sent from England who temporarily sold their services for the price of ship passage to the New World — met the labor requirements. These, however, did not prove satisfactory because they were not numerous enough to supply the demand and because it was difficult to keep them as slaves once they reached the frontier. To help solve the labor problem, Negro slaves were imported from Africa.

The first Negro slaves in the English Colonies were landed by a Dutch privateer at Jamestown in 1619. They were sold to the colonial government, which in turn sold them to planters along the James River. It was not until 1630 that a second cargo of Negroes was sold in the Virginia settlements. From 1635 on, a small number was imported nearly every year, partly from England and New Netherlands, but mostly from the West Indies. Despite the shortage of labor, Negroes were not popular at first, and even in 1690 there were only 5,000 in the tobacco colonies. However at the end of the seventeenth century the English Government restricted kidnaping and attempted to check the sending of convicts to America. As a result direct slave trade with Guinea developed, and slaveholding began in earnest. It is estimated that there were 400,000 slaves in the Colonies in 1760 and that three-fourths of them were in the southern Colonies. The slaves made up about two-fifths of the entire southern population . . .[3]

---

[3] Everett E. Edwards, "American Agriculture — The First 300 Years," *Yearbook of Agriculture, 1940,* pp. 180-181. Washington, D. C.: Government Printing Office, 1940.

Later when cotton became the important crop of the Old South after the invention of the gin, Negro slave labor seemed essential for clearing new lands and for planting and picking the crop. Had it not been for this large supply of labor during the eighteenth and early nineteenth centuries, it is doubtful whether the Cotton Belt could have expanded so rapidly or whether the Old South could have attained its high ante-bellum cultural stage. By 1808, when further importation of African slaves was prohibited, nearly 20,000 were being brought into the United States each year. They were never successful as laborers in the northeastern industrial states, and even in the Middle Atlantic States of Maryland and Virginia they were of doubtful value. Only in hot humid areas of the deep South, where Europeans experienced difficulty in performing physical labor, could Negro slaves be employed profitably. Because slaves were unprofitable in the North, that section of the country demanded abolition, while the Cotton Belt states became more convinced than ever that slavery was essential. The result was armed conflict between the two factions, and the ultimate emancipation of the Negro. Since that time the Negro problem both in the South and in the North has been a subject of much study and discussion.

Conflicts for Control of Anglo-America

By the early part of the seventeenth century, the English were entrenched along the Atlantic coast from Nova Scotia almost to Florida. The French dominated the Great Lakes and the Mississippi Valley and the Spanish held Florida, Texas, New Mexico, and all lands westward to the Pacific.

The main base of Russian America was on Baranof Island at Sitka, Alaska. No one disputed the Russian possession of the region around the Aleutian Islands, but in southeastern Alaska there were conflicting claims. The Spanish had sent out an expedition from Mexico, and claimed the coast as far north as 62° North Latitude. James Cook explored the Alaskan coast and claimed much of it for Great Britain. American clipper ships had traded up the West Coast, discovering the mouth of the Columbia River and the lands of the Northwest. Spain and Russia withdrew from the quarrel over the southern part of the area, leaving it to the United States and England. Spain relinquished her claims to the United States in the Treaty of 1819,[4] when Florida was purchased. In the early part of the nineteenth century Russia ceased to make any further advances in the territory.

The Territorial Growth of the United States and the Westward Movement

In the space of fifty years, 1803-1853, the United States attained its present continental size, acquiring much of the territory by purchase (Figure B–1). Following the Revolutionary War and the creation of the United States as a new nation on the North American Continent, the first land annexed was Louisiana in 1803. This territory had a complicated history. France had ceded Louisiana to Spain at the close of the French and Indian War to prevent it from falling into the hands of England. Spain, in accepting Louisiana, hoped to block the advance of the English colonists. She soon realized, however, that the advance of the new American republic could not be stopped, and hence returned Louisiana to France so that France could act as a barrier between the young United States and Spanish Texas.

Spain was dismayed when France immediately sold this territory to the neighbor she dreaded most. American pioneers in the Ohio Valley were demanding better treatment at New Orleans, their natural water outlet, and soon began to insist upon the purchase of that port by the United States. Some trans-Alleghenian people even threatened secession because their economic interests were more closely linked with the port at the mouth of the Mississippi River than with any of the American ports on the Atlantic Seaboard. President Jefferson, realizing the seriousness of the situation, opened negotiations with France for the purchase of New Orleans, and ultimately secured the entire Louisiana

---

[4] The treaty finally was ratified by Spain and the United States in 1821.

Territory for 15 million dollars. Although Congress had not authorized this purchase, Jefferson concluded the deal because he recognized the importance of this tract of land to the growing United States. Immediately he sent out an expedition under Lewis and Clark to explore the new territory. They ascended the Missouri River to its headwaters, crossed the Rocky Mountains, and descended the Snake and Columbia rivers to the Pacific Coast. Organized ex-

the land to settlers, giving them several times as much land for homesteading as the United States later offered to its land-hungry population. Mexico soon saw the mistake of permitting Americans to homestead in Texas and tried to discourage further settlement by making it unpleasant for those already there, thus precipitating the Texas War for Independence. After operating as an independent republic for nearly a decade, Texas was subsequently annexed by the United States.

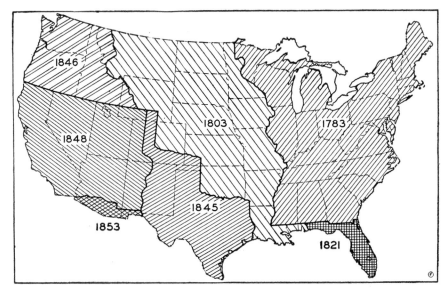

Figure B–1. Territorial Growth of the United States. (Adapted from map by the General Land Office of the United States.)

peditions were soon followed by trappers in the 1830's and 1840's. At this time the Great Plains were merely transit lands; no one was interested in occupying them or made any attempt to settle them.

Spain, having lost most of her colonial possessions in the New World, and realizing her inability to stop the territorial advance of the United States, sold Florida in 1821 to the new nation.

By 1820, settlers were moving westward rapidly. Meanwhile Mexico, having separated from Spain, controlled a broad area extending from Texas westward to the Pacific and as far north as the present northern boundary of California. Realizing that Texas should be occupied immediately, Mexico threw open

In the Mexican War which followed, the United States was victorious. Mexico then ceded to the United States all territory in dispute, established the Rio Grande as the southern boundary of Texas, and sold her the southwestern territories including California. In 1853 the Gadsden Purchase was negotiated to extend the boundary of the United States south of the Gila River Valley.

In Oregon the claims of the United States and England conflicted. The former demanded the territory as far north as the southern boundary of Alaska, 54° 40', on the basis of explorations by fur traders and by Lewis and Clark. England claimed the entire region because her trappers had descended the Fraser and Columbia rivers. The United States dispatched settlers over the Oregon Trail to clinch her claims. England also joined the race. The two countries compromised, however, on the 49th parallel, which had already been agreed upon as the boundary from the Lake of the Woods to the Rocky Mountains. This boundary was projected across the mountains without regard to relief. The only exception in the use of that parallel is Vancouver Island in British Columbia.

The purchase of Alaska from Russia in 1867 completed the acquisition of territory by the United States in Anglo-America.

The Formation of the Dominion of Canada

At the close of the French and Indian War, Canada became a part of the British Empire. Unlike the English colonies to the south, Canada remained loyal to Britain. The War of 1812 was largely a war between the United States and British Canada. At its close, the two countries agreed to abolish all fortifications along their common border and to maintain no navies on the Great Lakes. Since then, only customs houses mark the boundary between these two great nations on the longest unguarded international boundary in the world.

As England extended her domain to the Pacific Ocean need was felt for some type of home government. In 1867 the Dominion of Canada was organized. This included all of British North America north of the United States except Newfoundland and its colony, Labrador. In 1949 Newfoundland became a province of the Dominion of Canada.

In recent years Canada has attained virtual independence from the British Empire. It is practically an autonomous state — a rich and powerful unit in the British Commonwealth of Nations. With Anglo-America occupied and developed by two of the major English-speaking nations of the World, the United States of America and the Dominion of Canada, it seems certain that they will be drawn more closely together in the future. Their problems are largely the same in time of peace as well as in time of war.

Land Occupance and Land Utilization

The settlement and development of the West both in the United States and Canada resulted in the pre-emption of the best lands early in the twentieth century. Private ownership prevailed, and the frontier became a thing of the past.

As the pioneers took possession of the land they were overwhelmed by the abundance of the natural resources. As a result wasteful exploitation of resources was not only condoned in the midst of such abundance, but in many cases was encouraged. The vast forests occupied lands the settler wanted for cultivation, and hence he felt obligated to destroy them. Today a major part of the virgin timber has been destroyed, the wild game killed, and the top soil washed away through careless exploitation and cultivation. During the past two decades, however, Anglo-Americans have become more conservation-minded. They have seen that their economic system would have to be more closely attuned to nature, that they must avoid the mistakes of ignorance that have characterized the past, and that they must have enduring agriculture, permanent forestry, and lasting human communities.

The federal government realized that the maladjustment of man to land was a problem of nation-wide scope, and that the people involved were financially unable to better their situation, even if they knew how to improve conditions. The dry years of the early 1930's brought the matter before the nation in the alarming destruction of lands through wind erosion in the Dust Bowl of the High Plains. Severe soil erosion was also noted throughout the Southeast, and it soon became apparent that the soil, and other resources, were being wasted largely through ignorance. This national emergency led to the establishment of several government bureaus such as the Soil Conservation Service, the National Resources Board, and the Resettlement Administration. These agencies studied the problem of the land and its natural resources, and in many cases, made suggestions for the retirement of land from cultivation. They also moved some families from the poorest lands to those of higher productivity, but not always successfully owing to a number of causes, many of which are sociologic in character. Farming people become rooted to the soil. They prefer to remain in their native habitat even under a low standard of living rather than move to a more productive area where they might improve their conditions. When the habitat became untenable, such as in sections of the Dust Bowl, mass migration began. Many people such as the "Okies," migrated to good agricultural lands in California and other western states, resulting in an overcrowding of productive agricultural lands. Efforts by the government to prevent the destruction of natural resources, which has characterized so much of the nation's past, must be continued for the danger will be present always.

Regional Planning

Regional planning in its simplest terms is a political direction based upon the social and natural resource structure, rather than upon the outmoded statistical boundaries that were fixed to cope with problems that were paramount when the United States and Canada were young. If properly directed, regional planning will result in greater national efficiency and harmony. The Tennessee Valley Authority, discussed in detail in Chapter 6, has demonstrated clearly the desirability of unifying areas within the same major river drainage system for the common good of all living within its boundaries. More recently the Missouri Basin Commission has been planned, and if carried forward with the same energy and enthusiasm that TVA was in the 1930's, it should improve greatly a large part of the interior of the United States.[5]

Regional planning for large areas of like characteristics can be a good thing if the needs of the people are always kept foremost, but constant care must be exercised or the beneficial results might degenerate into a system of regimentation.

[5] Missouri Basin Survey Commission, *Missouri: Land and Water*. Washington, D. C.: Government Printing Office, 1953.

Index